Collins

Maths Now

7

Author
Mona Jhunjhunwala

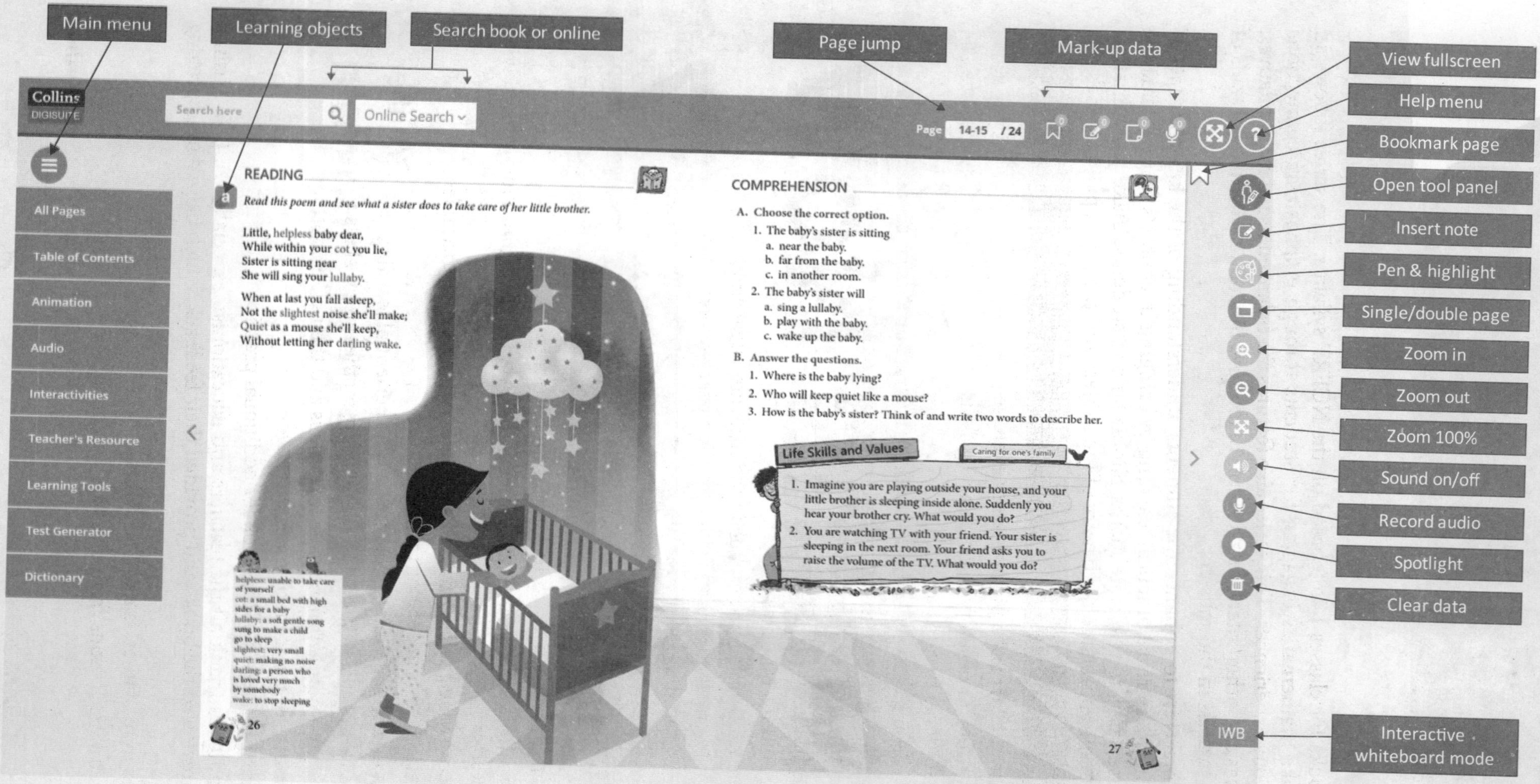

Student + Teacher			Teacher-only	
a animations	ia activities	g games	lp lesson plans	tn teacher's notes
ilt instructor-led tutorials	w worksheets	v videos	w worksheets	ak answer keys
	audio			

Preface

Maths Now is a series of eight books for classes 1 to 8 based on the NCERT syllabus. The series follows an activity-oriented approach to make mathematics engaging for students through emphasizing connections between mathematics and day-to-day experiences. This series also features the balanced use of manipulatives, virtual manipulatives, abstract ideas and other interesting features to improve inherent mathematical skills of students by creating foundational interest in the subject.

This series has been created with a view to enhance the students' understanding of the key concepts of mathematical problem-solving and to increase practical learning by bringing in contexts from outside the classroom. The main aim of the series is to eradicate maths phobia among students, make mathematical concepts crystal clear so that students appreciate the beauty of the subject and the role it plays in one's life.

Key Features

Let's Get Started Chapter starter in the form of a picture-based exercise

Mental Maths Objective-type questions to develop quick-thinking skills

Go Easy! Additional tips helping students to calculate quickly

Do You Know? Nuggets of information to add real-world context to abstract mathematical concepts

Common Errors Pointers highlighting common mistakes and misconceptions

Solved Examples Exercises with step-by-step solutions

Word Problems Textual questions based on real-life situations

Exercises In-text objective-type questions for quick review

Crossword and Puzzles Mathematical problems to stimulate the students' engagement

Maths Lab Activity Hands-on activity to connect concepts with their practical uses in real-life situations

Concept Map Graphic organizer to logically represent relationships between concepts under one topic

Key Concepts List to concisely give an overview of concepts in each topic

Chapter Revision Exercises at the end of each chapter for a comprehensive review

Skill Up!

- **Project** Practical activities to enhance real-world application of concepts
- **Life Skills** Questions to inculcate positive behaviour and add a layer of ethical thinking while solving practical mathematical questions
- **Mind Buzzer** Questions to provide challenging questions relating to real-life examples

Teacher's Notes Important tips related to concepts for the teacher

Worksheets Exercises that covers financial literacy, inferential and experiential learning

Reasoning Worksheet Questions to stimulate rational thinking using mathematical skills

Eminent Mathematicians Brief write-up on eminent mathematicians and their contributions

Poster Important points and formulae in the form of a pull-out page

Review Corner Variety of questions at the end of the book for additional practice

I would like to take this opportunity to thank all the teachers and educationist, especially Dr. C.B. Mishra, Prudence Group of School, who reviewed the books and provided their feedback, which helped in improving the quality of the content.

I would like to dedicate this series to my father, late Mr. S.P. Gupta.

Feedback, invaluable comments and suggestions from users are welcome.

Author

Mona Jhunjhunwala

Key Features

Different features interspersed within the book aim to provide active learning tools and techniques. These tools and techniques have been designed keeping in mind the 5E principle based on the constructivist approach to learning. These features can be used as learning strategies to enhance the understanding of key concepts of mathematics and increase practical learning and problem-solving by bringing in real-life contexts from outside the classroom.

Engage: To capture the attention of students, become mentally engaged and make connections between past and present knowledge

- Let's Get Started
- Common Errors
- Go Easy!
- Vedic Maths (classes 6 to 8)
- Eminent Mathematicians
- Poster

Explore: To enable the students to explore the concepts through hands-on activities, investigations, etc.

- Maths Lab Activity
- Crosswords
- Puzzles
- Mental Maths

Explain: To enable the students to understand the main ideas of the topics

- Learning Objectives
- Note
- Solved Examples
- Concept Map
- Key Concepts

Extend: To enable the students to stimulate thinking and apply prior and current knowledge to real-life situations

- Do You Know?
- Word Problems
- Skill Up!
  - Project
  - Life Skills
  - Mind Buzzer

Evaluate: To review, assess and evaluate what students have learnt

- Exercises
- Chapter Revision
- Reasoning Worksheet
- Worksheet
- Review Corner

Balanced use of Manipulatives, Virtual Manipulatives and Abstract Ideas!

About the Features

Engage

Let's Get Started
Picture-based chapter-opening exercise

Common Errors
Pointers highlighting common mistakes and misconceptions

Eminent Mathematicians
Brief write-up on eminent mathematicians and their contributions

Go Easy!
Shortcuts for easy and fast calculations

VEDIC MATHS
Shortcut techniques to solve mathematical calculations

Poster
Important points and formulae in the form of a pull-out page

Explore

Maths Lab Activity
Hands-on activity to help in improving investigation, reinforcement and extension of concepts just learnt

Mental Maths
Objective-type questions to develop quick-thinking skills

PUZZLE!
Questions in the form of a puzzle to stimulate engagement with the concepts

CROSSWORD
Questions in the form of a crossword to stimulate engagement with the concepts

Explain

Note
Pointers for better understanding of concepts

SOLVED EXAMPLES
Example exercises with step-by-step solutions

Concept Map
Logical representation of relationships between concepts in a chapter

Key Concepts
Definition of important terms and formulae given as bulleted list

Extend

Do you know?
Nuggets of information to add real-world context to abstract mathematical concepts

WORD PROBLEMS
Textual questions based on real-life situations

SKILL UP!

Project
Practical activities to enhance real-world application of concepts

Life Skills
Thought-provoking questions to help develop sensible life skills such as better awareness, empathy and attitude towards self and others

Mind Buzzer
Questions to arouse intellectual curiosity and encourage the students to think beyond the classroom

Evaluate

EXERCISE
In-text objective-type questions for quick review, assessment and evaluation

Chapter Revision
Chapter-end questions with varieties of objective and subjective-type questions

REASONING WORKSHEET
Questions to stimulate rational thinking using mathematical skills

WORKSHEET
Picture-based, fun problem-solving questions to reinforce concepts

REVIEW CORNER
Variety of questions at the end of the book for additional practice

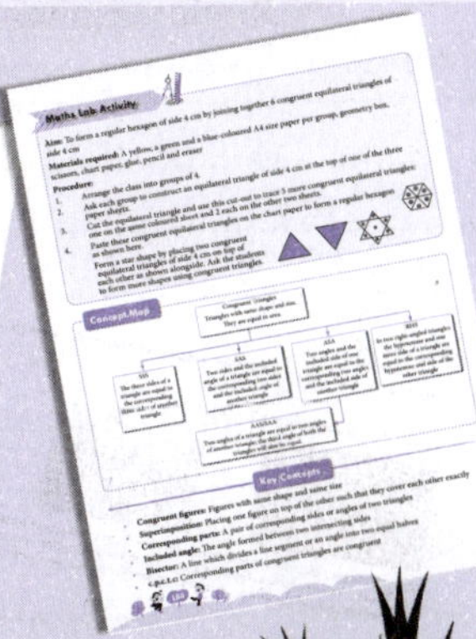

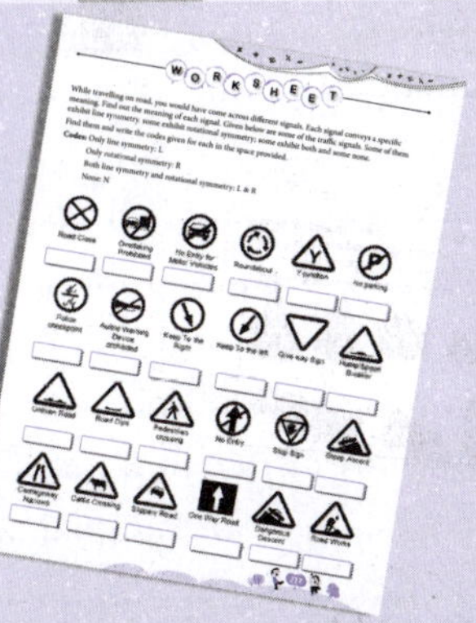

Maths Around Us
A two-page feature providing a variety of interesting information and activities that connect maths and Indian history, art, culture, real-life situations and financial literacy

Contents

Maths Around Us

INTRODUCTION TO BANKING

Have you ever been to a bank? Do you know what banks do? Let us familiarize ourselves with the role of a bank and services provided by it.

Bank: A bank is an institution that provides various financial services to its customers. It accepts deposits and lends or gives out loans for an agreement to return the amount to the bank, generally with an interest. Banks keep our money safe.

Deposit: The money that a bank accepts from public is called a deposit. In return, the bank gives some benefits to the depositor in the form of interest.

Loan: The money that a bank lends to public for purposes such as education, setting up a business, buying a house, a car, etc. is called a loan. The bank charges an interest on the loan amount. The interest is the extra money one pays back for the borrowed money or one receives from the bank for the deposited money.

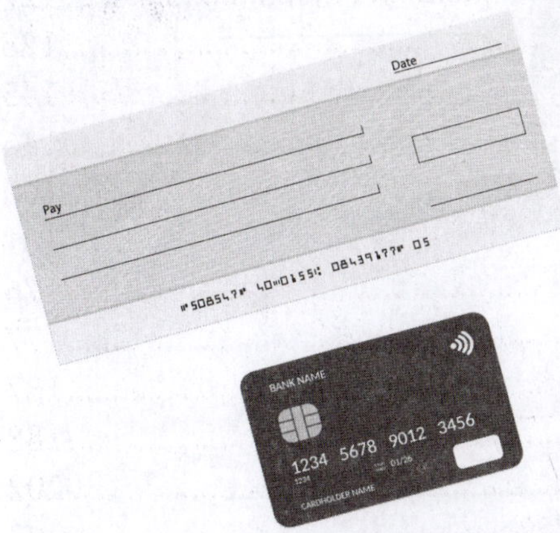

Cheque: It is a printed form that is a payment instruction from the account holder to his/her bank guiding to pay a sum of money to a specific person or an organization.

Debit card: An electronic card that a bank issues to its customers who have an account in that bank. It allows the card holder to access his/her account for making payments for goods and services or for withdrawing cash. This avoids the need for the card holder to go to bank branch for the above tasks.

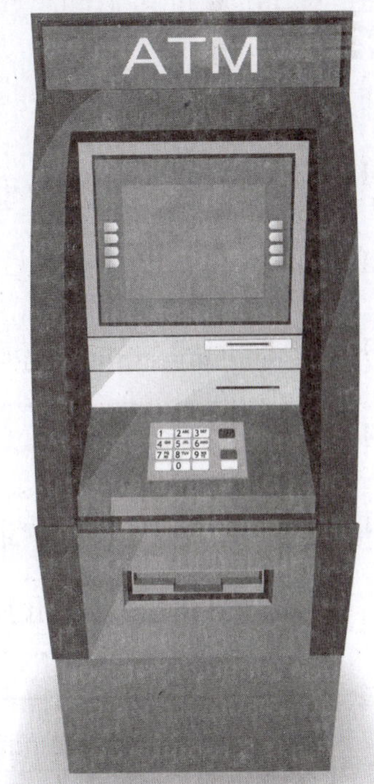

Credit card: An electronic card issued by a bank which gives the card holder an option to buy goods and services without making an actual cash payment. It is a type of borrowing for a short period of time. The card holder is expected to pay back the amount at a later date, failing which the bank charges an interest.

Automated Teller Machine (ATM): An ATM is basically a cash machine. It is an electronic machine which is operated by the customer himself. Using an ATM, customers can avail banking services like cash withdrawals, check account balance, transfer funds, etc.

To operate an ATM, the customer needs an ATM card (mostly a debit or credit card) issued by the respective bank.

The customer should insert the card in the machine and enter the Personal Identification Number (PIN).

If the PIN is correct, the machine allows the customer to make transactions.

Look at the image of a credit card given below. With the help of an elder or the Internet, find out what each part of the card stands for. Write your answer in the blanks provided.

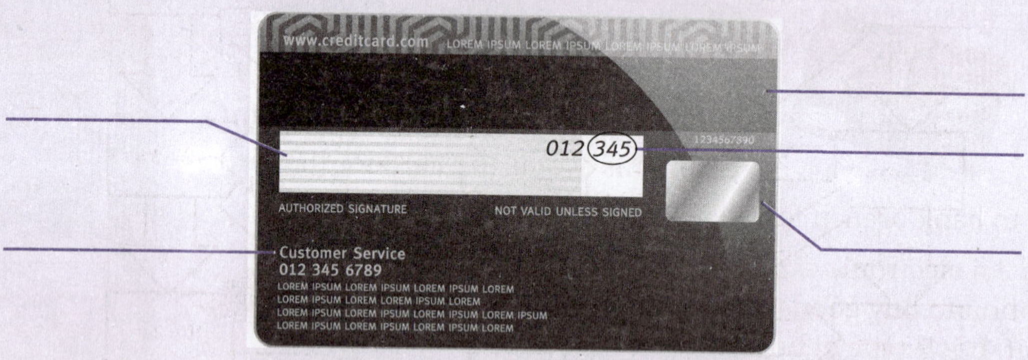

We need some of the above information related to a debit or credit card to complete a task. What is it and what information is required to complete this task? Write in the given space.

____

____

1 Integers

Learning Objectives

- To add and subtract integers
- To multiply and divide integers
- To understand properties of integers — closure, commutative and associative under all operations
- To understand distributive property of multiplication of integers over addition and subtraction

Let's Get Started

It was Christmas time! Lily was excited to receive gifts from her Secret Santa. Use the maze given here to find the gift she got!

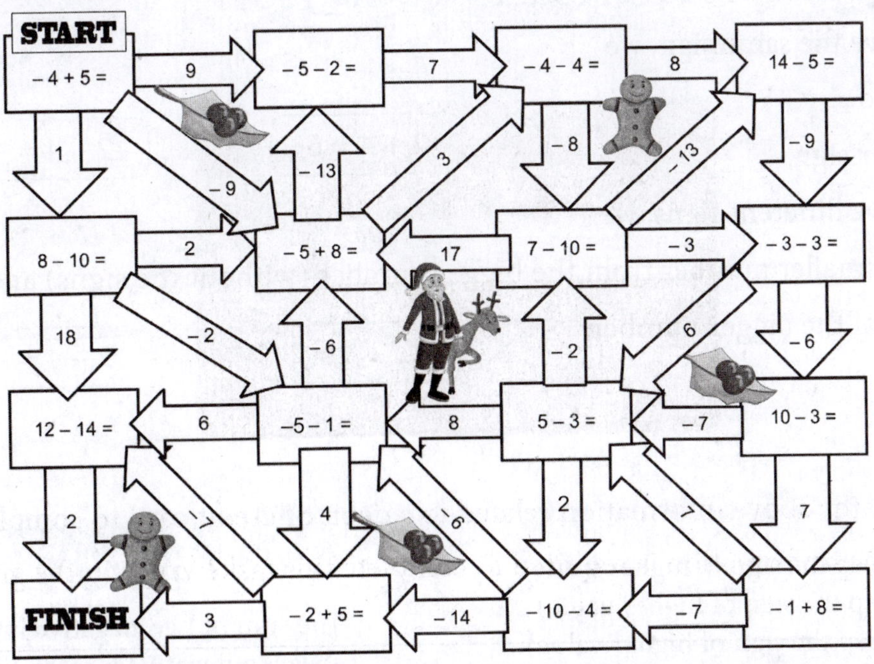

1. Consider all the results (numbers) that led to find Lily's gift. Arrange them in a descending order.
2. Represent all those numbers on a number line.

INTEGERS

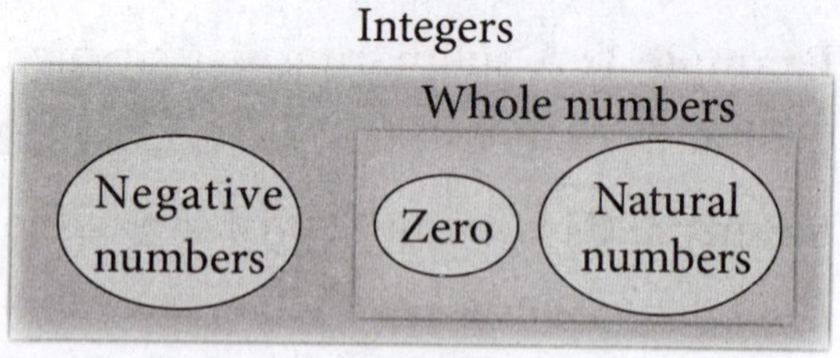

Integers are a collection of whole numbers along with the negative numbers. An integer does not have a decimal or fractional part. It may be positive (i.e., greater than 0), negative (i.e., less than 0) or zero.

Integers can be represented on a number line as follows:

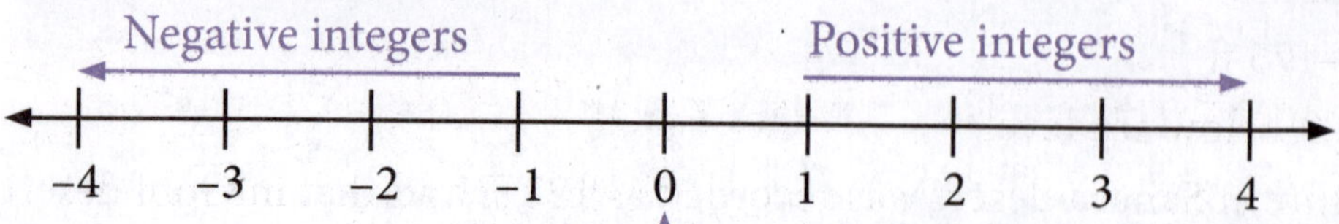

Zero is neither positive nor negative

We also come across integers in many real-life scenarios. The height above sea level is represented by a positive integer and the depth below sea level is represented by a negative integer. For example, if you are travelling over a mountain, then you could be at +1734 m above sea level. A fish underwater could be at –50 m from sea level. The temperature below 0°C is represented by a negative integer and above 0°C is represented by a positive integer. For example, the temperature at Shimla during nights in the winter season would be –5°C and that during the day might be 10°C.

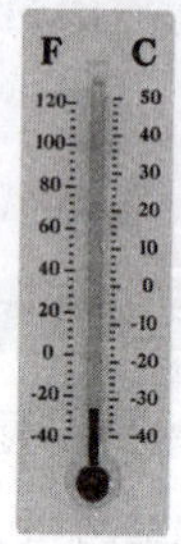

ADDITION AND SUBTRACTION OF INTEGERS

If two numbers have the same sign, we

- add them and
- then put their sign.

$2 + 4 = 6$ $-2 - 4 = -6$

If two numbers have different signs, we

- subtract the smaller number from the bigger number (without the signs) and
- put the sign of the bigger number.

$-2 + 4 = 2$ $2 - 4 = -2$

Go Easy!

Addition:

- + and + = + (keep the sign of higher value)
- – and – = – (keep the sign of higher value)
- + and – = + (keep the sign of higher value)
- – and + = – (keep the sign of higher value)

Mental Maths

The sum of two negative integers is always a negative integer. (True/False)

SOLVED EXAMPLES

Example 1: A submarine was situated at 300 ft below sea level. If it ascends 125 ft, what is its new position?

Solution: Given: Initial position of the submarine = 300 ft below sea level = –300 ft

Distance ascended by the submarine = +125 ft

To find: New position of the submarine

New position = (–300 + 125) ft = –175 ft

Therefore, the submarine is at 175 ft below sea level.

Example 2: One day, the temperature at Sahara desert was recorded as 128°F and that in Gobi desert was –45°F. What is the temperature difference between the two deserts on that day?

Solution: Given: The temperature at Sahara desert = 128°F

The temperature at Gobi desert = –45°F

To find: Difference in temperature between those two deserts

Difference in temperature = 128°F – (–45°F) = (128 + 45) °F = 173°F

Therefore, the difference in temperature between the two deserts on that day is 173°F.

EXERCISE 1A

1. **Add the following integers.**

   a. 45 and (–28) b. (–97) and (–56) c. (–132) and 81 d. (–77) and (–35)

2. **Subtract the following integers.**

   a. 15 from 38 b. (46) from –62 c. –73 from –101 d. –52 from 47

3. **Solve the following word problems.**

   a. It was –4°C during the night. The temperature rose by 9°C during the noon. What is the temperature now?

   b. A submarine is at a depth of 453 ft below sea level. It further descends by 87 ft. Where is the submarine now?

   c. A scuba diver has set a record of reaching a depth of 320 m in a sea. If another scuba diver has reached 280 m below sea level, how much more he must dive to break the record?

   d. The credit card bill of a person is ₹5000. He repaid an amount of ₹4200 and again purchased an item worth ₹1500. What is the outstanding amount that the person still owe the credit card company?

   e. At sunrise, the temperature outside was –15°C. By midday, it increased by 45°C. By evening, it fell to a third of the existing temperature and by night, a decrease of another 25°C was observed. What was the temperature by night?

PROPERTIES OF ADDITION AND SUBTRACTION OF INTEGERS

Closure Property

The sum or difference of two integers is also an integer. It is called the **closure property of addition and subtraction.**

For any two integers a and b, $a + b$ and $a - b$ is also an integer.

a	(–5)	10	(–9)	18	**Is it an integer?**
b	3	4	(–7)	(–12)	
a + b					
a – b					

Commutative Property

The sum obtained on adding two integers is the same irrespective of the order in which they are added. Therefore, addition is commutative for integers. It is called the **commutative property of addition.**

For any two integers a and b, $a + b = b + a$.

When the order of the numbers is changed, the difference obtained is different. Therefore, subtraction is not commutative for integers.

For any two distinct integers a and b, $a - b \neq b - a$.

a	8	(–6)	5	(–3)	
b	13	2	(–9)	(–7)	
a + b					**Is $a + b = b + a$? (Yes/No)**
b + a					
a – b					**Is $a - b = b - a$? (Yes/No)**
b – a					

Associative Property

a	3	(–6)	5	
b	(–5)	2	(–4)	
c	(–7)	4	(–8)	
a + (b + c)	3 + [(–5) + (–7)] = 3 + (–12) = (–9)			**Is $a + (b + c) = (a + b) + c$? (Yes/No)**
(a + b) + c	[3 + (–5)] + (–7) = (–2) + (–7) = (–9)			
a – (b – c)				**Is $a - (b - c) = (a - b) - c$? (Yes/No)**
(a – b) – c				

Note that $a + (b + c) = (a + b) + c$. Therefore, addition of integers is associative.

Note that $a - (b - c) \neq (a - b) - c$. Therefore, subtraction of integers is not associative.

For any three distinct integers a, b and c, $a + (b + c) = (a + b) + c$ but $a - (b - c) \neq (a - b) - c$.

Additive Identity

The number which when added to any number gives back the same number is called additive identity. Zero is an additive identity for whole numbers. Can zero be the additive identity for integers as well?

Find the following.

$(-4) + 0 =$ _____ $\quad 0 + (-12) =$ _____ $\quad$ _____ $+ 18 = 18 \quad$ _____ $+0=$ _____

On adding zero to any integer, we get the same integer.

Therefore, zero is the additive identity for integers.

For any integer a, $a + 0 = 0 + a = a$.

Additive Inverse

The additive inverse of an integer is that number which when added to its opposite gives zero. Thus, an integer and its opposite are called the additive inverses of each other.

Consider $4 + (-4) = 0$. Here, 4 is the additive inverse of (−4) and (−4) is the additive inverse of 4.

For any integer a, $-a$ is its opposite (or vice-versa) such that $a + (-a) = 0 = (-a) + a$.

Integer	(−5)	11	(−17)	24
Additive inverse	5	(−11)	17	(−24)

Mental Maths

1. Give a pair of integers whose product is (−85).
2. What is the sign of the product obtained on multiplying 3 positive and 7 negative integers?
3. What is the additive inverse of (−11)?

SOLVED EXAMPLES

Example 3: Fill in the blanks.

a. _____ $+ (-6) =$ _____ $+ 10 \quad$ b. $(-12) +$ _____ $= (-12) \quad$ c. $(-43) +$ _____ $= 0$

Solution:

a. $10 + (-6) = (-6) + 10 \quad$ b. $(-12) + 0 = (-12) \quad$ c. $(-43) + 43 = 0$

Example 4: Use a pair of integers to fill in the table given below. One has been done for you.

Condition	Sum	Difference
A negative integer	(−12) + 1 = (−11)	(−5) − (−1) = (−4)
Zero		
An integer smaller than one of the integers		
An integer greater than both the integers		

Solution:

Condition	Sum	Difference
A negative integer	(−12) + 1 = (−11)	(−5) − (−1) = (−4)
Zero	(−2) + 2 = 0	(−3) − (−3) = 0
An integer smaller than one of the integers	(−4) + 3 = (−1)	(−2) − 3 = (−5)
An integer greater than both the integers	4 + 3 = 7	7 − (−2) = 9

EXERCISE 1B

1. Fill in the blanks.

a. ______ + (−10) = 25 + ______

b. (−49) + ______ = 0

c. 14 + [____ + 8] = [____ + (−15)] + ____

d. (−32) + ______ = (−21) + ______

e. ______ + 0 = 100

2. Answer the following questions.

a. Write a pair of integers whose:

i. Sum is (−9)

ii. Difference is (−7)

iii. Sum is the additive identity of integers

iv. Difference is a positive integer

v. Sum is an integer smaller than both the integers

vi. Difference is an integer greater than one of the integers

b. Show that integers are closed under addition and subtraction.

c. Subtract the sum of −1878 and 878 from 2000.

d. Two golfers A and B played 6 rounds over three days. Look at the score given below and find out who took more shots and by how much.

	R1	R2	R3	R4	R5	R6
A	+6	−2	−1	+5	+3	−1
B	−3	+3	−3	+6	+5	−2

MULTIPLICATION OF INTEGERS

A bank employee had 5 bundles of 100 notes each. How many notes does he have?

Number of bundles with the employee = 5

Notes in each bundle = 100

Total number of notes with the employee = 5 × 100 = 500

Therefore, the bank employee has 500 notes.

5	×	100	=	500
Positive integer		Positive integer		Positive integer

Observe that when we multiply two positive integers, the product obtained is also a positive integer.

The product of two positive integers is always a positive integer.

Multiplication of a Positive and a Negative Integer

We know that multiplication is simply repeated addition.

For example, 3 × 5 = 3 + 3 + 3 + 3 + 3 = 15

Let us learn to multiply two integers using a number line.

Consider 4 × (–2).

Start from zero and move towards the left. Jump 2 steps 4 times and you will reach (–8).

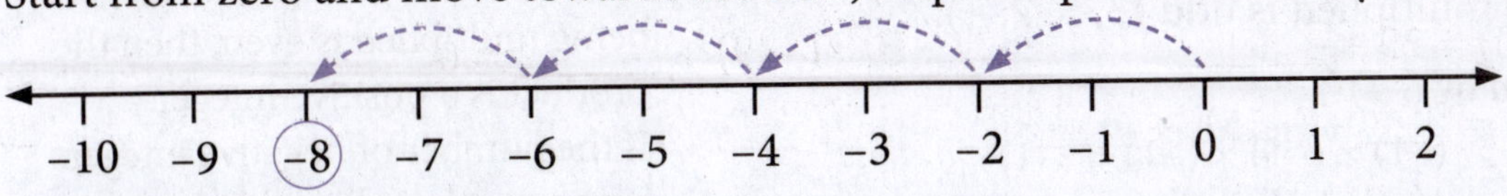

4 × (–2) = (–8)

Positive integer, Negative integer, Negative integer

Therefore, 4 × (–2) = (–8).

Consider (–2) × 3.

Start from zero and move towards the left. Jump 3 steps 2 times and you will reach (–6).

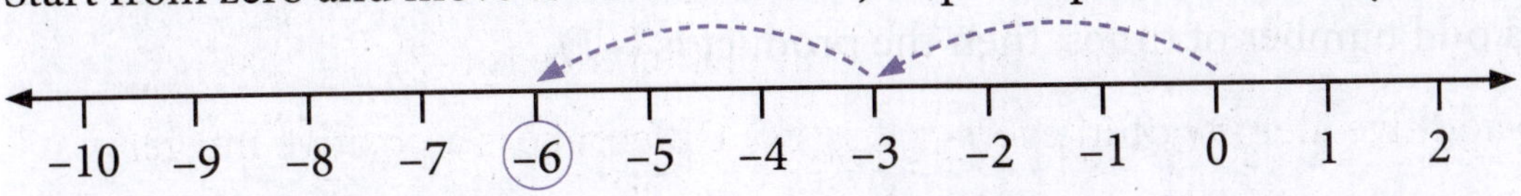

(–2) × 3 = (–6)

Negative integer, Positive integer, Negative integer

Therefore, (–2) × 3 = (–6).

What can you conclude from the above examples?

> The product of a positive integer and a negative integer is always a negative integer.

Multiplication of Two Negative Integers

Consider (–4) × (–2).

Start from zero and move opposite of (–2), that is, towards the right of zero. Jump 2 steps 4 times and you will reach +8.

(–4) × (–2) = 8

Negative integer, Negative integer, Positive integer

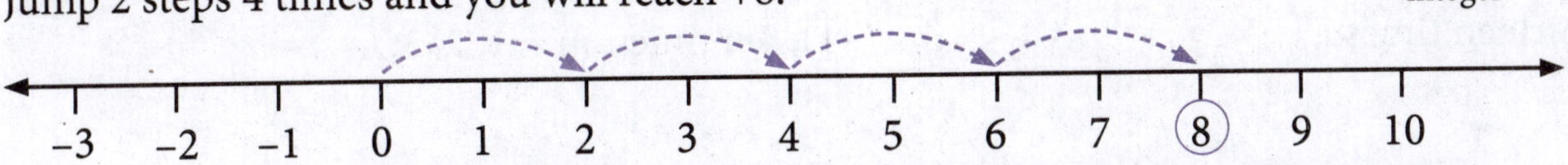

> The product of two negative integers is always a positive integer.

Product of Three or More Negative Integers

We have seen that the product of two negative integers is always a positive integer.

What will be the sign of the product when three or more negative integers are multiplied?

Observe the following examples.

(–3) × (–6) = 18

(–3) × (–6) × (–2) = 18 × (–2) = (–36)

(–3) × (–6) × (–2) × (–5) = (–36) × (–5) = 180

(–3) × (–6) × (–2) × (–5) × (–4) = 180 × (–4) = (–720)

We can conclude the following from the above examples:

- The product of two negative integers is a positive integer.
- The product of three negative integers is a negative integer.
- The product of four negative integers is a positive integer.
- The product of five negative integers is a negative integer.

+ × + = +

+ × – = –

– × + = –

– × – = +

Observe that the product is a positive integer when the number of negative integers that are multiplied is even (2, 4, 6...). The product is a negative integer when the number of negative integers that are multiplied is odd (3, 5, 7...).

Go Easy!

- If the number of negative integers being multiplied is even, then the product is a positive integer.
- If the number of negative integers being multiplied is odd, then the product is a negative integer.

Special case: Multiplication by (–1)

$(-1) \times (-1) = 1$ $\quad$ $(-1) \times (-1) \times (-1) = (-1)$

$(-1) \times (-1) \times (-1) = (-1)$ $\quad$ $(-1) \times (-1) \times (-1) \times (-1) \times (-1) = (-1)$

- If (–1) is multiplied even number of times, then the product is +1.
- If (–1) is multiplied odd number of times, then the product is (–1).

SOLVED EXAMPLES

Example 5: Find the products for the following.

a. $5 \times (-13)$ $\quad$ b. $(-21) \times 9$ $\quad$ c. $(-8) \times (-7)$ $\quad$ d. $(-3) \times (-2) \times 4 \times (-1)$

Solution:

a. $5 \times (-13) = (-65)$ $\quad$ b. $(-21) \times 9 = (-189)$

c. $(-8) \times (-7) = 56$ $\quad$ d. $(-3) \times (-2) \times 4 \times (-1) = 6 \times 4 \times (-1) = -24$

Example 6: Write whether the product is a positive or a negative integer in each case.

a. 4 positive and 4 negative integers $\quad$ b. 3 negative and 5 positive integers

c. (–1) thirteen times $\quad$ d. (–1), 3*m* times, *m* = 1, 2, 3...

Solution:

a. 4 positive and 4 negative integers: Positive integer

b. 3 negative and 5 positive integers: Negative integer

c. (–1) thirteen times: Negative integer

d. (–1), 3*m* times, *m* = 1, 2, 3... : Negative integer if *m* is odd and positive integer if *m* is even

PROPERTIES OF MULTIPLICATION OF INTEGERS

Closure Property

For any two integers *a* and *b*, $a \times b$ is also an integer.

Observe the following.

$12 \times 4 = 48$	$(-5) \times 3 = (-15)$	$8 \times (-6) = (-48)$	$(-11) \times (-7) = 77$

Is the product of any two integers an integer? ______

Are integers closed under multiplication? ______

Commutative Property

For any two integers a and b, $a \times b = b \times a$.

Observe and complete the following table.

a	b	$a \times b$	$b \times a$	Is $a \times b = b \times a$?
8	13	104	104	Yes
(–6)	2			
5	(–9)			
(–3)	(–7)			

Therefore, integers are commutative under multiplication.

Associative Property

For any three integers a, b and c, $a \times (b \times c) = (a \times b) \times c$.

Observe and complete the following table.

a	b	c	$a \times (b \times c)$	$(a \times b) \times c$
3	(–5)	(–7)	$3 \times [(-5) \times (-7)] = 3 \times 35 = 105$	$[3 \times (-5)] \times (-7) = (-15) \times (-7) = 105$
(–6)	2	4	$(-6) \times (2 \times 4) = (-6) \times 8 = (-48)$	$[(-6) \times 2] \times 4 = (-12) \times 4 = (-48)$
(–4)	(–3)	5		
8	3	(–5)		

From the above table, we find that $a \times (b \times c) = (a \times b) \times c$.

Therefore, integers are associative under multiplication.

Distributive Property

Distributive law of multiplication over addition:

For any three integers a, b and c, $a \times (b + c) = (a \times b) + (a \times c)$.

We know that multiplication of whole numbers is distributive over addition.

That is, $4 \times (2 + 6) = (4 \times 2) + (4 \times 6)$.

Let us see if this is true with respect to integers. Consider $(-4) \times (2 + 6)$.

$(-4) \times (2 + 6) = (-4) \times 8 = (-32)$

$[(-4) \times 2] + [(-4) \times 6] = (-8) + (-24) = (-32)$

$\Rightarrow (-4) \times (2 + 6) = (-4) \times 2 + (-4) \times 6$

Therefore, multiplication of integers is distributive over addition.

Distributive law of multiplication over subtraction:

For any three integers a, b and c, $a \times (b - c) = (a \times b) - (a \times c)$.

Consider $(-4) \times (2 - 6)$

$(-4) \times (2 - 6) = (-4) \times (-4) = 16$

$[(-4) \times 2] - [(-4) \times 6] = (-8) - (-24) = (-8) + 24 = 16$

$\Rightarrow (-4) \times (2 - 6) = (-4) \times 2 - (-4) \times 6$

Therefore, multiplication of integers is distributive over subtraction.

Multiplication by Zero

The product of a whole number and zero is always a zero.

On extending the same for integers, we have the following.

$(-4) \times 0 = 0$ $\quad 0 \times (-6) = 0$ $\quad 8 \times 0 = 0$ $\quad 0 \times (-11) = 0$

Therefore, the product of an integer with zero is zero.

For any integer a,
$a \times 0 = 0 \times a = 0$.

Multiplicative Identity

We know that 1 is the multiplicative identity for whole numbers. Can 1 be the multiplicative identity for integers as well?

Find the following.

$(-4) \times 1 =$ ______ $\quad 1 \times (-12) =$ ______ $\quad$ ______ $\times 18 = 18$ $\quad 7 \times 1 =$ ______

Therefore, 1 is the multiplicative identity for integers.

For any integer a, $a \times 1 = 1 \times a = a$.

SOLVED EXAMPLES

Example 7: Verify $[(-4) \times (-7)] \times (-2) = (-4) \times [(-7) \times (-2)]$

Solution: Consider LHS $= [(-4) \times (-7)] \times (-2) = 28 \times (-2) = (-56)$

RHS $= (-4) \times [(-7) \times (-2)] = (-4) \times 14 = (-56)$

LHS = RHS

Therefore, $[(-4) \times (-7)] \times (-2) = (-4) \times [(-7) \times (-2)]$

Example 8: Using distributive property of multiplication of integers, evaluate $(-17) \times [(-5) + (-3)]$.

Solution: Distributive property states $a \times (b + c) = (a \times b) + (a \times c)$.

$(-17) \times [(-5) + (-3)] = (-17) \times (-5) + (-17) \times (-3) = (85) + (51) = 136$

Thus, $(-17) \times [(-5) + (-3)] = 136$.

Example 9: Find the following products using distributive law.

a. 18×24 $\quad$ b. $(-25) \times 37$ $\quad$ c. $(-44) \times 6 - 44 \times (-4)$

Solution:

a. $18 \times 24 = 18 \times (20 + 4) = (18 \times 20) + (18 \times 4) = 360 + 72 = 432$

b. $(-25) \times 37 = (-25) \times (40 - 3) = (-25 \times 40) - (-25 \times 3) = -1000 + 75 = -925$

c. $(-44) \times 6 - 44 \times (-4) = (44) \times (-6) - 44 \times (-4) = 44 \times [(-6) - (-4)] = 44 \times (-2) = (-88)$

WORD PROBLEMS

We have seen different operations on integers. Let us solve a few problems using them.

Example 10: In a class test containing 20 questions, 3 marks are given for every correct answer and (–1) mark is given for every incorrect answer.

a. John attempts only 9 questions and gets all of them correct. What is his total score?

b. Olivia attempts all questions but gets 11 answers correct. What will be her score?

Solution: Given: Marks for one correct answer = 3; Marks for one incorrect answer = –1

a. To find: John's total score

Number of correct answers = 9

Marks for 9 correct answers = $9 \times 3 = 27$

Therefore, John's total score is 27.

b. To find: Olivia's total score

Number of correct answers = 11

Number of incorrect answers = $20 - 11 = 9$

Marks for 11 correct answers = $11 \times 3 = 33$

Marks for 9 incorrect answers = $9 \times (-1) = -9$

Total marks = $33 + (-9) = 24$

Therefore, Olivia's total score is 24.

Example 11: At 4 a.m., the temperature of a country was –2°C and after 6 hours, the temperature was 5°C.

a. Find the rise in temperature.

b. The temperature of another country was 3°C more than that of this country at 4 a.m. What is the temperature of the other country at 4 a.m.?

Solution: Given: Temperature at 4 a.m. = –2°C; Temperature after 6 hours, i.e., at 10 a.m. = 5°C

a. To find: Rise in temperature

Rise in temperature = 5°C – (–2°C) = 7°C

Therefore, the temperature rose by 7°C.

b. To find: Temperature of another country at 4 a.m.

Temperature of another country at 4 a.m. = –2°C + 3°C = 1°C

Therefore, the temperature of the other country at 4 a.m. is 1°C.

Example 12: The statement of account of a savings account of Mr. Ravi is as follows. Fill in the blank spaces. What will be the balance amount as on 5th March 2020?

Mr. Ravi
#2, Anjuna Enclave
Chromepet
Chennai

Account No: xxxxxxxxxx7902

From: 1/03/2020 To: 5/03/2020 Statement of account

Date	Narration	Withdrawal Amt.	Deposit Amt.	Closing Balance
1/03/2020	NEFT		4250.00	4250.00
2/03/2020	Salary Credited		8500.00	
3/03/2020	ATM Withdrawal	3500.00		
4/03/2020	Monthly Interest Credit		240.00	
5/03/2020	Monthly EMI	4825.00		

Solution:

Mr. Ravi
#2, Anjuna Enclave
Chromepet
Chennai

Account No: xxxxxxxxxx7902

From: 1/03/2020 To: 5/03/2020 Statement of account

Date	Narration	Withdrawal Amt.	Deposit Amt.	Closing Balance
1/03/2020	NEFT		4250.00	4250.00
2/03/2020	Salary Credited		8500.00	12750.00
3/03/2020	ATM Withdrawal	3500.00		9250.00
4/03/2020	Monthly Interest Credit		240.00	9490.00
5/03/2020	Monthly EMI	4825.00		4665.00

Therefore, the balance amount as on 5th March 2020 is ₹4665.

Example 13: Eva likes to bake. She has 5 aluminium muffin pans and 3 cast iron muffin pans holding 7 muffins each. She also has four stainless steel muffin pans that can hold 12 muffins each. If Eva fills all her muffin pans at once, how many muffins would that be?

Solution: Given: Number of aluminium pans = 5

Number of cast iron pans = 3

Number of muffins in each aluminium or cast iron pan = 7

Number of stainless steel pans = 4

Number of muffins in each stainless steel pan = 12

To find: Total number of muffins

Total number of muffins = $(7 \times 5) + (7 \times 3) + (12 \times 4) = 7 \times (5 + 3) + (12 \times 4)$

$= (7 \times 8) + 48 = 56 + 48 = 104$

Therefore, there would be 104 muffins altogether.

EXERCISE 1C

1. Write the nature of signs of the multiplicand and multiplier based on their product.

Sign of the product	Sign of the multiplicand	Sign of the multiplier
Positive		
Negative		

2. Find the following products.

a. (−13) × (−1) b. (−15) × 20 c. (−24) × (−1) × 9

d. (−1) × (−2) × (−3) × (−4) e. 8 × (−7) × (−6) f. 11 × (−9) × 5

3. Fill in the blanks to make each statement true.

a. (−7) × ______ = (−7) b. ______ × (−13) = (−117) c. (−14) × ______ = 0

d. (−15) × ______ = 120 e. ______ × (−5) = 50 f. (−11) × ____ = (−121)

4. Find the product using suitable properties.

a. (−16) × (−23) + (−16) × 37 b. 12 × 7 × 106 c. 98 × (−34)

d. 72 − (−18) × 72 e. 21 × (−29) + (−29) × 47 f. (−5) × (65 − 8)

5. Answer the following questions.

a	*b*	*c*
−6	7	−2
4	−9	−5
−21	−12	5

a. Verify the associative and distributive property of integers with respect to multiplication for the values of *a*, *b* and *c* given in the table.

b. A unit test consisting of 15 questions was held in a class. Three marks were given for each correct answer and (−1) mark for every incorrect answer. Also, for those questions that were attempted, 1 mark was given.

i. What is Liva's score if she attempted only 10 questions?

ii. James gets 8 incorrect and 7 correct answers. What is his score?

iii. Syria gets 6 correct and 5 incorrect answers. She also attempts the remaining questions. Calculate her score.

c. A process in pharmaceuticals requires the room temperature to be lowered from 28°C at the rate of 4°C per hour. What would be the room temperature attained in 9 hours after the process has begun?

d. A housewife along with a group of ladies sold bags of different sizes. She earns a profit of ₹25 on a purse and a loss of ₹20 on a vanity bag sold.

i. She received an order of 1050 vanity bags and 1000 purses. What is her profit or loss?

ii. How many purses must she sell to have neither profit nor loss, if the number of vanity bags sold is 750?

iii. How much profit/loss did she make in selling 325 purses and 513 vanity bags?

DIVISION OF INTEGERS

We have learnt about division of whole numbers. We also know that division is the inverse process of multiplication. Let us extend the same for integers.

Observe the following.

Multiplication statement	Corresponding division statements	
	Statement 1	Statement 2
$3 \times (-4) = (-12)$	$(-12) \div 3 = (-4)$	$(-12) \div (-4) = 3$
$(-7) \times 9 = (-63)$	$(-63) \div (-7) = 9$	$(-63) \div 9 = (-7)$
$(-6) \times (-5) = 30$	$30 \div (-5) = (-6)$	$30 \div (-6) = (-5)$

From the above table, we can conclude that

- division of a positive and negative integer is a negative integer.
- division of two negative integers is a positive integer.

Note

Divide the whole numbers first and then put the sign accordingly.

Find the following:

$(-50) \div 5 =$ ______ $(-75) \div (-3) =$ ______

$72 \div (-8) =$ ______ $(-64) \div 4 =$ ______

PROPERTIES OF DIVISION OF INTEGERS

Closure Property

For any two integers *a* and *b*, $a \div b$ need not be an integer.

Observe and complete the following.

$(-40) \div 2 =$ ______	$(-9) \div 27 =$ ______	$20 \div (-5) =$ ______	$(-30) \times (-9) =$ ______

Is the division of any two integers an integer? ________

Are integers closed under division? ________

Therefore, integers are not closed under division.

Commutative Property

For any two distinct integers *a* and *b*, $a \div b \neq b \div a$.

Observe and complete the following table.

a	b	$a \div b$	$b \div a$	Is $a \div b = b \div a$?
(−6)	2			
7	(−9)			
(−8)	(−4)			

Therefore, integers are not commutative under division.

Associative Property

For any three distinct non-zero integers a, b and c, $a \div (b \div c) \neq (a \div b) \div c$.

Consider the integers 18, 6 and 3.

$18 \div (6 \div 3) = 18 \div 3 = 9$

$(18 \div 6) \div 3 = 3 \div 3 = 1$

Therefore, $18 \div (6 \div 3) \neq (18 \div 6) \div 3$

It is clear that integers are not associative under division.

Note

Properties / Operations		INTEGERS			
		Addition	Subtraction	Multiplication	Division
Closed	Under	√	√	√	×
Commutative		√	×	√	×
Associative		√	×	√	×

Property of 1

For any integer a, $a \div 1 = a$.

Find the following.

$8 \div 1 =$ _____ $(-17) \div 1 =$ _____ $(-65) \div 1 =$ _____.

Therefore, any integer divided by 1 gives the same integer.

Mental Maths

a. $(-7) \div 1$

b. $0 \div (-21)$

c. $48 \div 1$

Property of 0

Similar to whole numbers, zero divided by a non-zero integer is always zero.

For any non-zero integer a, $0 \div a = 0$.

SOLVED EXAMPLES

Example 14: Evaluate the following.

a. $42 \div [(-15) + 8]$ b. $(-10) \div [(-20) \div 4]$ c. $[40 + (-100)] \div [(-9) + 29]$

Solution:

a. $42 \div [(-15) + 8] = 42 \div (-7) = (-6)$

b. $(-10) \div [(-20) \div 4] = (-10) \div (-5) = 2$

c. $[40 + (-100)] \div [(-9) + 29] = (-60) \div 20 = (-3)$

Example 15: What is the value of a if $a \times (-6) = 78$?

Solution: $a \times (-6) = 78 \Rightarrow a = 78 \div (-6) = (-13)$

Therefore, $a = (-13)$

Example 16: In a class test, (+4) marks are given for every correct answer and (–3) marks are given for every incorrect answer. Manu answered all the questions and scored 17 marks though she got 8 correct answers. How many incorrect answers did he attempt?

Solution: Given: Marks given for one correct answer = 4

Marks given for one incorrect answer = –3

Number of correct answers = 8

Manu's score = 17

To find: Number of incorrect answers attempted

Marks given for 8 correct answers = 8 × 4 = 32

Marks obtained for incorrect answers = 17 – 32 = –15

Number of incorrect answers = (–15) ÷ (–3) = 5

Therefore, Manu attempted 5 incorrect answers.

Example 17: A bakery owner earns a profit of ₹5 by selling a cake. While selling the previous day's items, he incurs a loss of ₹3 for every puff sold. During a day, he sold 65 cakes and few puffs of the previous day. Find the number of puffs sold by him if his net profit is ₹121.

Solution: Given: Profit earned by selling a cake = ₹5

Loss incurred by selling a puff = ₹3

Number of cakes sold = 65

Net profit = ₹121

To find: Number of puffs sold

Profit earned by selling 65 cakes = 65 × 5 = ₹325

Net profit = Profit earned by selling cakes – Loss incurred by selling puffs

121 = 325 – 3 × Number of puffs sold

Or, 3 × Number of puffs sold = 325 – 121 = ₹204

Number of puffs sold = 204 ÷ 3 = 68

Therefore, the owner sold 68 puffs during that month.

Example 18: Vani took altogether a loan of ₹55,800 from 3 banks located at different places. If she has taken the same amount from all the banks, how much loan amount did she get from each bank?

Solution: Given: Loan amount = ₹55,800

Number of banks = 3

To find: Loan amount in each bank

Loan amount in each bank = ₹55,800 ÷ 3 = ₹18,600

Therefore, each bank has given a loan amount of ₹18,600.

Example 19: An elevator descends into an underground column at the rate of 25 m/min. If the descent starts from 20 m above the ground level, how long will it take to reach –280 m?

Solution: Given: Initial height = + 20 m; final depth = –280 m; rate of descending = 25 m/min.

To find: Time taken to reach –280 m

Total distance travelled by the elevator = 20 – (–280) = 300 m

We know that Time = Total distance ÷ Rate of travel = (300) ÷ (25) = 12 minutes

Therefore, the elevator takes 12 minutes to reach –280 m.

EXERCISE 1D

1. Evaluate the following.

a. $(-64) \div 8$
b. $81 \div (-3)$
c. $14 \div [(-7) - (-5)]$
d. $[42 \div (-2)] \div (-7)$
e. $[(-39) \div 13] \div (8 - 11)$
f. $[120 \div (-4)] \div [6 - (-9)]$

2. Fill in the blanks.

a. $32 \div$ ______ $= 32$
b. ______ $\div (-54) = 1$
c. ______ $\div 1 = 99$
d. $(-123) \div$ ______ = not defined
e. $86 \div$ ______ $= (-1)$
f. $(-1) \div$ ______ $= 1$

3. Complete the following puzzle.

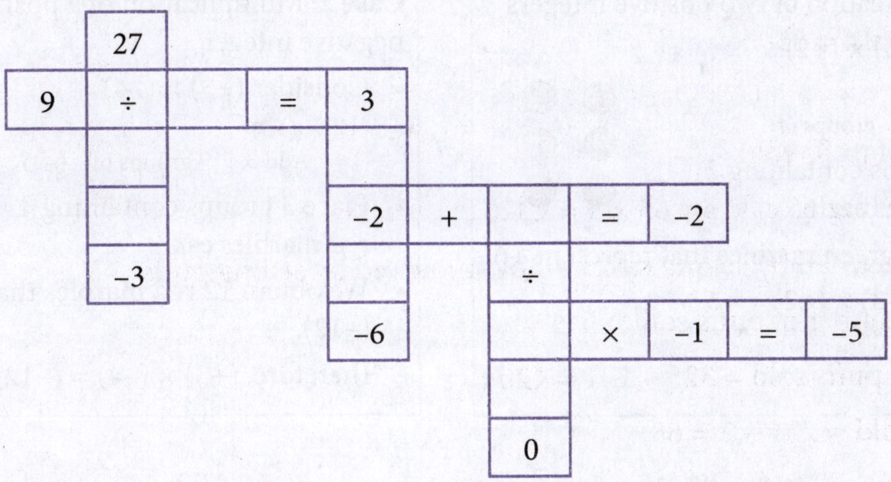

4. Answer the following questions.

a. Show that division is not associative by considering the integers 18, (–6) and 3.

b. A pair of integers is such that $x \div y = (-5)$. Write any 3 such pairs.

c. In an online quiz on sports, Mary loses points for every incorrect answer chosen. The table given below shows the points lost by her in two different quiz.

Quiz	Points lost for each wrong answer	Total points lost
1	4	44
2	7	91

In which quiz, did she give more wrong answers?

d. The profit obtained on selling smart phones is ₹2500 per piece and that on selling old mobiles with keypad is ₹900 per piece. During a month, a shopkeeper obtained a net profit of ₹17900. In this period, he sold 5 android mobiles. How many old mobiles did he sell in that period?

e. People from villages move to cities to seek employment opportunities. How many years will it take for 1216 people from a village to move to a city at a rate of 152 per year? Find the number of people who move to cities in 3 years.

MATHS LAB ACTIVITY

Aim: To multiply two integers

Materials required: Green and red coloured marbles

Instructions: The green marble represents +1 and the red marble represents (–1).

1 green marble and 1 red marble make a zero pair, i.e. $1 + (-1) = 0$.

A zero pair

● Represents green marbles

○ Represents red marbles

Procedure:

Case 1: Multiplication of two positive integers

- Consider $(+3) \times (+2)$

(+3) Add 3 × groups of (+2) 2

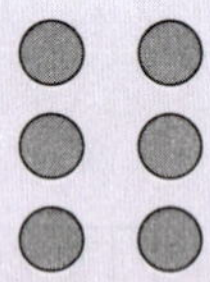

- Place 3 groups containing 2 green marbles each.
- We obtain 6 green marbles that represent +6.

Therefore, $(+3) \times (+2) = +6$

Case 2: Multiplication of a positive integer by a negative integer.

- Consider $(+3) \times (-4)$

(+3) Add 3 × groups of (–4) (–4)

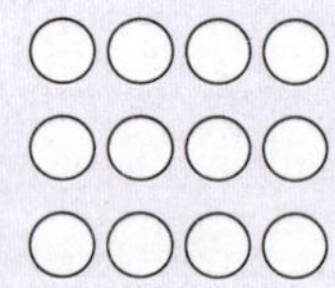

- Place 3 groups containing 4 red marbles each.
- We obtain 12 red marbles that represent (–12).

Therefore, $(+3) \times (-4) = (-12)$

Case 3: Multiplication of a negative integer by a positive integer.

- Consider $(-3) \times 2$

(–3) Take away 3 × groups of 2 2

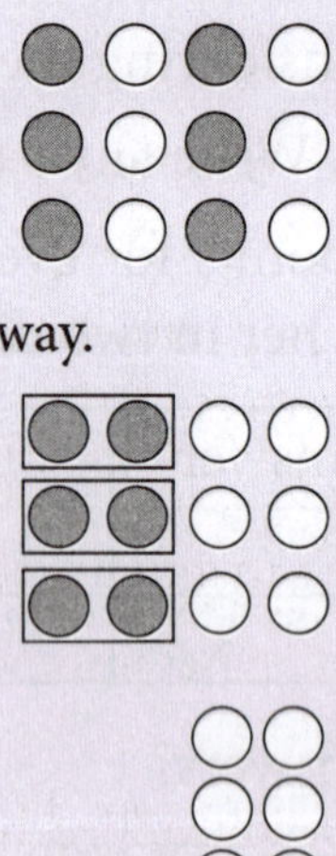

- There are no marbles to take away.
- Now take away 3 groups of 2 green marbles each.
- We obtain 6 red marbles that represent (–6).

Therefore, $(-3) \times 2 = (-6)$

Case 4: Multiplication of two negative integers

- Consider $(-3) \times (-4)$

(–3) Take away 3 × groups of (–4) (–4)

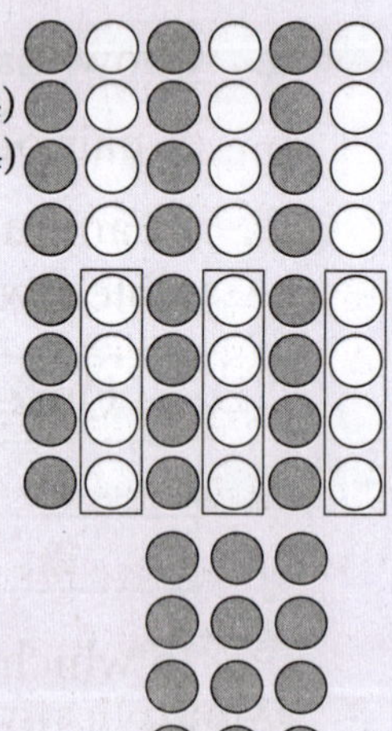

- There are no marbles to take away. So let us include 12 zero pairs.
- Now take away 3 groups of 4 red marbles each.
- We obtain 12 green marbles that represent (+12).

Therefore, $(-3) \times (-4) = +12$

Concept Map

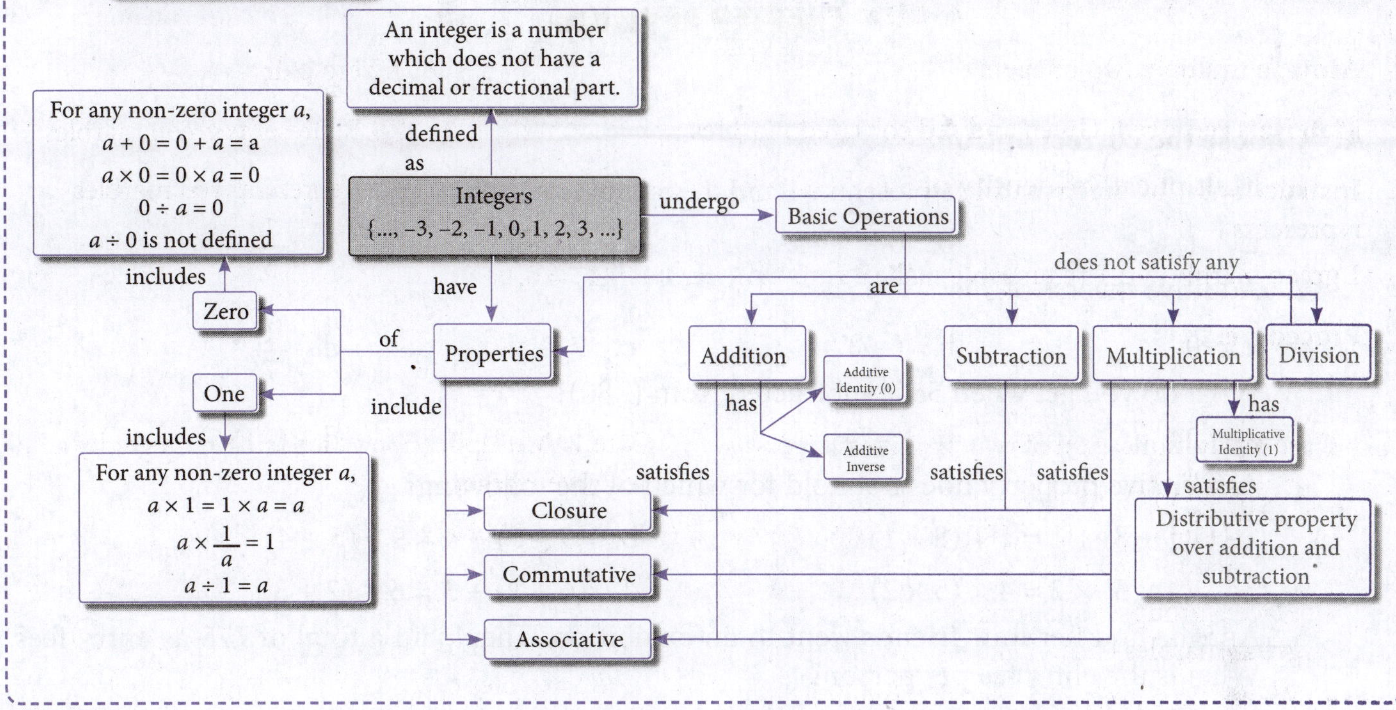

Key Concepts

- **Integers:** Numbers which do not have a decimal or fractional part
- **Closure:** The property of an operation (+, –, ×, ÷) in which the result obtained on performing the operation between any two integers should be an integer only
- **Commutativity:** The property of an operation (+, –, ×, ÷) in which the result obtained on performing the operation between any two integers should be the same irrespective of the order of numbers
- **Associativity:** The property of an operation (+, –, ×, ÷) in which the result obtained on performing the operation among any three integers is the same irrespective of the grouping of numbers without changing their order
- **Additive identity:** The number which when added to any number gives back the same number
- **Additive inverse:** The additive inverse of an integer is that number which when added to its opposite gives zero
- **Multiplicative identity:** The number which when multiplied by any number gives back the same number

CHAPTER REVISION

A. Choose the correct option.

1. Multiplicative identity of 5 is

 a. 1 b. 0 c. 5 d. $\frac{1}{5}$

2. Additive inverse of 7 is

 a. 0 b. (–7) c. 7 d. $\frac{1}{7}$

3. What do you get when 56 is subtracted from (–80)?

 a. 24 b. (–24) c. 136 d. (–136)

4. Associative property does not hold for which of the following?

 a. $(1 + 8) + 1 = 1 + (8 + 1)$ b. $(9 - 5) + 4 = 9 - (5 + 4)$

 c. $(4 \times 5) \times 2 = 4 \times (5 \times 2)$ d. $(6 + 2) + 3 = 6 + (2 + 3)$

5. Anagha and her four friends went to an exhibition. They paid a total of ₹75 as entry fees. What is the entry fee per person?

 a. ₹300 b. ₹18.75 c. ₹15 d. ₹75

B. Write T for true and F for false.

1. The sum of a positive and a negative integer is always a negative integer.
2. Division of integers is not associative.
3. The sign of the product of 5 negative and 3 positive integers is negative.
4. The additive identity for integers is 1.
5. Multiplicative inverse is the reciprocal of a number.

C. Evaluate the following.

1. $9 \times (4 + 15)$	2. $56 \times (5 + 10)$	3. $33 \times (40 - 10)$
4. $1560 \div (15 - 10)$	5. $2004 \div (501 - 167)$	6. $(-245) + 90 + (-140)$
7. $12 \div [(13) + (-13)]$	8. $(-5) \times (-4) \times (-6)$	9. $[95 - (-125)] \div [(-13) + 9]$

D. Take suitable integers and verify the following.

1. Subtraction is not commutative.
2. Multiplication is associative.
3. Division is not closed.
4. Multiplication is distributive over subtraction.
5. Product of odd number of negative integers is a negative integer.

E. Solve the following word problems.

1. A kite flew to a height of 50 ft. It rises at the rate of 2 ft per minute. How high will it be in 10 minutes?
2. On a particular day, the stock market value has reached to a maximum of 28000. If it loses 150 points every hour for 5 hours, what is its value after 5 hours?

3. In a competitive exam consisting of 100 questions, 2 marks are awarded for each correct answer and –1 for each wrong answer. If a student has written 70 correct answers and 30 wrong answers, what is his/her score?
4. The temperature of Bangalore on a sunny day was 20°C in the morning. The temperature increased by 19°C by noon. It remained at that temperature for 5 hours and then decreased by 15°C. What would be the temperature of the city at 8 p.m.?
5. Mukesh's breakfast costs ₹30 per day at a restaurant. If he deposits an amount of ₹510 in that restaurant, how many days can he have his breakfast there?

SKILL UP!

Project

1. The solar system is a planetary system consisting of the sun and other objects that orbit around it. Among all the objects, there are eight large planets. Find the minimum and maximum surface temperature of each planet. Find out why life is possible only on Earth. Make a presentation on the same.
2. Atom is the smallest constituent of matter. It has components, namely protons, neutrons and electrons. Find out the sign used for denoting protons and electrons. Find the number of protons and electrons in different atoms such as carbon, oxygen and nitrogen.

Life Skills

Underwater diving, as a human activity, is the practice of diving into water with special breathing equipment. What is the industrial standard depth limit for recreational divers? What are the various types, advantages and disadvantages of underwater diving?

On 11 July 2008, a team of divers rescued young Thai boys from a cave. Find out more about it.

Mind Buzzer

Write all the pairs of integers such that their product is 24. Find the pair that has the least sum.

Teacher's Notes

- Give problems such as 5 × 99, 5 × 999, 5 × 2999 and ask the students to find answers using distributive law of multiplication over addition and subtraction to understand the concept better.
- Give oral drills on the following: a. properties of integers and b. sign of the product (quotient) when integers are multiplied (divided).
- Draw a number line on the floor and make the students practice multiplication of integers on the number line by making them jump on the line drawn.

WORKSHEET

Solve the integer problems given in Table 1. Then, write the corresponding letters associated with the answers in Table 2 and find the secret message.

Table 1

(–39) – (–46)	R
2 × (–4) × 11	H
(54) ÷ (–6)	O
(–20) + 8	U
(–1) × (–7) × (–15)	A
62 + (–29)	T
11 + [(–40) ÷ 8]	N
43 – (–21)	S
5 × 4 × (–3)	L
[29 – (–3)] ÷ (–4)	T
(–10) × 0	M
20 ÷ [5 × (–2)]	I
(–17) + (–38)	N
(–2) × 3 × (–5) × (–1)	S
[(–60) ÷ (–12)] – 3	A
75 – 100	F
(–11) × (–4)	E

Table 2

0	2	(–8)	(–88)	64

(–2)	(–30)

(–25)	(–12)	6

33	(–9)

(–60)	44	(–105)	7	(–55)

Secret message

____

____

2 Fractions and Decimals

Learning Objectives

- To learn multiplication and division of fractions
- To solve word problems on fractions
- To understand multiplication and division of decimals
- To solve word problems on decimals

Let's Get Started

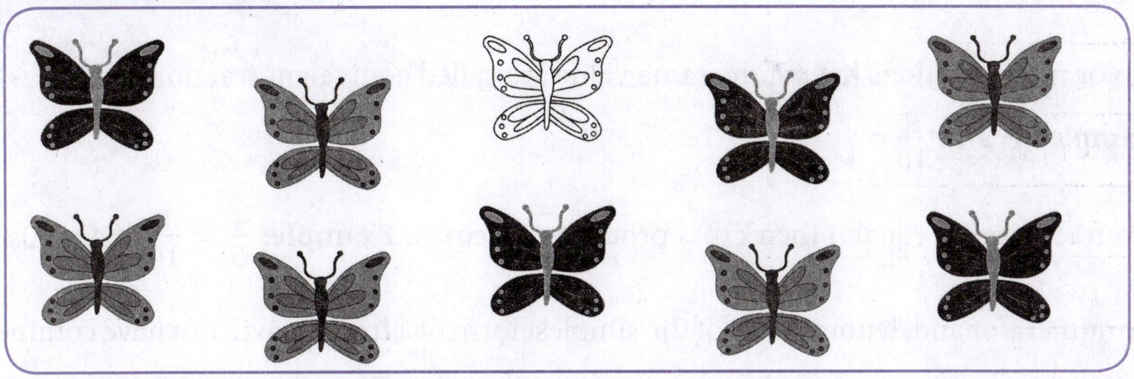

Observe the given picture and complete the table.

	Situation	Fractional representation	Type of fraction	Equivalent fraction
1.	Number of grey butterflies to total number of butterflies	$\frac{5}{10}$	Proper	$\frac{10}{20}$
2.	Number of black butterflies to total number of butterflies			
3.	Number of white butterflies to total number of butterflies			
4.	Number of grey butterflies to number of black butterflies			
5.	Number of white butterflies to number of black butterflies			
6.	Number of white butterflies to number of grey butterflies			

FRACTIONS

A **fraction** is a part of a whole or a collection. It is represented as $\frac{x}{y}$, where x is called the numerator and y is called the denominator of the fraction.

Let us quickly revise what we had learnt about fractions in Class 6.

> **Note**
> Each part must be equal for a fraction to be defined.

- Like fractions have the same denominators. **Examples:** $\frac{1}{10}, \frac{2}{10}, \frac{5}{10}, \frac{7}{10}$
- Unlike fractions have different denominators. **Examples:** $\frac{1}{5}, \frac{2}{3}, \frac{5}{7}, \frac{7}{10}$
- The numerator of a proper fraction is less than its denominator. **Examples:** $\frac{4}{5}, \frac{1}{3}, \frac{2}{7}, \frac{3}{10}$
- The numerator of an improper fraction is greater than its denominator.
  Examples: $\frac{8}{5}, \frac{5}{3}, \frac{11}{7}, \frac{3}{2}$
- Mixed fraction is the combination of a whole number and a proper fraction.
  Examples: $2\frac{1}{5}, 5\frac{2}{3}$
- Two or more fractions having the same value are called equivalent fractions.
  Example: $\frac{4}{5}$ and $\frac{8}{10}$
- Two fractions are equal if their cross products are equal. **Example:** $\frac{4}{5} = \frac{8}{10}$ if $4 \times 10 = 8 \times 5$
- The numerator and denominator of the simplest form of a fraction will not have common factors except 1. **Example:** The simplest form of $\frac{35}{25}$ is $\frac{7}{5}$.
- Like fractions can be compared by comparing the numerators. **Example:** $\frac{2}{10} < \frac{5}{10}$
- The sum or difference of like fractions can be found by adding or subtracting the numerators.
  Examples: $\frac{7}{10} + \frac{2}{10} = \frac{9}{10}$ and $\frac{7}{10} - \frac{2}{10} = \frac{3}{10}$
- Unlike fractions have to be converted into like fractions before comparing or adding or subtracting them.

  Example: Compare $\frac{1}{5}$ and $\frac{2}{3}$. $\frac{1}{5} \times \frac{3}{3} = \frac{3}{15}$ and $\frac{2}{3} \times \frac{5}{5} = \frac{10}{15}$. Therefore, $\frac{2}{3} > \frac{1}{5}$.

  Addition: $\frac{2}{3} + \frac{1}{5} = \frac{10}{15} + \frac{3}{15} = \frac{13}{15}$ Subtraction: $\frac{2}{3} - \frac{1}{5} = \frac{10}{15} - \frac{3}{15} = \frac{7}{15}$

MULTIPLICATION OF FRACTIONS

We know how to multiply whole numbers. We can multiply fractions in the same way. Let us learn how to multiply fractions.

Note

Convert the mixed fraction into improper fraction before multiplication and always retain the answer in its simplest form.

Multiplication of Fractions by Whole Numbers

To multiply a proper or an improper fraction by a whole number, multiply the whole number with the numerator of the fraction, and retain the denominator as it is.

Example 1: Multiply the following.

a. $\frac{1}{8}\times 5=\frac{1\times 5}{8}=\frac{5}{8}$ b. $\frac{4}{3}\times 2=\frac{4\times 2}{3}=\frac{8}{3}=2\frac{2}{3}$ c. $1\frac{6}{7}\times 5=\frac{13}{7}\times 5=\frac{13\times 5}{7}=\frac{65}{7}=9\frac{2}{7}$

Multiplication of Fractions by Fractions

To multiply a proper or an improper fraction by another fraction, multiply the numerators with the numerators and denominators with the denominators.

Example 2: Find the product.

a. $\frac{5}{8}\times\frac{7}{9}=\frac{5\times 7}{8\times 9}=\frac{35}{72}$ b. $\frac{8}{7}\times\frac{2}{5}=\frac{8\times 2}{7\times 5}=\frac{16}{35}$ c. $2\frac{3}{4}\times 1\frac{2}{3}=\frac{11}{4}\times\frac{5}{3}=\frac{11\times 5}{4\times 3}=\frac{55}{12}=4\frac{7}{12}$

Fraction as an Operator 'of'

The term 'of' represents multiplication.

Example 3: Solve the following.

a. How much is $\frac{2}{3}$ of 60 minutes?

$\frac{2}{3}$ of $60=\frac{2\times 60}{3}=\frac{120}{3}=40$

$\frac{2}{3}$ of 60 minutes is 40 minutes.

b. How much is $\frac{4}{9}$ of ₹180?

$\frac{4}{9}$ of $180=\frac{4\times 180}{9}=\frac{720}{9}=80$

$\frac{4}{9}$ of ₹180 is ₹80.

SOLVED EXAMPLES

Example 4: Find the products of the following.

a. $\frac{7}{9}\times 25=?$

Solution:

$\frac{7}{9}\times 25=\frac{7\times 25}{9}=\frac{175}{9}=19\frac{4}{9}$

$\frac{7}{9}\times 25=19\frac{4}{9}$

b. $2\frac{2}{5}\times 35=?$

Solution:

$2\frac{2}{5}\times 35=\frac{12}{5}\times 35=\frac{12\times 35}{5}=\frac{420}{5}=84$

$2\frac{2}{5}\times 35=84$

Example 5: Find the value of the following.

a. How much is $\frac{5}{7}$ of 4284?

Solution:

$$\frac{5}{7} \times 4284 = \frac{5 \times 4284}{7} = \frac{21420}{7} = 3060$$

$\frac{5}{7}$ of 4284 is 3060.

b. How much is $1\frac{4}{5}$ of 5240?

Solution:

$$1\frac{4}{5} \times 5240 = \frac{9}{5} \times 5240 = \frac{9 \times 5240}{5} = \frac{47160}{5} = 9432$$

$1\frac{4}{5}$ of 5240 is 9432.

EXERCISE 2A

1. **Find the product for each of the following.**

a. $2 \times \frac{1}{8}$ b. $10 \times \frac{5}{2}$ c. $5 \times \frac{3}{10}$ d. $\frac{5}{3} \times 99$

e. $\frac{3}{85} \times 45$ f. $100 \times \frac{6}{625}$ g. $\frac{13}{5} \times 80$ h. $\frac{56}{39} \times 10$

2. **Find the product of the following fractions.**

a. $\frac{1}{4} \times \frac{1}{5}$ b. $\frac{4}{5} \times \frac{10}{55}$ c. $\frac{5}{9} \times \frac{10}{8}$ d. $\frac{7}{8} \times \frac{7}{8}$

e. $\frac{8}{3} \times \frac{6}{5}$ f. $\frac{6}{10} \times 2\frac{7}{10}$ g. $\frac{4}{3} \times 5\frac{4}{5}$ h. $20\frac{3}{5} \times 3\frac{1}{10}$

3. **Find the value of the following.**

a. $\frac{1}{4}$ of 400 b. $\frac{1}{2}$ of 58 c. $\frac{1}{3}$ of 24 d. $\frac{1}{9}$ of 99

e. $\frac{2}{3}$ of 1200 f. $\frac{3}{5}$ of 345 g. $\frac{6}{5}$ of 400 h. $\frac{1}{8}$ of 160

RECIPROCAL OF A FRACTION

The reciprocal of a fraction is obtained by interchanging the position of the numerator and denominator.

Example 6: a. Reciprocal of $\frac{2}{5}$ is $\frac{5}{2}$. b. Reciprocal of $\frac{9}{4}$ is $\frac{4}{9}$.

c. Reciprocal of $3\frac{1}{2}$ is $\frac{2}{7}$. d. Reciprocal of 2 is $\frac{1}{2}$.

DIVISION OF FRACTIONS

We know that division is the inverse of multiplication. Thus, while dividing fractions, the division sign is changed to the multiplication sign and the given dividend is multiplied by the reciprocal of the divisor. Let us understand this with the help of some examples.

Division of Whole Numbers by Fractions

A whole number can be divided by a fraction by multiplying the given whole number by the reciprocal of the given fraction.

Example 7: Solve the following.

a. How many $\frac{1}{5}$ pieces will you get on cutting 3 apples into 5 pieces each?

$3 \div \frac{1}{5} = ?$

$3 \times \frac{5}{1} = \frac{3 \times 5}{1} = \frac{15}{1} = 15$

So, we will get 15 pieces.

b. How many $\frac{3}{4}$ m pieces will you get on cutting a 6 m piece of cloth?

$6 \div \frac{3}{4} = ?$

$6 \times \frac{4}{3} = \frac{6 \times 4}{3} = \frac{24}{3} = 8$

So, we will get 8 pieces.

Division of Fractions by Whole numbers

A fraction can be divided by a whole number by multiplying the given fraction by the reciprocal of the given whole number.

Example 8: Solve the following.

a. $\frac{5}{8} \div 5 = ?$

$\frac{5}{8} \times \frac{1}{5} = \frac{5}{40} = \frac{1}{8}$

So, $\frac{5}{8} \div 5 = \frac{1}{8}$

b. $\frac{8}{10} \div 24 = ?$

$\frac{8}{10} \times \frac{1}{24} = \frac{8}{240} = \frac{1}{30}$

So, $\frac{8}{10} \div 24 = \frac{1}{30}$

Division of a Fraction by Another Fraction

A fraction can be divided by another fraction by multiplying the first fraction by the reciprocal of the second fraction.

Example 9: Solve the following.

a. $\frac{2}{3} \div \frac{8}{9} = ?$

$\frac{2}{3} \times \frac{9}{8} = \frac{18}{24} = \frac{3}{4}$

Therefore, $\frac{2}{3} \div \frac{8}{9} = \frac{3}{4}$

b. $\frac{4}{7} \div \frac{20}{21} = ?$

$\frac{4}{7} \times \frac{21}{20} = \frac{84}{140} = \frac{3}{5}$

Therefore, $\frac{4}{7} \div \frac{20}{21} = \frac{3}{5}$

SOLVED EXAMPLES

Example 10. Divide the following fractions.

a. $\frac{4}{11} \div 20$

Solution:

$\frac{4}{11} \times \frac{1}{20} = \frac{4}{220} = \frac{1}{55}$

$\therefore \frac{4}{11} \div 20 = \frac{1}{55}$

b. $\frac{2}{3} \div \frac{8}{9} = ?$

Solution:

$\frac{2}{3} \times \frac{9}{8} = \frac{18}{24} = \frac{3}{4}$

$\therefore \frac{2}{3} \div \frac{8}{9} = \frac{3}{4}$

EXERCISE 2B

1. Match the fractions with their reciprocals.

Fractions a. $\frac{1}{3}$ b. $\frac{5}{6}$ c. $\frac{3}{1}$ d. $\frac{5}{9}$ e. $2\frac{1}{8}$ f. $3\frac{1}{2}$

Reciprocals i. $\frac{6}{5}$ ii. $\frac{9}{5}$ iii. $\frac{8}{17}$ iv. $\frac{2}{7}$ v. $\frac{1}{3}$ vi. 3

2. Divide the following.

a. $3 \div \frac{1}{4}$ b. $12 \div \frac{4}{9}$ c. $108 \div \frac{12}{8}$ d. $10 \div 7\frac{1}{8}$

3. Divide the following fractions by the given whole numbers.

a. $\frac{15}{2} \div 100$ b. $\frac{4}{3} \div 25$ c. $3\frac{2}{3} \div 44$ d. $2\frac{3}{11} \div 6$

4. Divide the following fractions by the given fractions.

a. $\frac{3}{17} \div \frac{9}{34}$ b. $\frac{56}{10} \div \frac{8}{5}$ c. $4\frac{7}{8} \div 3\frac{1}{2}$ d. $3\frac{1}{4} \div 5\frac{1}{3}$

WORD PROBLEMS ON FRACTIONS

Let us solve a few word problems on multiplication and division of fractions.

Example 11: Ethan ate $\frac{3}{5}$ of a cake. How much cake did he eat if there was $\frac{1}{2}$ kg cake?

Given: Ethan ate $\frac{3}{5}$ of $\frac{1}{2}$ kg cake

To find: $\frac{3}{5}$ of 500 g ($\frac{1}{2}$ kg = 500 g)

Solution: $\frac{3}{5} \times 500 = \frac{3 \times 500}{5} = \frac{1500}{5} = 300$

Therefore, Ethan ate 300 g of the cake.

Example 12: Gowravi used an orange to make $\frac{2}{3}$ glass of fruit pulp. How much fruit pulp can be made using 30 such oranges?

Given: 1 orange to make $\frac{2}{3}$ glass of fruit pulp   To find: $\frac{2}{3}$ of 30 = ?

Solution: $\frac{2}{3}\times 30=\frac{2\times 30}{3}=\frac{60}{3}=20$

Therefore, Gowravi can make 20 glasses of fruit pulp using 30 oranges.

Example 13: Equal pieces of half a watermelon need to be distributed among five children. How much does each child get?

Given: Equal pieces of $\frac{1}{2}$ of a watermelon are distributed among 5 children

To find: Each child's share

Solution: $\frac{1}{2}\div 5=?$ $\frac{1}{2}\times\frac{1}{5}=\frac{1}{10}$

Therefore, each child gets $\frac{1}{10}$ of the watermelon.

Example 14: How many quarters are there in a half?

To find: Number of quarters in one-half

Solution: $\frac{1}{2}\div\frac{1}{4}=\frac{1}{2}\times\frac{4}{1}=\frac{4}{2}=2$

Therefore, there are 2 quarters in a half.

EXERCISE 2C

Solve the following word problems.

1. Bari bought $2\frac{1}{2}$ kg of tomatoes and he also bought onions that were 3 times the weight of tomatoes. Find the weight of onions.
2. Harish had 30 pieces of sweets. If he ate $\frac{7}{10}$ of them in one week, how many pieces of sweets did he eat?
3. In a school, there are 480 children. If $\frac{1}{3}$ of them are boys, find the number of boys.
4. A student lives 5 km from the school. He travels $\frac{3}{5}$ km of the total distance by bus and walks the remaining distance. How far does he travel by bus?
5. A cylindrical rod of length $15\frac{1}{5}$ m is cut into 12 pieces. Find the length of each piece.
6. A bus travels a distance of 10 km in $\frac{1}{5}$ hours. How many kilometres will it travel in 5 hours?
7. Eva bought $\frac{3}{4}$ kg of ice cream. If she divides this quantity of ice cream into $\frac{1}{8}$ portion, how many servings can she make?
8. How do you share $\frac{1}{2}$ chapatti between two members equally?

DECIMALS

The fractions in which the denominators are 10 or multiples of 10 are called **decimals**. Decimal points divide decimal numbers into the whole number part and the decimal part, that is, tenths, hundredths, thousandths, etc. Some interesting facts about decimals are as follows:

- Decimal numbers having the same number of decimal places are called like decimals.
  Examples: 0.25, 10.67, 1.23
- Decimal numbers having different number of decimal places are called unlike decimals.
  Examples: 7.1, 0.324, 90.06
- Decimal numbers are compared by comparing the whole numbers; if they are same, then compare the decimal part of the given numbers. **Example:** 1.78 > 0.7
- Unlike decimal numbers are compared by converting them to like decimals. Add zeros to convert unlike decimals to like decimals. **Example:** Consider 6.5 and 8.547. These are unlike decimals. Adding zeros to 6.5 makes it 6.500. Now we can compare, add or subtract 6.500 and 8.547.
- Addition or subtraction of decimal numbers is similar to that of the whole numbers. We add or subtract the digits based on their place value.

Example 15: Find the following.

a. Add 35.356 and 45.15.

	1			1		
	3	5	.	3	5	6
+	4	5	.	1	5	0
	8	0	.	5	0	6

b. Subtract 28.732 from 59.45.

		8		14	4	10
	5	~~9~~	.	~~4~~	~~5~~	~~0~~
–	2	8	.	7	3	2
	3	0	.	7	1	8

MULTIPLICATION OF DECIMALS

We learnt how to add and subtract decimal numbers. Now let us learn to multiply decimal numbers.

Multiplication of Whole Numbers with Decimals and Decimals with Decimals

To multiply a whole number with a decimal number, first multiply the given numbers by ignoring the decimal point. Then count the number of digits after the decimal point and place the point in the product counting from right to left.

Example 16: 45 × 3.5 = 157.5   2.56 × 5.1 = 13.056

Multiplication of Decimals by 10, 100 and 1000

To multiply a decimal number by 10, 100 or 1000, shift the decimal point in the product to the right by as many number of places as there are zeros after one.

Example 17: The weight of an object is 85.378 g. Find the weight of 10, 100 and 1000 such objects.

Solution: Weight of 10 objects = 85.378 × 10 = 853.78 g

Weight of 100 objects = 85.378 × 100 = 8537.8 g

Weight of 1000 objects = 85.378 × 1000 = 85378 g

SOLVED EXAMPLES

Example 18: Find the product of the following decimal numbers.

a. 75.42 × 45

Solution: Multiply 7542 and 45 = 7542 × 45 = 339390

(There are 2 digits after decimal point in the multiplicand (75.42). So, put the decimal point before 2 digits from the right.)

Therefore, 75.42 × 45 = 3393.90

b. 85.05 × 6.57

Solution: Multiply 8505 and 657 = 8505 × 657 = 5587785

(In total, there are 4 digits after decimal point in the multiplication fact. So, put the decimal point before 4 digits from the right.)

Therefore, 85.05 × 6.57 = 558.7785

Example 19: Complete the table.

Decimals	× 10	× 100	× 1000
75.3056	753.056	a.	75305.6
850.678	b.	85067.8	c.

a. 7530.56

b. 8506.78

c. 850678

EXERCISE 2D

1. **Multiply the following whole numbers by decimals.**

a. 0.2 × 7 b. 1.3 × 8 c. 4.2 × 12 d. 1.23 × 7

e. 12.1 × 5 f. 45.25 × 10 g. 126.13 × 10 h. 5.76 × 100

2. **Find the product of the following.**

a. 0.3 × 0.5 b. 0.03× 1.5 c. 0.005 × 0.06 d. 12.3 × 1.7

e. 25.4 × 15.3 f. 78.3 × 0.03 g. 2.98 × 4.55 h. 2.687 × 0.8

3. **Complete the following table.**

	Decimals	× 10	× 100	× 1000
a.	0.1	1	10	100
b.	0.002		0.2	
c.	1.2309			1230.9
d.	23.3450	233.450		
e.	999.999	9999.99		
f.	1.00009			1000.09

DIVISION OF DECIMALS

We have learnt to add, subtract and multiply decimal numbers. Now let us learn to divide decimal numbers.

Division of Decimal Numbers by Whole Numbers

To divide a decimal number by a whole number, first divide the given decimal number as whole numbers, and then place the decimal point in the quotient after the number of decimal places as given in the decimal number. Remember to count from right to left.

Example 20: Solve the following.

a. $8.4 \div 4 = ?$

$$\frac{84}{10} \div 4 = \frac{84}{10} \times \frac{1}{4} = \frac{84}{40} = 2\frac{4}{40} \text{ or } 2\frac{1}{10} = 2.1$$

$\therefore$ $8.4 \div 4 = 2.1$

b. $16.5 \div 3 = ?$

$$\frac{165}{10} \div 3 = \frac{165}{10} \times \frac{1}{3} = \frac{165}{30} = 5\frac{15}{30} \text{ or } 5\frac{1}{2} = 5.5$$

$\therefore$ $16.5 \div 3 = 5.5$

Division of Decimal Numbers by Decimal Numbers

To divide two decimal numbers, first convert the divisor into a whole number by multiplying both the dividend and the divisor by 10 or 100 or 1000, etc., depending upon the number of decimal places in the given divisor, and then, divide them.

Example 21: Divide the following.

a. $7.5 \div 1.5 = ?$

$$\frac{75}{10} \div \frac{15}{10} = \frac{75}{10} \times \frac{10}{15} = 5$$

$\therefore$ $7.5 \div 1.5 = 5$

b. $24.84 \div 1.2 = ?$

$$\frac{2484}{100} \div \frac{12}{10} = \frac{2484}{100} \times \frac{10}{12} = \frac{207}{10} = 20.7$$

$\therefore$ $24.84 \div 1.2 = 20.7$

Division of Decimal Numbers by 10, 100 and 1000

To divide a decimal number by 10, 100 or 1000, the digits of the given decimal number and the quotient remain the same. Only the decimal point in the quotient is shifted to the left by as many number of places as there are zeros after one in the divisor.

Example 22: If we cut a twine of length 3857 m into 10, 100 and 1000 pieces respectively, then find the length of each twine.

Solution: $3857 \div 10 = 385.7$ m

$3857 \div 100 = 38.57$ m

$3857 \div 1000 = 3.857$ m

Mental Maths

1. What is the reciprocal of 6?
2. Find the number of one-fourths in 2.
3. What is the product of 2 and $\frac{3}{4}$?
4. $\frac{2}{3}$ of 18 is ______.
5. $0.2 \times 0.02 \div 0.002 =$ ______.

SOLVED EXAMPLES

Example 23: Divide the following decimal numbers.

a. 93.6 ÷ 6

Solution: Convert the decimal number to fraction: $93.6 = \frac{936}{10}$

Now divide: $\frac{936}{10} \div 6 = \frac{936}{10} \times \frac{1}{6} = \frac{936}{60} = 15\frac{36}{60} = 15\frac{6}{10} = 15.6$

$\therefore$ 93.6 ÷ 6 = 15.6

b. 12.5 ÷ 2.5

Solution: Convert the decimal number to fraction: $12.5 = \frac{125}{10}$ and $2.5 = \frac{25}{10}$

Now divide: $\frac{125}{10} \div \frac{25}{10} = \frac{125}{10} \times \frac{10}{25} = 5$

$\therefore$ 12.5 ÷ 2.5 = 5

Example 24: Complete the following table.

Number	÷ 10	÷ 100	÷ 1000
84569	a.	845.69	b.
7523678	752367.8	c.	d.

a. 8456.9

b. 84.569

c. 75236.78

d. 7523.678

EXERCISE 2E

1. Divide the following decimal numbers by whole numbers.

a. 0.2 ÷ 5 b. 1.2 ÷ 8 c. 3.5 ÷ 10 d. 0.008 ÷ 32

e. 0.49 ÷ 7 f. 5.25 ÷ 10 g. 200.13 ÷ 5.25 h. 243.81 ÷ 9.03

2. Divide the following decimal numbers by decimal numbers.

a. 7.95 ÷ 0.05 b. 49.6 ÷ 0.02 c. 0.49 ÷ 0.7 d. 2.62 ÷ 13.1

e. 0.32 ÷ 0.04 f. 1.86 ÷ 0.03 g. 7.28 ÷ 0.8 h. 0.696 ÷ 0.4

3. Complete the following table.

	Decimals	÷ 10	÷ 100	÷ 1000
a.	0.12	0.012	0.0012	0.00012
b.	15.78	1.578		
c.	250.056			0.250056
d.	138.23	13.823	1.3823	
e.	1.902			0.001902
f.	1000.0001		10.000001	

WORD PROBLEMS ON DECIMALS

Now, let us learn to solve word problems on multiplication and division of decimals.

Example 25: Pabita spends 1.5 hours every day in the garden. Find the number of hours she would spend in the garden for 15 days.

Given: 1.5 hours every day

To find: Number of hours spent in the garden in 15 days

Solution: $1.5 \times 15 = 22.5$

Therefore, in 15 days, Pabita would spent 22.5 hours in the garden.

Example 26: Sayan can run 10.3 km in 1 hour. How many kilometres can he run in 3.5 hours?

Given: 10.3 km in 1 hour

To find: Number of kilometres he can run in 3.5 hours

Solution: $10.3 \times 3.5 = 36.05$

Therefore, Sayan can run 36.05 km in 3.5 hours.

Example 27: The distance between Aizawl and Reiek is 29.67 km. If a cyclist covers 12.9 km per hour, then how much time will he take to travel from Aizawl to Reiek?

Given: Distance between the two places = 29.67 km

Distance covered in an hour = 12.9 km

To find: Total time taken to travel from Aizawl to Reiek

Solution: $29.67 \div 12.9 = ?$

First convert decimals to whole numbers: $29.67 = \frac{2967}{100}$ and $12.9 = \frac{129}{10}$

Then divide: $\frac{2967}{100} \div \frac{129}{10} = \frac{2967}{100} \times \frac{10}{129} = \frac{29670}{12900} = \frac{230}{100} = 2.3$

Therefore, the cyclist will reach Reiek in 2.3 hours.

Example 28: A two-wheeler covers a distance of 42.5 km in 2.5 hours. What is the average speed of the two-wheeler?

Given: Distance covered by a two-wheeler = 42.5 km

Time taken = 2.5 hours

To find: Average speed

Solution: Average speed = Distance covered ÷ Time taken

$$42.5 \div 2.5 = \frac{425}{10} \div \frac{25}{10} = \frac{425}{10} \times \frac{10}{25} = 17$$

Therefore, the average speed of the two-wheeler is 17 km per hour.

EXERCISE 2F

Solve the following word problems.

1. Nishat takes 0.5 hours to walk from home to her school and then to come back. How many hours does she spend walking to and fro from school in a week, considering Sunday is a holiday.
2. The side of an equilateral triangle is 3.6 m. What is its perimeter?
3. A bike covers a distance of 45.75 km in 1 litre of petrol. How far will it go if there is 3.5 litres of petrol?
4. The cost of 8 books is ₹1057.20. What is the cost of 1 book?
5. A wire measures 68.4 m. How many pieces of 1.5 m each can be cut from this wire?
6. Sophia bought 1.2 ℓ of oil for lighting the lamps. She used 0.02 ℓ of oil for each lamp. How many lamps will she be able to light?
7. A pumpkin weighing 9.5 kg costs ₹128.25. Find the cost of the pumpkin per kg.

Maths Lab Activity

Aim: To compute the fraction of a fraction using paper models

Materials required: Patty paper, colour pencils

Procedure:

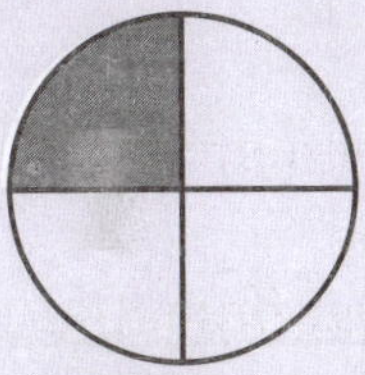

1. Consider an example for the multiplication of fractions, say $\frac{1}{2} \times \frac{1}{4}$.
2. Represent $\frac{1}{4}$ on a patty paper and shade it as shown.

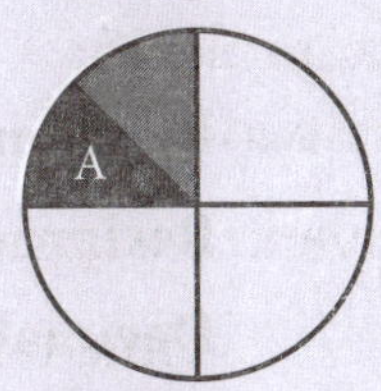

3. Divide $\frac{1}{4}$ part into two equal parts to represent $\frac{1}{2}$ of $\frac{1}{4}$ and name the part as A.
4. Now divide each part of the remaining whole into two equal parts as shown here.

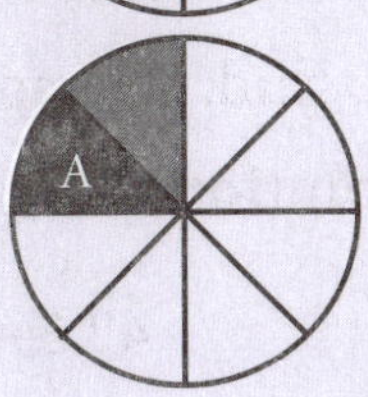

5. Now you will observe that the whole is first divided into 4 equal parts and each of the four parts is equally divided into 2 equal parts. So, now there are eight equal parts and A represents $\frac{1}{8}$ of the whole.

   That is, $\frac{1}{2} \times \frac{1}{4} = \frac{1 \times 1}{2 \times 4} = \frac{1}{8}$

6. Repeat the above steps to find the product of more fractions.

Conclusion: The activity will help to reinforce the concept of multiplication of fractions using paper models.

Concept Map

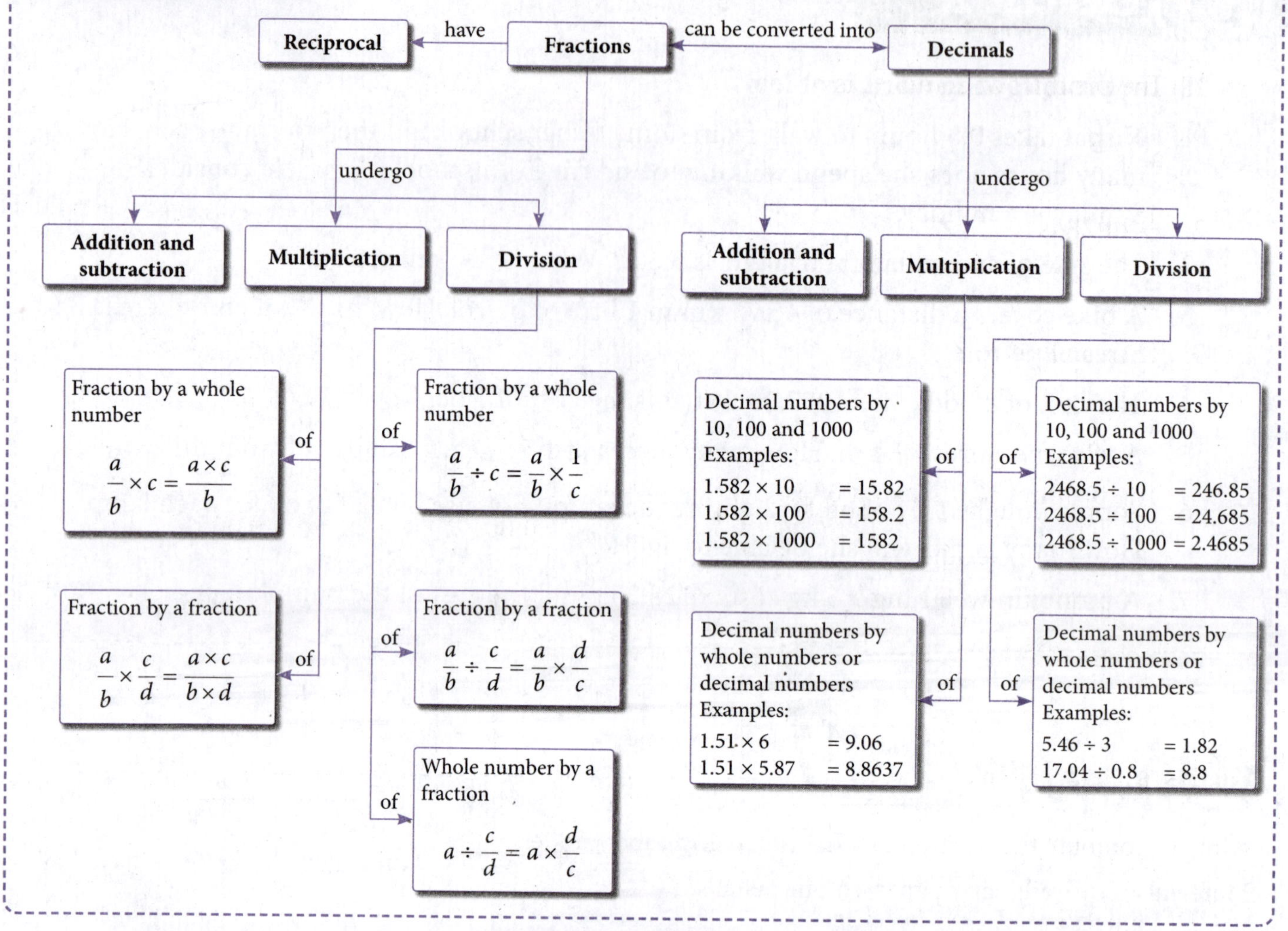

Key Concepts

- **Fraction:** It is a part of a whole or a collection
- **Reciprocal:** Inversing the position of numerator and denominator of the fraction
- **Decimal:** Fractions in which the denominators are 10 or multiples of 10

CHAPTER REVISION

A. Choose the correct option.

1. The product of 2 and $\frac{3}{2}$ is

   a. $\frac{3}{2}$ b. 2 c. 4 d. 3

2. $\frac{1}{2}$ of 28 is

   a. 3 b. 14 c. 8 d. 9

3. The value of $\frac{1}{4} \div \frac{1}{2}$ is

   a. $\frac{1}{8}$ b. $\frac{1}{6}$ c. $\frac{1}{2}$ d. $\frac{1}{3}$

4. The product of 0.25×0.005 is

   a. 0.025 b. 1.25 c. 0.00125 d. 0.005

5. The value of $1.25 \div 0.05$ is

   a. 0.25 b. 25 c. 25.15 d. 0.0075

B. Fill in the blanks.

1. $2 \times 4\frac{1}{2}$ is equal to ____________.
2. $\frac{3}{2} \div \frac{1}{2} =$ ____________
3. $\frac{1}{3}$ of 900 is ____________
4. $0.15 \times 0.5 =$ ____________
5. $25.36 \times 100 =$ ____________
6. $0.25 \div 0.50 =$ ____________

C. Write T for true and F for false.

1. The product of $\frac{3}{2}$ and $\frac{2}{3}$ is 1.
2. There are four one-fourths in 1.
3. $0.15 \times 0.5 = 0.025$.
4. $3.5 \div 10 = 0.35$.
5. The reciprocal of 3 is 0.3.
6. $\frac{1}{2}$ of 1000 is 500.

D. Match the following.

1.	$3 \times 5\frac{1}{2}$	a.	0.09
2.	$\frac{3}{8} \div \frac{1}{16}$	b.	135.2
3.	0.3×0.3	c.	0.1275
4.	1.352×100	d.	$\frac{33}{2}$
5.	$1.02 \div 8$	e.	7
6.	$3.5 \div 0.5$	f.	6

E. **Complete the following table.**

	Multiplication	Improper fraction	Mixed fraction
a.	$2 \times \frac{5}{3}$	$\frac{10}{3}$	$3\frac{1}{3}$
b.	$\frac{10}{11} \times \frac{5}{2}$	$\frac{50}{22}$	
c.	$2\frac{1}{2} \times \frac{8}{9}$		$2\frac{2}{9}$
d.	$\frac{10}{7} \times 4\frac{2}{7}$		$6\frac{6}{49}$
e.	$2\frac{1}{2} \times 8\frac{1}{3}$	$\frac{125}{6}$	

F. **Multiply the following.**

1. $20 \times \frac{1}{5}$
2. $\frac{5}{2} \times \frac{6}{10}$
3. $\frac{8}{5} \times \frac{9}{3}$
4. $\frac{9}{6} \times \frac{1}{3}$
5. $4\frac{1}{2} \times \frac{3}{5}$
6. $1\frac{3}{4} \times \frac{11}{8}$
7. $3\frac{1}{2} \times 4\frac{1}{4}$
8. $6\frac{1}{2} \times 7\frac{1}{5}$
9. 0.2 × 5
10. 0.06 × 12
11. 1.27 × 0.8
12. 0.003 × 0.01
13. 0.01 × 0.9
14. 12.5 × 0.5
15. 1.8 × 1.8
16. 0.03 × 1.03

G. **Divide the following.**

1. $5 \div \frac{2}{3}$
2. $\frac{1}{8} \div 18$
3. $12 \div \frac{1}{6}$
4. $\frac{5}{2} \div \frac{9}{2}$
5. $\frac{3}{2} \div \frac{1}{8}$
6. $3\frac{1}{2} \div \frac{1}{4}$
7. $5\frac{3}{2} \div \frac{3}{5}$
8. $30\frac{1}{2} \div 6\frac{1}{4}$
9. 3.5 ÷ 7
10. 9.5 ÷ 10
11. 78 ÷ 6.5
12. 100 ÷ 0.25
13. 8.125 ÷ 2.5
14. 6.2 ÷ 3.10
15. 31.5 ÷ 1.5
16. 4.2 ÷ 2.1

H. **Solve the following word problems.**

1. Jacob takes $\frac{1}{3}$ minutes to read a paragraph. How long will he take to read 5 paragraphs?
2. A packet of biscuits has $\frac{5}{4}$ calories of energy. How many calories of energy will 6 such packets have?
3. What should be multiplied with the fraction $\frac{4}{3}$ to get $\frac{5}{3}$?
4. Lucas reads 2.5 hours per day. How many hours does he spend reading in a week?
5. Mia spends ₹12.25 for 1 kg of dal. How much will she spend on 3.5 kg of dal?
6. If 4132.2 kg of sugar is packed in 97 bags, then how much sugar will each bag contain?

SKILL UP!

Project

Visit your school library and find out the number of different categories of books available in the library like science, maths, storybooks, comics, etc., and also the total number of books in the library. Now, find the fraction of each category of books in the library and compute each value in decimals too.

Life Skills

The students of Class 7 have a camp at school. They have decided to make roti and vegetables for dinner. One group of students went to the market to buy 2.5 kg of wheat flour for rotis. The price of wheat flour of different brands available in the market is given below.

Brand A	Brand B	Brand C	Brand C
₹21.2 per kg	₹100 for 5 kg	₹198 for 10 kg	₹78 for 4 kg

Choose the brand that will cost the least and find the amount to be paid for 2.5 kg of wheat flour.

Mind Buzzer

Jeje wants a toy that costs ₹151, and his friend Saroo wants one that costs exactly half of it. Saroo saves ₹5 in her money box every day. Jeje says he can give her money up to ₹1 if she is running short.

a. How many days would it take for Saroo to save enough so she can buy her toy with Jeje's help?

b. How much money does Jeje need to save every day so that he and his friend Saroo can buy their respective toys on the same day?

c. Will they have any money left after they have both bought their toys? If yes, then how much?

Teacher's Notes

- Assist the students to recall the concepts of fraction and decimal by explaining basic facts.
- Revision of the concepts like comparison, addition and subtraction of fractions and decimals can be done by giving a worksheet.
- Explain the importance of finding the reciprocal of fractions while dividing the fractions.
- Give more guided practice to the students when teaching how to divide decimal numbers by converting them to whole numbers first.
- Discuss the possible mistakes the students can make while multiplying and dividing decimal numbers by 10, 100 or 1000. Also, stress upon ways to avoid them.

WORKSHEET

The product of some of the given fractions is the same as the numbers in the clock given below. Find the products of each to find the numbers and then identify the letters. Draw a clock in the box provided and replace the numbers in the clock with these letters.

R	N	C	A	D	I	M	E	W	O
$\frac{5}{7}\times6\frac{1}{3}$	$2\times3\frac{1}{2}$	$2\times1\frac{1}{2}$	$\frac{1}{8}\times\frac{3}{2}$	$\frac{1}{8}\times\frac{3}{2}$	$13\times\frac{10}{26}$	$\frac{5}{8}\times\frac{1}{7}$	$121\times\frac{1}{11}$	$\frac{7}{2}\times\frac{1}{2}$	$2\frac{1}{12}\times2\frac{22}{25}$
T	**X**	**I**	**N**	**O**	**F**	**G**	**T**	**H**	**R**
$\frac{3}{2}\times5\frac{1}{3}$	$\frac{5}{3}\div\frac{1}{2}$	$15\div\frac{5}{3}$	$\frac{1}{8}\times\frac{3}{2}$	$\frac{1}{8}\times\frac{3}{2}$	$\frac{3}{2}\div\frac{1}{8}$	$\frac{2}{3}\times\frac{2}{3}$	$20\times\frac{1}{5}$	$\frac{1}{8}\times\frac{3}{2}$	$\frac{5}{7}\div\frac{5}{7}$
B	**K**	**A**	**U**	**L**	**M**				
$\frac{8}{7}\times1\frac{1}{6}$	$\frac{5}{2}\div\frac{1}{6}$	$1\frac{1}{2}\times\frac{4}{3}$	$\frac{1}{8}\times\frac{3}{2}$	$\frac{1}{8}\times\frac{3}{2}$	$2\frac{1}{2}\times4$				

3 Rational Numbers

Learning Objectives

- To define rational numbers
- To give examples for positive, negative and equivalent rational numbers
- To represent rational numbers on a number line
- To find the absolute value and compare rational numbers
- To add, subtract, multiply and divide rational numbers

Let's Get Started

Find the answer to the following question. Follow the instructions given below.

Why did the elephant cross the road?

R = $\frac{9}{10}$	N = $\frac{3}{11}$	E = 0.5	I = $\frac{1}{5}$	L = $\frac{5}{9}$
E = $\frac{3}{5}$	E = $\frac{4}{26}$	H = 0.09	E = 0.1	
V = $\frac{5}{8}$	R = $\frac{3}{22}$	A = $\frac{2}{3}$	T = $\frac{17}{22}$	
O = $\frac{7}{8}$	O = $\frac{4}{10}$	T = $\frac{2}{100}$	S = 0.23	

First convert all the given fractions to decimals and then arrange all the decimal numbers in ascending order. Write the letters corresponding to the answers in the boxes to find the answer to the above question.

RATIONAL NUMBERS

Look at the two groups given below.

Group A	Group B
$\frac{2}{3}$ $\frac{4}{1}$ $\frac{7}{5}$ $\frac{10}{9}$	$\frac{-2}{3}$ $\frac{4}{-1}$ $\frac{-7}{-5}$ $\frac{-10}{9}$

What are the numbers in Group A called? They are fractions.

Are the numbers in Group B fractions? No, they are not. They form a new category of numbers called **rational numbers**. Observe that a few numbers in Group B have a negative sign.

A **rational number** is defined as a number that can be expressed in the form $\frac{p}{q}$, where p and q are integers and $q \neq 0$.

SOLVED EXAMPLES

Example 1: Is 10 a rational number? Justify.

Solution: Yes, 10 is a rational number because 10 can be represented as $\frac{10}{1}$ where 10 (p) and 1 (q) are integers.

Example 2: Is the number $\frac{-5}{6}$ a rational number? Justify.

Solution: Yes, $\frac{-5}{6}$ is a rational number as it is represented in the form of $\frac{p}{q}$ where −5 (p) and 6 (q) are integers.

From the above two examples, it can be said that all integers and fractions are rational numbers. Is the vice-versa also true?

The figure given alongside shows the relation between different types of numbers that we have learnt so far.

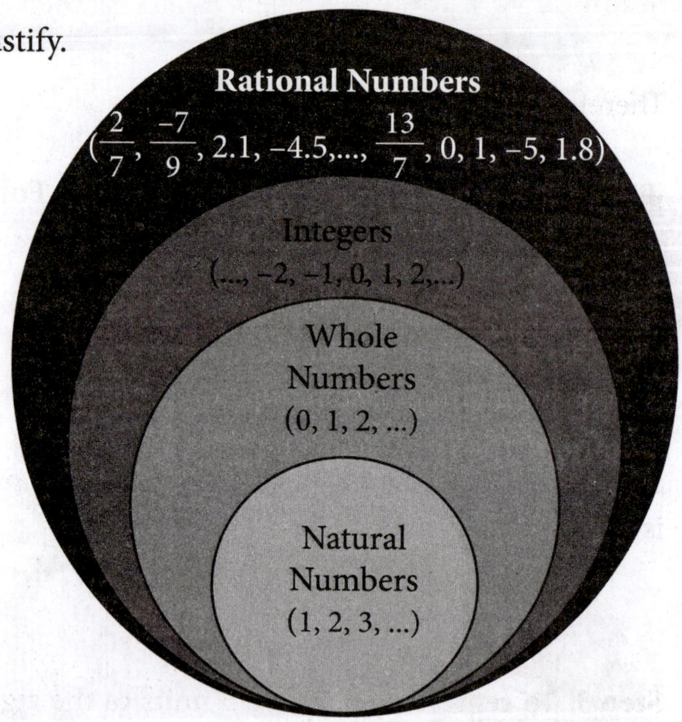

Positive and Negative Rational Numbers

Every rational number is either positive or negative except 0 which is neither a positive nor a negative rational number.

If both the numerator and denominator of a rational number are either negative or positive, then it is called a **positive rational number**. For example, $\frac{-2}{-7}, \frac{4}{5}$ are positive rational numbers.

If any of the numerator or denominator of a rational number is negative, then it is called a **negative rational number**. For example, $\frac{-2}{7}, \frac{4}{-5}$ are negative rational numbers.

REPRESENTATION OF RATIONAL NUMBERS ON A NUMBER LINE

We have learnt to represent integers and fractions on a number line. We can represent rational numbers also in the same way as we represent fractions.

Rational numbers are represented on an integer number line by dividing a unit into as many equal parts as the denominator of the rational number.

For example, $\frac{-1}{2}$ is represented on the number line by dividing each unit into two equal parts as shown below.

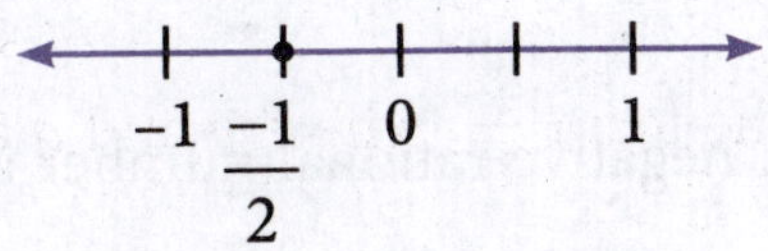

> **Note**
>
> On a number line, every positive integer lies to the right of 0 and every negative integer lies to the left of 0.

SOLVED EXAMPLES

Example 3: Is $\frac{3}{-8}$ a negative rational number?

Solution: We know that $\frac{3}{-8} = -\frac{3}{8}$

Therefore, $\frac{3}{-8}$ is a negative rational number.

Example 4: Is $\frac{-5}{-12}$ a positive rational number?

Solution: We know that $\frac{-5}{-12} = \frac{5\times(-1)}{12\times(-1)} = \frac{5}{12}$.

Therefore, $\frac{-5}{-12}$ is a positive rational number.

Example 5: Represent $\frac{5}{2}$ on the number line.

Solution: Step 1: Draw a number line such that distance between two consecutive numbers is 1 unit.

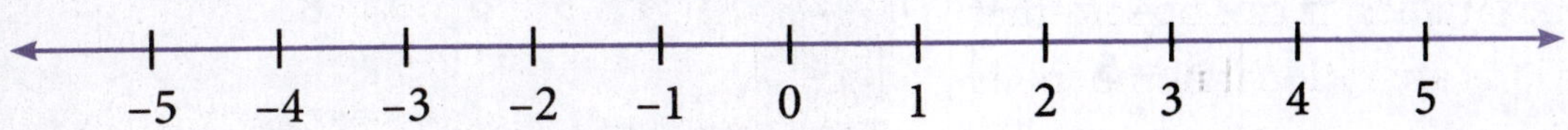

Step 2: Divide each unit into 2 equal parts as shown, as the denominator of the given rational number is 2.

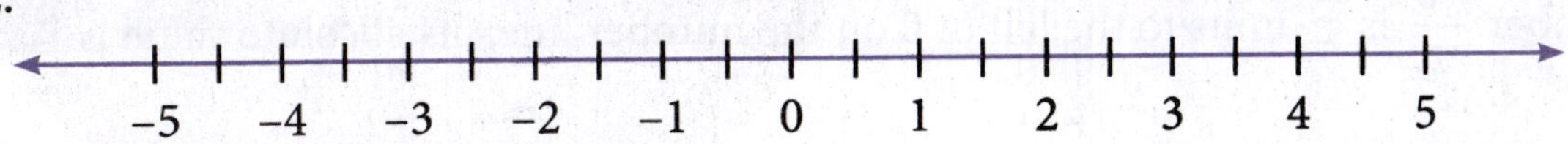

Step 3: To represent $\frac{5}{2}$, move 5 units to the right from 0 since it is a positive rational number and place a dot over the fifth division.

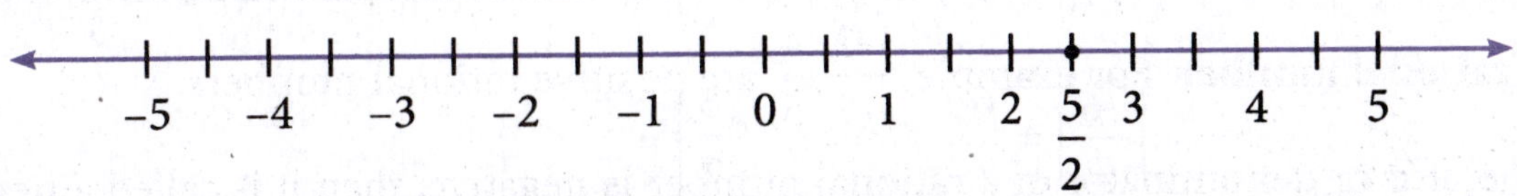

Example 6: Represent $-\frac{4}{3}$ on the number line.

Solution: Step 1: Draw a number line such that distance between two consecutive numbers is 1 unit.

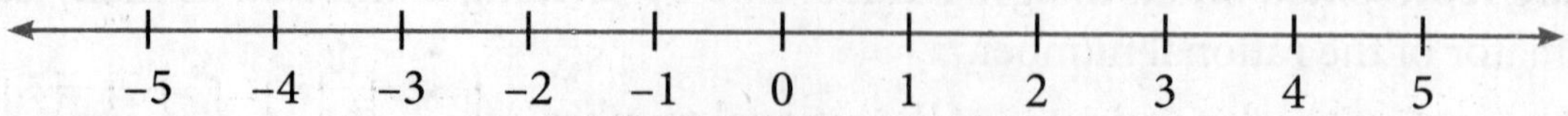

Step 2: Divide each unit into 3 equal parts, as the denominator of the given rational number is 3.

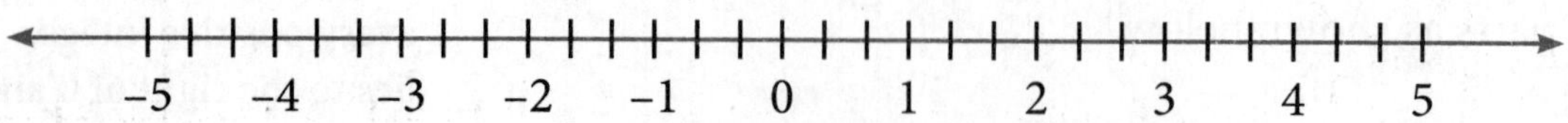

Step 3: To represent $-\frac{4}{3}$, move 4 units to the left from 0 since it is a negative rational number and place a dot over the fourth division.

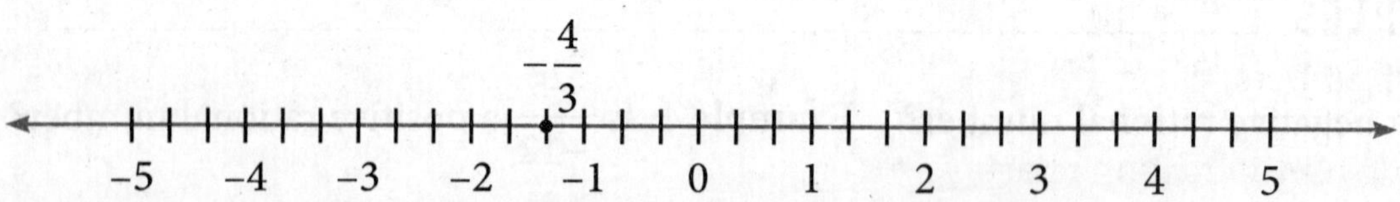

ABSOLUTE VALUE OF RATIONAL NUMBERS

Absolute value represents how far the number is from zero. In other words, we can say it is the positive version of the number. The absolute value of the integer 5 is written as $|5| = 5$ and the absolute value of the integer –5 is $|-5| = 5$, as it is 5 units to the left of 0 on the number line as shown below.

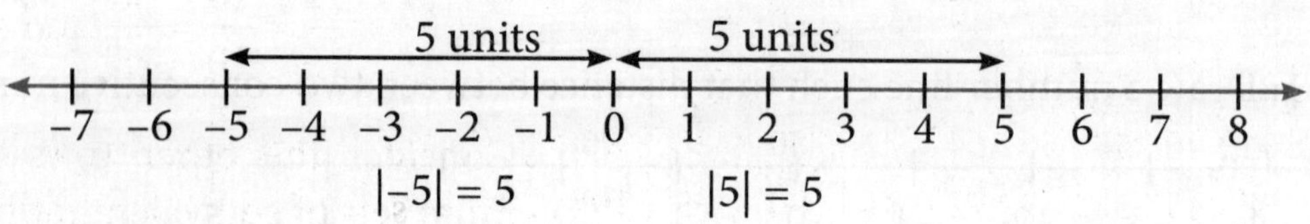

Similarly, the absolute value of the rational number $\frac{6}{7}$ is given by $\left|\frac{6}{7}\right| = \frac{6}{7}$.

As the rational number $\frac{-6}{7}$ is $\frac{6}{7}$ units to the left of 0 on the number line, its absolute value is $\frac{6}{7}$.

That is, $\left|\frac{-6}{7}\right| = \frac{6}{7}$.

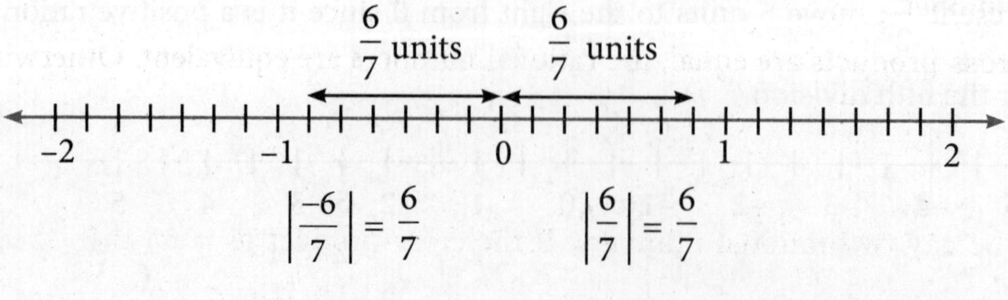

EQUIVALENT RATIONAL NUMBERS

Rational numbers having same or equal values are called equivalent rational numbers. Equivalent rational numbers of a given rational number can be obtained by either

- multiplying the numerator and denominator of the rational number by the same non-zero integer, or
- dividing the numerator and denominator of the rational number by the same non-zero integer.

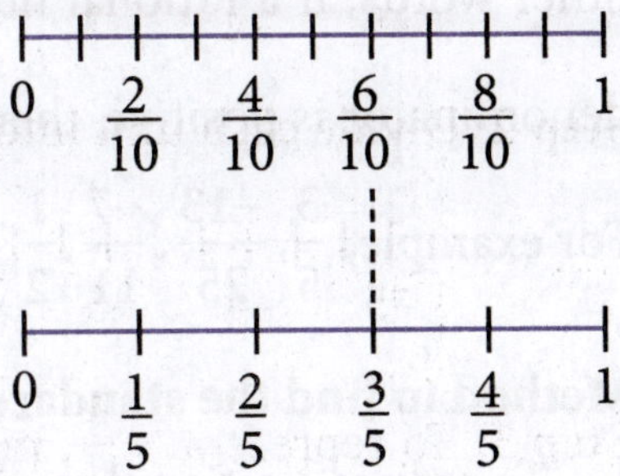

For example, consider $\frac{3}{5}$ and $\frac{6}{10}$.

$$\frac{3}{5}=\frac{3\times 2}{5\times 2}=\frac{6}{10}\Leftrightarrow \frac{6}{10}=\frac{6\div 2}{10\div 2}=\frac{3}{5}$$

It is clear that $\frac{3}{5}$ is the same as $\frac{6}{10}$. So, such rational numbers having the same values are called equivalent rational numbers.

Look at the following multiplication chart.

×	1	2	3	4	5	6	7	8	9	10	11	12
1	1	2	3	4	5	6	7	8	9	10	11	12
2	2	4	6	8	10	12	14	16	18	20	22	24
3	3	6	9	12	15	18	21	24	27	30	33	36
4	4	8	12	16	20	24	28	32	36	40	44	48
5	5	10	15	20	25	30	35	40	45	50	55	60
6	6	12	18	24	30	36	42	48	54	60	66	72
7	7	14	21	28	35	42	49	56	63	70	77	84
8	8	16	24	32	40	48	56	64	72	80	88	96
9	9	18	27	36	45	54	63	72	81	90	99	108
10	10	20	30	40	50	60	70	80	90	100	110	120
11	11	22	33	44	55	66	77	88	99	110	121	132
12	12	24	36	48	60	72	84	96	108	120	132	144

Consider any two rows. We can see the equivalent rational numbers.

For example, the row corresponding to the rational number $\frac{4}{5}$.

$$\frac{4}{5}=\frac{8}{10}=\frac{12}{15}=\frac{16}{20}=\frac{20}{25} \text{ and so on.}$$

Consider the other rows and write few more sets of equivalent rational numbers.

Check whether the two given rational numbers are equivalent or not

Step 1: Find the cross-product of the numerator of one rational number with the denominator of the other rational number.

Step 2: If the cross-products are equal, the rational numbers are equivalent. Otherwise, they are not equivalent.

Let $\frac{p}{q}$ and $\frac{r}{s}$ be any two rational numbers. If the cross-product $ps = rq$, then the given rational numbers are equivalent.

RATIONAL NUMBERS IN STANDARD FORM

In a rational number $\frac{p}{q}$, if the numerator (p) and the denominator (q) have no common factor other than 1 and the negative sign is only in the numerator, then it is said to be in the standard form. In other words, if a rational number $\frac{p}{q}$ is expressed in its lowest or simplest or reduced form and its denominator is positive, then it is said to be in the standard form.

For example, $\frac{3}{5}, \frac{-13}{25}, \frac{-7}{11}, \frac{1}{2}$ are rational numbers in the standard form.

Method to find the standard form:

1. To reduce a rational number to its standard form, divide its numerator and denominator by their highest common factor (HCF).
2. To find the standard form of a rational number with a negative integer as the denominator, divide it by their HCF with a minus sign.

SOLVED EXAMPLES

Example 7: Write two rational numbers equivalent to $\frac{2}{7}$.

Solution: Multiply or divide $\frac{2}{7}$ by the same non-zero integer to get equivalent rational numbers.

That is, $\frac{2 \times 2}{7 \times 2} = \frac{4}{14}, \frac{2 \times 3}{7 \times 3} = \frac{6}{21}$

$\therefore \frac{4}{14}$ and $\frac{6}{21}$ are the two rational numbers equivalent to $\frac{2}{7}$.

Example 8: Is $\frac{-7}{8}$ the same as $\frac{-21}{24}$?

Solution: Yes, $\frac{-7}{8}$ is the same as $\frac{-21}{24}$ as they have the same value as shown here.

$\frac{-21}{24} = \frac{-21 \div 3}{24 \div 3} = \frac{-7}{8}$.

So, they are equivalent rational numbers.

Example 9: Check whether the pair $\frac{15}{8}, \frac{12}{9}$ is equivalent.

Solution: We have $15 \times 9 = 135$ and $12 \times 8 = 96$.

Here $135 \neq 96$

$\therefore$ The given pair is not equivalent.

Example 10: Is $\frac{13}{57}$ in the standard form?

Solution: The HCF of 13 and 57 is 1.

So, $\frac{13}{57}$ cannot be simplified further.

Therefore, $\frac{13}{57}$ is in the standard form.

Example 11: Reduce each of the given rational numbers to its standard form.

a. $\frac{40}{24}$ b. $\frac{36}{-54}$

Solution: The HCF of 40 and 24 is 8.

Divide both numerator and denominator by 8.

$$\frac{40 \div 8}{24 \div 8} = \frac{5}{3}$$

$\therefore$ Standard form of $\frac{40}{24}$ is $\frac{5}{3}$.

Solution: The HCF of 36 and 54 is 18.

Divide both numerator and denominator by 18.

$$\frac{36 \div 18}{-54 \div 18} = \frac{-2}{3}$$

$\therefore$ Standard form of $\frac{36}{-54}$ is $\frac{-2}{3}$.

EXERCISE 3A

1. Classify the following rational numbers as positive or negative.

a. $\frac{-4}{9}$ b. $\frac{-2}{-9}$ c. $\frac{1}{-7}$ d. $\frac{9}{99}$ e. $\frac{-13}{-27}$ f. $-\frac{31}{72}$

2. Represent the following rational numbers on a number line.

a. $\frac{-1}{5}$ b. $\frac{5}{7}$ c. $\frac{7}{3}$ d. $\frac{-5}{4}$ e. $\frac{9}{2}$ f. $\frac{-3}{4}$

3. Write two equivalent rational numbers for each of the following.

a. $\frac{3}{5}$ b. $\frac{-4}{7}$ c. $\frac{1}{11}$ d. $\frac{5}{-6}$ e. $\frac{12}{16}$ f. $\frac{-10}{-50}$

4. Which of the following pairs represent the same rational number?

a. $\frac{2}{9}$ and $\frac{12}{54}$ b. $\frac{-3}{7}$ and $\frac{-12}{28}$ c. $\frac{3}{11}$ and $\frac{9}{22}$

d. $\frac{-2}{3}$ and $\frac{16}{24}$ e. $\frac{-6}{-17}$ and $\frac{18}{51}$ f. $\frac{1}{11}$ and $\frac{11}{111}$

5. Rewrite the following integers as rational numbers.

a. -3 b. 0 c. 1 d. 99 e. 50 f. -5

6. Write each of the given rational numbers in its standard form.

a. $\frac{50}{70}$ b. $\frac{-30}{195}$ c. $\frac{98}{112}$ d. $\frac{-13}{65}$ e. $\frac{25}{-525}$ f. $\frac{-13}{-117}$

COMPARING RATIONAL NUMBERS

We can use a number line to compare two rational numbers. We know that the number that is on the right side on the number line is greater than the number that is on the left side.

To compare two rational numbers using a number line, first convert them to equivalent rational numbers with same denominators. Represent those equivalent rational numbers on the number line and then compare. Consider the following example.

SOLVED EXAMPLES

Example 12: Compare $\frac{1}{5}$ and $\frac{2}{3}$. Which is greater?

Solution: Step 1: Find the LCM of the denominators. The LCM of 3 and 5 is 15.

Step 2: Convert the denominator of each rational number to the LCM obtained by multiplying with a suitable number.

Here, $\frac{1\times3}{5\times3}=\frac{3}{15}$ $\qquad$ $\frac{2\times5}{3\times5}=\frac{10}{15}$

Step 3: Represent the resultant rational numbers on the number line. As the denominator is 15, divide each unit into 15 equal parts.

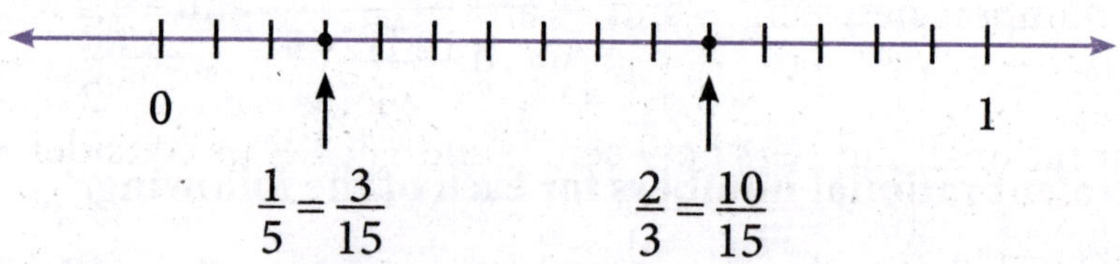

We notice that $\frac{1}{5}$ is to the left of $\frac{2}{3}$ on the number line. Therefore, $\frac{1}{5}$ is less than $\frac{2}{3}$. That is, $\frac{1}{5}<\frac{2}{3}$.

We can also compare rational numbers without using a number line. Consider the following example.

Example 13: Compare $\frac{3}{7}$ and $\frac{5}{6}$. Which is greater?

Solution: Convert the given rational numbers to equivalent rational numbers. The LCM of 7 and 6 is 42.

So, $\frac{3}{7}=\frac{3\times6}{7\times6}=\frac{18}{42}$ $\qquad$ $\frac{5}{6}=\frac{5\times7}{6\times7}=\frac{35}{42}$

As 18 < 35, we have $\frac{3}{7}<\frac{5}{6}$.

RATIONAL NUMBERS BETWEEN TWO RATIONAL NUMBERS

Look at the following table.

Integers	Number of integers between them
3 and 4	0 (no integers)
–5 and –6	0 (no integers)
0 and 4	3 (1, 2, 3)
–1 and –7	5 (–2, –3, –4, –5, –6)
0 and –3	2 (–1, –2)

From the above table, we can observe that there are only finite (limited) integers between any two non-consecutive integers and there are no integers between any two consecutive integers. Is the same true for rational numbers also? Let us try to find out by solving the following example.

SOLVED EXAMPLES

Example 14: Find four rational numbers between $\frac{1}{3}$ and $\frac{3}{4}$.

Solution: We first convert them into equivalent rational numbers with the same denominator.

The LCM of 3 and 4 is 12.

$\frac{1}{3}=\frac{1\times4}{3\times4}=\frac{4}{12}$ and $\frac{3}{4}=\frac{3\times3}{4\times3}=\frac{9}{12}$.

Clearly, $\frac{4}{12}<\frac{5}{12}<\frac{6}{12}<\frac{7}{12}<\frac{8}{12}<\frac{9}{12}$.

Therefore, four rational numbers between $\frac{1}{3}$ and $\frac{3}{4}$ are $\frac{5}{12},\frac{6}{12},\frac{7}{12}$ and $\frac{8}{12}$.

Are there only these four rational numbers between $\frac{1}{3}$ and $\frac{3}{4}$. Let us consider $\frac{1}{3}$ and $\frac{5}{12}$ to find out.

$\frac{1}{3}=\frac{1\times8}{3\times8}=\frac{8}{24}$ and $\frac{5}{12}=\frac{5\times2}{12\times2}=\frac{10}{24}$

So, $\frac{9}{24}$ is in between $\frac{1}{3}$ and $\frac{5}{12}$. Like this, we can continue to find more rational numbers between them.

Hence, there are infinite number of rational numbers between any two given rational numbers.

Example 15: Which of the following is greater: $\frac{-1}{5}$ or $\frac{-3}{4}$?

Solution: Step 1: Find the LCM of denominators. The LCM of 5 and 4 is 20.

Step 2: Convert the denominator of each rational number into the least common multiple.

$$\frac{-1\times4}{5\times4}=\frac{-4}{20} \qquad \frac{-3\times5}{4\times5}=\frac{-15}{20}$$

Step 3: Represent the resultant rational numbers on the number line. Since the denominator is 20, divide each unit into 20 equal parts.

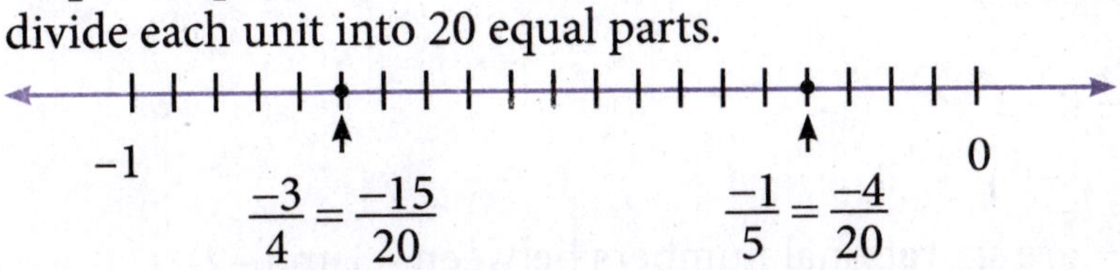

We can notice that $\frac{-1}{5}$ is to the right of $\frac{-3}{4}$ on the number line.

$\therefore$ $\frac{-1}{5}$ is greater than $\frac{-3}{4} \Rightarrow \frac{-1}{5}>\frac{-3}{4}$.

Example 16: Is $\frac{4}{9}$ greater than $-\frac{5}{8}$? Justify.

Solution: We know that a negative rational number lies to the left of zero, whereas a positive rational number lies to the right of zero on a number line. Hence, **a negative rational number is always less than a positive rational number.**

$\therefore \frac{4}{9} > -\frac{5}{8}$.

Example 17: Compare $-\frac{5}{8}$ and $-\frac{2}{5}$.

Solution: Firstly, ignore the signs and compare just the rational numbers, that is, $\frac{5}{8}$ and $\frac{2}{5}$.

The LCM of 8 and 5 is 40.

$$\frac{5}{8}=\frac{5\times5}{8\times5}=\frac{25}{40} \qquad \frac{2}{5}=\frac{2\times8}{5\times8}=\frac{16}{40}$$

Since 25 > 16, we have $\frac{5}{8} > \frac{2}{5}$.

$\Rightarrow -\frac{5}{8} < -\frac{2}{5}$.

> **Note**
>
> To compare any two rational numbers, first convert them to equivalent rational numbers with same denominators and then compare.

Example 18: List any four rational numbers between 2 and 3.

Solution: Write 2 and 3 as rational numbers with 5 as their denominator.

$$2=\frac{2\times5}{5}=\frac{10}{5} \qquad 3=\frac{3\times5}{5}=\frac{15}{5}$$

So, $\frac{10}{5}<\frac{11}{5}<\frac{12}{5}<\frac{13}{5}<\frac{14}{5}<\frac{15}{5}$ or $2<\frac{11}{5}<\frac{12}{5}<\frac{13}{5}<\frac{14}{5}<3$

Thus, $\frac{11}{5},\frac{12}{5},\frac{13}{5},\frac{14}{5}$ are four rational numbers between 2 and 3.

> **Note**
>
> To get n rational numbers between any two consecutive rational numbers, multiply the numerator and denominator of the given numbers by $(n + 1)$.

Example 19: List any six rational numbers between –3 and –2.

Solution: Write –3 and –2 as rational numbers with 7 as their denominator.

$$-3=\frac{-3\times7}{7}=\frac{-21}{7} \qquad -2=\frac{-2\times7}{7}=\frac{-14}{7}$$

So, $\frac{-21}{7}<\frac{-20}{7}<\frac{-19}{7}<\frac{-18}{7}<\frac{-17}{7}<\frac{-16}{7}<\frac{-15}{7}<\frac{-14}{7}$ or

$$-3<\frac{-20}{7}<\frac{-19}{7}<\frac{-18}{7}<\frac{-17}{7}<\frac{-16}{7}<\frac{-15}{7}<-2$$

Therefore, $\frac{-20}{7},\frac{-19}{7},\frac{-18}{7},\frac{-17}{7},\frac{-16}{7}$ and $\frac{-15}{7}$ are six rational numbers between –3 and –2.

EXERCISE 3B

1. Identify the greater rational number in each of the following.

a. $\frac{-4}{5}, \frac{-2}{3}$ b. $\frac{1}{5}, \frac{2}{7}$ c. $\frac{4}{9}, \frac{2}{11}$

d. $\frac{-11}{5}, \frac{-13}{5}$ e. $\frac{3}{7}, \frac{7}{3}$ f. $\frac{-5}{6}, \frac{-5}{9}$

2. Fill in the boxes with the correct symbol (< or > or =).

a. $\frac{-2}{9} \square \frac{-3}{18}$ b. $\frac{3}{5} \square \frac{14}{10}$ c. $\frac{3}{8} \square \frac{21}{56}$

d. $\frac{5}{13} \square \frac{19}{13}$ e. $\frac{-1}{6} \square \frac{-5}{30}$ f. $\frac{-1}{9} \square \frac{-1}{8}$

3. Arrange the following rational numbers in ascending order.

a. $\frac{2}{3}, \frac{4}{5}, \frac{3}{7}$ b. $\frac{-2}{5}, \frac{-4}{7}, \frac{-1}{3},$ c. $\frac{-3}{7}, 1, -2$

d. $3, -1, \frac{-8}{4}$ e. $\frac{-11}{12}, \frac{3}{5}, \frac{-13}{12}$ f. $\frac{-2}{7}, \frac{-1}{7}, \frac{-8}{7}$

4. List any four rational numbers between each of the following number pairs.

a. -2 and -1 b. 5 and 6   c. $\frac{-8}{5}$ and $\frac{-2}{3}$

d. $\frac{-1}{2}$ and $\frac{2}{3}$ e. $\frac{1}{3}$ and $\frac{4}{5}$ f. 0 and 1

OPERATIONS ON RATIONAL NUMBERS

Let us learn how to perform the basic operations (addition, subtraction, multiplication and division) on rational numbers. The same rules followed for integers and fractions are followed for rational numbers too.

Addition of Rational Numbers

Addition of rational numbers is similar to addition of fractions.

To add fractions, follow the steps given in the flowchart.

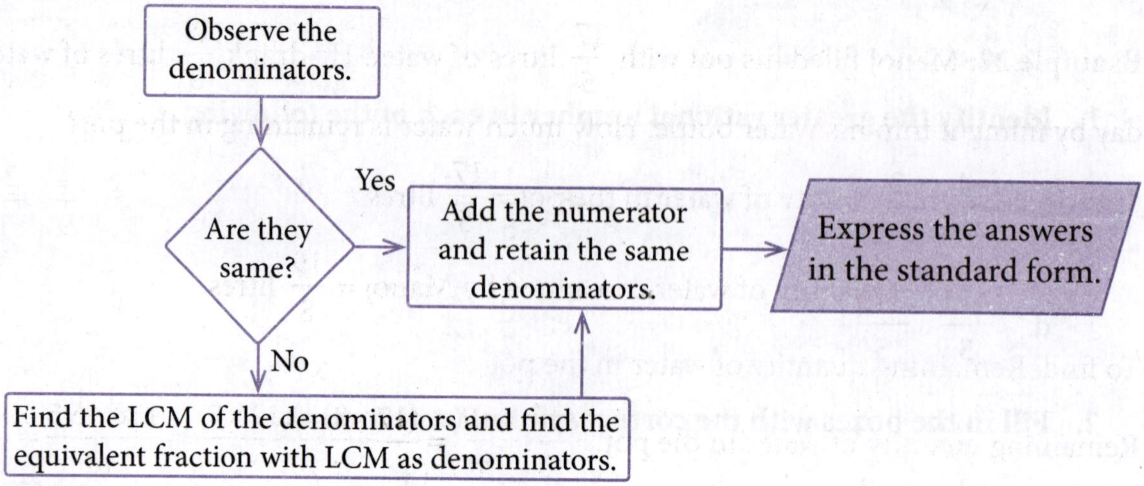

SOLVED EXAMPLES

Example 20: Diksha walked for $\frac{19}{8}$ km and jogged for $\frac{5}{6}$ km one morning. What is the distance covered by her altogether?

Solution: Given: Distance covered by walking = $\frac{19}{8}$ km

Distance covered by jogging = $\frac{5}{6}$ km

To find: Total distance covered

Total distance covered would be $\frac{19}{8} + \frac{5}{6}$.

Let us now find out the total distance covered by Diksha.

Total distance covered = $\frac{19}{8} + \frac{5}{6} = \frac{(19\times6)+(5\times8)}{48} = \frac{114+40}{48} = \frac{154}{48} = 3\frac{5}{24}$ km

$\therefore$ Diksha covered a distance of $3\frac{5}{24}$ km.

Additive Inverse

For a rational number $\frac{a}{b}$, $-\left(\frac{a}{b}\right)$ is the additive inverse such that $\frac{a}{b}+\left(-\frac{a}{b}\right) = 0$.

Example 21: Write the additive inverse of each of the following.

a. $\frac{-3}{8}$ b. $\frac{5}{11}$

Additive inverse of $\frac{-3}{8}$ is $-\left(\frac{-3}{8}\right)=\frac{3}{8}$.

Additive inverse of $\frac{5}{11}$ is $-\left(\frac{5}{11}\right)=-\frac{5}{11}$.

Subtraction of Rational Numbers

While subtracting integers, we add the additive inverse of the integer which is being subtracted. Similarly, while subtracting two rational numbers, we add the additive inverse of the rational number that is being subtracted, to the other rational number.

SOLVED EXAMPLES

Example 22: Manoj filled his pot with $\frac{17}{5}$ litres of water. He drank $\frac{19}{8}$ litres of water throughout the day by filling it into his water bottle. How much water is remaining in the pot?

Solution: Given: Quantity of water in the pot $= \frac{17}{5}$ litres

Quantity of water consumed by Manoj $= \frac{19}{8}$ litres

To find: Remaining quantity of water in the pot

Remaining quantity of water in the pot $= \frac{17}{5} - \frac{19}{8} = \frac{(17\times 8)-(19\times 5)}{40} = \frac{136-95}{40} = \frac{41}{40} = 1\frac{1}{40}$

$\therefore 1\frac{1}{40}$ litres of water was remaining in the pot.

Example 23: Add $\frac{2}{7}$ and $\frac{-3}{7}$.

Solution: Since the denominators are same, add the numerators keeping the same denominator.

$$\frac{2}{7}+\frac{-3}{7}=\frac{2+(-3)}{7}=\frac{2-3}{7}=\frac{-1}{7}$$

Example 24: Add $\frac{-3}{4}$ and $\frac{-2}{5}$.

Solution: Step 1: Find the LCM of the two denominators. The LCM of 4 and 5 is 20.

Step 2: Find the equivalent rational numbers of the given rational numbers with 20 as the denominator.

$$\frac{-3\times 5}{4\times 5}=\frac{-15}{20} \qquad \frac{-2\times 4}{5\times 4}=\frac{-8}{20}$$

Step 3: Add the two rational numbers and reduce the result obtained to the simplest form, if it is not.

$$\frac{-15}{20}+\frac{-8}{20}=\frac{-23}{20}$$

Therefore, $\frac{-3}{4}+\frac{-2}{5}=\frac{-23}{20}$.

Example 25: Subtract $\frac{5}{3}$ from $\frac{1}{6}$.

Solution: $\frac{1}{6}-\frac{5}{3}=\frac{1}{6}+\left(-\frac{5}{3}\right) = \frac{1+(-10)}{6}=\frac{-9}{6} = \frac{-9\div 3}{6\div 3}=\frac{-3}{2}$

Therefore, $\frac{1}{6}-\frac{5}{3}=\frac{-3}{2}$

Example 26: Find the difference: $\frac{-3}{8} - \frac{7}{11}$.

Solution: $\frac{-3}{8} - \frac{7}{11} = \frac{(-3\times11)-(7\times8)}{88} = \frac{-33-56}{88} = \frac{-89}{88} = -1\frac{1}{88}$

Therefore, $\frac{-3}{8} - \frac{7}{11} = -1\frac{1}{88}$.

Multiplication of Rational Numbers

Multiplication of rational numbers is similar to multiplication of fractions. Following are the rules to multiply rational numbers with an integer and a rational number.

Multiplying a rational number with an integer:

1. Multiply the numerator of the given rational number with the given integer, keeping the denominator unchanged.

$$\frac{a}{b} \times c = \frac{a \times c}{b}$$

2. Write the answer in standard form.

Multiplying a rational number with another rational number:

1. Product of two rational numbers $= \frac{\text{Product of their numerataors}}{\text{Product of their denominators}}$

$$\frac{a}{b} \times \frac{c}{d} = \frac{a \times c}{b \times d}$$

2. Write the answer in standard form.

Example 27: Anil earns ₹$\frac{950}{8}$ every hour. How much will he earn in three and half hours?

Solution: Given: Earnings per hour = ₹$\frac{950}{8}$

To find: Earnings in 3 and half hours

Earnings in 3 and half hours $= \frac{7}{2} \times \frac{950}{8} = 7 \times \frac{475}{8} =$ ₹$415\frac{5}{8}$

∴ Anil earns ₹$415\frac{5}{8}$ in three and half hours.

Reciprocal

Reciprocal of a rational number is obtained in the same way as for fractions.

For every non-zero rational number $\frac{a}{b}$, there exists a rational number $\frac{b}{a}$ such that $\frac{a}{b} \times \frac{b}{a} = 1$.

$\frac{b}{a}$ is the reciprocal of $\frac{a}{b}$ and vice versa.

For example, the reciprocal of $\frac{-2}{11}$ is $\frac{11}{-2}$ because $\frac{-2}{11} \times \frac{11}{-2} = 1$.

Similarly, the reciprocal of $\left(2 = \frac{2}{1}\right)$ is $\frac{1}{2}$ as $\frac{2}{1} \times \frac{1}{2} = 1$.

Division of Rational Numbers

To divide a rational number by another rational number, we multiply the rational number by the reciprocal of the other rational number. Here are the steps to divide $\frac{a}{b}$ by $\frac{c}{d}$ where a, b, c and d are non-zero integers.

Step 1: Find the reciprocal of $\frac{c}{d}$, i.e., $\frac{d}{c}$.

Step 2: Multiply $\frac{a}{b}$ with $\frac{d}{c}$. $\Rightarrow \frac{a}{b} \times \frac{d}{c} = \frac{a \times d}{b \times c}$

Step 3: Write the product $\frac{a \times d}{b \times c}$ in standard form.

That is, $\frac{a}{b} \div \frac{c}{d} = \frac{a}{b} \times \frac{d}{c} = \frac{a \times d}{b \times c}$

Example 28: Nakul had $4\frac{1}{2}$ cookies. He wanted to equally share them among his three friends. How much would each friend get?

Solution: Given: Number of cookies = $4\frac{1}{2}$, Number of friends = 3

To find: Each friend's share

Each friend's share = $4\frac{1}{2} \div 3 = \frac{9}{2} \times \frac{1}{3} = \frac{3}{2} = 1\frac{1}{2}$

$\therefore$ Each friend would get $1\frac{1}{2}$ cookies.

SOLVED EXAMPLES

Example 29: Multiply $\frac{-2}{9}$ by 3.

Solution: $\frac{-2}{9} \times 3 = \frac{-2 \times 3}{9} = \frac{-6}{9}$

$= \frac{-6 \div 3}{9 \div 3} = \frac{-2}{3}$

Therefore, $\frac{-2}{9} \times 3 = \frac{-2}{3}$.

Example 30: Find $\frac{-7}{9} \times \frac{3}{14}$.

Solution: $\frac{-7}{9} \times \frac{3}{14} = \frac{-21}{126}$

$= \frac{-21 \div 3}{126 \div 3} = \frac{-7}{42} = \frac{-7 \div 7}{42 \div 7} = \frac{-1}{6}$

Therefore, $\frac{-7}{9} \times \frac{3}{14} = \frac{-1}{6}$.

Example 31: Divide $\frac{-4}{7}$ by $\frac{8}{21}$.

Solution: $\frac{-4}{7} \div \frac{8}{21} = \frac{-4}{7} \times \frac{21}{8} = \frac{-4 \times 21}{7 \times 8} = \frac{-84}{56} = \frac{-84 \div 28}{56 \div 28} = \frac{-3}{2}$

Therefore, $\frac{-4}{7} \div \frac{8}{21} = \frac{-3}{2}$.

Example 32: Simplify: $\frac{2}{5} \div \left(\frac{-8}{15}\right)$.

Solution: $\frac{2}{5} \div \left(\frac{-8}{15}\right) = \frac{2}{5} \times \left(\frac{15}{-8}\right) = \frac{2 \times 15}{5 \times -8} = \frac{30}{-40} = \frac{30 \div 10}{-40 \div 10} = \frac{3}{-4}$

$\therefore \frac{2}{5} \div \left(\frac{-8}{15}\right) = \frac{3}{-4}$

EXERCISE 3C

1. **Find the sum of the following rational numbers.**
   a. $\frac{4}{7}$ and $\frac{-2}{7}$ b. $\frac{7}{16}$ and $\frac{1}{16}$ c. $\frac{-10}{33}$ and $\frac{-1}{33}$
   d. $\frac{4}{5}$ and $\frac{7}{8}$ e. $\frac{6}{11}$ and $\frac{-7}{5}$ f. $\frac{7}{-18}$ and $\frac{8}{21}$
2. **Subtract the following rational numbers.**
   a. $\frac{-7}{9}$ from $\frac{3}{5}$ b. $\frac{5}{6}$ from $\frac{7}{8}$ c. $\frac{1}{4}$ from $\frac{-3}{8}$
   d. $\frac{-5}{13}$ from $\frac{-6}{26}$ e. $\frac{15}{17}$ from $\frac{-13}{34}$ f. $\frac{-5}{-8}$ from $\frac{-3}{7}$
3. **Find the product of the given rational numbers.**
   a. $\frac{8}{11} \times \frac{6}{5}$ b. $\frac{-4}{9} \times \frac{7}{13}$ c. $\frac{25}{-6} \times \frac{9}{10}$
   d. $\frac{12}{-21} \times \frac{7}{10}$ e. $\frac{-12}{5} \times \frac{25}{-6}$ f. $\frac{5}{-27} \times \frac{-9}{20}$
4. **Solve the following.**
   a. $5 \div \frac{5}{-2}$ b. $\frac{-4}{9} \div 8$ c. $\frac{-18}{35} \div \frac{9}{-15}$
   d. $\frac{5}{11} \div \frac{-7}{3}$ e. $\frac{-7}{8} \div \frac{-3}{-4}$ f. $\frac{3}{2} \div \frac{12}{-7}$
5. **Write the additive inverse and reciprocal for each of the following rational numbers.**
   a. $\frac{-2}{7}$ b. $\frac{3}{11}$ c. -10 d. $\frac{-3}{-13}$ e. 100 f. $\frac{8}{19}$

WORD PROBLEMS ON RATIONAL NUMBERS

We have learnt to add, subtract, multiply and divide rational numbers. Let us now solve a few word problems involving them.

SOLVED EXAMPLES

Example 33: A recipe for trail mix requires $\frac{9}{4}$ cups of dry fruits, $\frac{7}{2}$ cups of sugar, and $\frac{1}{3}$ cup of coconut. How many cups of trail mix can be made with this recipe?

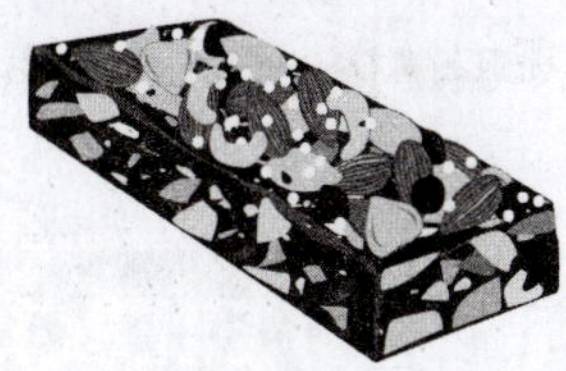

Solution: Given: Quantity of dry fruits = $\frac{9}{4}$ cups

Quantity of sugar = $\frac{7}{2}$ cups; Quantity of coconut = $\frac{1}{3}$ cup

To find: Total number of cups of trail mix

Total number of cups = $\frac{9}{4}+\frac{7}{2}+\frac{1}{3}=\frac{(9\times3)+(7\times6)+(1\times4)}{12}=\frac{27+42+4}{12}=\frac{73}{12}=6\frac{1}{12}$

$\therefore$ $6\frac{1}{12}$ cups of trail mix can be made with this recipe.

Example 34: A drum filled with rice weighs $\frac{400}{3}$ kg. If the empty drum weighs $\frac{55}{6}$ kg, find the weight of the rice in the drum.

Solution: Given: Weight of drum with rice = $\frac{400}{3}$ kg. Weight of empty drum = $\frac{55}{6}$ kg

To find: Weight of the rice in the drum

Weight of the rice in the drum = $\frac{400}{3}-\frac{55}{6}=\frac{(400\times2)-(55\times1)}{6}=\frac{800-55}{6}=\frac{745}{6}=124\frac{1}{6}$

$\therefore$ The weight of rice in the drum is $124\frac{1}{6}$ kg.

Example 35: A pen costs ₹$\frac{63}{5}$. Find the cost of 8 such pens.

Solution: Given: Cost of 1 pen = ₹$\frac{63}{5}$

To find: Cost of 8 pens

Cost of 8 pens = $8\times\frac{63}{5}=\frac{504}{5}=100.80$

$\therefore$ Cost of 8 pens is ₹100.80.

Example 36: A rope of length $\frac{140}{6}$ m is divided into 25 pieces. What is the length of each piece?

Solution: Given: Length of the rope = $\frac{140}{6}$ m, Number of pieces = 25

To find: Length of each piece of the rope

Length of each piece of the rope = $\frac{140}{6} \div 25 = \frac{140}{6} \times \frac{1}{25} = \frac{70}{3} \times \frac{1}{25} = \frac{14}{3} \times \frac{1}{5} = \frac{14}{15}$

$\therefore$ The length of each piece of the rope is $\frac{14}{15}$ m.

EXERCISE 3D

Solve the following word problems.

1. Two persons A and B planned to reach a point on the beach. They started from the same point P but took two different routes, PCQ and PDQ, respectively as shown in the picture. Find the distance travelled by each person and find who has travelled more distance.

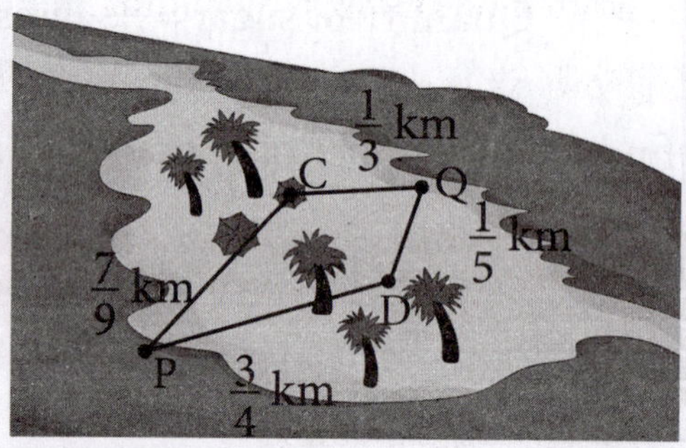

2. If the temperatures of two cold climate places P and Q are $\frac{98°}{5}$ and $\frac{82°}{7}$, then which place is colder and by how much?
3. If the cost of one litre of petrol is ₹$\frac{285}{4}$, find the cost of $\frac{3}{4}$ litres of petrol.
4. Raghu has purchased $\frac{31}{4}$ m of cloth. Out of this, he wanted to distribute $\frac{1}{4}$ m of cloth to each of his friends. Find the number of friends to whom he can distribute the cloth.
5. Danny has a dog named Al. Al eats $\frac{1}{3}$ of his food in the morning, $\frac{1}{4}$ in the afternoon and $\frac{2}{5}$ in the evening. What part of its food does Al eat during the day? How much of it is left?

Mental Maths

1. All rational numbers can be represented in the form of ____ where p and q are integers and $q \neq 0$.
2. All integers and fractions are ____________ numbers.
3. What is the standard form of $\frac{3}{-99}$?
4. The rational number $\frac{-14}{15}$ lies between the integers ____ and ____.
5. Find the sum of $\frac{3}{5}$ and $\frac{-1}{5}$.

Maths Lab Activity

Aim: To represent rational numbers on a number line

Materials required: Strips of paper

Procedure:

1. Draw a number line on a paper strip and mark the numbers from –1 to 1 as shown.

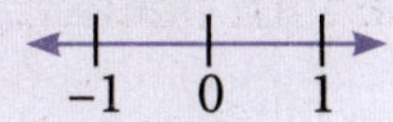

2. Ask the students to represent any rational number, say $\frac{1}{2}$, using the number line written on the strip by folding the strip into two equal halves between 0 and 1.

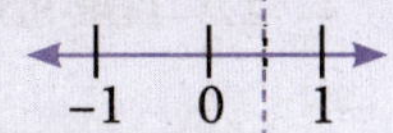

3. Next ask the students to represent the rational number $\frac{-1}{2}$ using the number line written on the strip by folding the strip into two equal halves between 0 and –1.

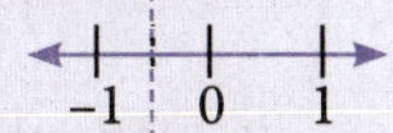

4. Now ask the students to represent the rational number $\frac{1}{3}$ using the strip of number line by folding the strip into three equal parts between 0 and 1.

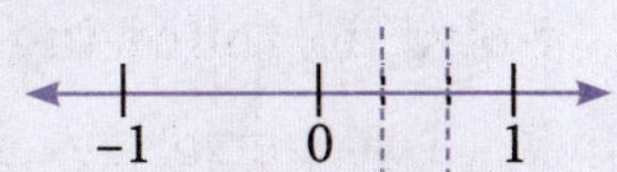

5. Explain to the students that in a similar manner, rational numbers are represented on a number line by dividing the number line into as many equal parts as the denominator of the given rational number.

Concept Map

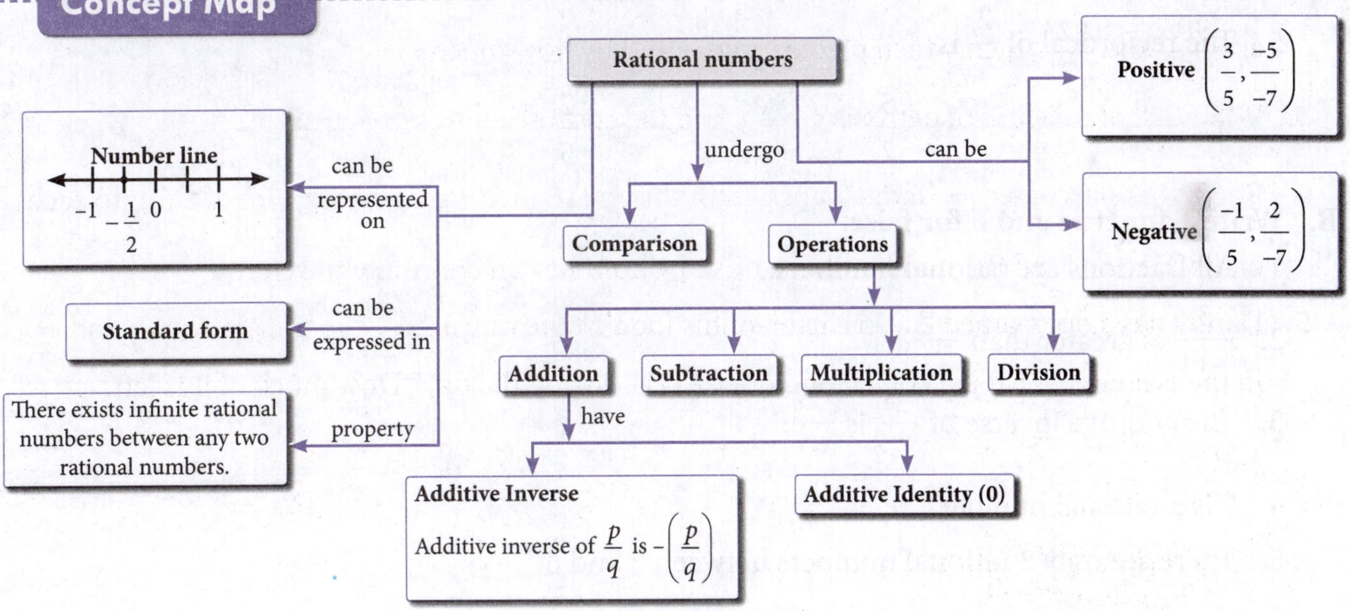

Key Concepts

- **Rational number:** A number which can be expressed in the form of $\frac{p}{q}$, where p and q are integers and $q \neq 0$
- **Additive inverse:** A number which when added to the given number gives 0
- **Reciprocal:** A number which when multiplied with the given number gives 1

CHAPTER REVISION

A. Choose the correct option.

1. The greatest among four rational numbers $\frac{2}{3}, \frac{1}{8}, \frac{-5}{6}, \frac{-2}{3}$ is

   a. $\frac{2}{3}$ b. $\frac{1}{8}$ c. $\frac{-5}{6}$ d. $\frac{-2}{3}$

2. The smallest among four rational numbers $\frac{-4}{12}, \frac{-4}{9}, \frac{-4}{13}, \frac{-4}{15}$ is

   a. $\frac{-4}{12}$ b. $\frac{-4}{9}$ c. $\frac{-4}{13}$ d. $\frac{-4}{15}$

3. Which of the following rational number is equivalent to $\frac{9}{11}$?

   a. $\frac{18}{20}$ b. $\frac{27}{44}$ c. $\frac{44}{55}$ d. $\frac{54}{66}$

4. The additive inverse of $\frac{2}{17}$ is

   a. $\frac{17}{2}$ b. $\frac{2}{17}$ c. $-\frac{2}{17}$ d. $-\frac{17}{2}$

5. The reciprocal of $\frac{2}{5}$ is

   a. $-\frac{5}{2}$ b. $\frac{5}{2}$ c. $\frac{2}{5}$ d. $-\frac{2}{5}$

B. Write T for true and F for false.

1. All fractions are rational numbers.
2. $\frac{3}{-11}$ is greater than $\frac{-9}{33}$.
3. The additive inverse of $\frac{-1}{2}$ is $\frac{2}{-1}$.
4. 0 is a rational number.
5. There are only 3 rational numbers between 2 and 6.

C. Fill in the blanks.

1. Every __________ rational number is always greater than 0 and every negative rational number is always __________ than 0.
2. The additive inverse of a rational number in the form $-\frac{a}{b}$ is ______.
3. The product of a rational number and its reciprocal is ________.
4. The number of rational numbers between any two rational numbers is ________.

5. To reduce a rational number to its standard form, divide the numerator and the denominator by their ____________.

D. Match the rational numbers with their equivalent rational numbers.

1. $\frac{-3}{5}$	a. $\frac{28}{49}$
2. $\frac{7}{-11}$	b. $\frac{-48}{78}$
3. $\frac{4}{7}$	c. $\frac{-15}{25}$
4. $\frac{-5}{9}$	d. $\frac{-21}{33}$
5. $\frac{8}{-13}$	e. $\frac{-15}{27}$

E. Represent the following rational numbers on a number line.

1. $\frac{-3}{7}$ 2. $\frac{-6}{5}$ 3. $\frac{-10}{4}$ 4. $\frac{3}{5}$ 5. $\frac{5}{3}$ 6. $\frac{7}{9}$

F. Simplify the following.

1. $5 \div \frac{10}{-3}$ 2. $\frac{-4}{9} + \frac{-5}{6}$ 3. $\frac{-18}{25} \times \frac{10}{-9}$

4. $\frac{5}{11} - \left(\frac{-7}{3}\right)$ 5. $\frac{-7}{8} + \frac{-3}{-4}$ 6. $\frac{6}{5} \div \frac{12}{-1}$

G. Solve the following word problems.

1. In a day, Ava spends $\frac{5}{4}$ hours reading a magazine and $\frac{6}{7}$ hours writing to finish her homework. How many hours does Ava spend reading and writing?
2. A cab travelled $\frac{2}{3}$ km due north and $\frac{3}{5}$ km due south. Find the total displacement of the cab?
3. Debal completes his work in $\frac{7}{9}$ days. Arun takes $\frac{3}{2}$ times more time than Debal to finish his work. Find the number of days that Arun needs to complete his work.
4. Rashmi bought $\frac{3}{2}$ chocolates and distributed among 6 members equally. Find each member's share.

SKILL UP!

Project

Which Greek mathematician came up with the concept of rational numbers? Is it true that all numbers are rational? Write a short note of about 100 words.

Life Skills

The following table shows the savings of six people who get the same amount of salary. Arrange them in increasing order of their savings. Also mention who saves the most and who saves the least.

Saving money is important. Do you think so? Give reasons.

Person	Savings (Part of the salary)
Anil	$\frac{1}{3}$
Ruma	$\frac{2}{5}$
Nikhil	$\frac{1}{4}$

Person	Savings (Part of the salary)
Faizal	$\frac{2}{3}$
Karthik	$\frac{3}{4}$
Joseph	$\frac{1}{2}$

Mind Buzzer

Build or write a word problem question on the given operation of rational numbers.

1. $11-\frac{13}{5}-\frac{33}{10}$

2. $\frac{183}{5}\times\frac{50}{3}$

Teacher's Notes

- Use a diagrammatic representation to explain the relationship between natural numbers, whole numbers, integers and rational numbers to the students. Elaborate that the group of rational numbers contains the natural numbers, whole numbers and also integers.
- The students can be given a few practice questions and asked to perform all the four operations for recapitulation.
- To give a better understanding, a number line can be used to explain all the operations on rational numbers.

WORKSHEET

Identify the figure by connecting the given dots in ascending order. Write the name of the figure in the space provided.
(*Hint*: Subtract the rational numbers and then compare them.)

____

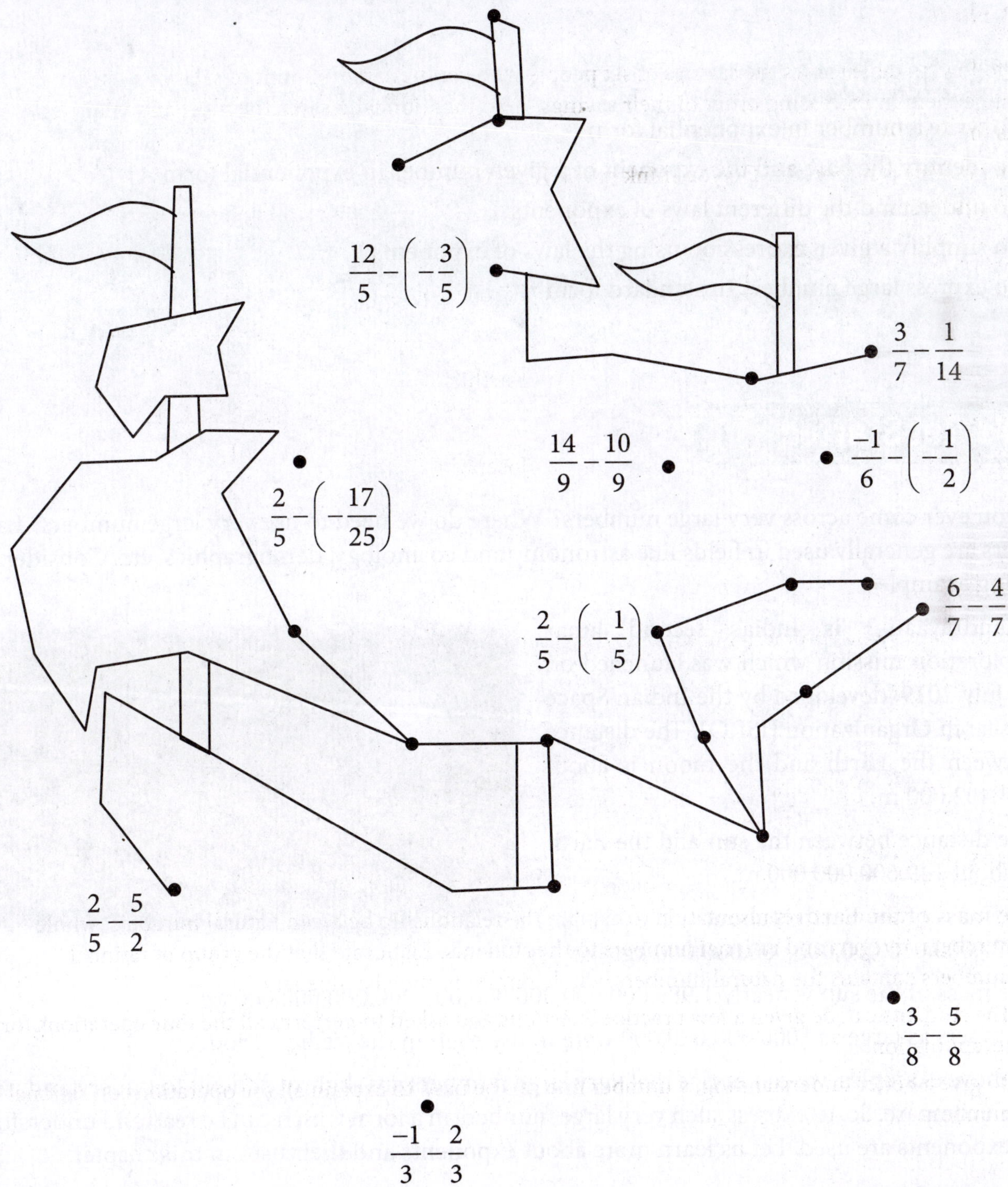

4 Exponents and Powers

Learning Objectives

- To write a number in exponential form
- To identify the base and the exponent of a given number in exponential form
- To understand the different laws of exponents
- To simplify a given expression using the laws of exponents
- To express large numbers in standard form

Let's Get Started

Have you ever come across very large numbers? Where do we need to use very large numbers? Large numbers are generally used in fields like astronomy and cosmology, demographics, etc. Consider the following examples.

- Chandrayaan-2 is India's second lunar exploration mission which was launched on 22 July 2019, developed by the Indian Space Research Organization (ISRO). The distance between the Earth and the moon is about 384,402,000 m.
- The distance between the sun and the Earth is about 149,600,000,000 m.
- The mass of the Earth is about 5,972,000,000,000,000,000,000,000 kg.
- The mass of the sun is nearly 1,989,000,000,000,000,000,000,000,000,000 kg.
- Numbers as large as 1000,000,000,000 were in use even in the Vedic period.

In the above examples, we can notice that very large numbers are slightly difficult to understand, read and even compare. So, to express such very large numbers in a form which can be read and understood easily, exponents are used. Let us learn more about exponents and their uses in this chapter.

EXPONENTS

Exponents are used to represent a number which is multiplied many times by itself. Exponents represent the repeated multiplication of the same number. In other words, using exponents, we can write very large numbers in a shorter form. Look at the example given below.

$5 \times 5 \times 5 \times 5 \times 5 \times 5 = 5^6$

The notation 5^6 stands for the short form of the product $5 \times 5 \times 5 \times 5 \times 5 \times 5 = 15,625$.

Here, '5' is called the base and '6' is called the **exponent** or **power** or **index**.

The number 5^6 is read as **five raised to the power of 6** or **sixth power** of 5.

This way of representing a number is known as the **exponential form**.

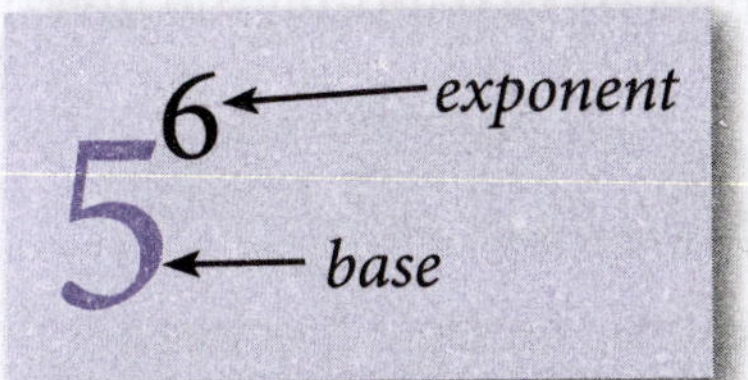

Note

An exponent tells how many times a number is multiplied by itself.

Writing Expanded Form using Exponents

In earlier classes, we have learnt how to write the expanded form of a given number. We use numbers such as 10, 100, 1000, etc. while writing the expanded form. For example, the expanded form of the number 5,41,862 is given by:

$$5,41,862 = 5 \times 1,00,000 + 4 \times 10,000 + 1 \times 1000 + 8 \times 100 + 6 \times 10 + 2 \times 10^0$$

We can write this in the exponential form as follows:

$$5,41,862 = 5 \times 10^5 + 4 \times 10^4 + 1 \times 10^3 + 8 \times 10^2 + 6 \times 10^1 + 2 \times 10^0$$

Expressing Numbers in Exponential Form

We can express a given number in the exponential form. Consider the following examples.

SOLVED EXAMPLES

Example 1: Express 2401 as a power of 7.

Solution: We can write 2401 as a product of its prime factors, that is:

$2401 = 7 \times 7 \times 7 \times 7$

As 7 appears 4 times as a factor, it can be written as $2401 = 7^4$.

Here, 7 is the base and 4 is the exponent or power. It is read as 7 raised to the power of 4.

Example 2: Write 324 using exponential notation.

Solution: First prime factorise the number and we get $324 = 2 \times 2 \times 3 \times 3 \times 3 \times 3$

Then express all the repeated factors in exponential form as shown.

$$324 = \underbrace{2 \times 2}_{\text{2 times}} \times \underbrace{3 \times 3 \times 3 \times 3}_{\text{4 times}}$$

So, $324 = 2^2 \times 3^4$

Note that in the above examples, the bases are numbers other than 10.

PUZZLE!

$2^? = 4^? = 16^? = 256$

$3^? = 9^? = 29^? = 729$

Comparing Numbers in Exponential Form

We can compare numbers in exponential form on the basis of the following rules:

- Terms with the same base: If the bases of the given terms are the same, then compare their exponents. The term with the greater exponent is the greater term.

  Example: Between 4^{11} and 4^{17}, 4^{17} is greater.

- Terms with the same exponents: If the exponents of the given terms are the same, then compare their bases. The term with the greater base is the greater term.

  Example: Between 2^8 and 6^8, 6^8 is greater.

- Terms with different bases and different exponents: First find their values by expanding the given terms, and then compare their values.

  Example: Which is greater: 7^3 or 5^4?

  $7^3 = 7 \times 7 \times 7 = 343$ and $5^4 = 5 \times 5 \times 5 \times 5 = 625$

  As $343 < 625$, we have $7^3 < 5^4$.

Do you know?

The name Google has been derived from the term googol.
1 googol = $1.0 \times 10^{100} = 10^{100}$

Terms with Negative Bases

Look at the given numbers.

$(-2)^2 = (-2) \times (-2) = 4$ Base = -2 and exponent = 2

$(-2)^3 = (-2) \times (-2) \times (-2) = -8$ Base = -2 and exponent = 3

- When a positive number is raised to any power, the answer is always positive.
- When a negative number is raised to the power of an odd natural number, the answer is negative. That is, $(-1)^{\text{odd natural number}} = -1$
- When a negative number is raised to the power of an even natural number, the answer is positive. That is, $(-1)^{\text{even natural number}} = 1$

EXERCISE 4A

1. Write the following products in exponent notation.

a. $7 \times 7 \times 7 \times 7 \times 7 \times 7$

b. $(-5) \times (-5) \times (-5)$

c. $\frac{8}{9} \times \frac{8}{9} \times \frac{8}{9} \times \frac{8}{9} \times \frac{8}{9}$

d. $\left(\frac{-3}{7}\right) \times \left(\frac{-3}{7}\right) \times \left(\frac{-3}{7}\right) \times \left(\frac{-3}{7}\right)$

e. $3 \times 3 \times 23 \times 23$

f. $8 \times 8 \times 8 \times 13 \times 13 \times 13$

g. $12 \times 12 \times 11 \times 11 \times 11$

h. $\frac{5 \times 5 \times 5 \times 5 \times 5}{11 \times 11 \times 11}$

i. $\frac{13 \times 13 \times 13 \times 13}{17 \times 17 \times 17 \times 17 \times 17 \times 17}$

j. $\frac{(-2) \times (-2) \times (-2)}{19 \times 19 \times 19 \times 19 \times 19}$

k. $\frac{(-6) \times (-6) \times (-6) \times (-6)}{(-7) \times (-7) \times (-7) \times (-7)}$

2. Express the following numbers as exponents of prime factors.

a. 64 b. 196 c. 324 d. $\frac{9}{25}$ e. $\frac{-1}{8}$

3. Evaluate the following.

a. 2^3 b. 3^2 c. 5^4 d. $(-4)^3$ e. $(-2)^7$

LAWS OF EXPONENTS

1. When we multiply two numbers whose bases are the same, then their powers are added. This is known as **product law of exponents.**

   $a^m \times a^n = a^{m+n}$, where a is any non-zero integer, m and n are any two integers.

2. (a) When we divide a number by another number whose bases are the same, then their powers are subtracted. This is known as **quotient law of exponents.**

   $$a^m \div a^n = \frac{a^m}{a^n} = a^{m-n} \text{ when } m > n$$

   (b) When bases are the same and we divide a number by another number, the number with the smaller power is shifted to the denominator if the greater power is in the denominator.

   When we shift a number from the numerator to the denominator or vice versa, the sign of its power changes. In this case,

   $$\frac{a^m}{a^n} = \frac{1}{a^{n-m}} \text{ when } m < n$$

   (c) $\frac{a^m}{a^n} = 1$ when $m = n$

Go Easy!

The number with smaller power is shifted from numerator to denominator so that the answer does not have a negative power.

Note

$$\frac{7^4}{7^4} = \frac{7 \times 7 \times 7 \times 7}{7 \times 7 \times 7 \times 7} = 1$$

or $\frac{7^4}{7^4} = 7^{4-4} = 7^0 = 1$

3. When a number with a power is raised to another power, the powers are multiplied. This is known as **power law of exponents.**

   $$\left(a^m\right)^n = a^{mn}$$

4. Any non-zero number raised to the power of 0 gives 1. This is known as **zero exponent law.**

   $a^0 = 1$

5. To convert negative power to positive, we need to take reciprocal of the number. This is known as **negative exponent law.**

   $$a^{-1} = \frac{1}{a} \qquad \left(\frac{a}{b}\right)^{-1} = \frac{b}{a}$$

Note

- 0^0 is not defined.
- Any number raised to power of 1 is equal to the number itself. For example, $3^1 = 3$

6. When we multiply two numbers with same exponents and different bases, we get:

$$a^m \times b^m = (ab)^m$$

This is known as **power of a product law.**

7. When we divide two numbers with same exponents and different bases, we get:

$$\frac{a^m}{b^m} = \left(\frac{a}{b}\right)^m$$

This is known as **power of a quotient law.**

SOLVED EXAMPLES

Example 3: Write the following products in exponential notation.

a. 5×5^2

$5 \times 5^2 = 5^{1+2}$ $[a^m \times a^n = a^{m+n}]$

$= 5^3$

b. $(-9)^4 \times (-9)^3$

$(-9)^4 \times (-9)^3 = (-9)^{4+3}$ $[a^m \times a^n = a^{m+n}]$

$= (-9)^7$

c. $\left(\frac{2}{3}\right)^2 \times \left(\frac{2}{3}\right)^3$

$\left(\frac{2}{3}\right)^2 \times \left(\frac{2}{3}\right)^3 = \left(\frac{2}{3}\right)^{2+3}$ $[a^m \times a^n = a^{m+n}]$

$= \left(\frac{2}{3}\right)^5$

d. $\left(\frac{-5}{7}\right) \times \left(\frac{-5}{7}\right)^3$

$\left(\frac{-5}{7}\right) \times \left(\frac{-5}{7}\right)^3 = \left(\frac{-5}{7}\right)^{1+3}$ $[a^m \times a^n = a^{m+n}]$

$= \left(\frac{-5}{7}\right)^4$

Example 4: Evaluate the following.

a. $2^5 \times 2^2$

$2^5 \times 2^2 = 2^{5+2}$ $[a^m \times a^n = a^{m+n}]$

$= 2^7$

$= 128$

b. $(-3)^4 \div (-3)$

$(-3)^4 \div (-3)^1 = (-3)^{4-1}$ $[a^m \div a^n = a^{m-n}]$

$= (-3)^3$

$= -27$

c. $\left(\frac{2}{5}\right) \times \left(\frac{2}{5}\right)^2$

$\left(\frac{2}{5}\right) \times \left(\frac{2}{5}\right)^2 = \left(\frac{2}{5}\right)^{1+2}$ $[a^m \times a^n = a^{m+n}]$

$= \left(\frac{2}{5}\right)^3$

$= \frac{8}{125}$

d. $\left(\frac{3}{4}\right)^2 \div \left(\frac{3}{4}\right)^5$

$\left(\frac{3}{4}\right)^2 \div \left(\frac{3}{4}\right)^5 = \left(\frac{3}{4}\right)^{2-5}$ $[a^m \div a^n = a^{m-n}]$

$= \left(\frac{3}{4}\right)^{-3} = \left(\frac{4}{3}\right)^3$ $\left[\left(\frac{a}{b}\right)^{-1} = \frac{b}{a}\right]$

$= \frac{64}{27} = 2\frac{10}{27}$

e. $\left(\frac{-4}{7}\right)^3 \times \left(\frac{-4}{7}\right)^0$

$$\left(\frac{-4}{7}\right)^3 \times \left(\frac{-4}{7}\right)^0 = \left(\frac{-4}{7}\right)^3 \times 1 \; [a^0 = 1]$$

$$= \left(\frac{-4}{7}\right)^3$$

$$= \frac{-64}{343}$$

f. $\left(\frac{-1}{6}\right)^{-1} \times \left(\frac{-1}{6}\right)^{-2}$

$$\left(\frac{-1}{6}\right)^{-1} \times \left(\frac{-1}{6}\right)^{-2} = \left(\frac{-1}{6}\right)^{-3} \quad [a^m \times a^n = a^{m+n}]$$

$$= \left(\frac{-6}{1}\right)^3$$

$$= -216$$

g. $\left(\frac{-2}{3}\right)^3 \times \left(\frac{6}{7}\right)^{-1}$

$$\left(\frac{-2}{3}\right)^3 \times \left(\frac{6}{7}\right)^{-1} = \frac{-8}{27} \times \frac{7}{6} \; [\left(\frac{a}{b}\right)^{-1} = \frac{b}{a}]$$

$$= \frac{-28}{81}$$

h. $\left(\frac{-4}{5}\right)^3 \div \left(\frac{125}{128}\right)^{-1}$

$$\left(\frac{-4}{5}\right)^3 \div \left(\frac{125}{128}\right)^{-1} = \frac{-64}{125} \div \frac{128}{125} \; [\left(\frac{a}{b}\right)^{-1} = \frac{b}{a}]$$

$$= \frac{-64}{125} \times \frac{125}{128}$$

$$= \frac{-1}{2}$$

i. $\left\{\left(\frac{-3}{4}\right)^{-1}\right\}^2$

$$\left\{\left(\frac{-3}{4}\right)^{-1}\right\}^2 = \left(\frac{-3}{4}\right)^{-1\times 2} \quad [(a^m)^n = a^{mn}]$$

$$= \left(\frac{-4}{3}\right)^2 \quad [\left(\frac{a}{b}\right)^{-1} = \frac{b}{a}]$$

$$= \frac{16}{9} = 1\frac{7}{9}$$

j. $\left[\left\{\left(\frac{-7}{9}\right)^{-1}\right\}^{-1}\right]^2$

$$\left[\left\{\left(\frac{-7}{9}\right)^{-1}\right\}^{-1}\right]^2 = \left(\frac{-7}{9}\right)^{-1\times(-1)\times 2} \quad [(a^m)^n = a^{mn}]$$

$$= \left(\frac{-7}{9}\right)^2$$

$$= \frac{49}{81}$$

k. $\frac{7}{9^{-1}} + \frac{1}{37^{-1}}$

$$\frac{7}{9^{-1}} + \frac{1}{37^{-1}} = 7 \times 9 + 37 \quad [a^{-1} = \frac{1}{a}]$$

$$= 63 + 37$$

$$= 100$$

l. $\left(\frac{2}{7}\right)^{-3} \div \left(\frac{7}{4}\right)^3$

$$\left(\frac{2}{7}\right)^{-3} \div \left(\frac{7}{4}\right)^3 = \left(\frac{7}{2}\right)^3 \div \left(\frac{7}{4}\right)^3 \quad \left[\left(\frac{a}{b}\right)^{-1} = \frac{b}{a}\right]$$

$$= \left(\frac{7}{2} \div \frac{7}{4}\right)^3 \quad \left[\frac{a^m}{b^m} = \left(\frac{a}{b}\right)^m\right]$$

$$= \left(\frac{7}{2} \times \frac{4}{7}\right)^3$$

$$= (2)^3 = 8$$

m. $\left(8^{-1}+12^{-1}\right)^{-1}$

$$\left(8^{-1}+12^{-1}\right)^{-1}=\left(\frac{1}{8}+\frac{1}{12}\right)^{-1} \quad [a^{-1}=\frac{1}{a}]$$

$$=\left(\frac{3+2}{24}\right)^{-1}$$

$$=\left(\frac{5}{24}\right)^{-1}$$

$$=\frac{24}{5}=4\frac{4}{5} \quad [a^{-1}=\frac{1}{a}]$$

n. $(-5)^0+\left(5^{-1}+5\right)^0$

$$(-5)^0+\left(5^{-1}+5\right)^0=1+1 \quad [a^0=1]$$

$$=2$$

Common Errors

$(8^{-1}+12^{-1})^{-1} \neq 8+12$. We need to take reciprocals of 8 and 12, their LCM and then add.

o. $\dfrac{7^{n+1}-2\times 7^n}{7^n-7^{n-1}}$

$$\frac{7^{n+1}-2\times 7^n}{7^n-7^{n-1}}=\frac{7^n(7-2)}{7^n(1-7^{-1})} \quad [7^n \text{ is the HCF}]$$

$$=\frac{5}{1-\frac{1}{7}}=\frac{5}{\left(\frac{7-1}{7}\right)}=5\div\frac{6}{7}$$

$$=\frac{5\times 7}{6} \quad [5\div\frac{6}{7}=5\times\frac{7}{6}]$$

$$=\frac{35}{6}=5\frac{5}{6}$$

Note

When there is a + or a – sign in the numerator/denominator of a fraction, the numbers cannot be reduced by dividing by their common factors. If all terms in the numerator and denominator have a common factor, the HCF gets cancelled because of the multiplication sign between the HCF and the brackets both in the numerator and in the denominator.

p. $\dfrac{10\times 2^n-3\times 2^{n+1}}{3\times 2^{n+1}-2^{n+1}}$

$$\frac{10\times 2^n-3\times 2^{n+1}}{3\times 2^{n+1}-2^{n+1}}=\frac{5\times 2\times 2^n-3\times 2^{n+1}}{3\times 2^{n+1}-2^{n+1}} \quad [\text{HCF of all 4 terms is } 2^{n+1}]$$

$$=\frac{5\times 2^{n+1}-3\times 2^{n+1}}{3\times 2^{n+1}-2^{n+1}}$$

$$=\frac{2^{n+1}(5-3)}{2^{n+1}(3-1)}$$

$$=\frac{2}{2}=1$$

Mental Maths

Calculate:

a. $2^{-3}\times 3^{-3}\times 6^3$

b. $\left(\frac{-4}{5}\right)^2\div\left(\frac{5}{4}\right)^{-3}$

c. $\left(2^3\right)^2$

d. $\dfrac{\left(\frac{-4}{5}\right)}{4}\times 5^2$

Example 5: Find the value of n in the following.

a. $8 \times 2^n = 2^{10}$

$\Rightarrow 2^3 \times 2^n = 2^{10}$

$\Rightarrow 2^{n+3} = 2^{10}$ $[a^m \times a^n = a^{m+n}]$

$\Rightarrow n + 3 = 10$ [As bases are same]

$\Rightarrow n = 10 - 3$

$\Rightarrow n = 7$

b. $6^n + 6^{n+1} = 42$

$\Rightarrow 6^n + 6^n \times 6 = 42$ $[a^{m+n} = a^m \times a^n]$

$\Rightarrow 6^n(1+6) = 42$ [Taking 6^n common]

$\Rightarrow 6^n \times 7 = 42$

$\Rightarrow 6^n = \frac{42}{7}$

$\Rightarrow 6^n = 6^1$

$\Rightarrow n = 1$ [As bases are same]

c. $2^{n+1} - 3 \times 2^n = -8$

$\Rightarrow 2^n \times 2 - 3 \times 2^n = -8$ $[a^{m+n} = a^m \times a^n]$

$\Rightarrow 2^n(2-3) = -8$ [Taking 2^n common]

$\Rightarrow -2^n = -2^3$

$\Rightarrow 2^n = 2^3$ [Multiplying both the sides by -1]

$\Rightarrow n = 3$ [As bases are same]

d. $6^n - 2 \times 3^n = 3^n$

$\Rightarrow (2 \times 3)^n - 2 \times 3^n = 3^n$ [Splitting 6 into its factors]

$\Rightarrow 2^n \times 3^n - 2 \times 3^n = 3^n$ $[(ab)^m = a^m \times b^m]$

$\Rightarrow 3^n(2^n - 1) = 3^n$

$\Rightarrow 2^n - 1 = 1$ [Dividing both the sides by $3n$]

$\Rightarrow 2^n = 2^1$

$\Rightarrow n = 1$ [As bases are same]

EXERCISE 4B

1. Evaluate the following.

a. $\left(\frac{3}{8}\right)^2$

b. $\left(\frac{-4}{7}\right)^3$

c. 11×7^2

d. $(-4)^2 \times (-5)^3$

e. $(-1 \times 9)^3$

f. $8^0 \times 99^0$

g. $5(17^0 + 19^0)$

h. $\left(\frac{4}{9}\right) \times \left(\frac{4}{9}\right)^2$

i. $\left(\frac{10}{11}\right) \times \left(\frac{10}{11}\right)^2 \times \left(\frac{10}{11}\right)^{-3}$

j. $\left(\frac{25}{27}\right)^{-1} \times \left(\frac{25}{27}\right)^2$

k. $\left(\frac{3}{5}\right)^3 \div \left(\frac{3}{5}\right)^2$

l. $\left(\frac{15}{17}\right)^{-3} \div \left(\frac{15}{17}\right)^{-2}$

m. $\left(\frac{3}{4}\right)^3 \times \left(\frac{2}{3}\right)^2$

n. $\left(\frac{6}{10}\right)^3 \times \left(\frac{5}{9}\right)^2$

o. $9 \times \left(\frac{15}{45}\right)^3 \times \left(\frac{5}{9}\right)^{-2}$

p. $\left(\frac{7}{23}\right)^3 \times \frac{1}{23} \times \left(\frac{7}{23}\right)^{-2}$

q. $\left\{\left(\frac{16}{36}\right)^3 \times \left(\frac{4}{9}\right)^{-2}\right\}^3$

r. $(2^{-1} + 3^{-1})^{-2}$

s. $(-9)^0 - (9^{-1} + 9)^0$

t. $\dfrac{3}{8^{-1}} - \dfrac{4}{6^{-1}}$

u. $\left[\left\{\left(\dfrac{-7}{9}\right)^{-1}\right\}^{-1}\right]^2$

v. $\left\{6^{-1} + \left(\dfrac{6}{5}\right)^{-1}\right\}^2$

w. $\dfrac{4^{n+1} - 3 \times 4^n}{4^n - 4^{n-1}}$

2. Find the value of *n* in the following.

a. $11^n \times 11^2 = 11^9$

b. $14^{2n} \times 14^{1-n} = 14^5$

c. $4^{2n} \times 4^n = 2^{12}$

d. $81 \times 3^n = 3^5$

e. $7^{2n} = 49 \times 7^n$

f. $5^{3n} = 125 \times 5^n$

g. $8^n + 8^{n+1} = 72$

h. $9^{n+1} - 2 \times 9^n = 7$

i. $\left(\dfrac{4}{9}\right)^3 \div \left(\dfrac{4}{9}\right)^2 = \left(\dfrac{2}{3}\right)^n$

STANDARD NOTATION

Standard notation is used to represent large numbers that occur in scientific study in a convenient way. It saves the effort of counting many trailing zeros in large numbers. Standard notation is also known as scientific notation.

In standard notation, a number is written as the product of

- an integer or a decimal number from 1.0 to 10 (10 is not included.) and
- a power of 10

SOLVED EXAMPLES

Example 6: Express the following numbers in standard form.

a. 56000

b. 23000000

c. 956.8

d. 3792000

Solution:

a. $56000 = 5.6 \times 10000 = 5.6 \times 10^4$

b. $23000000 = 2.3 \times 10000000 = 2.3 \times 10^7$

c. $956.8 = 9.568 \times 10^2$

d. $3792000 = 3.792 \times 1000000 = 3.792 \times 10^6$

Example 7: Multiply the following.

a. 9.8×10^4

b. 2.1304×10^4

Solution:

a. $9.8 \times 10^4 = 98000$

b. $2.1304 \times 10^4 = 21304$

Example 8: Write 729365 in expanded form using powers of 10.

Solution: $729365 = 7 \times 10^5 + 2 \times 10^4 + 9 \times 10^3 + 3 \times 10^2 + 6 \times 10^1 + 5 \times 10^0$

EXERCISE 4C

1. **Write the following numbers in expanded form using powers of 10.**

   a. 38245 b. 653752 c. 8467382

2. **Write the numeral for the numbers given in expanded form.**

   a. $5 \times 10^5 + 2 \times 10^4 + 1 \times 10^3 + 7 \times 10^2 + 6 \times 10^1 + 8 \times 10^0$

   b. $9 \times 10^4 + 2 \times 10^3 + 8 \times 10^2 + 5 \times 10^1 + 4 \times 10^0$

3. **Write the following in standard form.**

   a. 24000 b. 120000 c. 7390000

4. **Multiply the following.**

   a. 7.25×10^4 b. 3.15×10^7

Maths Lab Activity

Aim: To calculate 2^{30} and 3^{20} in diverse ways

Materials required: Two chart papers, pens and sheets of paper for each group

Procedure:

Hint: $a^{mn} = (a^m)^n$

1. Arrange the class into groups of 2 each.
2. Each pair will calculate 2^{30} and 3^{20} using various laws of exponents.
3. The different ways of calculating will be written on the two chart papers for the class.
4. The fastest way of doing the calculation will be highlighted.

Concept Map

Laws of Exponents

- $a^m \times a^n = a^{m+n}$
- $a^m \div a^n = a^{m-n}$
- $(a^m)^n = a^{mn}$
- $a^{-1} = \frac{1}{a}$
- $a^0 = 1$
- $\left(\frac{a}{b}\right)^{-1} = \frac{b}{a}$
- $(ab)^m = a^m \times b^m$

Key Concepts

- **Exponent:** Used to represent a number which is multiplied many times by itself or the repeated multiplication of the same number
- In standard notation, a number is written as the product of
  - an integer or a decimal number from 1.0 to 10 (10 is not included.)
  - a power of 10

CHAPTER REVISION

A. Choose the correct option.

1. Pick the odd one out.

   a. 2^6 b. 3^6 c. 4^3 d. 8^2

2. Pick the odd one out.

   a. 2.5×10^3 b. $2^2 \times 5^4$ c. $2^4 \times 5^2$ d. $5^2 \times 10^2$

3. Pick the odd one out.

   a. $-7^2(a-b)$ b. $(a-b)-7^2$ c. $7^2(b-a)$ d. $-\{7^2(a-b)\}$

4. $\{(2^{-1}+4^{-1})^{-1}\}^{-1} =$

   a. 6   b. $\frac{1}{6}$ c. 0.75   d. $\frac{4}{3}$

5. $(2^4 + 2^2)^0 =$

   a. 0   b. 1   c. 20   d. 2^6

6. $\left(\frac{2}{3^{-1}} - \frac{3}{2^{-1}}\right)^2$

   a. 0   b. 1   c. 2   d. 4

B. Fill in the blanks.

1. In 7^8 the base is ______ and the exponent is ______.
2. In $(-2)^3$ the base is ______ and the exponent is ______.
3. $(-9)^4$ should be multiplied by ______ to get $(-9)^4$.
4. $(-5)^2$ should be divided by ______ to get $(-5)^{-3}$.
5. The reciprocal of $\left(\frac{-3}{2}\right)^{-1}$ is ______.
6. The reciprocal of $\frac{2^{-1}}{3^{-1}}$ is ______.

C. Match the following.

1. $(2^{-1})^{-2}$	a. 0
2. $2^0 + 3^0$	b. 1
3. $(3^2-2^3)^4$	c. 2
4. $(4^3-2^6)^3$	d. 3
5. $3^2 - (3^2 + 3)$	e. 4

D. Write T for true and F for false.

1. $2^3 = 3^2$.
2. $(-5)^3 = -5^3$.
3. $(-6)^2 = -6^2$.
4. $29000 = 2.9 \times 10^3$.
5. If $4n = 32$, $n = 5$.

E. Evaluate the following.

1. $(-6)^{-1} \times (-4)^2$
2. $(-5 \times 6)^2$
3. $\left(\frac{1}{9}\right)^{-1} - 3 \div (9)^{-2}$
4. $\left\{10^{-1} + \left(\frac{10}{3}\right)^{-1}\right\}^2$
5. $(4^{-1} - 6^{-1})^{-2}$
6. $\left(\frac{11}{13}\right)^3 \times 13 \times \left(\frac{11}{13}\right)^{-2}$

SKILL UP!

Project

"Give me one grain of rice for the first square of the chessboard, two grains for the next square, four for the next, eight for the next and so on for all 64 squares, with each square having double the number of grains as the square before." In which place did the incidence take place? Read the Legend of the Ambalappuzha Paal Payasam and write briefly about this story.

What will be the number of rice grains on the 10th and the 20th square of the chessboard?

Life Skills

On an average, about 170 billion litres of water is wasted every year all over the world. How many litres of water is wasted every month? Write your answer in standard notation.

Mind Buzzer

There are 86,400 seconds in a day. How many days long is a second? Express your answer in scientific notation.

Teacher's Notes

- Introduce the chapter by asking students to cite some real-life examples of large numbers and explain how exponents are useful in expressing such numbers.
- Discuss the various laws of exponents and simplification based on them.

WORKSHEET

Solve the questions given in the boxes and colour the picture by matching the answers obtained. Also, write the laws of exponents used to solve each question in the box.

Green

$7^0 =$

Pink

$2^2 \times 2^5 =$

Blue

$11^{-1} =$

Orange

$6^2 \div (-4)^2 =$

Brown

$(3^2)^3 =$

Yellow

$\dfrac{3^6}{3^2} =$

Red

$5^3 \times 2^3 =$

5 Algebraic Expressions

Learning Objectives

- To recall the terminology used in algebra
- To identify like and unlike terms
- To learn about types of algebraic expressions
- To add, subtract and multiply algebraic expressions
- To simplify and evaluate value of given algebraic expressions

Let's Get Started

We learnt about algebra in Class 6. Let us recall a few concepts learnt by solving the given questions.

1. Look at the given expressions and complete the table.

	Is it an algebraic expression? Write yes or no.	Terms	Coefficients	
			Numerical	Literal
1. $a + b + c$	Yes	a, b, c	One	a, b, c
2. $l \times b$				
3. $7 + 5 = 12$				
4. $5n + 1$				
5. $4 \times 7 = 28$				
6. $m^2 + 2mn$				

2. Identify the pattern and frame an expression for the given series.

   a. 5, 10, 15, 20, 25, ….

   b. 3, 4, 7, 10, 13, …

ALGEBRAIC EXPRESSIONS

We have learnt that **algebra** is a branch of mathematics in which letters or symbols and numbers are used. The value of the letters or symbols may change according to the problem. The use of letters allows us to write generalized formulae.

We also learnt that **algebraic expressions** are formed by combining variables and constants, which are usually joined by plus and/or minus signs. Table 5.1 gives the difference between a variable and a constant.

Table 5.1 Difference between constant and variable

Constant	Variable
• It is a quantity that has a fixed value. • It has one particular value. • Examples: 3, 59, 101, –11, –76, etc.	• It is a quantity that does not have a fixed value. • It can take various numerical values. • It is denoted usually by letters of the alphabet. Examples: x, y, L, m, t, etc.

Powers of Variables

The variable x means x^1. The base is x and the power or exponent or index is 1. So, the value of x is taken once.

The variable x^2 means $x \times x$. The base is x and the power is 2. So, x should be multiplied by 'x' two times. In general, x^2 is read as 'x squared'.

The variable x^3 means $x \times x \times x$. The base is x and the power is 3. So, x should be multiplied by 'x' three times. x^3 is read as 'x cubed'.

Similarly, y^2z means $y \times y \times z$ and ab^2 means $a \times b \times b$.

TERMS OF AN EXPRESSION

Terms and Factors of a Term

In an algebraic expression, a term is a constant, a variable or a combination of constants and variables joined by multiplication or division sign. A term may be the product of a constant and a variable.

Consider the expression $(2a^2 + 5b)$. To form this expression, we:

1. first formed $2a^2$ separately as a product of 2, a and a;
2. then formed $5b$ separately as a product of 5 and b; and
3. finally added the two parts ($2a^2$ and $5b$) formed separately to get the expression $2a^2 + 5b$.

So, the parts of an expression which are first formed separately and then added are called the **terms** of the expression.

Note that the terms of an expression can have a negative sign too. For example, the expression $(3p^2 - 7pq)$ consists of two terms, $3p^2$ and $(-7pq)$. The term $3p^2$ is a product of 3, p and p. We can also say that 3, p and p are the **factors** of the term $3p^2$. Here, 3 is called the numerical factor, p and p are called the literal factors of $3p^2$. Similarly, the term $(-7pq)$ is a product of (-7), p and q, where (-7) is the numerical factor, and p and q are the literal factors.

So, a term is a product of its factors.

The terms and factors of the term of an expression can be represented as shown in the figure alongside.

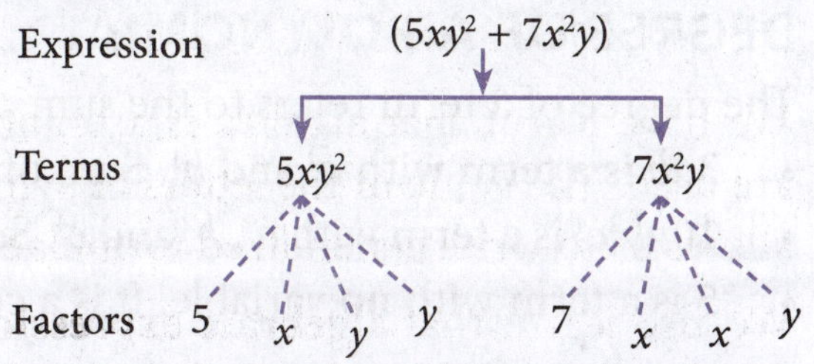

A term having only a number and no variables as its factor is called a **constant term**. For example, in the expression $(5x + 6)$, 6 is the constant term.

Coefficients

Any factor of a term is called the **coefficient** of the product of the remaining factors of the term. For example, in the expression $(-7pq)$:

(-7) is the coefficient of pq,

p is the coefficient of $(-7q)$,

q is the coefficient of $(-7p)$.

A numerical factor is called the **numerical coefficient** of the term, while a literal factor (which is a variable or a combination of variables) is called the **literal coefficient** of the term. So, in the expression $(-7pq)$, (-7) is the numerical coefficient and pq is the literal coefficient.

Note

When the coefficient of a term is +1, we need not write it.
Example: $1p$ is written as p.
When the coefficient is (-1), we indicate it with a minus sign.
Example: $(-1p)$ is written as $-p$.

Like and Unlike Terms

Terms having the same literal factors, that is, the same variable raised to the same power, are called like terms. For example, the terms x, $2ax$ and $-3ax$ are like terms as they have the same variable x raised to the same power 1. Similarly, the terms z^2, $2z^2$ and $-2z^2$ are like terms as they have the same variable z raised to the same power 2.

Terms having different literal factors, that is, different variables or different powers of the same variables, are called unlike terms. For example, the terms y, y^2 and $2y^3$ are unlike terms.

TYPES OF ALGEBRAIC EXPRESSIONS

An algebraic expression that has only one term is called a **monomial.** For example, $4xy$, $-2n$, $5a^2b$ and qr are monomials.

An algebraic expression that has two terms is called a **binomial**. For example, $x + y$, $-a + 6$, $m^2n - 3n$ and $y + 8x$ are binomials.

An algebraic expression that has three terms is called a **trinomial**. For example, $x^2 - 2x - 15$, $7a - 2b + c$ and $5m^3 + 3n + 11mn$ are trinomials.

Common Errors

The expression $4x - 2z + x$ is not a trinomial as the terms $4x$ and x are like terms . $4x - 2z + x = 5x - 2z$, which is a binomial.

An algebraic expression that has four terms is called a **quadrinomial**. For example, $a + 2b - c + \frac{1}{2}$ and $6p^2 + 2q - 5r + 12$ are quadrinomials.

An algebraic expression with one or more terms having positive integral powers of the variable is called a **polynomial**. A polynomial may be a monomial, binomial, trinomial or a quadrinomial. So, all the examples considered above are polynomials. In a polynomial, the power of the variable cannot be negative or fractional. For example, $3s + \frac{5}{t^2}$ is not a polynomial as the power of t in $\frac{5}{t^2}$ is -2, which is a negative integer.

DEGREE OF A POLYNOMIAL

The degree of a term refers to the sum of all the powers of the variables in the term. Examples:

- $3ab$ is a term with a^1 and b^1. Sum of the powers = 1 + 1 = 2. So, the degree of $3ab$ is 2.
- $10ab^2c^4$ is a term with a^1, b^2 and c^4. Sum of the powers = 1 + 2 + 4 = 7. So, the degree of $10ab^2c^4$ is 7.
- 5 is a term with no variable. It is a constant. So, its degree is 0.

The degree of a polynomial refers to the highest power of variables among the different terms in the polynomial.

- When an algebraic expression has only one variable, then the highest power of the variable gives the degree of the expression or polynomial. For example, in the polynomial $9a^2 + 5a - 3$, the only variable is a and its highest power in the given expression is 2. So, the degree of the polynomial is 2.
- When an algebraic expression has more than one variable, first find the degree of each term by adding the powers of each variable. Then the highest degree of the terms gives the degree of the expression or polynomial. For example, in the polynomial $2u^3v + 5uv^2 - 3v$, there are two variables u and v. The degree of each term: $2u^3v$ is 3 + 1 = 4, $5uv^2$ is 1 + 2 = 3 and $3v$ is 1. So, the degree of the polynomial is 4 as the highest degree among the terms is 4.

EXERCISE 5A

1. **Write the coefficient of m in the following terms.**
   a. $15m$ b. $2mn$ c. $-29a^2m$ d. $-m$ e. $-6my$ f. m
2. **Write the numerical coefficient of the following terms.**
   a. $11c$ b. $-36k$ c. $-11abc$ d. $15h^2$ e. c f. $5j$
3. **Write the literal coefficient of the following terms.**
   a. $13t$ b. $4.5c$ c. $-2st$ d. $-h^2$ e. $-4a^2c$ f. $17s$
4. **Identify the like terms in the following.**
   a. $p, pq, 2p, -qp, 4pq$ b. $a, -a^2, -6a, 9a^2, a^2$ c. $7p, -3q, q, -p, 5pq$
5. **Identify polynomials in the given expressions.**
   a. $9x + 1$ b. $\frac{2}{x} - 1$ c. $\frac{1}{b} + 3$ d. $x - 1$ e. 200 f. $10ab + a - b$
6. **Write down the degrees of the following polynomials.**
   a. $3a^2 + 6a + 3$ b. $11ab^2 - 10ac + 4$ c. $18ab + 15a - abc$

FINDING THE VALUE OF AN EXPRESSION BY SUBSTITUTION

We can find the value of an algebraic expression by substituting the value of the variable in the expression. Let us understand this by solving the following example.

> **Note**
> Substitution means putting the value of a variable in the given expression.

Example 1: If $a = -2$, $b = 3$, $c = -3$, find the value of:

a. $a^2 - c$

$a^2 - c = (-2)^2 + 2$
$= 4 + 2$
$= 6$

b. $a^3 - c^3$

$a^3 - c^3 = (-2)^3 - (-3)^3$
$= -8 - (-27)$
$= -8 + 27 = 19$

c. $(a + b - c)^2$

$(a + b - c)^2 = \{-2 + 3 - (-3)\}^2$
$= \{4\}^2$
$= 16$

Mental Maths

If $a = -2$ and $b = 5$, calculate the following:

1. $a(a + b)$ 2. $(b - a)(b + a)$ 3. $\{a - (a - b)\}^2$ 4. $(ab)^3$

USING ALGEBRAIC EXPRESSIONS TO FORM FORMULAS AND RULES

We have learnt different formulae in arithmetic and geometry as well as rules for number patterns. These formulae and rules can be expressed in a concise and general form using algebraic expressions. Consider the following examples.

Shape	Perimeter	Area	Explanation
Triangle	$a + b + c$	$\frac{1}{2} b \times h$	For perimeter, the 3 sides of the triangle are denoted by *a*, *b* and *c*. For area, base and height of the triangle are denoted by *b* and *h*, respectively.
Equilateral triangle	$3a$	$\frac{\sqrt{3}}{4} a^2$	Here, the length of each side of the equilateral triangle is denoted by *a*.
Rectangle	$2(l + b)$	$l \times b$	Here, length and breadth of the rectangle are denoted by *l* and *b*, respectively.
Square	$4a$	a^2	The length of each side of the square is denoted by *a*.

- Number of diagonals that can be drawn from a vertex in a polygon is given by $n - 3$, where n is the number of sides of the polygon.

  Total number of diagonals that can be drawn in a polygon = $\frac{n(n-3)}{2}$

- For triangular numbers, the base (or bottom) of the triangle is first made of dots. The number of dots in each row is one less than the number of dots in the row below it. The topmost row has one dot.

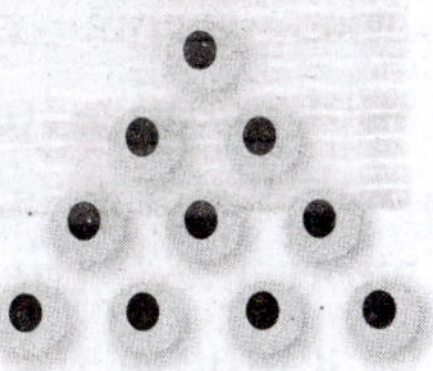

  Number of dots used to form the triangle = 4 + 3 + 2 + 1.

  Total number of dots = $\frac{n(n+1)}{2}$, where n is the number of dots at the base and n is not equal to 1.

  So, nth triangular number = $\frac{n(n+1)}{2}$.

  3, 6, 10, 15, 21 are triangular numbers.

If the formula or algebraic expression for a given quantity is known, then we can calculate the value of the quantity. Look at the following examples.

SOLVED EXAMPLES

Example 2: Find the area and perimeter of a square of side 3 cm.

Solution: Area of square = $a^2 = 3^2 = 9$

Perimeter of square = $4a = 4 \times 3 = 12$ cm

Example 3: Find the number of diagonals that can be drawn for a hexagon.

Solution: A hexagon has 6 sides, that is, $n = 6$.

So, $\frac{n(n-3)}{2} = \frac{6(6-3)}{2} = \frac{6 \times 3}{2} = 9$.

Number of diagonals that can be drawn in a hexagon = $\frac{n(n-3)}{2}$

Example 4: Find the tenth triangular number.

Solution: $n = 10$

Tenth triangular number = $\frac{n(n+1)}{2} = \frac{10(10+1)}{2} = \frac{10 \times 11}{2} = 55$.

EXERCISE 5B

1. **If $a = -3$, $b = 4$, $c = -5$, find the value of:**
   a. $a^2 - c^2$ b. $a^3 - b - c^3$ c. $(a + b + c)^3$
2. **Find the area and perimeter of a square of side 4 cm.**
3. **Find the number of diagonals that can be drawn for a pentagon.**
4. **Find the fifth triangular number.**

ADDITION AND SUBTRACTION OF ALGEBRAIC EXPRESSIONS

Like terms can be added or subtracted to get one term. Unlike terms cannot be added or subtracted. They can only be joined by a plus or minus sign.

We can add or subtract algebraic expressions with multiple positive and negative like terms using any of the following two ways:

1. Row or horizontal method
   a. For addition, put a + sign between the expressions. For subtraction, put a – sign between the expressions and while subtracting, change the signs of all terms in the second expression.
   b. Separate the like terms.

Go Easy!

Some points that need to be followed while adding or subtracting algebraic expressions are given below:

- When there is a plus (+) sign outside a bracket and we remove the bracket, the signs of terms inside the bracket do not change. So, a '+' sign indicates all the + or – signs would remain the same.

  Example: $4x + y + (2x - 3)$

  $= 4x + y + 2x - 3$

  $= 4x + 2x + y - 3 = 6x + y - 3$

- When there is a minus '–' sign outside a bracket and we remove the bracket, the signs of terms inside the bracket change. That is, – sign changes to + sign and + sign changes to – sign. So, a '–' sign indicates all the + or – signs change to their opposite signs.

  Example: $4x + y - (2x - 3)$

  $= 4x + y - 2x + 3$

  $= 4x - 2x + y + 3 = 2x + y + 3$

c. Rearrange the terms and write all the positive like terms together followed by all the negative like terms.

d. Add all the positive like terms separately and the negative like terms separately.

e. Find the difference of the two like terms obtained in the previous step.

2. Column or vertical method
   - Arrange the like terms one below the other.
   - For addition, add the terms.
   - For subtraction, change the signs of the terms in the second row and then add.

SOLVED EXAMPLES

Example 5: Add the following algebraic expressions.

a. a, 1

$a + 1$

b. $4a$, $2a$

$4a + 2a = 6a$

c. a, $-a$

$a + (-a) = a - a$
$= 0$

d. a, $-2a$

$a + (-2a) = a - 2a$
$= -a$

e. $5a - 2b - c$, $4a + b + c$

$5a - 2b - c + (4a + b + c) = 5a - 2b - c + 4a + b + c = 5a + 4a - 2b + b - c + c$
$= 9a - b$

Example 6: Add the following algebraic expressions using column method.

a.
$$\begin{array}{rr} a & +\,6b \\ -a & +\,3b \\ \hline & +\,3b \\ \hline \end{array}$$

b.
$$\begin{array}{rrr} 8a & -\,2b & -\,c \\ a & +\,b & +\,c \\ \hline 9a & -\,b & \\ \hline \end{array}$$

c.
$$\begin{array}{rrrr} -7a & -\,11b & -\,5c & \\ -5a & -\,3b & +\,c & +\,7 \\ \hline -12a & -\,14b & -\,4c & +\,7 \\ \hline \end{array}$$

Example 7: Subtract the second expression from the first in the following:

a. a, a

$a - a = 0$

b. $-r$, $-s$

$-r - (-s) = -r + s$

c. z, 18

$z - 18$

d. a, $-4a$

$a - (-4a) = a + 4a$
$= 5a$

e. $9a + b$, $-a - 3b$

$9a + b - (-a - 3b) = 9a + b + a + 3b$
$= 9a + a + b + 3b$
$= 10a + 4b$

f. $a - b - c$, $4a + b$

$a - b - c - (4a + b) = a - b - c - 4a - b$
$= a - 4a - b - b - c$
$= -3a - 2b - c$

Example 8: Subtract the second expression from the first using column method.

a.
$$\begin{array}{rr} 9a & +\,b \\ -\,a & -\,3b \\ (+) & (+) \\ \hline 10a & +\,4b \\ \hline \end{array}$$

b.
$$\begin{array}{rrr} 8a & -\,2b & \\ a & +\,b & -\,c \\ (-) & (-) & (+) \\ \hline 7a & -\,3b & +\,c \\ \hline \end{array}$$

c.
$$\begin{array}{rrrr} 9x & -10y & -\,z & +\,3 \\ -\,9x & -\,7y & -\,z & \\ (+) & (+) & (+) & \\ \hline 18x & -\,3y & & +\,3 \\ \hline \end{array}$$

EXERCISE 5C

1. Add the following algebraic expressions.

a. $2d, -8d, +3d$ b. $-2e, 4e, 2e^3$ c. $17a + 11b, -9a - 8b$

d. $9a - 7b + 3c, 6a + b - c$ e. $20x - 10y + z, -20x + 10y - z$

f. $17f + g - 7gh, 13f + 3g + 5hg, 2f - 4gh$

g. $8a^3 + 7a^2 + 4a + 3, -2a^3 + a^2 + 10, 6a^3 + 3a + 1$

h. $c + 9a + 13b, 2b + 3a + 2c, 2b + c - a$

i. $\begin{array}{r} 9a - 8 \\ 9a + 9 \\ \hline \end{array}$ j. $\begin{array}{r} -a + 15b + 32c \\ 6a - 2b - 6c \\ \hline \end{array}$ k. $\begin{array}{r} x - y - 25z \\ -2x - 8y + 13z - 40 \\ \hline \end{array}$

2. Subtract the second expression from the first in the following.

a. $12a, -a$ b. $14ba, 14ab$ c. $-abc, 4cab$ d. $d + 5, 2d$

e. $t^3 - t^2, 3t^3 + t^2$ f. $23a - b + 8c, a + 11b - 8c$ g. $r - s + 15, s + 15$

h. $\begin{array}{r} 6a + b - 9c \\ -6a - 7b + 3c \\ \hline \end{array}$ i. $\begin{array}{r} 5a + 8b - 14c \\ -3a - 3b \\ \hline \end{array}$ j. $\begin{array}{r} 9e - 34s - u + su \\ -4e - 23s - 9u + us \\ \hline \end{array}$

3. Take away $3e + 4r - 5t$ from $6e + 5r - 9t$.

4. By how much does $15a + 14b - c$ exceed $5a + 11b - c$.

5. Take away $9a + 11b$ from the sum of $4a + 6b - 2c$ and $8a + b - 4c$.

6. From the sum of $17a + 12b - 8c$ and $7a + 8b - 10c$, subtract $12a + 13b - 10c$.

7. If $A = 12b - 10c + 6d$, $B = 9b - c + 3d$ and $C = a + b + c$, find:

a. $A + B$ b. $A + B + C$ c. $B - C$ d. $2A - C$

MULTIPLICATION OF ALGEBRAIC EXPRESSIONS

Multiplication of numbers is distributive over addition and subtraction.

So, $a(b + c) = ab + ac$

- **Multiplication of a monomial by a monomial**

For multiplication of a monomial by a monomial, the numerical coefficients of both the monomials are multiplied followed by the literal coefficients of the monomials.

- **Multiplication of a monomial by a binomial or a trinomial**

The monomial is multiplied by each term of the binomial or trinomial.

- **Multiplication of a binomial by a binomial or a trinomial**
  - Row method
    a. The first term from the first expression is multiplied by all terms of the second expression.
    b. The second term from the first expression is multiplied by all terms of the second expression. The terms are then rearranged by writing all the like terms together.
    c. The like terms are added to get the final answer.
  - Column method
    a. The first term from the left of the second expression is multiplied by all terms of the first expression and the answer is written in the first line.
    b. The second term from the left of the second expression is multiplied by all terms of the first expression and the answer is written in the second line.
    c. Then the like terms are added.

SOLVED EXAMPLES

Example 9: Multiply the following.

a. $5g, -2$

$5g \times -2 = -10g$

b. $-7r, -6rs$

$-7r \times (-6rs) = +42r^2s$

c. $a, 3b, -c$

$a \times 3b \times (-c) = -3abc$

d. $9f, 0, -11g$

$9f \times 0 \times (-11g) = 0$

e. $-a, \frac{1}{2}, \frac{a}{2}$

$-a \times \frac{1}{2} \times \frac{a}{2} = \frac{-a^2}{4}$

f. $7a, 2a - b$

$7a(2a - b) = 7a \times 2a - 7a \times b$
$= 14a^2 - 7ab$

g. $y + z, y - 2z$

$(y + z)(y - 2z) = y(y - 2z) + z(y - 2z)$
$= y^2 - 2yz + yz - 2z^2$
$= y^2 - yz - 2z^2$

h. $a + 3b - c, a - b$

$(a + 3b - c)(a - b) = (a - b)(a + 3b - c)$
$= a(a + 3b - c) - b(a + 3b - c)$
$= a^2 + 3ab - ac - ab - 3b^2 + bc$
$= a^2 + 2ab - ac - 3b^2 + bc$

Example 10: Multiply the following algebraic expressions using column method.

a.
$$\begin{array}{rr} +7b & -4c \\ \times & +2c \\ \hline 14bc & -8c^2 \\ \hline \end{array}$$

b.
$$\begin{array}{rrr} a & +2b & \\ \times\ b & -a & \\ \hline ab & +2b^2 & \\ -2ab & & -a^2 \\ \hline -ab & +2b^2 & -a^2 \\ \hline \end{array}$$

c.
$$\begin{array}{rrrrr} 2e & +7f & -4 & & \\ \times\ e & +f & & & \\ \hline 2e^2 & +7ef & -4e & & \\ & +2ef & & +7f^2 & -4f \\ \hline 2e^2 & +9ef & -4e & +7f^2 & -4f \\ \hline \end{array}$$

EXERCISE 5D

1. Multiply the following algebraic expressions.

a. $\begin{array}{r r} & 3b \quad -c \\ \times & +7b \\ \hline \end{array}$

b. $\begin{array}{r r} & 2x \quad +y \\ \times & x \quad -y \\ \hline \end{array}$

c. $\begin{array}{r r} & 3a \quad +b \\ & \times 5b \quad -2a \\ \hline \end{array}$

d. $2a(a + b)$ e. $-3r(2r - 7)$ f. $(2a^2 + 3a + 1)1.5a$ g. $-(6e - 11)(e - f)$

h. $(12a^2 + 5)(2a^2 - 1)$ i. $(0.2a + 3)(a - 5)$ j. $-2(5ab + 4)(2b - a)$

k. $(x+2)\left(\dfrac{x}{4}-7\right)$ l. $(xy + 1)(y - x + 3)$ m. $(5x + 1)(a + x + 3)$ n. $(xy+y+2)(x+1)$

2. Simplify the following.

a. $2a + (3a - b + a)$ b. $a + (4a - a) + (7a - a)$ c. $11b - a + 2(3a - b)$

d. $5 + (11b - b) + 2(3a - b)$ e. $5p + (3p + q - 7p) - q$ f. $8kl - 6k + 4(lk - k + lk)$

g. $3r - 7s + (3r - s + s) + (7s - r)$ h. $-a + [b - \{-(a - b + a)\}]$

i. $2a - a - 2\{a + (2a - a) - a\}]$ j. $a + [a - a\{a^2 + a(a - a) - a^2\}]$

k. $4a(1 + 2b) + 2(3a + ab)$ l. $2y^2 + y(y - 3) - 3(y^2 - 4)$

3. Multiply the following and verify the result for $x = 1$ and $y = -1$.

a. $\dfrac{x}{3}(x^2 + 3x - 6)$ b. $(5a + 4)(2a - 1)$ c. $6(x + 2y)(3x + y)$ d. $(x - y + 3)(2x - 1)$

Maths Lab Activity

Aim: To understand the concept of substitution and multiplication

Materials required: 4 boxes for digit chits – labelled as *A*, *B*, *C* and *D*, 1 box for the questions (simplification) on variables *A*, *B*, *C* and *D*; scissors, pencils and rulers; 4 chits each for digits 1 to 9 and for digits from –1 to –9 and 1 chit each for the simplification question as given in the tables below.

Chits for boxes A, B, C and D

–9	–4	9	4
–8	–3	8	3
–7	–2	7	2
–6	–1	6	1
–5	0	5	0

$A(B + 1)$	$(A + B)(C + D)$	$A(B + C + D)$
$B(C - 1)$	$(A + C)(B + D)$	$B(A + C + D)$
$C(D + 2)$	$(B - A)(D - C)$	$C(A + B + D)$
$D(A - 2)$	$(D - B)(C - A)$	$D(A + B + C)$

Procedure:

1. Arrange the class in 4 groups. Each group will be given a box labelled *A, B, C* or *D* with a set of digit chits put in each of the boxes. The teacher will have the box containing chits with simplification questions.
2. Each group will have two team leaders for answering the questions after discussion in the group.
3. Two students will be in charge of keeping the score on the green board. Each correct answer will win 1 point. There will be no negative marking.
4. For every round of questions, a chit from box *A, B, C* and *D* will be taken out by a player from that group. With these values of *A, B, C* and *D*, each group is required to solve the simplification problem on the chit taken out by the teacher.
5. As soon as the teacher writes the simplification problem on the board, each group will be given approximately 1 minute to calculate the answer for the same.
6. At the end of the quiz, the team with the highest score will be the winner.

Concept Map

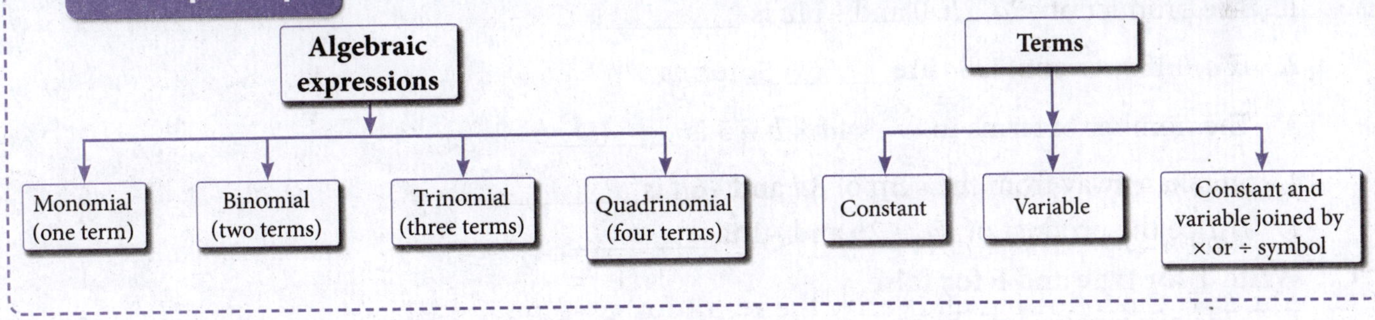

Key Concepts

- **Term:** A constant, a variable or a combination of constants and variables joined by multiplication or division sign
- **Coefficient:** A factor of a term is the coefficient of the product of the remaining factors in the term
- **Like Terms:** Terms having the same variable and the same power for each variable
- **Unlike Terms:** Terms not having the same variable or the same power for each variable
- **Algebraic expression:** A combination of terms joined by plus or minus sign
- **Degree of a term:** Sum of all the powers of the variables in the term
- **Degree of a polynomial:** Highest of all the degrees of the terms in the polynomial

CHAPTER REVISION

A. Choose the correct option.

1. $4a \times bc + 4a^2 - b + 5$ is a polynomial of degree ________.
   a. 0 b. 1 c. 2 d. 3
2. Pick the odd one out.
   a. $a(5a - 15)$ b. $5a(a - 3)$ c. $5a(3 - a)$ d. $(a - 3)5a$
3. $3y - 3y(z + 1) + 3z(y - 1) =$
   a. $3yz - 3z$ b. $-3z$ c. $6y - 6z$ d. $3y - 3z$
4. $(a - b)7 - 7(b - a) =$
   a. 0 b. $7a - 7b$ c. $14a - 14b$ d. $7(a - b)(b - a)$
5. $(0.5a + 1) - 0.5a =$
   a. $-0.25a^2$ b. $-0.5a$ c. 1 d. $-0.25a^2 - 0.5a$

B. Fill in the blanks.

1. The product of $-9a$, $2b$, 0 and $-11c$ is ________.
2. $18a$, $145a$, $\frac{a}{2}$ and $-28a$ are ________ terms.
3. The number of terms in $\frac{x}{2} + 4a \times b - 5$ is ________.
4. $5d$ taken away from the sum of $8d$ and $-6d$ is ________.
5. Thrice the product of $4a$, $-2b$ and -1 is ________.

C. Write T for true and F for false.

1. 17 is not a polynomial.
2. $12abc$ and $-12bca$ are like terms.
3. The coefficient of a in $-45ad$ is $45d$.
4. The degree of the polynomial $ab^3 - 3abc + ab$ is 3.
5. The degree of the polynomial $100a$ is 1.
6. Unlike terms can be added.
7. The sum of like terms is another like term.

D. Match the following.

1. $\frac{5a(a-1)}{5}$ 2. $(a + 1)(a - 1)$ 3. $\frac{a}{2}(2-4a)$ 4. $\frac{-1}{2}(-4a+2)$ 5. $a(a + 1) - 2a^2$

a. $a^2 - 1$ b. $-2a^2 + a$ c. $-1 + 2a$ d. $a^2 - a$ e. $-a^2 + a$

E. Answer the following questions.

1. Find the sum of the following.
   a. $15y + 18z, -15y + 10z - 11$ b. $8a + 12b, 2b + c, -a + 2b - c$
2. Subtract the first expression from the second in the following.
   a. $20y + 10z, -11y + 8z - 15$ b. $7a + 13b, -12a + 19b - 17c$
3. Multiply the following.
   a. $6p(p - 3q)$ b. $(4r - s)(50 - 7s)$ c. $(4 + a)(a + b - 1)$ d. $5(r + s)(r - 2s)$

e. $(9e + 7f - 5)(e + f)$ f. $(6x + 7y - 2)(2x + y)$

4. If $A = b - c$, $B = 9b - c + 3$ and $C = a + b$, find:

a. $(A + B)C$ b. $A + B + C$ c. $B(A - C)$ d. $2B - A$

5. If $a = -2$, $b = 2$, $c = -5$, find the value of the following.

a. abc b. $a(b + c)$ c. $b(a + c)^2$ d. $\frac{a+b}{c}$

6. Find the area and perimeter of a rectangle of length 5 cm and breadth 3 cm.

SKILL UP!

Project

For a 20/20 cricket series played by India in the current year, tabulate the runs scored by two of your favourite Indian cricketers for each match of the entire series. You may use the newspaper or TV or the Internet to collect the data. Also tabulate the numbers of 4s and 6s scored by each player. Frame algebraic expressions for calculating the average runs of the two cricketers for the series, percentage of 4s and percentage of 6s out of the total runs scored by a cricketer. Using these expressions, calculate the average runs scored by the cricketers, the percentage of their 4s and 6s and compare these values for the two cricketers.

Life Skills

Mawsynram in Meghalaya is one of the wettest places in the world.

Using internet, find the rainfall in Mawsynram for 4 consecutive days in May and June. If a, b, c and d respectively represent the rainfall on 4 consecutive days of a week, write an expression to calculate the average rainfall for 4 days.

If you intend to make a travel itinerary for Mawsynram, would it be better to go in May or in June. Why?

Mind Buzzer

Simplify the following.

a. $(a + 1)(a - 1) - a(a - 1)$ b. $(r - s)2 + 3(r + s) - (r - s)$

c. $(a - b)5 + 3(a + b) - (a - 2b)$ d. $(a + 1)(a + 2) + (a - 1)(a - 3)$

e. $(a + 1)(a - 2) - (a + 2)(a - 1)$

Teacher's Notes

- Begin the lesson by revision of the basic concepts learnt in class 6.
- Encourage the students to practise questions to reinforce the rules for addition, subtraction and multiplication of algebraic expressions.
- With the help of real-life examples, discuss the situations where algebraic expressions are needed.

WORKSHEET

In Class 6 (Algebra chapter), we played a game based on Snakes and Ladders. Let us play the same game with a slight difference.

The rules of the game are almost the same, except that it will be played **with 2 dice, one of black colour and one of white.**

x represents score on the black dice. y represents score on the white dice.

Positive value of any expression represents a ladder, that is, moving forward.

Negative value of an expression represents a snake, that is, moving backward.

Home 100 and 99		98 $-x^2 - y$	97	96	95 $-2(x + y)$	94	93	92	91
81	82	83	84	85	86	87	88 $3x - 2y$	89	90
80	79	78 $2y - 3$	77	76	75	74	73	72	71 xy
61	62	63	64	65	66 $y - x^2$	67	68	69	70
60	59	58	57 $x(x + y)$	56	55	54 $3x - 2$	53	52	51
41	42	43 $2y + 3$	44	45	46	47	48	49	50 $-xy$
40	39	38	37	36 $2x + 4$	35	34	33	32	31
21 $10 - y$	22	23	24	25	26	27 $3y - 4$	28	29	30
20	19	18	17	16	15	14	13	14	11
Start	2	3	4	5 $3(x + y)$	6	7	8	9	10

6 Linear Equations in One Variable

Learning Objectives

- To identify equations and frame equations
- To solve simple equations using different methods and verify the solution
- To apply the concept to solve real-life problems

Let's Get Started

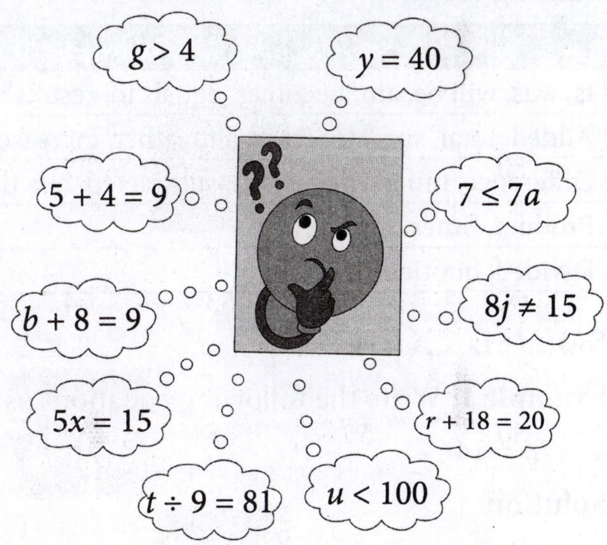

What is an equation?

An equation is an algebraic statement in which one expression is equal to another.

$4 + 3 = 7$ is an example of a numerical equation, as this equation has only numerals.

An algebraic statement in which instead of = sign, <, >, ≠, ≤, or ≥ symbol is used is not an equation. For example, $g > 4$, $7 \leq 7a$, $8j \neq 15$, $U < 100$, $5 + 4 = 9$ are not equations.

larger > smaller

= equal	> greater than	≥ greater than or equal
≠ not equal	< less than	≤ less than or equal

All equations consist of a left side, an equal sign and a right side.

In an equation, LEFT SIDE = RIGHT SIDE, that is, LHS = RHS.

The following is the general pattern.

Equation	Left side	Equal sign	Right side
$x+2=1$	$x+2$	=	1
$x-5=0$	$x-5$	=	0

Constants	Variables
+2, 1	x
−5, 0	x

Write any five formulae you have learnt in Physics and Geometry. Are they equations?

LINEAR EQUATION

A linear equation is an equation of a line. It may have one or two variables. The power of the variables is always one. In this chapter, we will study about linear equations in one variable. When we solve an equation, we find the value (answer/solution/ root) of the unknown variable.

> **Do you know?**
> The word linear is derived from the Latin word '*linearis*' which means resembling a line and the word equation means 'is equal to'.

Solution/Root of an Equation

A value which satisfies an equation (makes LHS of the equation = RHS of the equation) is called a solution or root of the equation. So, a value for which the equation holds true is a solution of the equation. When we solve an equation (find its answer/solution), we find the value of the unknown variable.

Phrases such as 'a value which satisfies the equation' or 'a value for which the equation holds true' actually convey that when that particular value is put in the equation, then LHS becomes equal to the RHS.

Understanding the relation between the following phrases and the corresponding symbols will make learning easier.

Word(s)	Symbol
Is, was, will be, am, becomes, equals to, results in, gives	=
Added, total, sum, together, altogether, increased, more than	+
Difference, minus, decreased, subtracted, less than, take away	−
Product, times, multiply	×
Divided, quotient	÷

SOLVED EXAMPLES

Example 1: Write the following equations as statements:

a. $7a = 14$ b. $y + 4 = 10$ c. $3(a + 5) = 18$

Solution:

a. Given: $7a = 14$

$7a$ means seven times a.

Seven times a is (will be, becomes, equal to, results in) 14.

b. Given: $y + 4 = 10$

For + we can write added, total, sum, together, altogether, increased by, more than. So, the statements can be any of the following:

i. 4 added to y is 10 ii. y increased by 4 becomes 10.

iii. Sum of y and 4 is equal to 10. iv. 4 more than y results in 10.

v. Total of y and 4 is equal to 10.

c. Given: $3(a + 5) = 18$

$(a + 5)$ can be written as the sum of a and 5. As we want this answer to be multiplied by 3, our statements can be the following:

i. Thrice the sum of a and 5 is 18.

ii. Three times the sum of a and 5 is 18.

iii. 5 is added to a and the result is multiplied by 3 to get 18.

iv. The product of 3 and the sum of a and 5 gives 18.

SOLVING AN EQUATION

A linear equation can be solved by using any of the following methods:

1. Trial and error method
2. Method of balancing
3. By cross-multiplication and transposing of terms by changing addition into subtraction and vice versa

> **Note**
> Solving an equation means finding the value of the unknown variable in the equation.

Trial and Error Method

In this method, we try to find a solution by substituting (putting) some suitable values in the given equation. If the LHS of the equation becomes equal to RHS, then the equation is satisfied and the substituted value is a solution. If LHS is not equal to RHS (LHS ≠ RHS), then we try some other value.

> **Note**
> Simple equations have a unique solution. There is only one possible solution for a simple equation. Other values cannot make LHS of the equation equal to RHS.

SOLVED EXAMPLES

Example 2: Write the following statements as equations. Write a solution (by trial and error) for the equations such that L.H.S = RHS.

a. Twice h is 5 more than 3.

b. Thrice p gives the sum of first three odd numbers.

c. Half the sum of x and 5 becomes 1.

Solution:

a. Given: Twice h is 5 more than 3.

Twice h means 2 multiplied by h, that is, $2h$. More means '+' and is means '='.

$2h = 3 + 5 = 8$

Here, LHS = $2h$ and RHS = 8.

- If we put $h = 1$, we get $2h = 2 \times 1 = 2$ which does not make LHS = RHS.
- If we put $h = 2$, we get $2h = 2 \times 2 = 4$ which does not make LHS = RHS.
- If we put $h = 3$, we get $2h = 2 \times 3 = 6$ which does not make LHS = RHS.
- If we put $h = 4$, we get $2h = 2 \times 4 = 8$ or $8 = 8$ which makes LHS = RHS.

So, by trial and error, we conclude that $h = 4$ satisfies the equation.

Thus, $h = 4$ is a solution of the equation.

b. Given: Thrice p gives the sum of first three odd numbers.

Thrice p means 3 multiplied by p, i.e., $3p$. Sum means '+' and gives means '='.

$3p = 1 + 3 + 5 = 9$

Here LHS = $3p$ and RHS = 9.

If we put $p = 1$, we get $3p = 3 \times 1 = 3$ which does not make LHS = RHS.

If we put $p = 2$, we get $3p = 3 \times 2 = 6$ which does not make LHS = RHS.

If we put $p = 3$, we get $3p = 3 \times 3 = 9$ or $9 = 9$ which makes LHS = RHS.

So, by trial and error, we conclude that $p = 3$ satisfies the equation.

Thus, $p = 3$ is a solution of the equation.

c. Given: Half the sum of x and 5 becomes 1.

Sum of x and 5 is $(x + 5)$. Half the sum is $\frac{(x+5)}{2}$.

Becomes means =. So, we get $\frac{(x+5)}{2} = 1$. Here LHS = $\frac{(x+5)}{2}$ and RHS = 1

If we put $x = 0$, we get $\frac{(x+5)}{2} = \frac{(0+5)}{2} = 2.5$ which does not make LHS = RHS.

If we put $x = 1$, we get $\frac{(x+5)}{2} = \frac{(1+5)}{2} = 3$ which does not make LHS = RHS.

If we put $x = -1$, we get $\frac{(x+5)}{2} = \frac{(-1+5)}{2} = 2$ which does not make LHS = RHS.

If we put $x = -2$, we get $\frac{(-2+5)}{2} = 1.5$ which does not make LHS = RHS.

If we put $x = -3$, we get $\frac{(-3+5)}{2} = 1 = 1$ which makes LHS = RHS.

So, by trial and error, we conclude that $x = -3$ satisfies the equation.

Thus, $x = -3$ is a solution of the equation.

Method of Balancing

In a beam balance or a weighing balance, we need to put equal weights on both the sides to make both the sides balanced with each other. If we add some extra weight on one side of the balance, we need to add the same weight on the other side to make the beam balanced. Similarly, for removing (subtracting), multiplying or dividing some weight from one side of a balance, we need to remove (subtract), multiply or divide the same weight from the other side of the balance so that the beam is balanced.

If weight of 1 jar = w, weight of 2 jars = $\mathbf{2w = 1}$ **kg** for the beam to be balanced.

$\mathbf{2w = 1.}$

So, $\mathbf{w = \frac{1}{2}}$ **kg.**

In the above beam balance, on one side we have a weight of 1 kg, whereas on the other side, we have 2 jam jars of equal weights. The beam is balanced. This means that the weight of each jar is $\frac{1}{2}$ the weight on the other side.

Now, if we add one more jar on the right side, we need to add a weight of 500 g on the left side to make the beams balanced.

Same technique is applied in simple equations also. **If we add/subtract/multiply/divide both sides of an equation by the same number, the equation remains unchanged.**

SOLVED EXAMPLES

Example 3: Solve the following equations by adding, subtracting, multiplying or dividing both sides of the equations by the same number.

a. $x + 1 = 4$ b. $a - 6 = 5$ c. $12 = \frac{d}{2}$

d. $7y = 4y - 6$ e. $5a - 9a = 8$

Solution:

a. Given: $x + 1 = 4$

To get just the variable x on the LHS, subtract 1 from both sides of the equation.

$$x+1-1=4-1$$

$$x=3$$

Thus, the value of x is 3.

b. Given: $a - 6 = 5$

To remove the numbers from the LHS, add 6 to both sides of the equation.

$$a-6+6=5+6$$

$$a=11$$

Thus, the value of a is 11.

c. Given: $12 = \frac{d}{2}$

Multiply both sides by 2.

$$12\times 2=\frac{d}{2}\times 2$$

$$24=d \text{ or } d=24$$

Thus, the value of d is 24.

d. Given: $7y = 4y - 6$

Subtract $4y$ from both sides of the equation.

$$7y-4y=4y-6-4y$$

$$3y=-6$$

$$y=-2$$

Thus, the value of y is −2.

e. Given: $5a - 9a = 8$

Simplify the above equation.

$$5a-9a=8$$

$$-4a=8$$

Multiply both sides by (−1).

$$-4a(-1)=8(-1)$$

$$4a=-8$$

$$a=-2$$

Thus, the value of a is −2.

Cross-Multiplication and Transposing of Terms

If there is no addition or subtraction in an equation (except when terms are put in brackets), we can cross-multiply to solve a simple equation. We assume that there is a cross (×) on the '=' sign and according to our requirement, we can transpose terms in the numerator of one side to the denominator of the other side and vice versa.

In cross-multiplication, if $\frac{a}{b} = \frac{c}{d}$, then $a \times d = b \times c$.

SOLVED EXAMPLES

Example 4: Solve the following equations by the method of cross-multiplication:

a. $\dfrac{2a}{7} = \dfrac{4}{1}$

b. $15a = 45$

Solution:

a. Given: $\dfrac{2a}{7} = \dfrac{4}{1}$

On cross multiplication, we get

$2a \times 1 = 7 \times 4$

So, $a = \dfrac{7 \times 4}{1 \times 2}$

Thus, the value of a is 14.

b. Given: 15a = 45

To calculate the value of a, we need to remove 15 from LHS. We can do so by multiplying 45 by the reciprocal of 15, that is, $\dfrac{1}{15}$.

$15a = 45$

$a = \dfrac{45}{15} = 3$

Thus, the value of a is 3.

Shortcut of cross-multiplication

If on the LHS and RHS of an equation, we do not have a '+' or a '–' sign in the denominator (numerator) and both the denominators (numerators) have a common factor, then we can divide both by their HCF and the equation will remain unchanged.

Transposing Terms

Changing of terms from one side of the equal sign to the other is called transposing of terms. When transposing terms from one side of the equal sign to the other, remember the following:

a. When a positive number is taken from LHS of an equation to RHS, the sign of the number becomes negative. The converse is also true. That is, + sign from LHS becomes – sign on RHS and vice versa.

b. Put all the terms containing the variable on one side of the equal sign and all the constants on the other side.

c. An equation remains the same even when the expressions on the LHS and RHS are interchanged.

Adding/subtracting on both sides Subtracting 9 from both sides, $x + 9 = 12 \Rightarrow x + 9 - 9 = 12 - 9 \Rightarrow x = 3$	**Transposing** Transposing the constant to RHS, $x + 9 = 12 \Rightarrow x = 12 - 9 \Rightarrow x = 3$
Multiplying/dividing both sides Dividing both sides by 3, $3x = 12 \Rightarrow \dfrac{3x}{3} = \dfrac{12}{3} \Rightarrow x = 4$	**Transposing** Transposing the coefficient of x, $3x = 12 \Rightarrow x = \dfrac{12}{3} = 4$

SOLVED EXAMPLES

Example 5: Solve the following equations.

a. $\frac{x}{8}=\frac{7}{4}$ b. $\frac{5x}{3}=15$ c. $11y=\frac{22}{7}$

d. $\frac{a}{2}=\frac{1}{2}-a$ e. $\frac{b}{2}+\frac{b}{3}=20$ f. $\frac{a+1}{2}+\frac{a}{5}=-2-1$

Solution:

a. Given: $\frac{x}{8}=\frac{7}{4}$

Use cross-multiplication:

$x=\frac{7}{4}\times 8$

$x=14$

Thus, the value of x is 14.

b. Given: $\frac{5x}{3}=15$

Use cross-multiplication:

$x=15\times\frac{3}{5}$

$x=9$

Thus, the value of x is 9.

c. Given: $11y=\frac{22}{7}$

Use cross-multiplication:

$y=\frac{22}{7}\times\frac{1}{11}$

$y=\frac{2}{7}$

Thus, the value of y is $\frac{2}{7}$.

d. Given: $\frac{a}{2}=\frac{1}{2}-a$

$\frac{a}{2}+a=\frac{1}{2}$

$\frac{a+2a}{2}=\frac{1}{2}$

$\frac{3a}{2}=\frac{1}{2}$

Use cross-multiplication:

$a=\frac{1}{2}\times\frac{2}{3}=\frac{1}{3}$

Thus, the value of a is $\frac{1}{3}$.

e. Given: $\frac{b}{2}+\frac{b}{3}=20$

$\frac{3b+2b}{6}=20$

$\frac{5b}{6}=20$

Use cross-multiplication:

$b=20\times\frac{6}{5}$

$b=24$

Thus, the value of b is 24.

f. Given: $\frac{a+1}{2}+\frac{a}{5}=-2-1$

$\frac{5(a+1)+2a}{10}=-3$

Use cross-multiplication:

$5a+5+2a=-30$

$7a+5=-30$

$7a=-30-5$

$7a=-35$

$a=\frac{-35}{7}=-5$

Thus, the value of a is –5.

Example 6: Find the value of x in the following equations.

a. $\frac{2x-1}{10}-\frac{x-3}{5}=\frac{5x+1}{10}$ b. $\frac{1}{4}(x-3)-\frac{1}{3}(x-4)=\frac{2x}{5}$

Solution:

a. Given: $\frac{2x-1}{10}-\frac{x-3}{5}=\frac{5x+1}{10}$

Simplifying the above equation, we get:

$$\frac{(2x-1)-2(x-3)}{10}=\frac{5x+1}{10}$$

Cancelling 10 on both sides, we get:

$$(2x-1)-2(x-3)=5x+1$$
$$2x-1-2x+6=5x+1$$
$$5=5x+1$$
$$5-1=5x$$
$$5x=4$$
$$x=\frac{4}{5}$$

Thus, the value of x is $\frac{4}{5}$.

b. Given: $\frac{1}{4}(x-3)-\frac{1}{3}(x-4)=\frac{2x}{5}$

$$\frac{(x-3)}{4}-\frac{(x-4)}{3}=\frac{2x}{5}$$
$$\frac{3(x-3)-4(x-4)}{12}=\frac{2x}{5}$$
$$\frac{3x-9-4x+16}{12}=\frac{2x}{5}$$
$$\frac{-x+7}{12}=\frac{2x}{5}$$

Use cross-multiplication:

$$5(-x+7)=24x$$
$$-5x+35=24x$$
$$35=24x+5x \Rightarrow 29x=35$$
$$x=\frac{35}{29}=1\frac{6}{29}$$

Thus, the value of x is $1\frac{6}{29}$.

FRAMING AN EQUATION FROM A SOLUTION

If the solution of an equation is $t = 4$, we can frame many equations from the solution by adding, subtracting, multiplying or dividing the same number from both LHS and RHS of the equation.

1. $t=4$
   $t\times 2=4\times 2$
   $2t=8$
2. $t=4$
   $t+6=4+6$
   $t+6=10$
3. $t=4$
   $t\div 2=4\div 2$
   $t\div 2=2$
4. $t=4$
   $t-5=4-5$
   $t-5=-1$

Go Easy!

For easier understanding, look at the change of signs in the following equations:

a. $4+3=7$
   $4=7-3$ or $3=7-4$ or $4+3-7=0$

b. $\frac{2}{3}\div\frac{1}{2}=\frac{2}{3}\times\frac{2}{1}=\frac{4}{3}$

c. $\frac{2}{3}\times x=6$, then $x=6\times\frac{3}{2}$

d. If $\frac{x}{3}=6$, then $x=6\times\frac{3}{1}=\frac{18}{1}=18$ (as reciprocal of $\frac{1}{3}=\frac{3}{1}$).

EXERCISE 6A

1. Solve the following equations by adding, subtracting, multiplying or dividing both sides of the equations by the same number.

a. $x + 5 = 3$ b. $a - 3 = 5$ c. $7a = 14$ d. $z \div 9 = 6$ e. $8 = 16d$

f. $5a + a = 12$ g. $a - 3a = 8$ h. $6p = -9 + 9$ i. $4y = 2y - 5$ j. $19a = -38$

2. Frame four equations having the solution $d = 5$.

3. Solve the following equations and verify your answer by substituting the value of the variable separately in LHS and RHS.

a. $8x = 21 + 5x + 9$ b. $\frac{27}{x} = \frac{3}{5}$ c. $8x - 14 = -2x + 6$

d. $2d + \frac{1}{4} = \frac{3}{4} + d$ e. $1.8a = a + 16$ f. $a + 0.04 = 5a - 7.08$

4. Solve the following equations.

a. $2x + 1 = 9$ b. $15 - 6a = -3$ c. $3d - 4d + 8d = 28$

d. $0.25c + 5 = 0.5c - 2.5$ e. $-7(a - 4) = 14$ f. $5(a + 2) - 3(a - 1) = 3$

g. $27 - 3a = a + 3a - 8$ h. $11 - 3(q - 4) = 8q + 4$ i. $0.08a = 3 - 0.1a$

j. x % of 200 g = 50 g k. $\frac{x}{7} + \frac{x}{14} = 9$ l. $\frac{x}{2} + 4 = \frac{x}{3} - 5$

m. $\frac{a+1}{2} = \frac{a-1}{3}$ n. $\frac{4a+1}{a-1} = 7$ o. $\frac{x}{7} - \frac{x-1}{5} = 5$

p. $\frac{e-4}{3} - \frac{e}{2} = 1$ q. $\frac{x+1}{3} - \frac{x-1}{5} = 14$ r. $\frac{x-4}{11} - 1 = \frac{2x}{11}$

APPLICATIONS OF SIMPLE EQUATIONS IN REAL LIFE

When we do not know a value, why do we call it 'x' or some other letter of the English alphabet? We do so because it makes the understanding of the problem easier for us.

SOLVED EXAMPLES

Example 7: Ten subtracted from five times a number gives 100. Find the number.

Solution: Let the number be x.

Five times the number = $5x$

$5x - 10 = 100$

$5x = 100 + 10 = 110$

$x = \frac{110}{5} = 22$

Thus, the number is 22.

Example 8: The sum of three consecutive even natural numbers is 48. Find the numbers.

Solution: Let the three consecutive even natural numbers be $x, x+2, x+4$.

$$x+x+2+x+4=48$$
$$3x+6=48$$
$$3x=48-6$$
$$3x=42$$
$$x=\frac{42}{3}=14$$
$$x+2=14+2=16$$
$$x+4=14+4=18$$

Thus, the three consecutive numbers are 14, 16 and 18.

Example 9: The length of a rectangle is thrice its breadth. If the perimeter of the rectangle is 120 m, find its length and breadth.

Solution: Let the breadth of the rectangle be x.

Length of the rectangle = $3x$

$$\text{Perimeter}=2(l+b)$$
$$120=2(3x+x)$$
$$120=2\times 4x$$
$$120=8x \text{ or}$$
$$8x=120$$
$$x=\frac{120}{8}=15$$

Thus, Breadth = x = 15 m

Length $=3x=3\times 15=45$ m

Example 10: The denominator of a fraction is 5 more than its numerator. If 2 is added to both the numerator and the denominator, the fraction becomes $\frac{2}{3}$ Find the fraction.

Solution: Let the numerator of the fraction be x.

Denominator = $x + 5$

Required fraction = $\frac{x}{x+5}$

If 2 is added to both numerator and denominator, we get

$$\frac{x+2}{x+5+2}=\frac{2}{3}\Rightarrow\frac{x+2}{x+7}=\frac{2}{3}$$

Use cross-multiplication:

$$3(x+2)=2(x+7)$$
$$3x+6=2x+14$$
$$3x-2x=14-6$$
$$x=8$$

Numerator = x = 8

Denominator = x + 5 = 8 + 5 = 13

Thus, the required fraction is $\frac{8}{13}$.

Example 11: Javed is five times as old as John. After 4 years, he will be 3 times as old as John. Find the present ages of Javed and John.

Solution: Present ages

Let John's age = x years

Javed's age = $5x$ years

After 4 years,

John's age = $(x + 4)$ years

Javed's age = $(5x + 4)$ years

$$5x+4=3(x+4)$$
$$5x+4=3x+12$$
$$5x-3x=12-4$$
$$2x=8$$
$$x=\frac{8}{2}=4$$

John's age = x = 4 years.

Javed's age = $5x = 5 \times 4 = 20$ years.

Thus, at present John's age is 4 years and Javed's age is 20 years.

EXERCISE 6B

Answer the following.

1. Seven added to a number gives 100. Find the number.
2. Fifteen times a number added to half the number gives 62. Find the number.
3. The sum of two consecutive natural numbers is 69. Find the numbers.
4. If the sum of two consecutive odd numbers is 84, find the numbers.
5. If the sum of three consecutive even numbers is 114, find the numbers.
6. The angles of a triangle are in the ratio 3 : 4 : 5. Find the angles.
7. Two supplementary angles differ by 20°. Find the angles.
8. Two numbers are in the ratio 5 : 9 and their difference is 24. Find the numbers.
9. Two numbers are in the ratio 3 : 4. If 2 is subtracted from each number, the ratio becomes 2 : 3. Find the numbers.
10. The sum of one-fourth of a number and 6 is 22. Find the number.
11. In a class of 30 students, the number of girls is two-third of the number of boys. Find the number of girls in the class.
12. The present age of Bhuvan is 5 years and his father's age is 28 years. In how many years will the father's age be twice the age of his son?
13. The sum of the digits of a two-digit number is 10. The unit's digit is four times the ten's digit. Find the numbers.
14. The difference in the digits of a two-digit number is 1. If the digits are interchanged, the new number becomes 9 more than the old number. Find the number.
15. The numerator of a fraction is 1 more than the denominator. If 5 is subtracted from both the numerator and the denominator, the fraction becomes 2. Find the number.

Common Errors

$$\frac{x}{5} - \frac{x-1}{3} = \frac{x}{15}$$

$$\Rightarrow \frac{3x - 5x - 5}{15} = \frac{x}{15} \quad ✗$$

To avoid this error, put the entire numerator in brackets as follows:

$$\frac{x}{5} - \frac{(x-1)}{3} = \frac{x}{15}$$

$$\Rightarrow \frac{3x - 5(x-1)}{15} = \frac{x}{15}$$

$$\Rightarrow 3x - 5x + 5 = x$$

$$\Rightarrow -2x + 5 = x$$

$$\Rightarrow 3x = 5$$

$$\Rightarrow x = \frac{5}{3} = 1\frac{2}{3} \quad ✓$$

Maths Lab Activity

Aim: To demonstrate that an equation remains balanced if the same number is added, subtracted, multiplied or divided on both sides of an equation

Materials required: Beam balance, weights each of 50 g, 100 g, 200 g

Procedure:

1. Put weights of 100 g on both sides of the beam balance. Let the students say what they observe.
2. Add a weight of 100 g on the left side. What is the observation?
3. Now add a weight of 100 g on the right side as well. What is the observation?
4. Similarly, subtract 100 g from one side and then from the other side. What is the observation?
5. Remove all previous weights from the beam balance and put 50 g on both sides of the beam. What happens?
6. Next place (100 + 50) g extra on both sides. What is the observation?
7. With 200 g on both sides, the beams are balanced.
8. Remove (100 + 50) g first from one side and then the other side of the beam balance. What is the observation?

Conclusion: Like a beam balance, an equation remains balanced if the same number is added, subtracted, multiplied or divided on both sides of an equation.

Concept Map

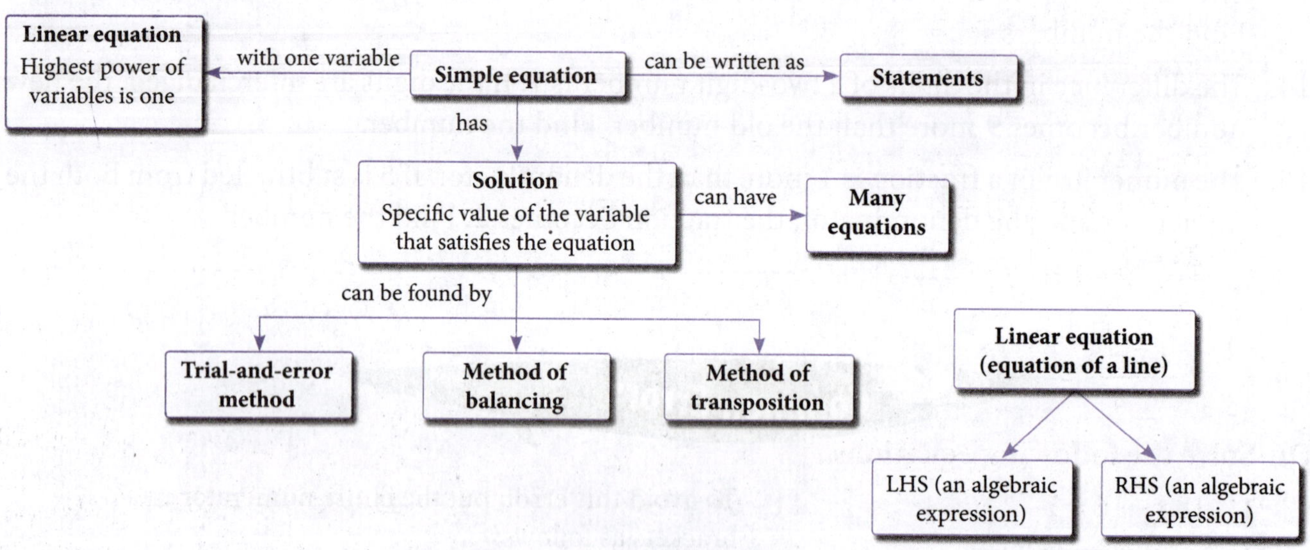

Key Concepts

- **Equation:** An algebraic statement in which one expression is equal to another
- **Linear equation:** An equation of a line
- **Solution/root of an equation:** A value which satisfies an equation

CHAPTER REVISION

A. Choose the correct option.

1. Pick the odd one out.

   a. $y > 5$ b. $y < 5$ c. $y = 5$ d. $y \neq 5$

2. If $3b - \frac{1}{4} = 2$, then $b = ?$

   a. 0.75 b. 0.25 c. 1.75 d. −1.6

3. Pick the odd one out.

   a. $6a = 12$ b. $42a - 84 = 0$ c. $a + 18 = 20$ d. $76a \div 38 = 0$

4. For what value of f will the expressions $5f + 14$ and $7 - 2f$ be equal?

   a. 1 b. −1 c. −14/3 d. 7

B. Write T for true and F for false.

1. If both sides of an equation are multiplied by a negative number, the equation remains unchanged.
2. If reciprocal is taken of both sides of an equation, the equation remains unchanged.
3. A linear equation can have two variables.
4. The power of the variable(s) is always one in a linear equation.
5. $2x + 18 = 3x$ and $4x + 36 = 6x$ have the same solution.

C. Match the following.

1. $0.7x - 1.8 = 0.5x$	a. 3
2. $4.4x - 33 = 2.2$	b. 4
3. $5x - (4x + 8) = -x$	c. 5
4. $-\{-6 + 3(x - 4)\} = 0$	d. 6
5. $\frac{2x}{5} - x + 1 = -2$	e. 8
6. $x - \frac{x+5}{4} = 1$	f. 9

D. Solve the following equations.

1. $18x + 16 = 7$
2. $11 - 6b = -9$
3. $-4e + 9e + 3e = 28 + 3e$
4. $0.75c + 5 = 0.7c$
5. $\frac{x}{33} - \frac{x-1}{3} = 2$
6. $\frac{3x-4}{14} - 1 = \frac{2x}{28}$

E. Answer the following questions.

1. The sum of two consecutive even numbers is 118. Find the numbers.
2. Two complementary angles differ by 20°. Find the angles.
3. The sum of one-sixth of a number and 7 is 22. Find the number.
4. Jane is 15 years older than Ganesh. She is four times as old as Ganesh. Find their present ages.

5. The sum of three consecutive odd numbers is 117. Find the numbers.
6. The sum of the digits of a two-digit number is 9. If the digits are reversed, the new number exceeds the old number by 27. Find the number.
7. Rahman is 5 years older than Mohan. 5 years ago Rahman was one and a half times Mohan's age. Find Rahman's age now.
8. Amit is 24 years older than his son. After 11 years, he will be thrice the age of his son. Find the age of the son two years from now.
9. The number of children who went for cable car ride in an amusement park was one-fourth of the number of children who went for striking cars. If the total number of children who went for the two rides was 150, find the number of children who went for the cable car ride.
10. Nungsang is 20 years older than Hafizur. Four years from now, Nungsang will be twice Hafizur's age. Find their present ages.

SKILL UP!

Project

In ancient Egyptian times, problems with variables were known by a different name. With the help of the Internet, find out what it was called then and prepare a brief write-up on the same including information on the following:

- What method was used then to solve problems that had variables?
- Name of the book which gives a collection of such problems.
- A few examples of the problems on simple equations used during that time.

Life Skills

Prepare a travel itinerary of 5 days with an approximate budget for a leisure trip from Mumbai to Pune for you and your family. It is a time for everyone in the family to enjoy themselves. Remember to keep scope for small changes and be flexible as long as the total budget does not get disturbed!

Mind Buzzer

1. Goa is one of the most popular tourist destinations in India. What is the distance by road between Goa and Mumbai? If a car travels from Mumbai to Goa at an average speed of 60 km/h, how much time will it take to reach Goa keeping an extra time of 2 hours to stopover for meals.
2. Solve the following equations:

a. $\frac{1}{x} - \frac{2}{x-1} = \frac{5}{x(x-1)}$ b. $5x - 10.5 = 2(3 - 0.5x)$

Teacher's Notes

- Ask students to write the various formulae they have learnt in Physics and Geometry. Explain the meaning of equations and linear equations.
- Explain the various ways of solving a linear equation. Encourage students to use any of the methods that they are most comfortable with.
- Using real-life examples, explain to the students the use of linear equations in practical situations.

WORKSHEET

A travel agent charges ₹x per adult per day for a 7-day trip to Maharashtra. There is no extra charge for a child below 2 years.
The charge for a child from 2 to 5 years is one-fourth of the charge for an adult.
The charge for a child from 5 to 12 years is three-fourth of the charge for an adult.

Based on the above rates, calculate the following.

1. A group of 6 adults, 1 infant, 1 child aged 4 years and 2 children aged 8 and 10 years, respectively, is charged a total of ₹86,800. Find x, the charge per adult.
2. Find the charge for 2 adults, one child aged 3 years and one child aged 11 years.
3. Find the charge for 6 adults.
4. Find the charge for 8 adults, one child aged 6 years and one infant.
5. Find the charge for 6 adults, two children aged 6 years and 10 years, and one child aged 3 years.

7 Ratio, Proportion and Unitary Method

Learning Objectives

- To express the given quantities as ratios in the simplified form
- To understand the concepts of ratio, proportion and unitary method
- To apply these concepts to solve real-life problems

Let's Get Started

Which are the fastest and the second fastest trains in India?

With respect to their average speeds, compare the speeds of Vande Bharat Express, Gatimaan Express and Shatabdi Express. How fast/slow is each of the trains compared to the other?

RATIO

- A ratio is a comparison between two or more quantities which are of the same kind.
- In a ratio, the first quantity is divided by the second. So, a ratio can be expressed as a fraction.
- The fraction $\frac{a}{b}$ is different from $\frac{b}{a}$ if $a \neq b$. Similarly, the ratio $a : b$ is different from $b : a$ if $a \neq b$.
- The different terms in a ratio are separated by colon signs (:).
- $a : b$ is read as a is to b. $a : b :$ c is read as a is to b is to c.
- The first term in a ratio is called **antecedent** and the second term is called the **consequent**.

PROPERTIES OF RATIO

- All quantities in a ratio should be of the same kind. Quantities of different kinds cannot be compared with each other. The height of one person cannot be compared to the weight of another person.
- All quantities in a ratio should have the same unit. If the units are different, all the quantities are converted into the same unit and then expressed as a ratio.
- A ratio is a pure number. It does not have a unit. For example, if we have the ratio

  $3 \text{ cm} : 5 \text{ cm} = \frac{3 \text{ cm}}{5 \text{ cm}}$, the units get cancelled and the ratio does not have a unit.

- A ratio is said to be in the simplest form when the HCF of the numerator and the denominator is 1.
- When the numerator and the denominator of a fraction are both multiplied or divided by the same non-zero number, the fraction remains the same.

  For example, $\frac{2}{3} = \frac{2}{3} \times \frac{5}{5} = \frac{10}{15}$ and $\frac{12}{16} = \frac{12}{16} \div \frac{4}{4} = \frac{3}{4}$

  Similarly, if all terms of a ratio are multiplied or divided by the same non-zero number, the ratio remains the same.

  For example, $2 : 3 = 2 \times 5 : 3 \times 5 = 10 : 15$ and $12 : 16 = 12 \div 4 : 16 \div 4 = 3 : 4$

- Increase or decrease ratio and multiplying factor

  $$\text{Increase or decrease ratio} = \frac{\text{Old value}}{\text{New value}}$$

  $$\text{Multiplying factor} = \frac{\text{New value}}{\text{Old value}}$$

  If a quantity increases in the ratio 2 : 3 (old value that is the antecedent is less than the new value that is the consequent), multiplying factor = 3 : 2.

  If a quantity decreases in the ratio 3 : 2 (old value that is the antecedent is more than the new value that is the consequent), multiplying factor = 2 : 3.

COMPARING RATIOS

Equivalent Ratios

Two ratios are said to be equivalent ratios if their simplified values are the same. To compare two ratios, we can compare them the way we compare fractions. Let us compare 2 : 3 and 4 : 5.

- Convert them into like fractions

  $\frac{2}{3}$ and $\frac{4}{5}$

  $\frac{2}{3}=\frac{2}{3}\times\frac{5}{5}=\frac{10}{15}$ and $\frac{4}{5}=\frac{4}{5}\times\frac{3}{3}=\frac{12}{15}$

  10 < 12.

  So, 2 : 3 < 4 : 5.

- Cross-multiply

  $\frac{2}{3}$ and $\frac{4}{5}$

  $\frac{2}{3} \times \frac{4}{5} = 2 \times 5$ ___ 4×3

  or 10 < 12.

  So, 2 : 3 < 4 : 5.

- Multiply each ratio by the LCM of the denominators

  $\frac{2}{3}$ and $\frac{4}{5}$

  $\frac{2}{3}\times 15$, $\frac{4}{5}\times 15$

  10 < 12

  So, 2 : 3 < 4 : 5.

To arrange ratios in ascending or descending order, convert each ratio into a fraction, arrange the fractions in ascending or descending order and write the answer in ratio form.

SOLVED EXAMPLES

Example 1: Express the following ratios in the simplest form.

a. 60 : 130 b. 2.1 : 7 c. $2\frac{1}{3}:3\frac{2}{5}:1$

d. ₹1.50 : 250 paise e. 200 minutes : 5 hours f. 1 kg : 750 g

Solution:

a. Given: 60 : 130

$\frac{60}{130}=\frac{6}{13}$

$=6:13$

Thus, the value is 6 :13.

b. Given: 2.1 : 7

$\frac{2.1}{7}=\frac{2.1\times10}{7\times10}$

$=\frac{21}{70}$

$=3:10$

Thus, the value is 3 : 10.

c. Given: $2\frac{1}{3}:3\frac{2}{5}:1$

Multiply each term of the ratio by the LCM of the denominators.

$2\frac{1}{3}:3\frac{2}{5}:1=\frac{7}{3}:\frac{17}{5}:1$

$=\frac{7}{3}\times15:\frac{17}{5}\times15:1\times15$

$=35:51:15$

Thus, the value is $35:51:15$.

d. Given: ₹1.50 : 250 paise

Here, ₹1.50 = 1.50 × 100 = 150 paise

₹1.50 : 250 paise $=\frac{150 \text{ paise}}{250 \text{ paise}}$

$\frac{150 \text{ paise}}{250 \text{ paise}}=\frac{150}{250}$

$=\frac{150\div50}{250\div50}=\frac{3}{5}=3:5$

Thus, the value is 3 : 5.

Note

If a ratio has 3 or more terms, it cannot be simplified by simply dividing the terms by each other. That is, *a* : *b* : *c* is not equal to *a* / *b* / *c*.

e. Given: 200 minutes : 5 hours

5 hours = 5 × 60 = 300 minutes

$$200 \text{ minutes} : 5 \text{ hours} = \frac{200 \text{ minutes}}{300 \text{ minutes}}$$

$$\frac{200 \text{ minutes}}{300 \text{ minutes}} = \frac{200}{300}$$

$$= \frac{2}{3}$$

$$= 2:3$$

Thus, the value is $2:3$.

Example 2: If $A : B = 25 : 7$ and $B : C = 14 : 5$, find $A : C$ and $A : B : C$.

Solution: Given: $A : B = 25 : 7$ and $B : C = 14 : 5$

$$\frac{A}{B} = \frac{25}{7} \text{ and } \frac{B}{C} = \frac{14}{5}$$

$$A:C = \frac{A}{C} = \frac{A}{B} \times \frac{B}{C}$$

$$\text{So, } \frac{A}{C} = \frac{25}{7} \times \frac{14}{5}$$

$$= \frac{10}{1} = 10:1$$

Thus, the value of $A:C$ is $10:1$.

$$\frac{A}{B} = \frac{25}{7} \text{ and } \frac{B}{C} = \frac{14}{5}$$

Now, LCM of 7 and 14 is 14. (As B is in the middle of $A : B : C$, we need to make the B part in both the ratios equal by finding the LCM of the B parts).

$$\frac{A}{B} = \frac{25}{7} \times \frac{2}{2} = \frac{50}{14} \text{ and } \frac{B}{C} = \frac{14}{5} \times \frac{1}{1} = \frac{14}{5}$$

$A : B : C = 50 : 14 : 5$

Thus, the value of $A : B : C$ is $50 : 14 : 5$.

f. Given: 1 kg : 750 g

1 kg = 1000 g

$$1 \text{ kg} : 750 \text{ g} = \frac{1000}{750}$$

$$\frac{1000 \text{ g}}{750 \text{ g}} = \frac{1000}{750}$$

$$= \frac{1000 \div 250}{750 \div 250}$$

$$= \frac{4}{3} = 4:3$$

Thus, the value is $4:3$.

Example 3: The sides of a triangle are in the ratio 5 : 6 : 7. The perimeter of the triangle is 36 cm. Find the sides of the triangle.

Solution: Ratio of sides = 5 : 6 : 7

Total of terms of the ratio = 5 + 6 + 7 = 18

$$\text{First side} = \frac{5}{18} \times 36 = 10 \text{ cm}$$

$$\text{Second side} = \frac{6}{18} \times 36 = 12 \text{ cm}$$

$$\text{Third side} = \frac{7}{18} \times 36 = 14 \text{ cm}$$

Go Easy!

Another method to solve Example 3:

Let the sides of the triangle be $5x$, $6x$ and $7x$.

Perimeter = 36 cm

$$5x + 6x + 7x = 36$$

$$18x = 36$$

$$x = \frac{36}{18} = 2 \text{ cm}$$

First side = $5 \times 2 = 10$ cm

Second side = $6 \times 2 = 12$ cm

Third side = $7 \times 2 = 14$ cm

Thus, the sides of the triangle are 10 cm, 12 cm and 14 cm.

Example 4: The profit of a company increases every month in the ratio 5 : 8. If the profit earned in April is ₹1,20,000, find the profit earned in May.

Solution: Let the profit earned in May = ₹x

$$\text{Increase ratio} = \frac{\text{Old value}}{\text{New value}}$$

$$\frac{5}{8} = \frac{120000}{x}$$

$$x = \frac{120000 \times 8}{5}$$

$$x = 24000 \times 8 = 192000$$

Thus, the profit earned in May is ₹1,92,000.

Common Errors

Students tend to write the total of ratios instead of the total of terms of the ratio. Here, we are adding the parts of one ratio and not adding two different ratios.

Example 5: For a puja ₹1, ₹2 and ₹5 coins are needed in the ratio 15 : 8 : 10. If the total money value of these coins is ₹4050, find the number of coins of each kind.

Solution: Let the number of ₹1 coins be $15x$.

Number of ₹2 coins = $8x$.

Number of ₹5 coins = $10x$

Money value of ₹1 coins = ₹$15x$

Money value of ₹2 coins = ₹$16x$

Money value of ₹5 coins = ₹$50x$

$$15x + 16x + 50x = 4050$$

$$81x = 4050$$

$$x = \frac{4050}{81}$$

$$x = 50$$

Number of ₹1 coins = $15x = 15 \times 50 = 750$

Number of ₹2 coins = $8x = 8 \times 50 = 400$

Number of ₹5 coins = $10x = 10 \times 50 = 500$

Thus, the number of coins are 750, 400 and 500.

EXERCISE 7A

1. Express the following ratios in the simplest form.

a. 10 : 50 b. 1.2 : 24 c. 0.25 : 0.5 d. $2\frac{1}{2} : 1\frac{1}{3}$

e. $\frac{3}{4} : \frac{5}{6} : \frac{2}{3}$ f. $2\frac{1}{5} : 2\frac{9}{10} : \frac{3}{15}$ g. 1.2 : 3.6 : 6 h. 5 m 50 cm : 6 m

i. 15 days : 24 days j. 150 g : 1 kg k. 45 minutes : 1 hour

l. 9 months: $1\frac{1}{2}$ years m. ₹5 : 90 paise

2. In a class of 40 students, there are 25 boys. Find the ratio of:

a. the number of boys to the number of girls.

b. the number of girls to the number of boys.

c. the number of girls to the total number of students.

3. If X : Y = 3 : 5 and Y : Z = 14 : 9, find: a. X : Z b. X : Y : Z

4. A and B are given pens in the ratio 6 : 7. B and C are given pens in the ratio 14 : 15.

a. Find the ratio of pens given to A and C.

b. If the total number of pens given to A and C is 36, find the ratio of the number of pens A, B and C gets.

5. Arrange the ratios 3 : 5, 2 : 7 and 4 : 15 in ascending order.
6. If $a : b = 3 : 4$, find $(a + 2b) : (3a + b)$.
7. The angles of a triangle are in the ratio $\frac{1}{2} : \frac{1}{3} : \frac{1}{6}$. Find the angles.
8. For a prize distribution, ₹810 has to be divided among the first, second and third prize winners in the ratio 4 : 3 : 2. Find the share of each winner.
9. The price of an article increases every year in the ratio 4 : 5. If the price in 2018 is ₹128, find the price in 2019.
10. The price of a laptop decreases every year in the ratio 15 : 14. If the price in 2018 is ₹30,000, find its price in 2019.

PROPORTION

The number of pastries given to A and B are in the ratio 80 : 160 and the number of pastries given to C and D are in the ratio $\frac{1}{70} : \frac{1}{35}$.

What can we say about the two simplified ratios? Are they equivalent ratios?

Note

Two ratios are said to be equivalent ratios if their simplified values are the same.

If $a : b = c : d$, we say that a, b, c and d are in proportion. This can be written as $a : b :: c : d$ and read as $a : b$ is proportional to $c : d$. The symbol for proportion is '::'.

a, b, c and d are respectively called the first, second, third and fourth proportional. As a and d are at two ends, they are called **extremes**. As b and c are towards the middle, they are called **means**. In a proportion, **product of means = product of extremes.**

Note

Extreme means the furthest from the middle, that is, at the beginning or at the end.

So, $b \times c = a \times d$.

Proportion: Four quantities are said to be in proportion if the ratio of the first two quantities is equal to the ratio of the last two quantities. The first two quantities should be of the same kind and the last two quantities should be of the same kind. All four quantities may not be of the same kind.

Note

For proportion minimum four quantities are needed. If there are three quantities and the terms continued or mean proportion are used, the middle quantity is repeated.

Continued proportion: Three quantities a, b and c are said to be in continued proportion if the ratio of the first quantity to the second is equal to the ratio of the second quantity to the third, that is, $\frac{a}{b} = \frac{b}{c}$.

$$b^2 = ac$$

Thus, $b = \sqrt{ac}$

We can also say that, b is the mean proportion between a and c. c is the third proportional to a and b.

SOLVED EXAMPLES

Example 6: Find whether 4 kg, 12 kg, ₹7, ₹21 are in proportion or not.

Solution: The first two quantities have the same unit. The third and fourth quantities have the same unit.

Ratio of the first two quantities = $\frac{4}{12} = \frac{1}{3}$

Ratio of the last two quantities = $\frac{7}{21} = \frac{1}{3}$

Ratio of the first two quantities = Ratio of the last two quantities

So, the given quantities are in proportion.

OR

Product of means = 4 × 21 = 84

Product of extremes = 12 × 7 = 84

Product of means = Product of extremes

So, the given quantities are in proportion.

Example 7: Find the value of x in the proportion 22 : 6 :: x : 3.

Solution: Given: 22 : 6 :: x : 3

$$\frac{22}{6} = \frac{x}{3}$$

$$\frac{11}{3} = \frac{x}{3}$$

$$x = 11$$

OR

Product of means = Product of extremes

$$6x = 22 \times 3$$

$$x = \frac{22 \times 3}{6} = 11$$

Thus, the value of x is 11.

Example 8: Find the mean proportion between 18 and 72.

Solution: Let the mean proportion be x.

18, x and 72 are in continued proportion.

Since the quantities are in continued proportion, the second quantity will be repeated.

$$\frac{18}{x} = \frac{x}{72}$$

$$x^2 = 18 \times 72$$

$$x^2 = 2 \times 3 \times 3 \times 2 \times 2 \times 2 \times 3 \times 3 = 2^4 \times 3^4$$

$$x = 2^2 \times 3^2 = 4 \times 9 = 36$$

Thus, the value of x is 36.

Example 9: Find the third proportional to 7 and 14.

Solution: Let the third proportional be x.

7, 14 and x. (As there are 3 quantities, the second quantity will be repeated).

$$\frac{7}{14} = \frac{14}{x}$$

$$x = \frac{14 \times 14}{7}$$

$$x = 28$$

Thus, the value of x is 28.

Example 10: Find the fourth proportional to 13, 4, 39.

Solution: Let the fourth proportional be x.

13, 4, 39 and x.

$$\frac{13}{4} = \frac{39}{x}$$

$$x = \frac{39 \times 4}{13}$$

$$x = 12$$

Thus, the value of x is 12.

EXERCISE 7B

1. **Find whether the following numbers are in proportion or not.**

   a. 5, 10, 7, 14 b. 0.2, $\frac{1}{2}$, 2, 0.5

2. **Find the value of x in the following proportions.**

   a. $11 : 2 :: x : 6$ b. $0.25 : x :: \frac{1}{2} : 2$

3. **If 16, x and 25 are in continued proportion, find the value of x.**

4. **Find the mean proportion between the following.**

   a. 28 and 63 b. 0.4 and 0.9 c. 12 and 48 d. 72 and 98

5. **Find the third proportional to the following.**

   a. 5 and 15 b. $\frac{2}{13}$ and $\frac{8}{13}$ c. 0.4 and 0.8 d. 10 and 20

6. **Find the fourth proportional to the following.**

   a. 33, 27, 11 b. 16, 12, 8 c. 14, 5, 28 d. 45, 15, 6

UNITARY METHOD

The method used to calculate the value of several quantities of the same kind by first finding the value of one (unit) such quantity.

Unitary method is used to find the value of quantities which change with respect to each other in one of the following ways:

Note

Unit means one.
Vary means to change.
Variation means change.

- **Direct variation:** If an increase in one quantity brings a corresponding increase in the other quantity (or vice versa), the two quantities are said to be in direct variation. If two quantities a and b vary directly, $\frac{a}{b}$ is constant for all pairs of values of a and b.
- **Inverse variation:** If an increase in one quantity brings a corresponding decrease in the other quantity (or vice versa), the two quantities are said to be in inverse variation. If two quantities a and b vary inversely, ab is constant for all pairs of values of a and b.

SOLVED EXAMPLES

Example 11: The cost of 15 similar pens is ₹45. Find the cost of 20 such pens.

Solution: As more are the number of pens, more is the total cost. So, this is a case of direct variation.

Cost of 15 pens = ₹45

Cost of 1 pen = $\frac{45}{15}$ = ₹3

Cost of 20 pens = 20×3 = ₹60

Note

In problem sums, we should start the statement with the variable whose value is to be found so that the unknown value is at the end of the statement.

OR

Pens	15	20
Cost (in ₹)	45	x

As this is a case of direct variation, we have:

$$\frac{15}{45}=\frac{20}{x} \quad \left(\frac{a}{b} \text{ is constant for all pairs of values of } a \text{ and } b.\right)$$

$$x=\frac{20\times45}{15}=60$$

Thus, the cost of 20 pens is ₹60.

Example 12: 9 litres of water are required to fill 6 similar bottles. Find the volume of water needed to fill 8 such bottles.

Solution: As more are the number of bottles, more is the volume of water needed. So, this is a case of direct variation.

Volume of water needed to fill 6 bottles = 9 litres

Volume of water needed to fill 1 bottle = $\frac{9}{6}=\frac{3}{2}$ litres

(Do not convert into decimals because further simplification will be done in the next step.)

Volume of water needed to fill 8 bottles = $\frac{3}{2}\times8=12$ litres

Thus, the volume of water needed to fill 8 bottles is 12 litres

Go Easy!

No. of bottles	6	8
Volume (in litres)	9	x

As this is a case of direct variation, we have:

$$\frac{6}{9}=\frac{8}{x}$$

$$\Rightarrow x=\frac{8\times9}{6}=12$$

Volume of water needed to fill 8 bottles = 12 litres

Example 13: 5 men can do a work in 12 days. How long will 6 men take to do the same work?

Solution: As more are the number of men doing a work, less is the time taken. So, this is a case of inverse variation.

Time taken by 5 men = 12 days

Time taken by 1 man = (12 × 5) days

Time taken by 6 men = $\frac{12\times5}{6}=10$ days

Thus, the time taken by 6 men is 10 days.

Go Easy!

No. of men	5	6
No. of days	12	x

As this is a case of inverse variation, we have: $5\times12=6\times x$

$$\Rightarrow x=\frac{5\times12}{6}=10 \text{ days}$$

Example 14: A camp had food for 60 people for 75 days. 15 more people came to the camp. How long will the food last?

Solution: As more are the number of people who would consume the given amount of food, lesser is the time for which the food will last. So, this is a case of inverse variation.

New total number of people = 60 + 15 = 75

Number of days the food will last for 60 people = 75

Number of days the food will last for 1 person = 60 × 75. (The same quantity of food will last longer for 1 person than for 60 people.)

Number of days the food will last for 75 people = $\frac{60\times75}{75}=60$

Thus, the food will last for 60 days for 75 people.

EXERCISE 7C

Solve the following questions.

1. The cost of 15 similar chocolates is ₹60. Find the cost of 20 such chocolates.
2. 105 litres of water are required to fill 7 similar containers. Find the volume of water needed to fill 9 such containers.
3. 8 men can do a work in 45 days. How long will 12 men take to do the same work?
4. A camp had food for 90 people for 50 days. 10 more people came to the camp. How long will the food last?
5. A camp had food for 80 people for 50 days. How long will the food last if the number of people increases to 125?
6. The cost of 2 dozen bananas is ₹96. Find the cost of 15 bananas.
7. The cost of 15 similar chocolates is ₹90. How many chocolates can be bought for ₹126?
8. 12 men can reap a field in 65 days. How many men are needed to reap the field in 60 days?

MATHS LAB ACTIVITY

Aim: To understand the concept of proportion, mean proportion and continued proportion

Materials required: Four boxes for containing number chits for A, B, C and D and one box for containing the proportion questions for A, B, C and D; scissors, pencils and rulers for making small chits for each number or question shown in the tables below.

A	B	C	D
2	4	2	4
4	16	4	8
8	36	8	10
10	64	10	12
12	100	12	16
16	144	16	36

Questions
Pick a chit each from A, B, C and D. Are A, B, C and D in proportion?
Pick a chit each from A, B, and C. Are A, B and C in continued proportion?
Pick a chit each from B, C and D. Is B the mean proportion between C and D?

Procedure:

1. Arrange the class into 4 groups. Give each group a box named A, B, C or D with a set of digit chits put in each of the boxes. The teacher will have the box of questions.
2. Each group will have two team leaders for answering the questions after discussion in the group.
3. Two students can be in charge of recording the score on the green board. One point will be given for every correct answer. There will be no negative marking.
4. The teacher will read out question chits one by one from her box and conduct the activity like a quiz by giving each group a time of approximately 1 minute to think of the answer.

At the end of the quiz, the team with the highest total will be the winner.

Concept Map

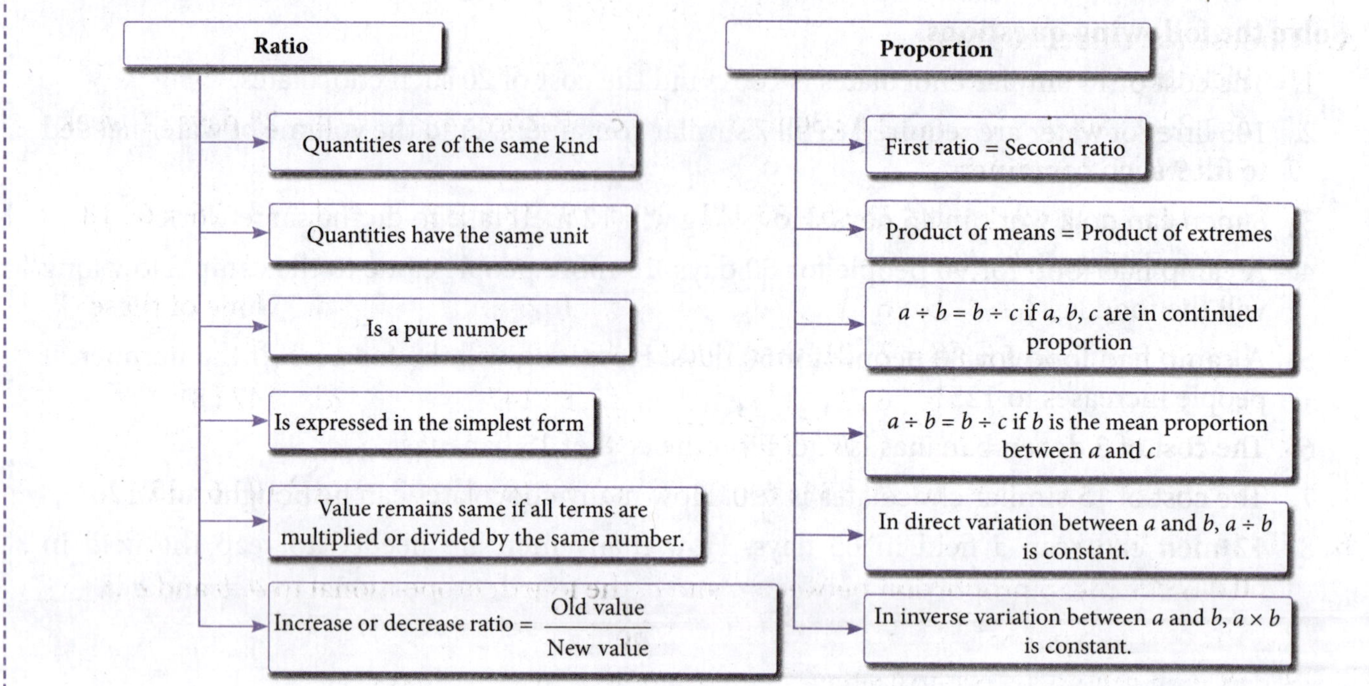

Key Concepts

- **Ratio:** A comparison between two or more quantities which are of the same kind
- **Antecedent:** The first term in a ratio
- **Consequent:** The second term in a ratio
- **Proportion:** Four quantities are said to be in proportion if the ratio of the first two quantities is equal to the ratio of the last two quantities
- **Continued proportion:** Three quantities *a*, *b* and *c* are said to be in continued proportion if the ratio of the first quantity to the second is equal to the ratio of the second quantity to the third
- **Unitary method:** The method used to calculate the value of several quantities of the same kind by first finding the value of one (unit) such quantity
- **Direct variation:** If an increase in one quantity brings a corresponding increase in the other quantity (or vice versa), the two quantities are said to be in direct variation
- **Inverse variation:** If an increase in one quantity brings a corresponding decrease in the other quantity (or vice versa), the two quantities are said to be in inverse variation

CHAPTER REVISION

A. Choose the correct option.

1. Pick the odd one out.
   a. 2 kg : 500 g b. 2 h : 30 min c. 1 score : 4 d. 28 days : 1 week
2. Pick the odd one out.
   a. 14 : 7 :: 18 : 9 b. 15 : 5 :: 33 : 11 c. 9 : 18 :: 1 : 2 d. 13 : 26 = 6 : 18
3. $a : b = 7 : 5$, $(a + b) : (a - b) =$
   a. 1 : 1 b. 6 : 1 c. 1 : 6 d. None of these
4. If $A : B = 4 : 7$ and $C : B = 2 : 21$, then find $C : A$.
   a. 1 : 6 b. 6 : 1 c. 8 : 147 d. 147 : 8
5. $A : B = 3 : 5$, $C : A = 2 : 7$, $A : B : C = ?$
   a. 6 : 21 : 35 b. 21 : 35 : 6 c. 6 : 10 : 35 d. 10 : 6 : 35

B. Fill in the blanks.

1. If b is the mean proportion between a and c, the fourth proportional to a, b and c is ____.
2. The cost of 5 books is ₹1375. The cost of 15 books is ₹_______.
3. 18 men can do a work in 15 days. 6 men can do it in _____ days.
4. If 7A = 3B, 5A : 7B = _______.
5. If 7A = 5B and B = 4C, A : B : C = ________.

C. Write T for true and F for false.

1. If a, b and c are in continued proportion, b is the mean proportion between a and c.
2. If ₹1275 is divided between A and B in the ratio $\frac{1}{5} : \frac{1}{10}$, A gets ₹425.
3. If 6 men can do a work in 8 days, 12 men can do it in 16 days.
4. The ratio of 1 week to a fortnight is greater than the ratio of 6 months to a year.
5. The fourth proportional to 11, 22 and 33 is 44.

D. Match the following.

1. 2.5 : 7.5	a. 3 : 1
2. 1 year : 73 days	b. 1 : 3
3. 3 decades : 10 years	c. 2 : 1
4. 1 : 0.5	d. 5 : 1
5. Half a day : 24 h	e. 1 : 2

E. Answer the following questions.

1. Which number should be added to each term of the ratio 7 : 11 to make it equal to 2 : 3?
2. Arrange the ratios 4 : 5, 5 : 9 and 8 : 15 in descending order.
3. If 32, x and 50 are in continued proportion, find the value of x.
4. The cost of 12 dozen bangles is ₹264. Find the cost of 5 dozen bangles.

5. It takes 7 days to read a book if 45 pages are read every day. How long will it take to read the book if 35 pages are read every day?
6. Which number should be subtracted from each term of the ratio 14 : 13 to make it equal to 7 : 6?
7. For a ceremony ₹1, ₹2 and ₹5 coins are needed in the ratio 9 : 8 : 5. If the total money collected is ₹2500, find the number of coins of each kind.
8. The profit of a company increases every month in the ratio 4 : 5. If the profit earned in March is ₹2,50,000, find the profit earned in April.
9. The price of a phone decreases every year in the ratio 9 : 8. If the price in 2019 is ₹12,000, find its price in 2018.

SKILL UP!

Project

For the current month, find the expenditure of your family on the following items. Express the expenditure on these items as a ratio.

1. Electricity bill
2. Phone bills
3. Grocery
4. Conveyance
5. Fruits and vegetables
6. Miscellaneous articles

Life Skills

The expenditure and savings of Amit are in the ratio 7 : 5. The income and expenditure of Aryan are in the ratio 10 : 6. Who is saving more if both are earning ₹60,000 per month? Both boys are aged 25 years. Is it wise to save what they are saving at their age?

Mind Buzzer

On many maps the scale is written like 1 : 10,000. What does it mean? It means that 1 unit on map represents 10,000 units in reality. If the distance between two places on the map is 5 cm, how much will it be in reality?

Teacher's Notes

- Explain the various properties of ratio and how to compare ratios.
- Make students simplify two ratios to check if their values are same. Using these equal ratios, explain the concept of proportion and the various properties of proportion.
- Through real-life examples explain the concept of direct and inverse variation.

WORKSHEET

Maya is 13 years old and Radha is 5 years old. When Maya is given 10 chocolates by her grandparents, Radha is given 20 chocolates. When Maya is given 5 chocolates, Radha is given 10. Radha is always being given double the number of chocolates than those given to Maya because she is younger than Maya.

Now answer the following questions:

1. What is the ratio of the number of chocolates given to Maya and Radha?

   ____

2. How many chocolates does each of them get if the total number of chocolates distributed is 45?

   ____

3. If Maya gets 13 chocolates, how many does Radha get?

   ____

4. If Radha gets 18 chocolates, how many does Maya get?

   ____

5. If the ratio of the number of chocolates which Radha and Geeta get is 4 : 3, find:

   a. the ratio of the number of chocolates given to Maya and Geeta.

   ____

   b. the ratio of the number of chocolates given to Maya, Radha and Geeta.

   ____

   c. the ratio of the number of chocolates given to Radha, Maya and Geeta.

   ____

8 Percentage and Its Applications

Learning Objectives

- To understand the concept of percentage
- To convert fraction to percentage and vice versa
- To convert decimal to percentage and vice versa
- To convert ratio to percentage and vice versa
- To apply the concept of percentage in real-life situations
- To understand the concept of profit and loss
- To learn how to calculate simple interest

Let's Get Started

Match the fractions and the decimals by colouring them with the same colour. One has been done for your reference.

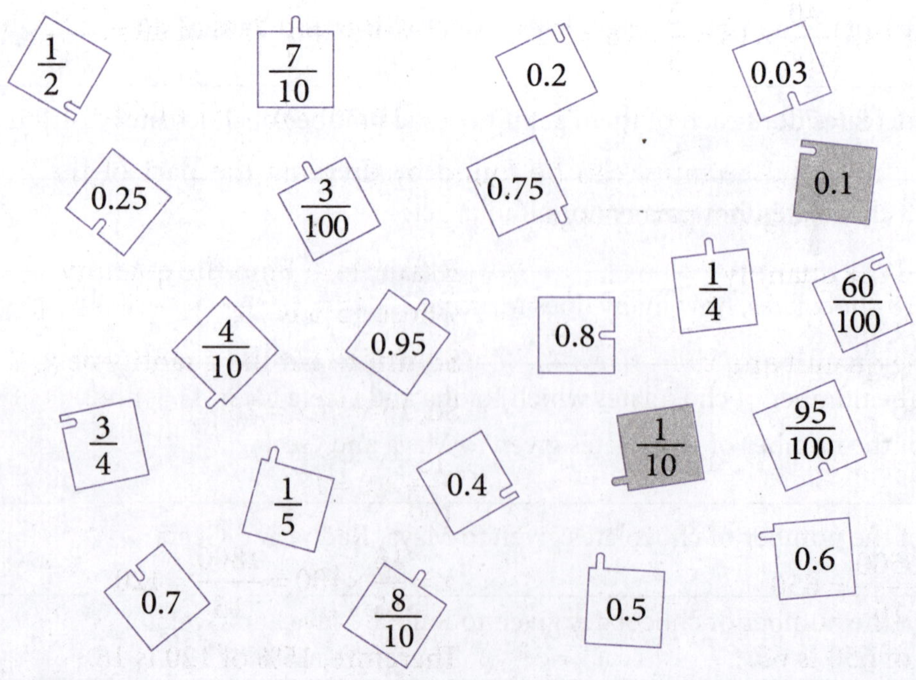

PERCENTAGE

A percentage is a part or portion of a whole expressed as a fraction with 100 as denominator. It is denoted by the symbol % that means hundredths.

For example, 8% means eight out of hundred or eight hundredths.

35% means thirty-five out of hundred or thirty-five hundredths.

> **Do you know?**
> The word per cent is derived from the Latin word '*per centum*' which means per hundred.

Pictorial Representation of Percentage

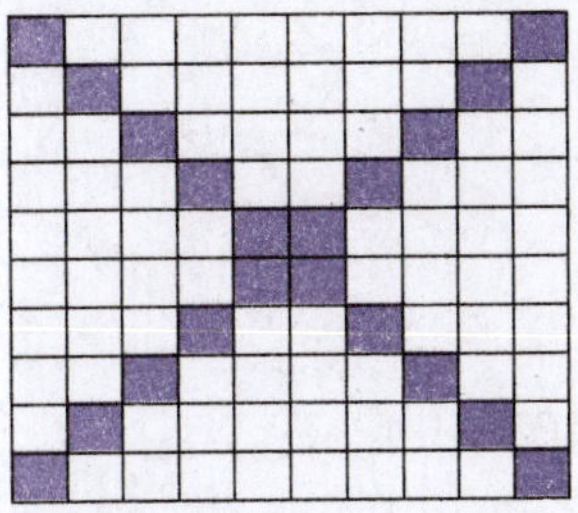

Observe the given figure. 20 squares are shaded out of 100 squares.

The shaded part of the grid is represented as $\frac{20}{100}$. This is written as 20% and read as 20 per cent.

The unshaded part of the grid is represented as $\frac{80}{100}$. This is written as 80% and read as 80 per cent.

PERCENTAGE OF A GIVEN QUANTITY

Deepak was at a mall and bought a pair of sports shoes at 50% discount. If it was priced at ₹400, how much did he pay for it?

As the shoes were at a 50% discount, Deepak paid half the price for them.

That is, 50% of ₹400 = $\frac{50}{100} \times 400 = 200$

So, Deepak paid ₹200 for the shoes.

- The per cent of a part of a given whole quantity can be calculated by multiplying the given quantity by the percentage.

Example 1: What is 40% of 18?

Solution: 40% of 18 = $\frac{40}{100} \times 18 = \frac{2}{5} \times 18 = 7.2$

Therefore, 40% of 18 = 7.2

Example 2: Find 75% of 40.

Solution: 75% of 40 = $\frac{75}{100} \times 40 = \frac{3}{4} \times 40 = 30$

Therefore, 75% of 40 = 30.

> **Note**
> Express the percentage as a fraction while multiplying.

- The whole or the total quantity can be found by dividing the part of the whole quantity by the given percentage.

Example 3: Find the quantity whose 10% is 65.

Solution: Let the quantity be x.

So, 10% of x = 65

$\frac{10}{100} \times x = 65$

$x = \frac{65}{10} \times 100 = \frac{6500}{10} = 650$

Therefore, 10% of 650 is 65.

Example 4: Find the quantity whose 15% is 18.

Solution: Let the quantity be x.

So, 15% of x = 18

$\frac{15}{100} \times x = 18$

$x = \frac{18}{15} \times 100 = \frac{1800}{15} = 120$

Therefore, 15% of 120 is 18.

SOLVED EXAMPLES

Example 5: Find the percentage of the shaded part in the following grids.

a. 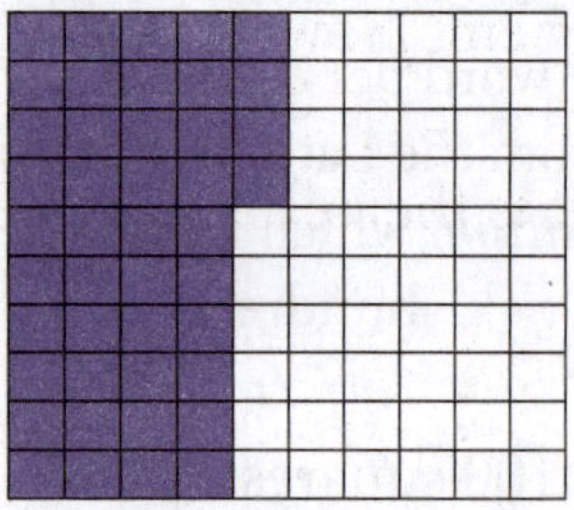 $= \frac{44}{100} = 44\%$

b. 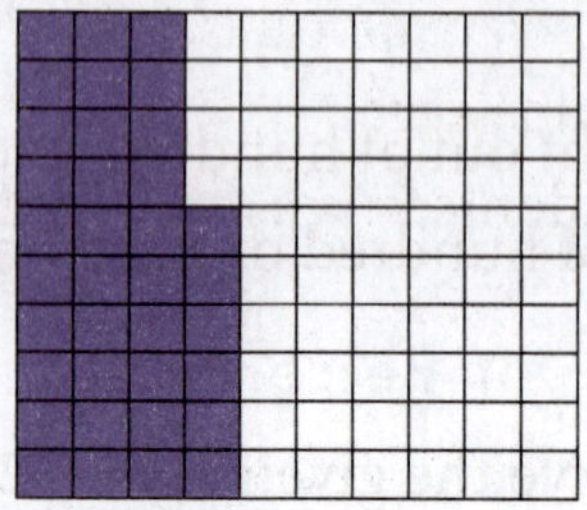 $= \frac{36}{100} = 36\%$

Example 6: Find the percentage of the given quantity.

a. 25% of 200

$$\frac{25}{100} \times 200 = \frac{1}{4} \times 200 = 50$$

25% of 200 is 50.

b. 81% of 500

$$\frac{81}{100} \times 500 = 81 \times 5 = 405$$

81% of 500 is 405.

Example 7: Find the total quantity if its:

a. 8% is 12.

$$\frac{8}{100} \times x = 12$$

$$x = \frac{12}{8} \times 100 = \frac{1200}{8} = 150$$

Therefore, 8% of 150 is 12.

b. 33% is 66.

$$\frac{33}{100} \times x = 66$$

$$x = \frac{66}{33} \times 100 = 200$$

Therefore, 33% of 200 is 66.

EXERCISE 8A

1. **Find the percentage of the given quantity.**

   a. 2% of 7 b. 60% of 2482 c. 3.5% of 35 d. 1% of 1000

   e. 2% of 5 minutes f. 15% of 1 hour g. 50% of 50 paise h. 25% of ₹5000

   i. 5% of 500 g j. 30% of 2 kg k. 7% of 3 litres l. 120% of 750 mℓ

2. **Find the total for the following.**

   a. 14% of it is 70 b. 20% of it is 380 c. 2% of it is 1234

   d. 7% of it is 280 e. 5% of it is 80 ℓ f. 90% of it is 50 kg

3. **Solve the following word problems.**

   a. Ravi scored 18 marks out of 25 in maths unit test. What is the percentage of marks scored by him?

   b. In a movie theatre, 30% of the people were men, 45% of the people were women and the remaining were children. Find the percentage of children in the theatre.

c. Raju spent 10% of his salary on entertainment. If he earns ₹24,500, how much did he spend on entertainment?

d. In an exam, there were 48 questions. A student answered 25% of them. How many questions did he answer?

e. There are 550 students in a school and 310 of them are boys. What is the percentage of girls?

FRACTIONS AND PERCENTAGES

Sita ate $\frac{2}{5}$ of the cake. What percentage of the cake did she eat? To find the percentage, we multiply by 100.

$\frac{2}{5} \times 100 = 40\%$

So, Sita ate 40% of the cake.

Let us learn how to convert fractions to percentages and percentages to fractions.

Convert Fraction to Percentage

A fraction can be converted to a percentage by multiplying the given fraction by 100. Represent the answer with the per cent symbol.

Example 8: Convert $\frac{1}{5}$ to percentage.

Solution: $\frac{1}{5} \times 100 = 20\%$

Example 9: Express $\frac{7}{12}$ as percentage.

Solution: $\frac{7}{12} \times 100 = 58.33\%$

Convert Percentage to Fraction

A percentage can be converted to a fraction by dividing the given percentage by 100. The answer should be in its simplest form without the per cent symbol.

Example 10: Convert 14% to a fraction.

Solution: $14\% = \frac{14}{100} = \frac{7}{50}$

So, $14\% = \frac{7}{50}$

Example 11: Convert 68% to a fraction.

Solution: $68\% = \frac{68}{100} = \frac{34}{50} = \frac{17}{25}$

So, $68\% = \frac{17}{25}$

DECIMALS AND PERCENTAGES

Convert Decimal to Percentage

Now let us learn how to convert a given decimal to a percentage.

A decimal number can be converted to a percentage by multiplying the given decimal number by 100. Represent the answer with the per cent symbol.

Example 12: Convert 0.5 to percentage.

Solution: $0.5 \times 100 = 50.0$

So, $0.5 = 50\%$

Example 13: Convert 1.6 to percentage.

Solution: $1.6 \times 100 = 160.0$

So, $1.6 = 160\%$

Convert Percentage to Decimal

A given percentage can be converted to decimal by converting the percentage to a fraction and then to decimal.

Example 14: Convert 7% to decimal.

Solution: $7\% = \frac{7}{100} = 0.07$

Example 15: Convert 12.25% to decimal.

Solution: $12.25\% = \frac{1225}{10000} = 0.1225$

RATIOS AND PERCENTAGES

Convert Ratio to Percentage

A ratio can be converted to a percentage by representing the given ratio as a fraction, and then converting the fraction to a percentage.

Example 16: Convert 2:5 to percentage.

$2:5 = \frac{2}{5} \Rightarrow \frac{2}{5} \times 100 = \frac{200}{5} = 40\%$

Example 17: Convert 8:40 to percentage.

$8:40 = \frac{8}{40} \Rightarrow \frac{8}{40} \times 100 = \frac{800}{40} = 20\%$

Convert Percentage to Ratio

A given percentage can be converted to a ratio by expressing it as a fraction with denominator 100. Simplify the fraction and represent the same as ratio.

Example 18: Convert 35% to ratio.

$35\% = \frac{35}{100} = \frac{7}{20} = 7:20$

Example 19: Convert 80% to ratio.

$80\% = \frac{80}{100} = \frac{8}{10} = \frac{4}{5} = 4:5$

EXERCISE 8B

1. **Convert the following fractions to percentages.**

   a. $\frac{1}{2}$ b. $\frac{2}{3}$ c. $\frac{5}{4}$ d. $\frac{3}{4}$ e. $5\frac{1}{2}$

2. **Convert the following percentages to fractions.**

   a. 30% b. 85% c. 68% d. 45% e. 1%

3. **Convert the following decimals to percentages.**

   a. 0.05 b. 0.67 c. 1.5 d. 12.05 e. 0.001

4. **Convert the following percentages to decimals.**

   a. 8% b. 14% c. 88% d. 60% e. 51%

5. **Convert the following ratios to percentages.**

   a. 1 : 7 b. 1 : 8 c. 2 : 9 d. 5 : 12 e. 3 : 4

6. **Convert the following percentages to ratios.**

   a. 10% b. 96% c. 125% d. 92% e. 22%

APPLICATIONS OF PERCENTAGE

We learnt that percentages are another way of comparing quantities. In our everyday life, percentage is used widely in different areas. Some of them are as follows:

- Percentage of a quantity = Given quantity × 100
- Percentage of marks scored = $\frac{\text{Marks scored}}{\text{Total marks}} \times 100$
- Percentage of increase or decrease in the price of commodities = $\frac{\text{Amount of increase/decrease}}{\text{Actual price}} \times 100$
- Percentage of discount on sales = $\frac{\text{Amount of discount}}{\text{Price of commodity}} \times 100$
- Percentage of depreciation (decrease) of the value of equipment and vehicles = $\frac{\text{Amount of depreciation}}{\text{Value of equipment}} \times 100$

INCREASE OR DECREASE AS PER CENT

Sometimes, we need to find out the increase or decrease in a given quantity as percentage. For example, if the height of a plant increases from 2 m to 3 m, then we can say that the height increased by 50%.

To convert the increase or decrease in a given quantity as a percentage of the initial value, we can use the following formulae.

$$\text{Percentage increase} = \frac{\text{Increase in amount}}{\text{Original amount}} \times 100\%$$

$$\text{Percentage decrease} = \frac{\text{Decrease in amount}}{\text{Original amount}} \times 100\%$$

Example 20: The price of a house decreased from ₹20,00,000 to ₹15,00,000. Find the percentage decrease.

We have, original price = ₹20,00,000; new price = ₹15,00,000

So, decrease in price = ₹20,00,000 – ₹15,00,000 = ₹5,00,000

$$\text{Percentage decrease} = \frac{\text{Decrease in amount}}{\text{Original amount}} \times 100\%$$

$$= \frac{\cancel{500000}^{1}}{\cancel{2000000}_{\cancel{4}_{1}}} \times \cancel{100}^{25} = 25\%$$

Therefore, the price decreased by 25%.

SOLVED EXAMPLES

Example 21: Out of 100 students, one-fifth like dancing, one-fourth like singing and the rest of them like reading books.

a. What percentage of students like dancing?

b. What percentage of students like singing?

c. What percentage of students like reading?

Solution: Given: Number of students = 100, Those who like dancing = $\frac{1}{5}$

Those who like singing = $\frac{1}{4}$, Those who like reading books = ?

To find: Percentage of students who like dancing, singing and reading

a. Percentage of students who like dancing = $\frac{1}{5} \times 100 = 20\%$

b Percentage of students who like singing = $\frac{1}{4} \times 100 = 25\%$

c. Number of students who like reading = 100 – (20 + 25) = 55

Percentage of students who like reading = 55%

> **Note**
> All the parts that form the whole when added together gives the whole or 100%.

Example 22: In an examination, Gagana scored 85%. If the total marks were 600, then find the marks scored by her?

Solution: Given: Percentage of marks scored = 85%

Total marks = 600

To find: Marks obtained out of 600

$$\frac{85}{100} \times 600 = 85 \times 6 = 510$$

Therefore, Gagana scored 510 marks out of 600.

Example 23: The weight of a baby increased from 8 kg to 10 kg. Find the percentage increase in the weight of the baby.

Solution: Given: Weight of the baby increased from 8kg to 10 kg

To find: Percentage increase in the weight of baby

Increase in weight = (10 – 8) kg = 2 kg

Percentage of increase in baby's weight = $\frac{2}{8} \times 100 = \frac{200}{8} = 25$

Therefore, there is 25% increase in the weight of the baby.

Example 24: The cost of a dress has decreased from ₹950 to ₹475. Find the percentage of decrease in the cost of the dress.

Solution: Given: Decrease in the cost of the dress = from ₹950 to ₹475

To find: Percentage of decrease in the cost of the dress

Amount of decrease in the cost = ₹950 – ₹475 = ₹475

Percentage of decrease in the cost = $\frac{475}{950} \times 100 = \frac{1}{2} \times 100 = 50$

Therefore, there is a 50% decrease in the cost of the dress.

PROFIT AND LOSS

Every day, we buy or sell goods or items and even avail different services. There may be profit or loss while buying and selling.

Shopkeepers buy goods from wholesalers or manufacturers and sell them. The price at which an item is bought is called the **cost price** of the item. In short, it is written as CP.

Shopkeepers may sell the goods at a higher price than the cost price or sometimes, at a lower price than the cost price. The price at which an item is sold is called the **selling price** of the item. In short, it is written as SP. To calculate these, follow the steps given in the flow chart below.

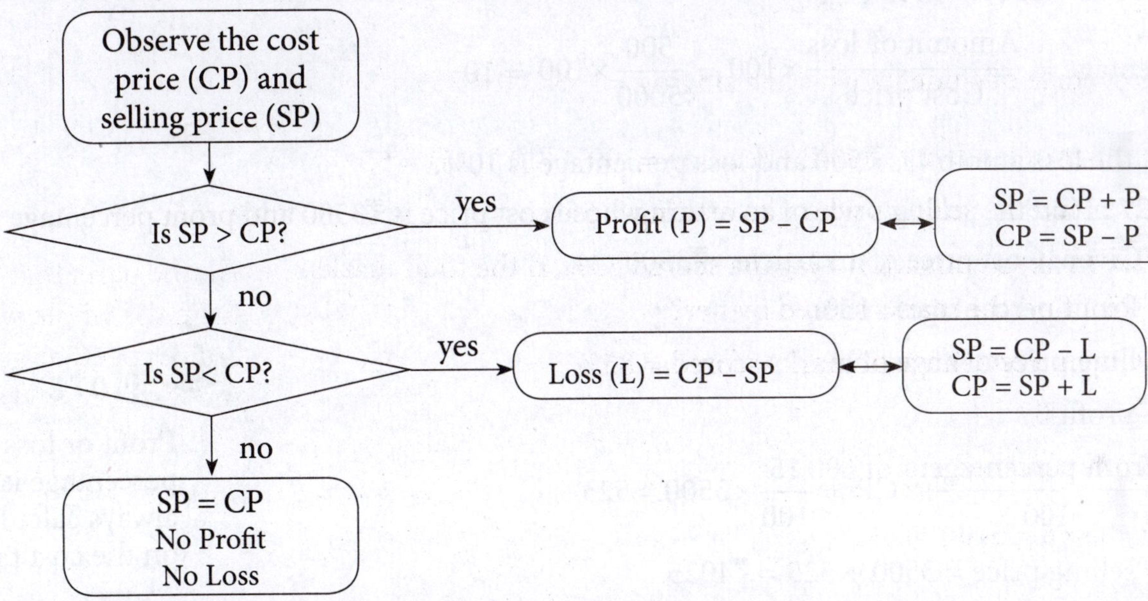

Profit or loss can be converted to a percentage. We can find the percentage of profit or loss if we know the amount of profit or loss. Similarly, we can also find the amount of profit or loss if we know the percentage of profit or loss.

Profit or loss percentage = $\left(\frac{\text{Amount of profit/loss}}{\text{Cost price}} \times 100\right)\%$

Let us consider a few examples to understand this.

SOLVED EXAMPLES

Example 25: Shivam bought tea powder at ₹80 per kg from the wholesaler. He sold the tea powder at ₹100 per kg. What will be his profit percentage?

Solution: Given: Cost price of tea powder = ₹80 per kg

Selling price of tea powder = ₹100 per kg

To find: Profit percentage

Selling price > cost price

∴ Profit = 100 − 80 = 20

$$\text{Profit percentage} = \frac{\text{Amount of profit}}{\text{Cost price}} \times 100 = \frac{20}{80} \times 100 = 25$$

Therefore, the profit percentage is 25%.

Example 26 : Spriha bought a bread toaster at ₹5000 and sold it for ₹4500. Find the loss and loss percentage.

Solution: Given: Cost price of the toaster = ₹5000

Selling price of the toaster = ₹4500

To find: Loss amount and loss percentage

Selling price < cost price

∴ Loss = 5000 − 4500 = 500

$$\text{Loss percentage} = \frac{\text{Amount of loss}}{\text{Cost price}} \times 100 = \frac{500}{5000} \times 100 = 10$$

Therefore, the loss amount is ₹500 and loss percentage is 10%.

Example 27 : Find the selling price of an article whose cost price is ₹3500 and profit percentage is 15%.

Solution: Given: Cost price of an article =₹3500

Profit percentage = 15%

To find: Selling price of an article

SP = CP + profit

$$\text{Profit} = \frac{\text{Profit percentage}}{100} \times \text{CP} = \frac{15}{100} \times 3500 = 525$$

Therefore, selling price = 3500 + 525 = ₹4025.

Note

Profit or loss percentage is always calculated on the cost price.

OVERHEAD EXPENSE

Revanth bought furniture for ₹25,000. He had to pay an extra amount of ₹1500 for transportation and assembly of the parts.

The extra amount that he paid apart from the original cost of the item is known as **overhead expense.** Transportation charges, installation charges, amount spent on repairs, taxes, etc. come under overhead expenses. To calculate the overall profit or loss, we should consider the overhead expenses along with CP, that is, add overhead expenses to the original CP. Consider the following example.

Example 28: Revanth bought furniture for ₹25,000. He had to pay an extra amount of ₹1500 for transportation and assembly. After a year, he sold it for ₹22,500. Find his loss percentage.

Solution: Given: CP of the furniture = ₹25,000, Overhead expenses = ₹1500

SP of the furniture = ₹22,500

To find: Loss percentage

New CP = Original CP + Overhead expense

= ₹25,000 + ₹1500 = ₹26,500

Loss = CP − SP = 26,500 − 22,500 = ₹4000

$$\text{Loss percentage} = \frac{\text{Amount of loss}}{\text{Cost price}}\times 100 = \frac{4000}{26500}\times 100 = 15.09\%$$

So, the loss percentage is 15.09%.

EXERCISE 8C

Solve the following word problems.

1. A student secures 90 marks in his first test and 75 marks in the second test. Find the percentage decrease.
2. What is the percentage decrease on a DVD recorder that is priced down from ₹2890 to ₹1053?
3. An article bought for ₹800 was sold for ₹1200. Find the gain percentage.
4. A shopkeeper sells two books at ₹480. On one book, he gains 10% and on the other, he loses 10%. Find the overall profit or loss percentage incurred.
5. A fruit seller bought a box of apples for ₹500. However, he was forced to sell them at ₹400 because they had started to get spoilt. Find the loss percentage.
6. Jacob bought a bike for ₹45,300 and spent ₹12,500 on repairs. If he sells it for ₹75,000, will he get a profit or a loss?
7. The price of an article has increased from ₹300 to ₹400. What is the percentage increase?
8. Complete the following table.

	Cost Price (₹)	Selling Price (₹)	Loss (₹)	Profit (₹)	Profit/Loss (%)
a.	80	90	–		
b.	353	300		–	
c.	1250		150	–	
d.		3500	–	600	

SIMPLE INTEREST

In real life, we might come across instances when we need to calculate interest.

- Interest may be earned on bank deposits
- Interest may be paid on bank loans

The sum of money deposited or loaned (borrowed) is known as the **principal.**

The extra amount of money charged on the loan borrowed or earned on the deposited money is known as the **interest.**

The sum of the principal and the interest is called the **amount.**

That is, **Amount = Principal + Interest**

The rate of interest is the interest earned or charged on every 100 rupees for 1 year. This is also known as the rate per cent per annum. Per annum (p.a.) means for each year.

$$\text{Interest} = \frac{\text{Principal} \times \text{Rate of interest}}{100}$$

When the interest is calculated on the same principal at the same rate of interest throughout a given period of time, it is called **simple interest.**

$$\text{Simple interest (SI)} = \frac{\text{Principal (P)} \times \text{Time (T)} \times \text{Rate of interest (R)}}{100}$$

$$\text{Percentage of interest} = \frac{\text{Interest in rupees}}{\text{Loan/Deposit amount}} \times 100$$

Note

$A = P + I$

$A = P + \left(\frac{P \times R \times T}{100}\right)$

$A = P\left(1 + \frac{R \times T}{100}\right)$

Let us solve a few examples to learn how to calculate the terms discussed above.

SOLVED EXAMPLES

Example 29: Isabella takes a loan of ₹50,000 at 15% per annum. Find the interest she has to pay at the end of one year.

Solution: Given: Principal = ₹50,000, Rate of interest = 15%

To find: The interest to be paid at the end of 1 year

$$\text{Interest} = \frac{\text{Principal} \times \text{Rate of interest}}{100}$$

$$\text{Interest} = \frac{50000 \times 15}{100} = 7500$$

Therefore, Isabella has to pay ₹7500 as interest at the end of 1 year.

Example 30: Mitali deposits ₹45,000 in a bank at 8% per year. Find the amount she gets after 4 years.

Solution: Given: Principal = ₹45,000, Rate of interest = 8% and Time = 4 years

To find: Amount

Amount = Principal + Interest

$$\text{Simple interest} = \frac{\text{Principal} \times \text{Time} \times \text{Rate of interest}}{100}$$

$$\text{Simple interest} = \frac{45000 \times 4 \times 8}{100} = 14{,}400$$

Amount = 45000 + 14400 = 59400

Therefore, she will get ₹59,400 after 4 years.

Example 31: Manohar pays an interest of ₹10,500 for 2 years on a sum of ₹75,000. Find the rate of interest.

Solution: Given: Principal = ₹75,000, Time = 2 years and Interest = ₹10,500

To find: Rate of interest

$$\text{Simple interest} = \frac{\text{Principal} \times \text{Time} \times \text{Rate of interest}}{100}$$

$$10500 = \frac{75000 \times 2 \times \text{Rate of interest}}{100}$$

$$\text{Rate of interest} = \frac{10500 \times 100}{75000 \times 2} = 7\%$$

Therefore, the rate of interest is 7%.

Example 32 : What will be the rate of interest per annum if the sum doubles itself in 5 years?

Solution: Given: Time = 5 years and the principal doubles in 5 years

To find: Rate of interest

Let the principal be ₹100. So, after 5 years, amount will be ₹200.

Amount = Principal + Interest

200 = 100 + Interest

So, Interest for 5 years = 100

$$\text{Simple interest} = \frac{\text{Principal} \times \text{Time} \times \text{Rate of interest}}{100}$$

$$100 = \frac{100 \times 5 \times \text{Rate of interest}}{100}$$

$$\text{Rate of interest} = \frac{100 \times 100}{100 \times 5} = 20$$

Therefore, the rate of interest per annum is 20%.

Mental Maths

1. What is 15% of 1500?
2. 20% of which number is 420?
3. If SP = 10 and CP = 40, then what is the percentage of loss?
4. The price of petrol is increased from ₹78 to ₹80. Find the percentage increase.
5. What is the simple interest, when P = 2000, T = 2 years and R = 2%?

EXERCISE 8D

1. Complete the following table.

	Principal	Time	Rate	Interest	Amount
a.	₹10,000	2 years	5%		
b.	₹8500		10%		₹9350
c.		6 years	15%	₹490.5	
d.	₹2,30,000	10 years		₹2,87,500	₹5,17,500
e.		3 years	2%	₹60	

2. Shilpa takes a loan of ₹3,00,000 at the rate of 15% for 1 year. Calculate the simple interest.

3. Rahul invests ₹25,000 annually at the rate of 6% for 3 years in a recurring deposit. How much amount will he get at the end of 3 years?

4. How much time will it take for a principal of ₹20,000 to give ₹1000 as interest at 5% per annum?

5. A sum of ₹28,000 amounts to ₹35,000 in 4 years. What is the rate of interest?

6. What sum would yield an interest of ₹400 in 3 years at 3% per annum?

7. At what rate of simple interest will the sum of money double itself in 6 years?

8. In what time will ₹300 amount to ₹360 at the rate of 5% p.a. simple interest?

MATHS LAB ACTIVITY

Aim: To deduce the general formula for simple interest

Materials required: Notebook, pen

Procedure:

1. Consider an amount as principal, say ₹10,000 and choose a rate of interest, say 10%.
2. Calculate the interest for a year using the following formula:

   $$\text{Interest} = \frac{\text{Principal} \times \text{Rate of interest}}{100}$$

   Thus, interest for the chosen amount for 1 year $= \frac{10000 \times 10}{100} = ₹1000$
3. Now calculate the interest for the second year for the same principal and rate of interest.

   Interest for the chosen amount for 2nd year $= \frac{10000 \times 10}{100} = ₹1000$

   Therefore, the total interest for 2 years = 1000 + 1000 = ₹2000
4. Then calculate the interest for 8 consecutive years by adding the interest for each respective year.
   Interest for 8 years = ₹8000

   (1000 + 1000 + 1000 + 1000 + 1000 + 1000 + 1000 + 1000)
5. Now we know the general formula for calculating the interest for 1 year is $\frac{P \times R}{100}$.

   So, the interest for T years would be $\frac{P \times R \times T}{100}$,

   where P = Principal, R = Rate of interest and T = Time

   $$\text{So, Simple interest} = \frac{\text{Principal} \times \text{Time} \times \text{Rate of interest}}{100}$$
6. Now calculate the simple interest for the same principal and rate of interest chosen earlier for 8 years.
   Principal = ₹10,000, Rate of interest = 10%, Time = 8 years

   Therefore, Simple interest $= \frac{10000 \times 8 \times 10}{100} = 8000$
7. Now compare the simple interest calculated by adding interest for each year and using the formula. You will find that both answers are the same.
8. Now try calculating the simple interest by choosing different principal, time and rate of interest.

Concept Map

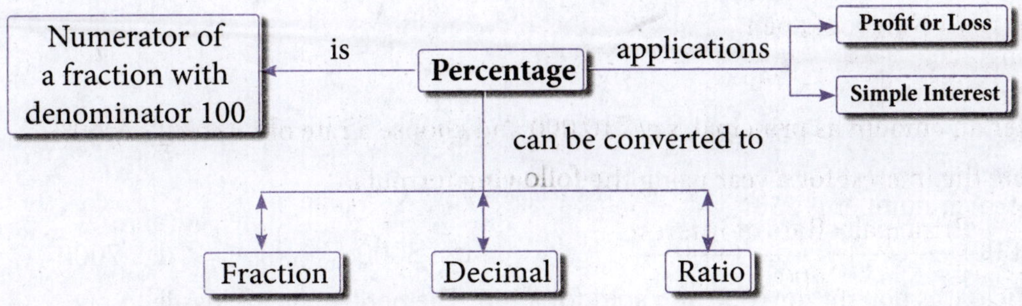

Key Concepts

- **Per cent**: A number expressed as a fraction with denominator 100
- **Cost price**: Total cost incurred by the shopkeeper to buy an item
- **Selling price:** The price at which the shopkeeper sells an item
- **Profit:** Excess amount which is more than the cost price
- **Loss:** Deficit amount which is less than the cost price
- **Principal:** The money borrowed or deposited
- **Interest:** The extra amount paid on borrowed or deposited money
- **Amount:** The sum of principal and interest
- **Rate of interest:** The interest on ₹100 for 1 year, known as the rate per cent per annum

CHAPTER REVISION

A. Choose the correct option.

1. 10% of 180 is

   a. 80 b. 18 c. 90 d. 60

2. 5% of which number is 250?

   a. 5000 b. 6000 c. 3000 d. 7000

3. An article was bought for ₹300 and sold for ₹240. The percentage of loss is

   a. 20% b. 5% c. 25% d. 15%

4. The cost of petrol is increased from ₹72 to ₹78. The percentage increase is

   a. 7.6% b. 7.7% c. 8% d. 8.3%

5. The simple interest for a sum of ₹10,000 at the rate of 3% for 2 years is

   a. ₹200 b. ₹600 c. ₹800 d. ₹1000

B. Fill in the blanks.

1. 0.03 converted to percentage is ________.
2. ________ % of 480 is 72.
3. The price of a book is decreased by 10%. Its actual price was ₹250. The new price is ________.
4. To convert a fraction to a percentage, we multiply it with ________.
5. The formula to calculate simple interest is ________.

C. Write T for true and F for false.

1. 80% of 100 is 80.
2. 75% on being converted into fraction is $\frac{1}{2}$.
3. Per cent means hundredths.
4. 15 out of 60 is 20%.
5. If an article is bought for ₹80 and sold for ₹100, loss is incurred.

D. Match the following.

1. 2% of 40	a. 20
2. 8% of 70	b. 5.34
3. 15% of 780	c. 357.5
4. 10% of 200	d. 5.6
5. 6% of 89	e. 117
6. 55% of 650	f. 0.8

E. Find the percentage of the following.

1. 30% of 5 metres
2. 5% of 600 g
3. 8% of 1 litre
4. 12% of 8 cm
5. 3% of 2 km
6. 6% of 900 mℓ
7. 16% of ₹480
8. 7% of 50 paise

F. Complete the following table.

	Fractions	Decimals	Percentages
1.	$\frac{1}{2}$	0.5	50%
2.		0.75	
3.	$\frac{2}{5}$		
4.			125%
5.	$\frac{6}{7}$		
6.		0.33	
7.	$\frac{1}{8}$		12.5%

G. Find the following.

1. SP = ₹200 CP = ₹150 Profit percentage = ?
2. SP = ₹1500 CP = ₹1400 Profit percentage = ?
3. SP = ₹9400 CP = ₹8000 Profit percentage = ?
4. CP = ₹250 SP = ₹200 Loss percentage = ?
5. CP = ₹5100 SP = ₹5000 Loss percentage = ?
6. CP = ₹7420 SP = ₹7300 Loss percentage = ?

H. Calculate the missing values.

	Principal (P)	Rate of interest (R)%	Time (T)	Simple interest (SI)	Amount (A)
1.	₹2000	3%	1 year	₹60	
2.		8%	2 years	₹560	
3.	₹8000	2.5%			₹8600
4.			4 years	₹100	₹2600
5.	₹7000	5%			₹8750
6.	₹10,000		10 years	₹1250	
7.	₹25,000	11%			₹30,500

I. Solve the following word problems.

1. Harish saves ₹900 out of a total monthly salary of ₹14,400. Find his percentage of savings.
2. A total of 2700 cookies was bought in a school. If the children ate 2430 cookies then, what percentage of cookies is left?
3. Jacob has a collection of different cars. 27 out of them are red in colour and they make 60% of the collection. How many cars does he have in all?

4. By selling a T-shirt for ₹999, the shopkeeper gains ₹60. Find the percentage of gain.
5. Rahul bought a bag of rice for ₹1000 and sold it for ₹1250. Calculate his profit or loss percentage.
6. The population of a city was 95,897 in 2010 and decreased to 95,300 in 2015. What is the percentage decrease?
7. The price of rice is increased from ₹52 to ₹58 per kg. What is the percentage of increase?
8. The price of a top is decreased by 2%. The original price was ₹599. What is the decreased price of the top?

SKILL UP!

Project

Visit nearby banks and find out new schemes of deposits. Compare the rates of interest for different duration of time offered by different banks. Write a brief report on various deposit schemes and state which bank would be ideal for saving money.

Life Skills

A wildlife protection movement called Project Tiger was started in 1973 at Jim Corbett National Park, Uttarakhand, India to guard the Royal Bengal Tigers. This project was targeted at tiger protection in different areas throughout India.

India has a suitable climate and it is home to 70% of tigers in the world. Project Tiger has helped boost the tiger population from 1200 in 1970 to 3500 in 1990. In 2006, there were 1411 tigers which increased to 1706 in 2011 and 2226 in 2014, 3890 in 2016.

Now answer the following questions.

1. What is the % change in tiger population compared to 1970 and 1990?
2. What is the % change in tiger population compared to 2006 and 2016?
3. Find out the present population of tigers in India.

Mind Buzzer

A test was divided into two parts: Parts A and B. If 75% of the students could answer questions in Part A correctly, 55% could answer questions in Part B correctly and 20% could not answer both the parts, find the percentage of students who could answer both the parts correctly.

Teacher's Notes

- Introduce the topic using real-life situations where the concepts of percentage, profit or loss and interest are used.
- Guide students to write down the given information first before solving the questions.
- Explain the calculation of interest, percentage, etc., based on different scenarios.

WORKSHEET

Look at the grid shown below and complete the given table.

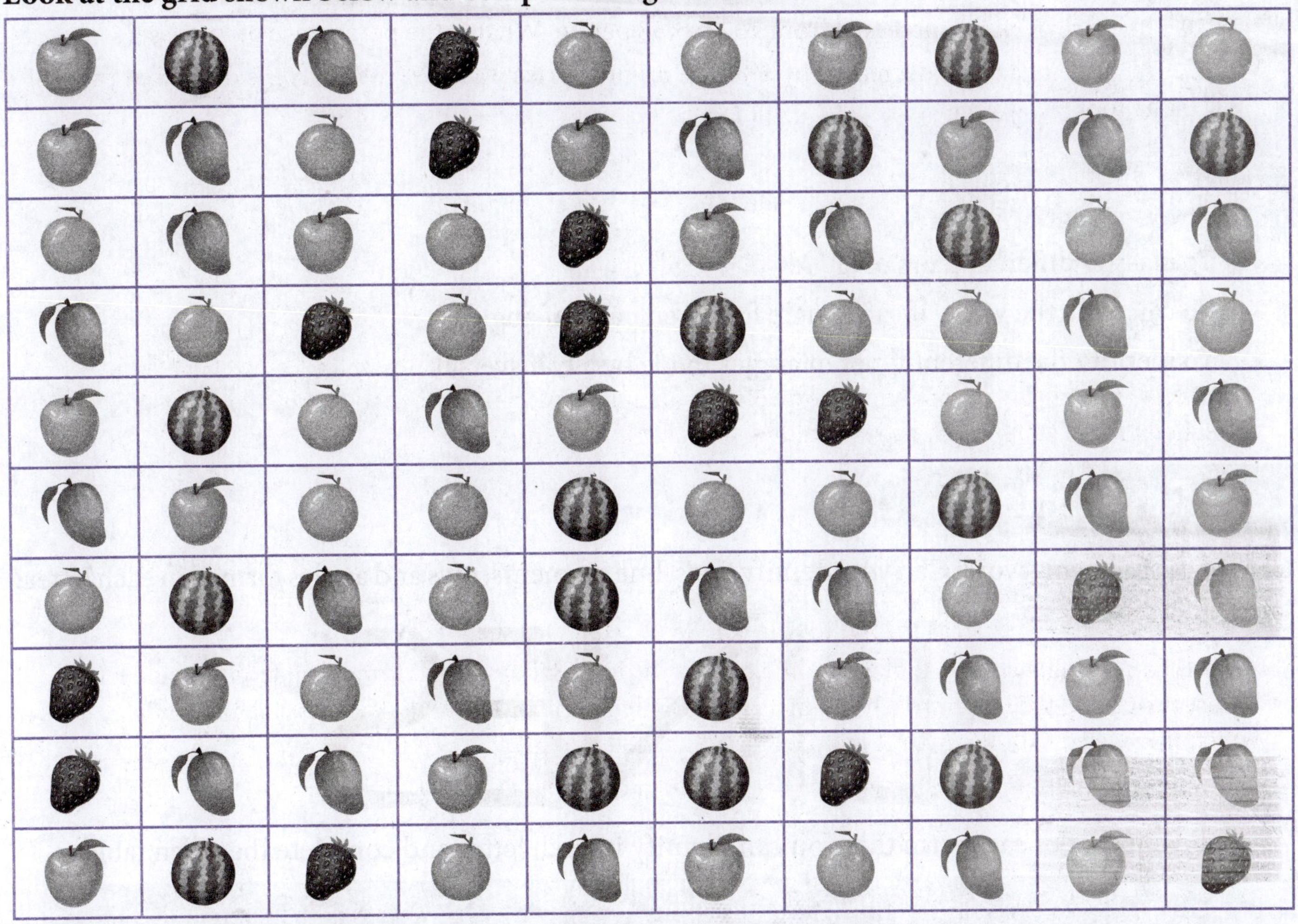

Fruits		How many	Fraction	Decimal	Percentage
Apple					
Orange					
Mango					
Watermelon					
Strawberry					

9 Lines and Angles

Learning Objectives

- To classify different pairs of angles
- To calculate the value of each angle for given pairs of angles
- To identify the different types of angles made by a transversal

Let's Get Started

Look at the following word. Can you identify lines, line segments, rays and angles formed in each letter?

Write the number of each term that you can identify in each letter and complete the given table.

Letter	Lines	Line segments	Rays	Angles
L				
I				
N				
E				
S				

In Class 6, we learnt about some basic geometrical terms. Let us recall that.

Plane 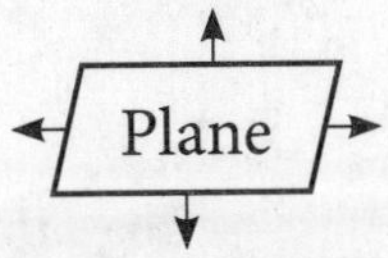	• A plane is a flat surface that extends infinitely in all directions. • It has length and breadth but no thickness.
Point •X	• A point marks an exact location in a plane. • It has no length, breadth and thickness. • It is represented by a dot and named with a capital letter.
Line segment 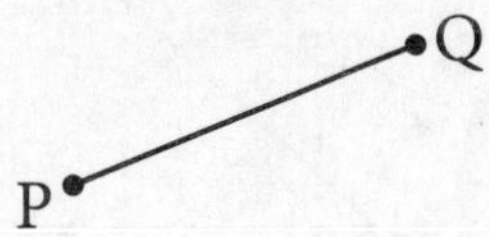	• A line segment is the shortest straight path (distance) between two points in a plane. • It has two end points and a definite length. • It is denoted by the symbol $\overline{PQ}$ and named with two capital letters or by a single small letter.
Line 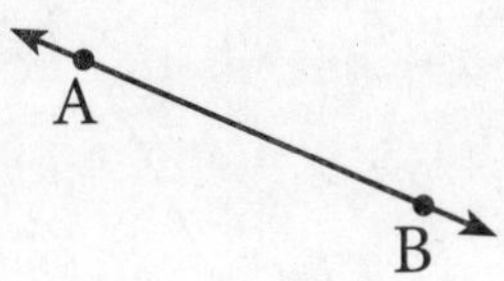	• When we extend the two end points of a line segment in both directions endlessly, we get a line. • There are infinite points on a line. • A line has no end points and thus no definite length. • It is denoted by the symbol $\overleftrightarrow{AB}$ and named with two capital letters or by a single small letter.
Ray 	• A ray is a part of a line with a fixed starting point and continues endlessly in the other direction. • It has one end point (which is its starting point) and does not have a definite length. • It is denoted by the symbol $\overrightarrow{OP}$.
Angle 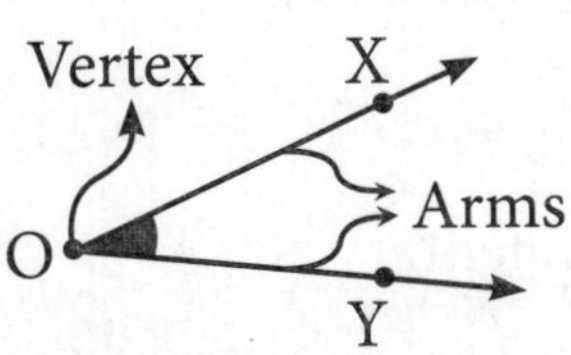	• An angle is formed when two lines or line segments or rays meet at a common point. • The point where the two lines or line segments or rays meet is called the vertex of the angle. Here, O is the vertex. • The two lines or line segments or rays that form the angle are called its arms. Here, OX and OY are the arms. • An angle is denoted by the symbol ∠ and named with either one capital letter or one small letter or three capital letters of the English alphabet. Here, the angle is ∠O or ∠XOY or ∠YOX. • The unit used for measuring an angle is called degree and its symbol is °. • Types of angles are: 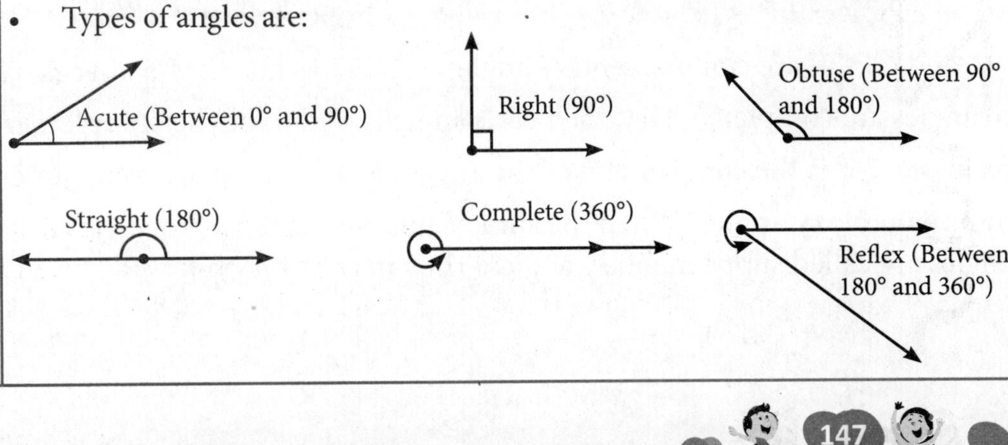

MORE ABOUT ANGLES

Pairs of Angles

There are a few pairs of angles that satisfy some important properties.

1. **Adjacent angles** are a pair of angles which lie next to one another and have:
   - a common arm,
   - a common vertex,
   - the non-common arms located on either side (or opposite sides) of the common arm.

Look at the given figure. The hands of the clock form adjacent angles.

- ∠POR and ∠QOR have the common arm OR.
- ∠POR and ∠QOR have the common vertex O.
- the non-common arms OP and OQ lie on either side of the common arm OR.

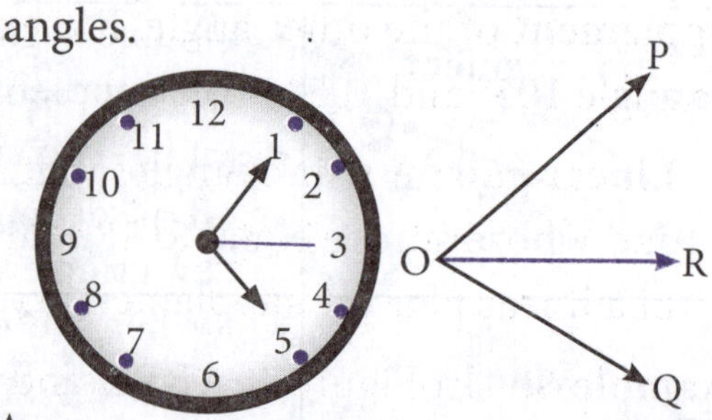

So, ∠POR and ∠QOR are adjacent angles.

Example 1: Consider the figures given alongside.

In Figure 1, are ∠AOB and ∠AOC adjacent angles?

Solution: ∠AOB and ∠AOC share a common vertex (O) and a common arm (OA), but the non-common arms (OC, OB) are not on either side of the common arm. So, they are not adjacent angles.

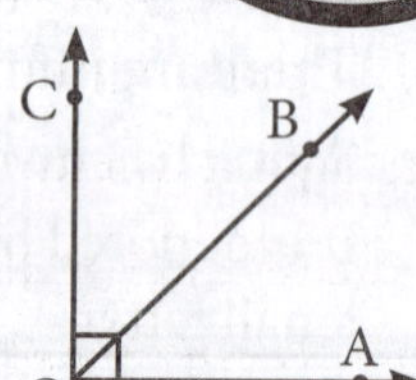

Figure 1

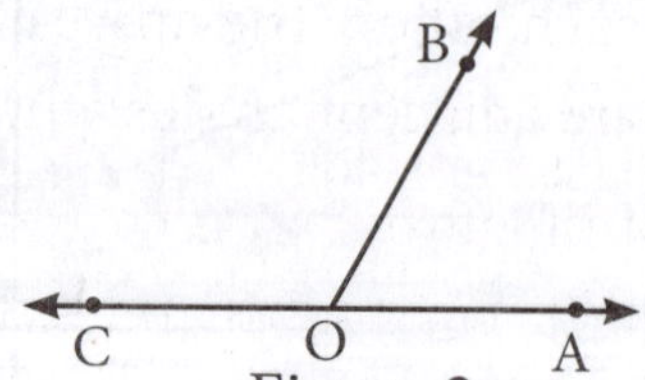

Figure 2

In Figure 2, are ∠AOC and ∠BOC adjacent angles? Why?

2. **Complementary angles**: When the sum of the measures of two angles is equal to 90°, the pair of angles are called complementary angles. They may or may not be adjacent angles.

   Consider the following examples.

Common Errors

Here, ∠*a* and ∠*b* share a common arm but do not share a common vertex. Hence, ∠*a* and ∠*b* are not adjacent angles.

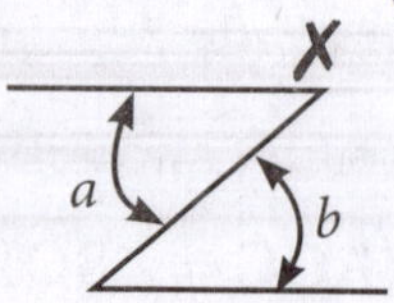

Example 2:

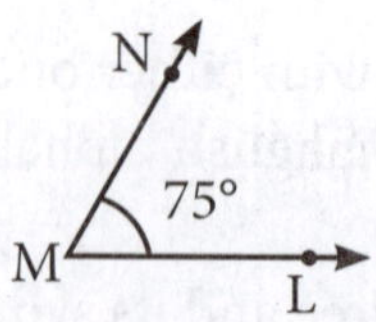

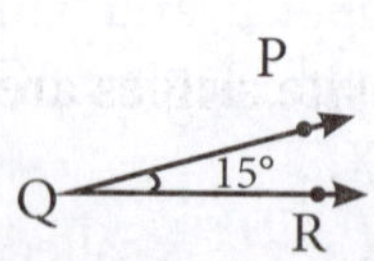

∠NML + ∠PQR = 75° + 15° = 90°

∠NML and ∠PQR are complementary angles.

Example 3:

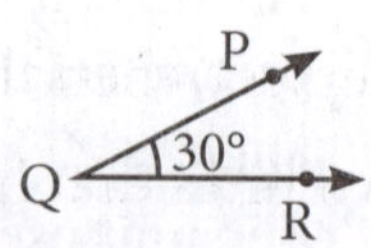

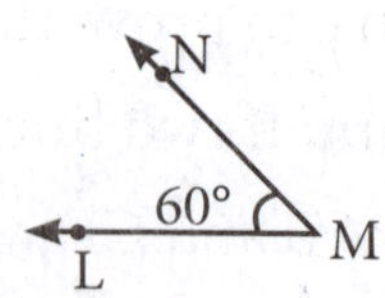

∠PQR + ∠LMN = 30° + 60° = 90°

∠PQR and ∠LMN are complementary angles.

If two angles are complementary, then each angle is said to be the **complement** of the other angle.

For example, 75° is the complement of the angle 15° and 15° is the complement of the angle 75°.

3. **Supplementary angles**: When the sum of the measures of two angles is equal to 180°, the pair of angles are called supplementary angles. They may or may not be adjacent angles.

Example 4:

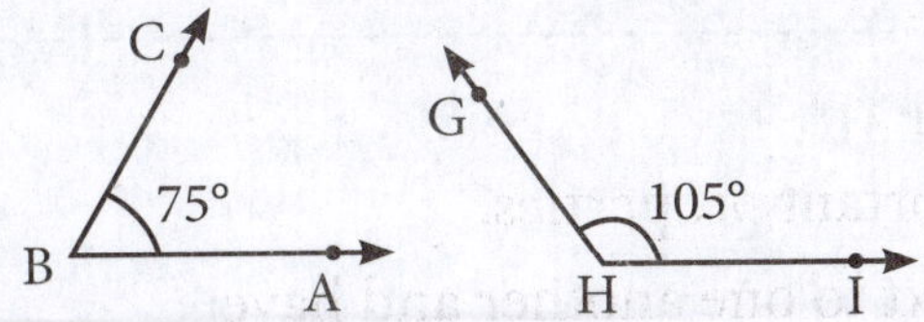

Example 5:

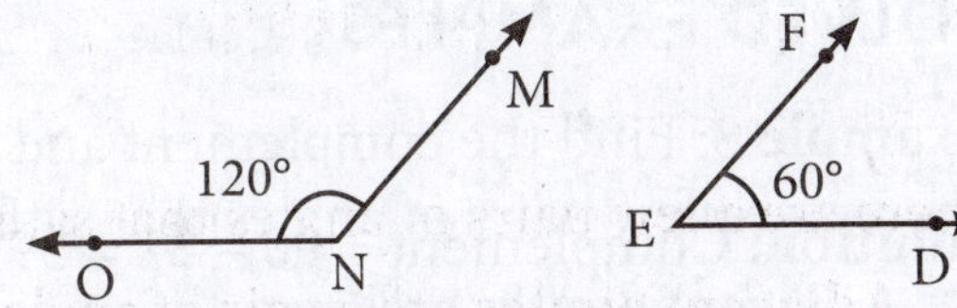

∠ABC + ∠GHI = 75° + 105° = 180°

∠ABC and ∠GHI are supplementary angles.

∠MNO + ∠DEF = 120° + 60° = 180°

∠MNO and ∠DEF are supplementary angles.

If two angles are supplementary, then each angle is said to be the **supplement** of the other angle. For example, 75° is the supplement of the angle 105° and 105° is the supplement of the angle 75°.

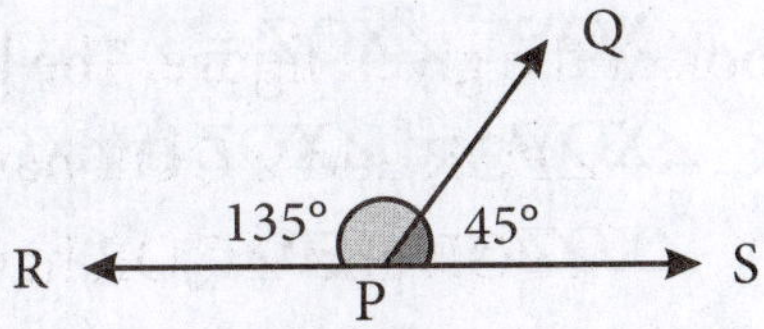

Figure 1

4. **Linear pair:** A pair of angles that are adjacent, form a straight line and whose sum is equal to 180° are called a linear pair. The angles in a linear pair are supplementary.

Example 6: In Figure 1, ∠RPQ and ∠SPQ form a straight line and are adjacent to each other. The angles are supplementary (135° + 45° = 180°). So, ∠RPQ and ∠SPQ are adjacent angles which form a linear pair.

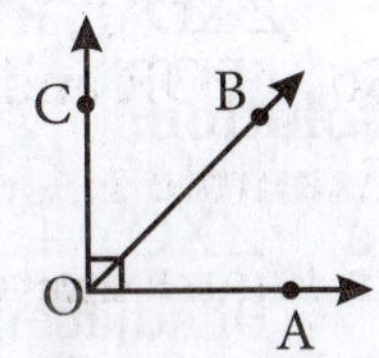

Figure 2

In Figure 2, ∠AOB and ∠BOC are adjacent to each other but do not form a straight line. So, ∠AOB and ∠BOC are adjacent angles which do not form a linear pair.

5. **Vertically opposite angles:** When two lines intersect or meet each other at a point, a pair of angles form opposite to each other at the common vertex. These angles are called vertically opposite angles. Vertically opposite angles so formed are equal.

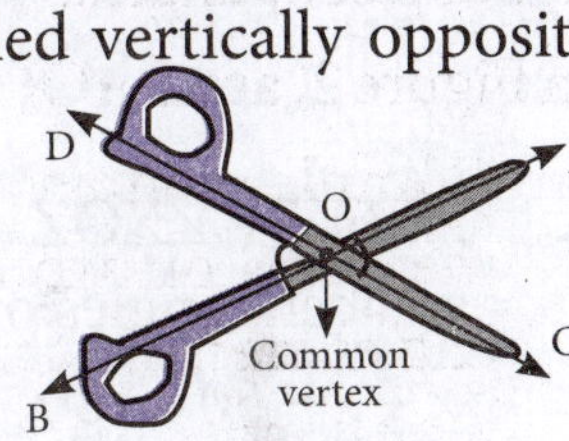

Example 7: In the given figure, ∠AOC and ∠BOD are vertically opposite angles.

∠AOD and ∠BOC are also vertically opposite angles.

∠AOC = ∠BOD and ∠AOD = ∠BOC

So, vertically opposite angles are a pair of angles that share a common vertex but have no common arms and are equal.

Let us try to prove the following statement or theorem.

Theorem: If two lines intersect, then the vertically opposite angles are equal.

Given: AB and CD are two lines that intersect at O.

The lines make the following angles: ∠AOC, ∠AOD, ∠BOD, ∠BOC

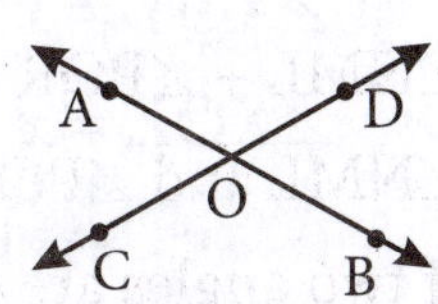

To prove: ∠AOC = ∠BOD

Proof: ∠AOC + ∠AOD = 180° (linear pair) (i)

∠AOD + ∠BOD = 180° (linear pair) (ii)

From (i) and (ii), we find that

∠AOC + ∠AOD = ∠AOD + ∠BOD

Therefore, ∠AOC = ∠BOD.

Similarly, we can prove that ∠AOD = ∠BOC.

SOLVED EXAMPLES

Example 8: Find the complement and supplement of 31°.

Solution: Complement = 90 – 31 = 59°

Supplement = 180 – 31= 149°

Example 9: In the given figure, YOZ is a straight line and OX is a ray. Calculate the following.

a. $\angle XOY$ if $\angle XOZ = 112°$

b. $\angle XOY$ if $\angle XOZ = 3\angle XOY$

c. $\angle XOY$ and $\angle XOZ$ if $\angle XOY = x$ and $\angle XOZ = x - 50$

d. $\angle XOY$ and $\angle XOZ$ if $\angle XOY : \angle XOZ = 3 : 7$

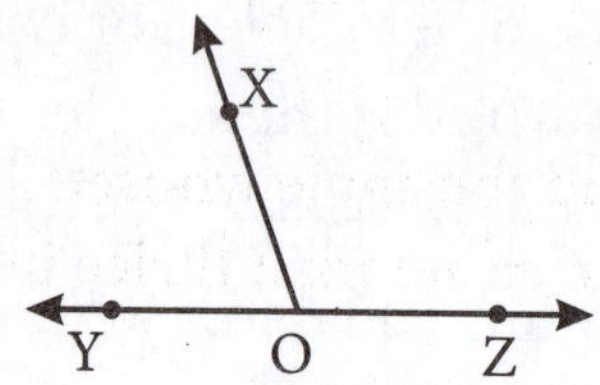

Solution:

a. $\angle XOY + \angle XOZ = 180°$ [Linear pair or sum of adjacent angles on a straight line]

$$\angle XOY + 112° = 180°$$

$$\angle XOY = 180° - 112°$$

$$\angle XOY = 68°$$

b. $\angle XOY + \angle XOZ = 180°$ [Linear pair or sum of adjacent angles on a straight line]

$$\angle XOY + 3\angle XOY = 180°$$

$$4\angle XOY = 180°$$

$$\angle XOY = \frac{180°}{4} = 45°$$

c. $\angle XOY + \angle XOZ = 180°$ [Linear pair or sum of adjacent angles on a straight line]

$$x + x - 50 = 180$$

$$2x - 50 = 180$$

$$2x = 180 + 50$$

$$2x = 230$$

$$x = \frac{230}{2} = 115°$$

$$\angle XOY = x = 115°$$

$$\angle XOZ = x - 50$$

$$= 115 - 50 = 65°$$

d. Let $\angle XOY = 3x$ and $\angle XOZ = 7x$.

$\angle XOY + \angle XOZ = 180°$ [Linear pair or sum of adjacent angles on a straight line]

$$\angle XOY + \angle XOZ = 180°$$

$$3x + 7x = 180°$$

$$10x = 180°$$

$$x = \frac{180°}{10°} = 18°$$

$$\angle XOY = 3x = 3 \times 18 = 54°$$

$$\angle XOZ = 7x = 7 \times 18 = 126°$$

Note

Pair means two. The term linear pair can be used for two adjacent supplementary angles. For more than two such angles, we write sum of adjacent angles on a straight line.

Example 10: In the given figure, AB and CD are two lines intersecting at O. Calculate ∠AOD, ∠AOC, ∠BOD and ∠BOC if ∠AOD : ∠AOC = 2:1.

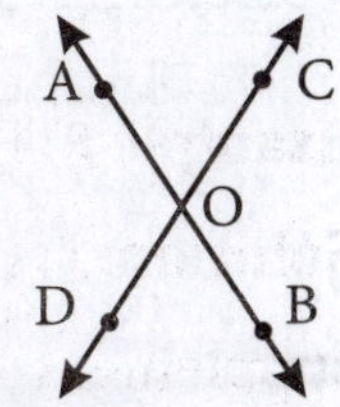

Solution: Let $\angle AOD = 2x$ and $\angle AOC = x$

$\angle AOD + \angle AOC = 180°$ [Linear pair or sum of adjacent angles on a straight line]

$2x + x = 180°$

$3x = 180°$

$x = \frac{180°}{3} = 60°$

$\angle AOD = 2x = 2 \times 60 = 120°$

$\angle AOC = x = 60°$

$\angle BOD = \angle AOC = 60°$ (Vertically opposite angles)

$\angle BOC = \angle AOD = 120°$ (Vertically opposite angles)

Example 11: Find the angle whose supplement is 20° more than thrice its complement.

Solution: Let the angle be $x°$.

Complement = $(90 - x)°$

Supplement = $(180 - x)°$

$180 - x = 3(90 - x) + 20$

$180 - x = 270 - 3x + 20$

$3x - x = 290 - 180$

$2x = 110$

$x = 55°$

Thus, the angle is 55°.

Example 12: Find the angle whose complement is $\frac{1}{3}$ of its supplement.

Solution: Let the angle be $x°$.

Complement = $(90 - x)°$

Supplement = $(180 - x)°$

$90 - x = \frac{180 - x}{3}$

$3(90 - x) = 180 - x$

$270 - 3x = 180 - x$

$270 - 180 = 3x - x$

$2x = 90$

$x = \frac{90}{2} = 45°$

Thus, the angle is 45°.

Mental Maths

Find the complement of 80°.

Linear pair of 90° is _____°.

EXERCISE 9A

1. **Find the complement of:**

   a. 40° b. 85°

2. **Find the supplement of:**

   a. 62° b. 137°

3. **Find the angle which is equal to its complement.**
4. **An angle is 40° more than its supplementary angle. Find the angle.**
5. **Find the angle whose supplement is 10° more than twice its complement.**
6. **Find the angle whose complement is $\frac{1}{3}$ of its supplement.**

7. **In the given figure, AOC is a straight line. OB and OD are rays. Calculate the following:**

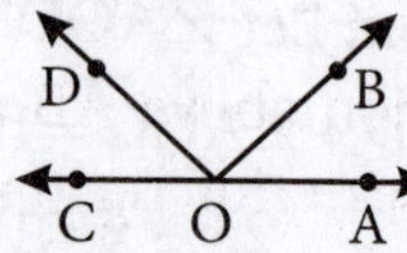

   a. $\angle AOB$ if $\angle BOC = 110°$
   b. $\angle COD$ if $\angle AOD = 130°$
   c. $\angle AOB$ if $\angle BOD = 90°$ and $\angle COD = 30°$
   d. $\angle COD$ if $\angle AOB = 45°$ and $\angle BOD = 85°$
   e. $\angle AOB$ if $\angle AOB : \angle BOD : \angle DOC = 2:4:3$
   f. $\angle BOD$ if $\angle AOB = x - 10$ and $\angle BOD = 3x$ and $\angle COD = x + 10$

8. **In the given figure, AB and CD are two lines intersecting at O. Calculate the following:**

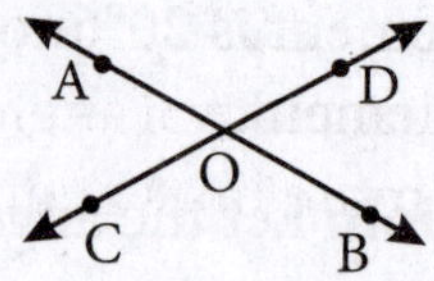

   a. $\angle AOD$, $\angle BOD$ and $\angle BOC$ if $\angle AOC = 50°$
   b. $\angle AOD$, $\angle AOC$, $\angle BOD$ and $\angle BOC$ if $\angle AOD = 2\angle AOC$
   c. $\angle AOD$, $\angle AOC$, $\angle BOD$ and $\angle BOC$ if $\angle AOD : \angle AOC = 5:4$

PARALLEL LINES AND TRANSVERSAL

We know that when two lines meet at a point, they are called intersecting lines. The point where they meet is known as the point of intersection of the lines.

Intersecting lines

Two lines in a plane which never meet each other and are at the same perpendicular distance from each other throughout are called **parallel lines.** The symbol for parallel is ||. To show that two lines are parallel, we make similar arrow heads on both the lines.

Parallel lines

Transversal: A line which passes through two or more lines at different points is called a transversal.

In the first figure, the line *m* intersects the two lines AB and CD at only one point O. So, *m* is not a transversal.

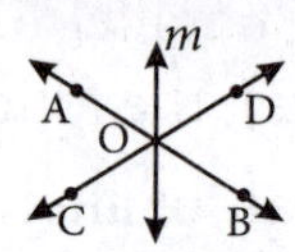

In the second figure, the line *m* intersects the two lines AB and CD at two different points P and Q. So, *m* is a transversal.

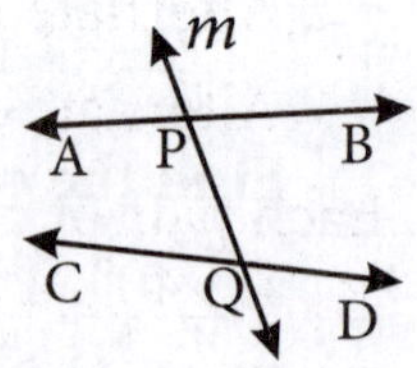

Angles Made by a Transversal

When two or more lines are cut by a transversal, the following angles are formed:

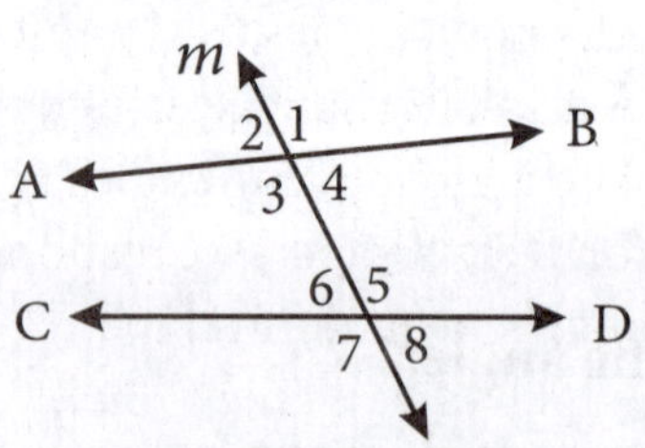

AB and CD are intersecting lines (not parallel)

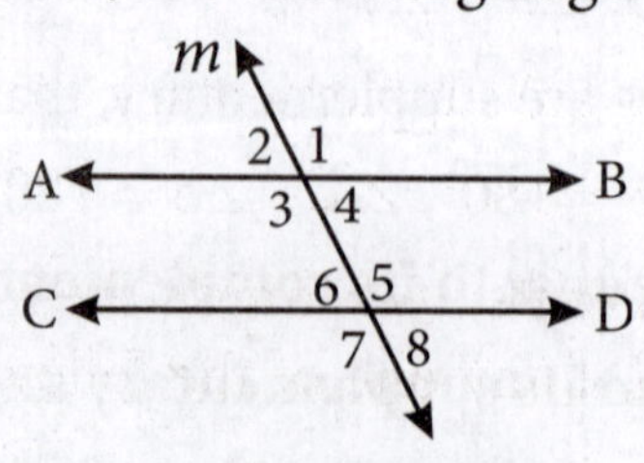

Lines AB and CD are parallel lines (non-intersecting)

AB and CD are two lines cut by the transversal *m*. In the first figure, AB and CD are not parallel. In the second figure, AB and CD are parallel.

The regions between AB and CD are the interior regions.

So, **interior angles** are formed between AB and CD. $\angle 3$, $\angle 4$, $\angle 5$ and $\angle 6$ are the interior angles.

The region above AB and the region below CD are the exterior regions. So, **exterior angles** are formed above AB and below CD. $\angle 1$, $\angle 2$, $\angle 7$ and $\angle 8$ are the exterior angles.

> **Note**
> Vertically opposite angles and linear pairs are formed because of intersecting lines. They are not dependent on the lines being parallel or not parallel.

In both the given figures, vertically opposite angles are $\angle 1 = \angle 3$, $\angle 2 = \angle 4$, $\angle 5 = \angle 7$, $\angle 6 = \angle 8$ and linear pairs are

$\angle 1 + \angle 2 = 180°$, $\angle 2 + \angle 3 = 180°$, $\angle 3 + \angle 4 = 180°$, $\angle 1 + \angle 4 = 180°$, $\angle 5 + \angle 6 = 180°$, $\angle 6 + \angle 7 = 180°$, $\angle 7 + \angle 8 = 180°$, $\angle 5 + \angle 8 = 180°$.

Following pairs of angles are formed by a transversal when it intersects two or more lines at distinct points.

> **Note**
> Where the prefix co is added as in co-interior and corresponding angles, both angles are on the same side of the transversal.

Pairs of angles	Description	Angles in the given figures
Alternate interior angles	A pair of interior angles formed on either side of the transversal and do not form a linear pair.	$\angle 4$ and $\angle 6$, $\angle 3$ and $\angle 5$
Alternate exterior angles	A pair of exterior angles formed on either side of the transversal and do not form a linear pair.	$\angle 1$ and $\angle 7$, $\angle 2$ and $\angle 8$
Corresponding angles	A pair of angles formed on the same side of the transversal in which one is an interior angle and the other is an exterior angle, but not forming a linear pair.	$\angle 1$ and $\angle 5$, $\angle 4$ and $\angle 8$, $\angle 2$ and $\angle 6$, $\angle 3$ and $\angle 7$
Co-interior angles	A pair of interior angles formed on the same side of the transversal. They are also called allied or conjoined angles.	$\angle 3$ and $\angle 6$, $\angle 4$ and $\angle 5$

Properties of Angles Made by a Transversal with Parallel Lines

When two parallel lines are cut or intersected by a transversal (as in the given figure), the following three conditions are true:

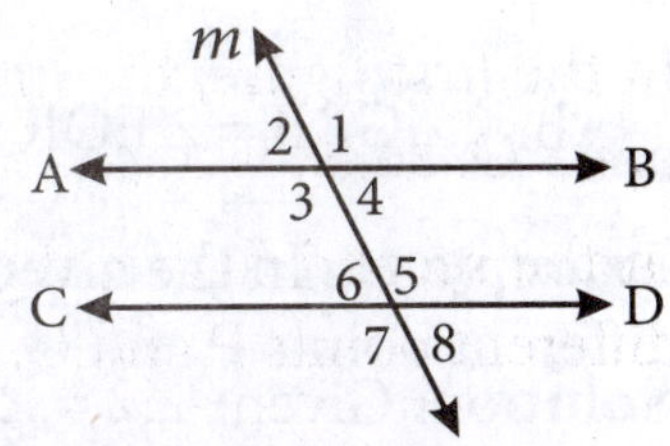

1. Each pair of alternate angles are equal in measure.
   - Alternate interior angles are equal. $\angle 4 = \angle 6$, $\angle 3 = \angle 5$
   - Alternate exterior angles are equal. $\angle 1 = \angle 7$, $\angle 2 = \angle 8$
2. Each pair of corresponding angles are equal in measure. $\angle 1 = \angle 5$, $\angle 4 = \angle 8$, $\angle 2 = \angle 6$, $\angle 3 = \angle 7$
3. Each pair of co-interior angles are supplementary, that is, they add up to 180°. $\angle 3 + \angle 6 = 180°$, $\angle 4 + \angle 5 = 180°$

> **Note**
> Alternate angles by default means alternate interior angles. Alternate interior angles generally form a Z shape. Corresponding angles form an F shape.

Conversely, when a transversal cuts two lines, then the given lines are said to be parallel if any one of the following conditions is true.

1. Alternate angles are equal.
2. Corresponding angles are equal.
3. Co-interior angles are supplementary.

> **Note**
> Lines which are parallel to the same straight line are parallel to one another. If $l \parallel m$ and $m \parallel n$, then $l \parallel n$.

SOLVED EXAMPLES

Example 13: If AB and CD are two parallel lines cut by a transversal *m* and $\angle 3 = 42°$, then find $\angle 1, \angle 2, \angle 4, \angle 5, \angle 6, \angle 7$ and $\angle 8$.

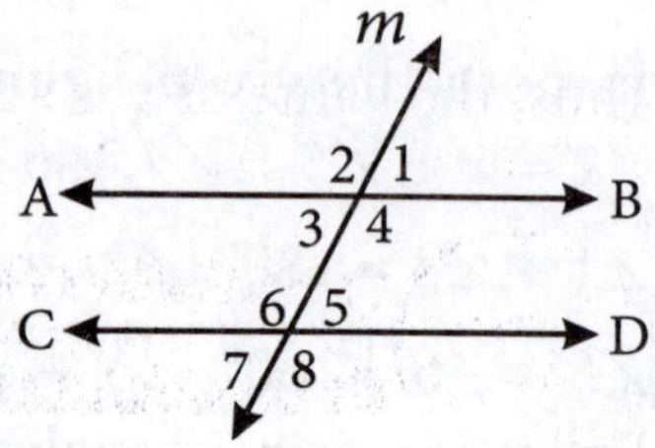

Solution: $\angle 2 + \angle 3 = 180°$ (Linear pair)

$\angle 2 + 42° = 180°$

$\angle 2 = 180° - 42° = 138°$

$\angle 1 = \angle 3 = 42°$ (Vertically opposite angles)

$\angle 4 = \angle 2 = 138°$ (Vertically opposite angles)

$\angle 5 = \angle 1 = 42°$ (Corresponding angles)

$\angle 6 = \angle 4 = 138°$ (Alternate interior angles)

$\angle 7 = \angle 3 = 42°$ (Corresponding angles)

$\angle 8 = \angle 4 = 138°$ (Corresponding angles)

Example 14: In the given figure, AB || CD and EF || GH. If ∠OPQ = 75°, calculate the following.

a. ∠EOA   b. ∠GRB

Solution:

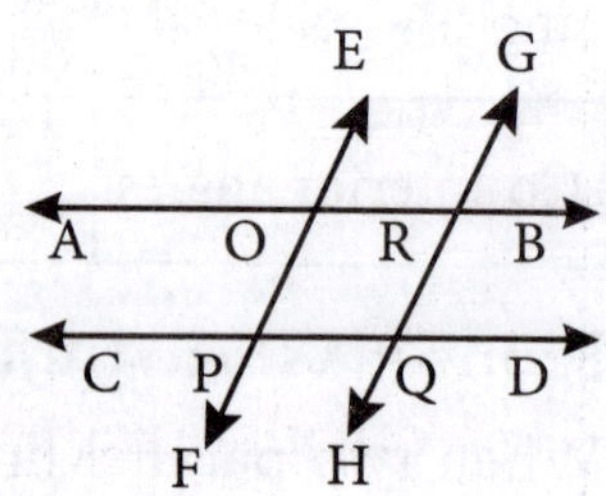

a. $\angle EOR = \angle OPQ = 75°$ (Corresponding angles as AB || CD)

$\angle EOA + \angle EOR = 180°$ (Linear pair)

$\angle EOA + 75° = 180°$

$\angle EOA = 180° - 75° = 105°$

b. $\angle GRB = \angle EOR = 75°$ (Corresponding angles as EF || GH)

Example 15: In the given figure, AB || CD, AB || EF, $\angle 2 = \angle 75°$ and $\angle 4 = 105°$. Prove that CD || EF.

Solution: Given: $\angle 2 = \angle 75°$ and $\angle 4 = 105°$

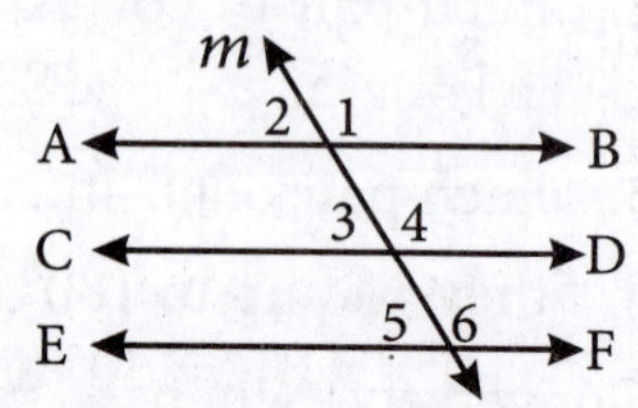

$\angle 5 = \angle 2 = 75°$ (Corresponding angles as AB || EF)

$\angle 3 + \angle 4 = 180°$ (Linear pair)

$\angle 3 = 180° - \angle 4$

$\angle 3 = 180° - 105° = 75°$

So, $\angle 3 = \angle 5$.

CD || EF as corresponding angles are equal.

Example 16: In the given figure AB || CD, calculate x.

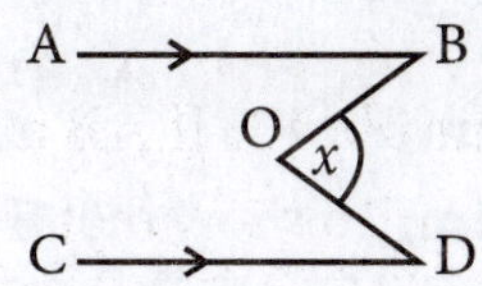

Solution: Through O we draw a line XY || AB || CD.

$a = 50°$ (Alternate interior angles)

$b = 70°$ (Alternate interior angles)

$x = a + b$

$= 50 + 70 = 120°$

Thus, the value of x is 120°.

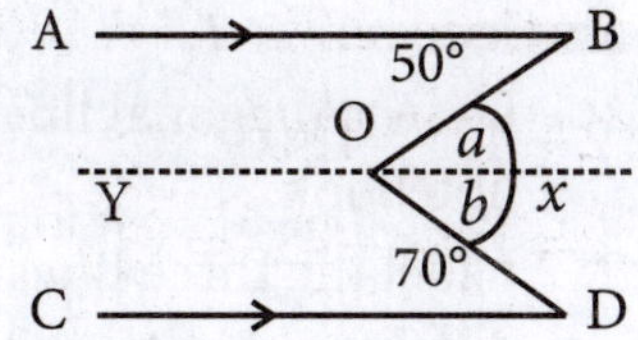

EXERCISE 9B

1. AB and CD are two parallel lines.

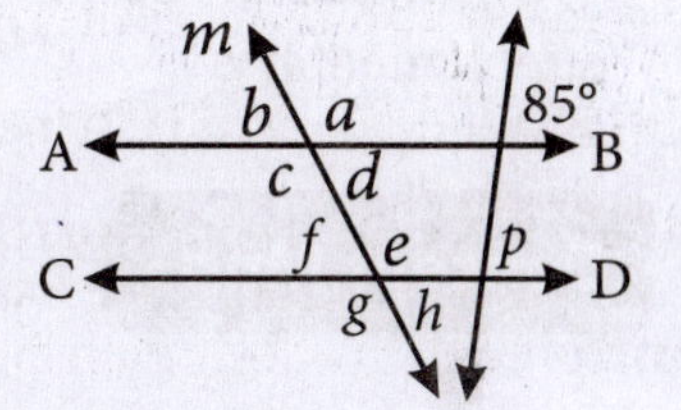

a. If $a = 50°$, find b, c, d, e, f, g and h.

b. If $h = 80°$, find d and c.

c. If $a = 2y - 10$ and $g = y + 20$, find a and b.

d. If $c : f = 4 : 5$, find g.

e. If $f = 5x$ and $d = x + 40$, find h.

f. Calculate p.

2. If ∠2 = 55° and ∠4 = 125°, prove that AB || CD.

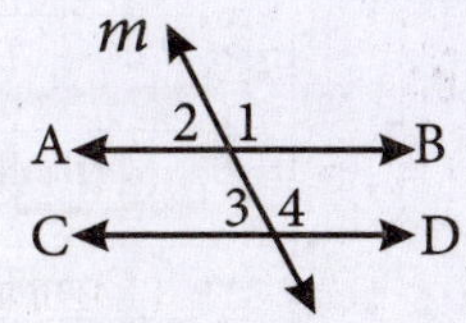

3. In the given figure, AB || CD and EF || GH. If ∠OPC = 60°, calculate the following.

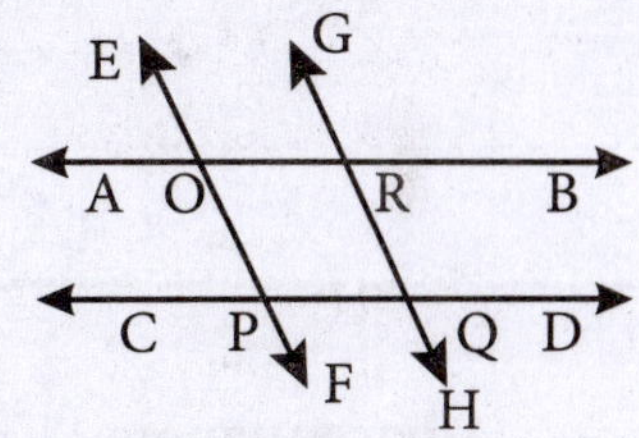

a. ∠ROP

b. ∠EOR

c. ∠GRB

d. ∠GQC

4. In the given figure, AB || CD and CD || EF. If ∠2 = 37°, find

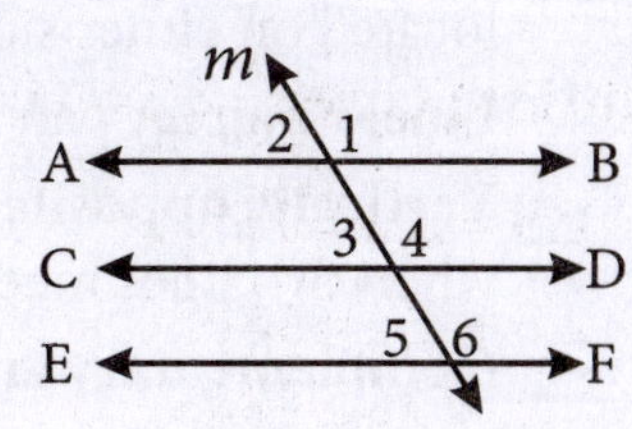

a. ∠5

b. ∠4

5. In the given figure, AB || DC and BCE is a straight line. If ∠ABC = 50° and ∠BAC : ∠ACB = 2 : 3, find ∠ACD.

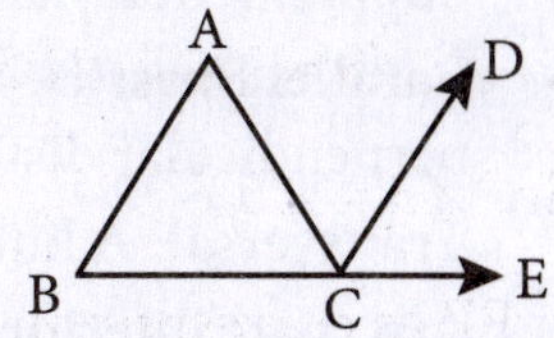

6. ABCD is a parallelogram. If ∠A = 73°, find ∠BCE.

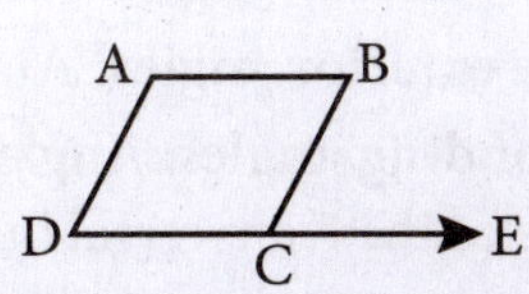

Maths Lab Activity

Aim: To show that if two parallel lines are cut by a transversal, the co-interior angles (i.e., interior angles formed on the same side of the transversal) are supplementary

Materials required: A page of single line notebook, glue stick, scissors and colour pencils

Procedure:

1. Draw a diagonal line cutting or intersecting any two lines of a single line notebook.
2. Label the three lines and angles, and colour the co-interior angles using different colours as shown.

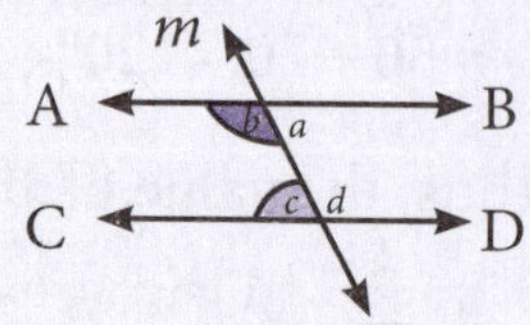

3. Cut a pair of co-interior angles *b* and *c* and place them adjacent to each other on a sheet of paper as shown such that *b* and *c* have a common vertex and are adjacent angles.

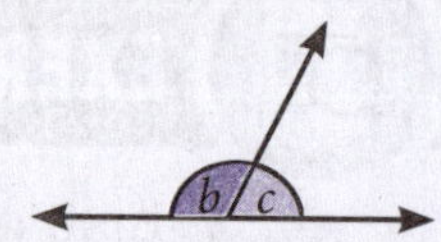

4. We find that the co-interior angles form a straight line. Therefore, they are supplementary.

Concept Map

Pairs of angles
- Adjacent angles
- Linear pair
- Vertically opposite angles
- Complementary angles
- Supplementary angles

Parallel lines
- Interior alternate angles are equal
- Exterior alternate angles are equal
- Corresponding angles are equal
- Co-interior angles are supplementary

Key Concepts

- **Adjacent angles:** Two angles with a common arm, a common vertex and the uncommon arms located on either side of the common arm
- **Linear pair:** A pair of adjacent angles which form a straight line
- **Vertically opposite angles:** A pair of angles which are formed opposite to each other at a vertex when two lines meet each other. They are equal.
- **Complementary angles:** The sum of two angles which add up to 90°
- **Supplementary angles:** The sum of two angles which add up to 180°
- **Parallel lines:** Two lines in a plane which never meet each other and are at the same perpendicular distance from each other throughout
- **Transversal:** A line that intersects two or more lines at different points
- **Alternate interior angles:** Angles formed in the interior on either side of the transversal
- **Alternate exterior angles:** Angles formed in the exterior on either side of the transversal
- **Corresponding angles:** Angles (one in the interior and the other in the exterior) formed on the same side of the transversal but not forming a linear pair
- **Co-interior angles:** Angles formed in the interior on the same side of the transversal

CHAPTER REVISION

A. Choose the correct option.

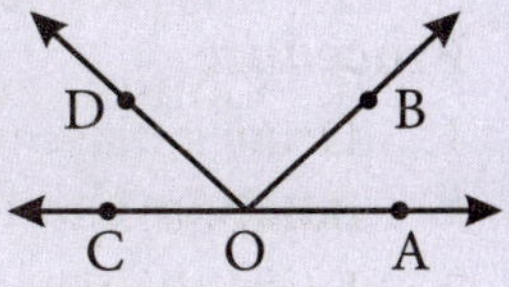

1. Which of the following pairs of angles are adjacent angles?
   a. ∠AOB and ∠AOD b. ∠AOB and ∠BOD
   c. ∠COD and ∠COB d. ∠COD and ∠COA
2. In the above figure, which of the following pairs of angles are supplementary angles?
   a. ∠AOB and ∠AOD b. ∠AOB and ∠BOD
   c. ∠COD and ∠DOA d. ∠COD and ∠COA
3. Which of the following is not true for a linear pair?
   a. Supplementary angles b. Complementary angles
   c. Adjacent angles d. Add up to 180°
4. Two lines cut by a transversal may not be parallel if
   a. Vertically opposite angles are equal
   b. Corresponding angles are equal
   c. Alternate angles are equal
   d. Co-interior angles add to 180°
5. Which of the following is not a pair of complementary angles?
   a. 75°, 15°
   b. Acute angles of an isosceles right-angled triangle
   c. Acute angles of an isosceles triangle
   d. Acute angles of a right-angled triangle

B. Fill in the blanks.

1. Adjacent angles on a straight line are __________.
2. The complement of 68° is ________.
3. The supplement of 68° is ________.
4. The angle vertically opposite to 50° will measure _______.
5. Conjoined angles add to ________.

C. Write T for true and F for false.

1. Two supplementary angles can both be acute angles.
2. Two supplementary angles can both be obtuse angles.
3. Two complementary angles can both be acute angles.
4. Two complementary angles can be vertically opposite angles.
5. Each of the co-interior angles may be a right angle.

D. Match the following.

1.	Alternate angles	a.	Allied angles
2.	Vertically opposite angles	b.	Are always equal
3.	Complementary angles	c.	May be interior or exterior
4.	Supplementary angles	d.	16°, 74°
5.	Conjoined angles	e.	74°, 106°

E. Answer the following.

1. In the given figure, AOC is a straight line and OB is a ray. Calculate the following.

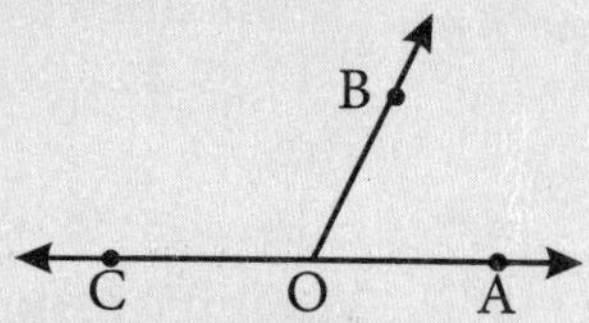

   a. $\angle AOB$ if $\angle BOC = 100°$

   b. $\angle AOB$ if $\angle BOC = 2\angle AOB$

   c. $\angle AOB$ and $\angle BOC$ if $\angle AOB = x$ and $\angle BOC = x + 20$

   d. $\angle AOB$ and $\angle BOC$ if $\angle AOB : \angle BOC = 2 : 3$

   e. $\angle BOC$ if $\angle AOB = x - 15$ and $\angle BOC = 2x$

2. In the given figures AB || CD || EF, calculate x.

a.

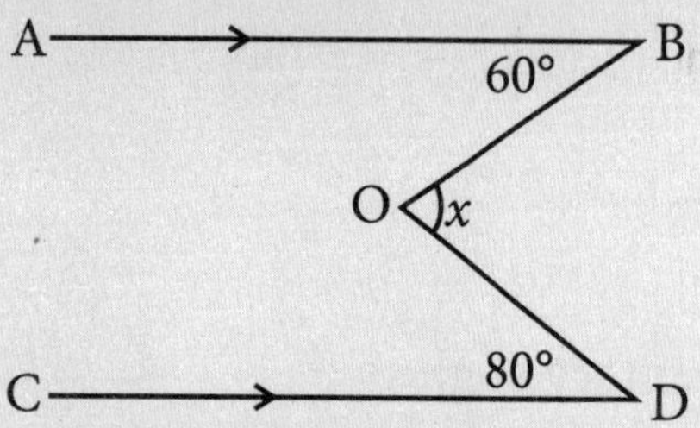

b.

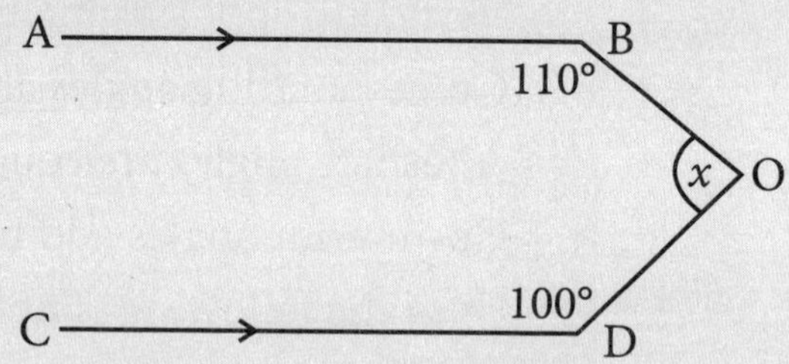

c.

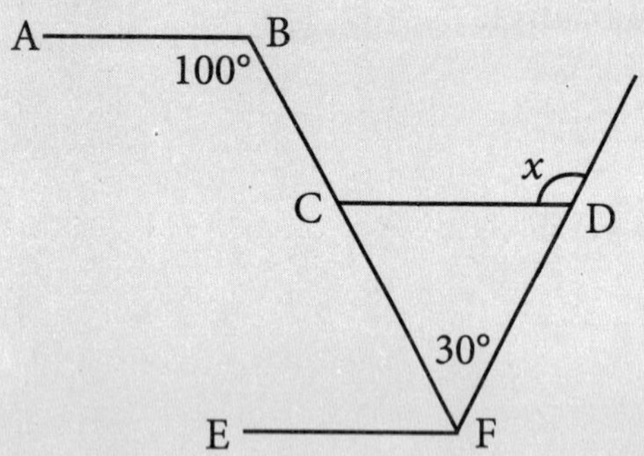

d.

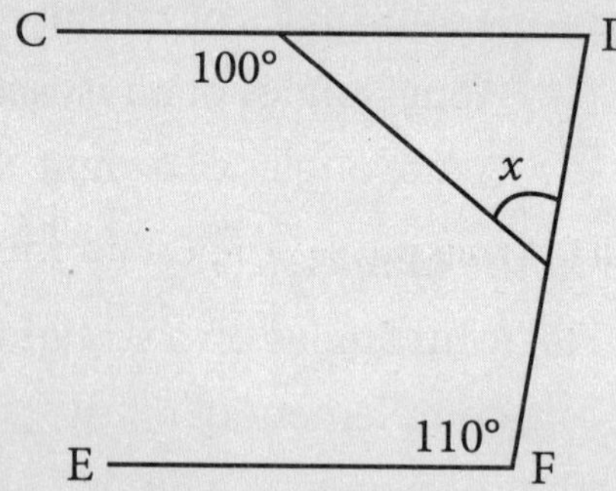

SKILL UP!

Project

The Dhola–Sadiya Bridge, also referred to as the Bhupen Hazarika Setu, is a beam bridge in India.

Identify some parallel and intersecting lines in it. Also, try to identify and mark pairs of angles which are adjacent, supplementary or complementary.

1. Which northeast states of India does the bridge connect? The bridge is constructed over which river?
2. Which is the longest bridge in India?
3. Which under-construction bridge is expected to become the longest bridge in India?

Life Skills

Ask students to measure with protractor and identify some complementary, supplementary angles and some linear pairs of angles in the classroom.

Mind Buzzer

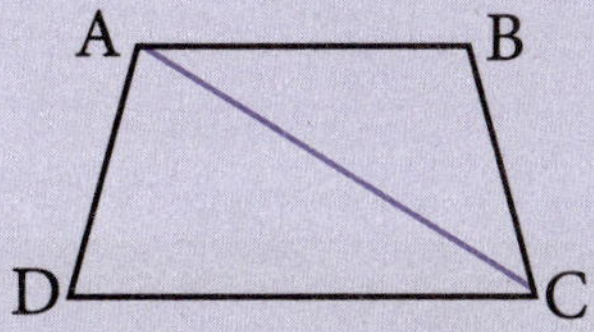

ABCD is an isosceles trapezium with AB || CD. If $\angle B = 110°$, $\angle BCA = \angle ACD - 10°$. Find $\angle ACD$.

Teacher's Notes

- Introduce the lesson by asking children to identify parallel and intersecting lines in the classroom.
- Encourage the students to identify the various pairs of angles in their surroundings.
- Help the students understand what happens when parallel lines are cut by a transversal and vice versa.
- Using solved examples, guide the students to calculate the missing angle from a given pair of angles.

WORKSHEET

Help Surbhi solve the given puzzle by finding all the missing angles and collect the items at each level to decorate the Christmas tree given at the top.

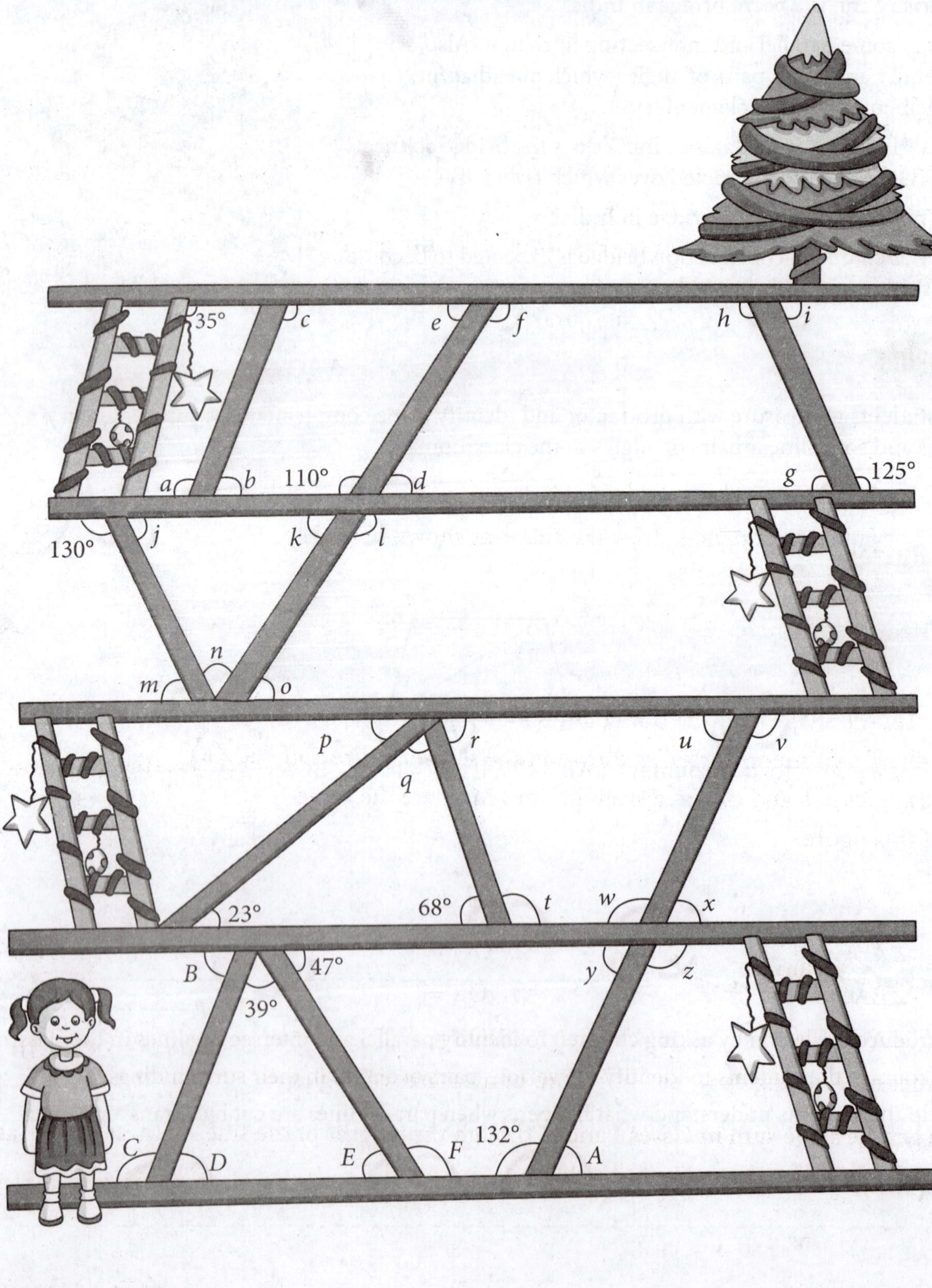

10 Triangles and Their Properties

Learning Objectives

- To verify angle sum property and exterior angle property of a triangle and apply it in real-life problems
- To understand the relation between the sum or difference of two sides of a triangle and its third side
- To verify Pythagoras theorem and understand how to apply it

Let's Get Started

Using only a ruler and a pencil, draw the shape as shown here. The three sides can be of any length.

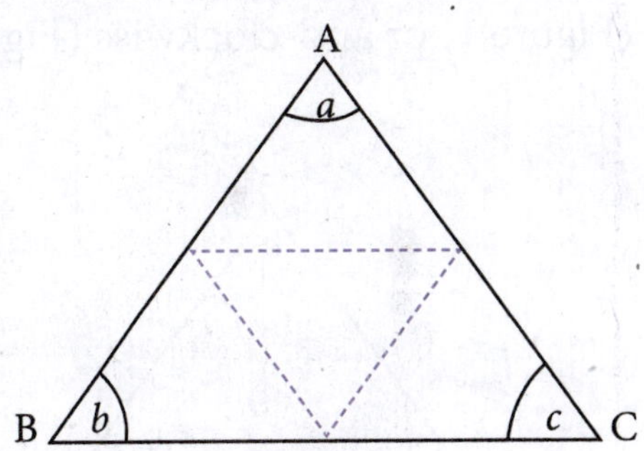

Case I

Case I: Measure the three angles a, b and c of the shape using a protractor. Add the measures of the angles.

Case II: Cut the shape over the dotted lines and place angles a, b and c to share a common vertex as shown in the second figure. Do the three angles a, b and c form a straight line? Measure the three angles of this figure.

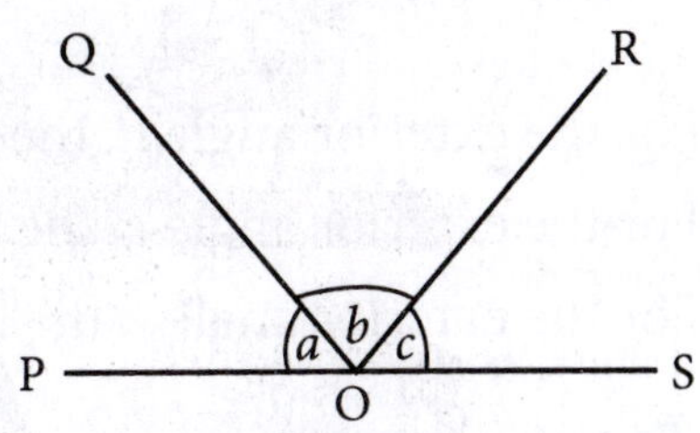

Case II

Case I	Case II
∠ABC =	∠POQ =
∠BAC =	∠QOR =
∠ACB =	∠ROS =

Sum of measures of angles = Sum of measures of angles =

Did you get the same sum in Cases I and II though the lengths of the sides of these shapes are different? Let us learn more about this shape.

TRIANGLE

A triangle is a closed figure made of three line segments. A triangle has six parts or elements. These elements are the three sides and the three angles.

Vertex (plural: vertices) of a triangle is a point where two of its sides meet.

Vertices: A, B and C

Sides: AB, AC and BC

Angles: ∠A, ∠B and ∠C

or ∠BAC, ∠ABC and ∠ACB

or ∠CAB, ∠CBA and ∠BCA

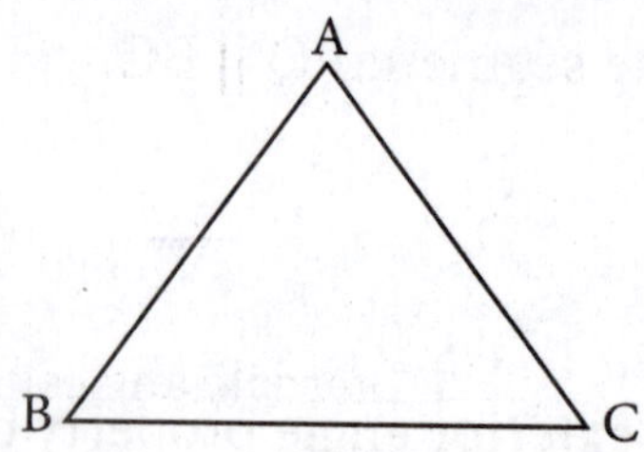

Side opposite to vertex A = BC

Side opposite to vertex B = AC

Side opposite to vertex C = AB

Types of Angles in a Triangle

Interior angles: Every triangle has three interior angles. The interior angles in the triangles below are *a*, *b* and *c*.

Exterior angles: For every interior angle formed at the vertex of a triangle, an exterior angle is formed by extending one of the two sides of the triangle meeting at that vertex. The two exterior angles that can be formed at the vertex of a triangle are the same. So, in the following figures, *d*, *e* and *f* are the three exterior angles of the triangle.

To draw all the three exterior angles of a triangle, extend all the three sides either clockwise (Figure 1) or anti-clockwise (Figure 2).

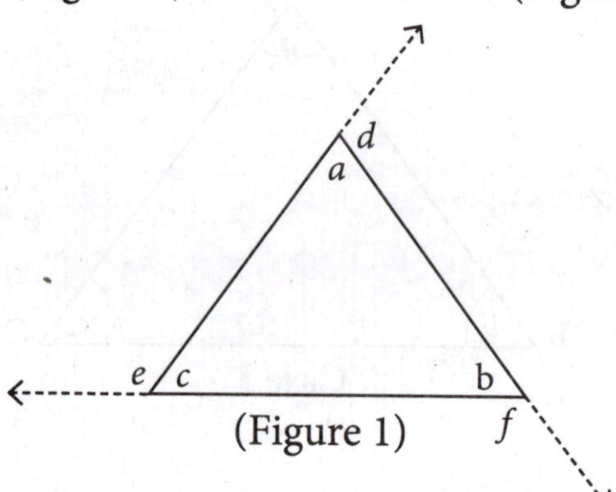

(Figure 1)

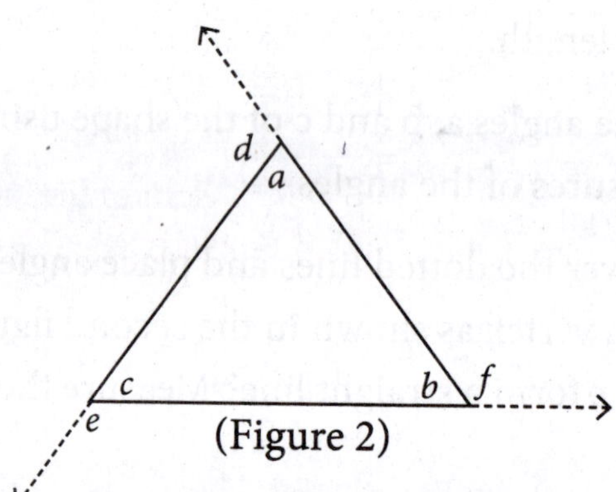

(Figure 2)

> **Note**
> Sum of the three exterior angles of a triangle is 360°.

For the exterior angle *d*, the interior adjacent angle is *a* and the interior opposite angles are *b* and *c*.

For the exterior angle *e*, the interior adjacent angle is *c* and the interior opposite angles are *a* and *b*.

For the exterior angle *f*, the interior adjacent angle is *b* and the interior opposite angles are *a* and *c*.

> **Note**
> A statement in mathematics that can be proved to be true by logical reasoning is called a theorem.
> The validity of a statement can be established by verification or a proof.
> The establishment or confirmation of the truth or accuracy of a theory is called verification.
> A sequence of steps or statements based on logical arguments that establishes the truth of a theorem is called the proof.

Sum of Angles of a Triangle

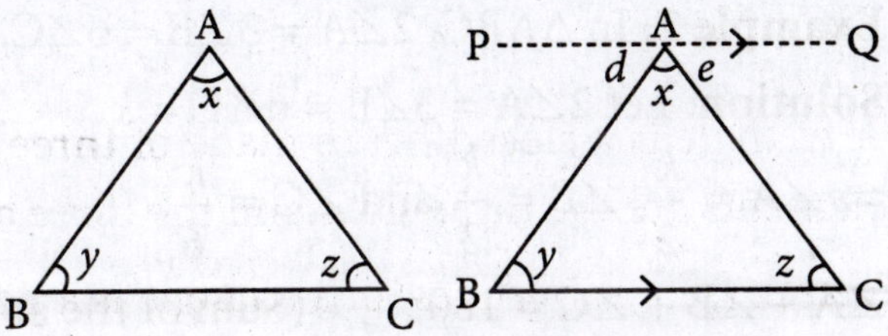

Theorem 1: *The sum of the interior angles of a triangle is 180°.*

Given: A triangle ABC with interior angles x, y and z.

To prove: $x + y + z = 180°$

Construction: Through A we draw a line segment PQ || BC.

Proof:

Statement	Reason
(i) $d = y$	Alternate angles
(ii) $e = z$	Alternate angles
(iii) $d + x + e = 180°$	Sum of adjacent angles on a straight line
$\Rightarrow y + x + z = 180°$	From (i) and (ii)
$\Rightarrow x + y + z = 180°$	

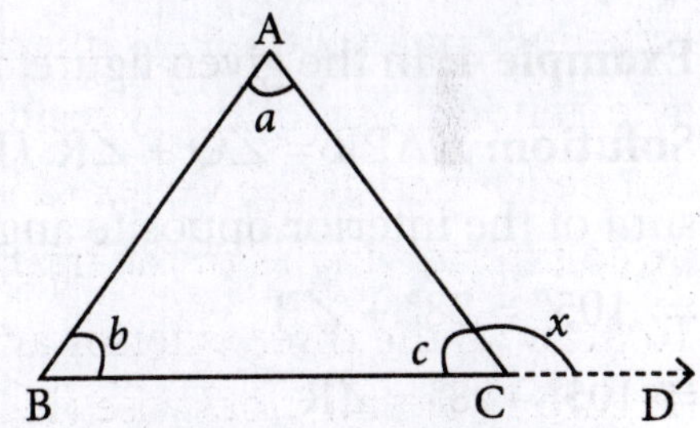

Theorem 2: *If a side of a triangle is extended, the exterior angle so formed is equal to the sum of the two interior opposite angles.*

Given: A triangle ABC with interior angles a, b and c.

Construction: We extend BC to D to form the exterior angle x.

Proof:

Statement	Reason
(i) $c + x = 180°$	Linear pair
(ii) $a + b + c = 180°$	Sum of the angles of a triangle
(iii) $c + x = a + b + c$ $\Rightarrow x = a + b$	From (i) and (ii)

SOLVED EXAMPLES

Example 1: In ΔABC, ∠A : ∠B = 2 : 3 and ∠C = 50°. Calculate ∠A, ∠B and ∠C.

Solution:

Let ∠A = $2x$ and ∠B = $3x$.

∠A + ∠B + ∠C = 180° (Sum of the angles of a triangle)

$\Rightarrow 2x + 3x + 50° = 180° \Rightarrow 5x = 180° - 50° \Rightarrow 5x = 130° \Rightarrow x = \frac{130}{5} \Rightarrow x = 26°$

∠A = $2x = 2 \times 26 = 52°$

∠B = $3x = 3 \times 26 = 78°$

Example 2: In ΔABC, $2\angle A = 3\angle B = 6\angle C$. Calculate $\angle A$.

Solution: Let $2\angle A = 3\angle B = 6\angle C = k$

$\Rightarrow \angle A = \frac{k}{2}, \angle B = \frac{k}{3}$ and $\angle C = \frac{k}{6}$

$\angle A + \angle B + \angle C = 180°$ (Sum of the angles of a triangle)

$\Rightarrow \frac{k}{2} + \frac{k}{3} + \frac{k}{6} = 180° \Rightarrow \frac{3k+2k+k}{6} = 180° \Rightarrow \frac{6k}{6} = 180° \Rightarrow k = 180°$

$\angle A = \frac{k}{2} = \frac{180}{2} = 90°, \quad \angle B = \frac{k}{3} = \frac{180}{3} = 60°, \quad \angle C = \frac{k}{6} = \frac{180}{6} = 30°.$

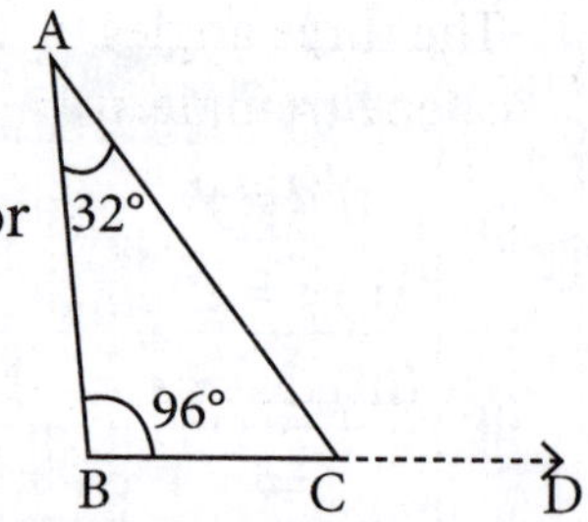

Example 3: In ΔABC, $\angle A = 32°$ and $\angle B = 96°$. Calculate the value of the exterior angle at C.

Solution: $\angle ACD$ is the exterior angle at C. (Exterior angle of a triangle is equal to the sum of the interior opposite angles)

$\angle ACD = \angle A + \angle B \Rightarrow \angle ACD = 32° + 96° = 128°.$

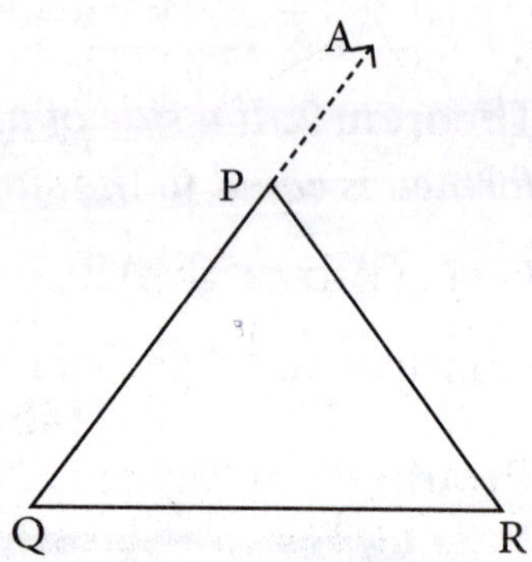

Example 4: In the given figure, $\angle APR = 105°$ and $\angle Q = 28°$. Calculate $\angle R$.

Solution: $\angle APR = \angle Q + \angle R$. (Exterior angle of a traingle is equal to the sum of the interior opposite angles)

$\Rightarrow 105° = 28° + \angle R$

$\Rightarrow 105° - 28° = \angle R$

$\Rightarrow \angle R = 77°.$

EXERCISE 10A

Answer the following questions.

1. In ΔABC, $\angle A = 70°$ and $\angle C = 50°$. Calculate $\angle B$.
2. In ΔABC, $\angle A : \angle B : \angle C = 4 : 5 : 6$. Calculate $\angle A$, $\angle B$ and $\angle C$.
3. In ΔPQR, $\angle P = x$, $\angle Q = x - 40$ and $\angle R = x + 10$. Calculate $\angle Q$.
4. In ΔABC, $\angle A : \angle B = 3 : 4$ and $\angle C = 40°$. Calculate $\angle A$.
5. In ΔABC, $4\angle A = 6\angle B = 12\angle C$. Calculate $\angle B$.
6. In ΔABC, $\angle A = 64°$ and $\angle B = 37°$. Calculate the value of the exterior angle at C.
7. Calculate the value of x and y in the figures.

a.

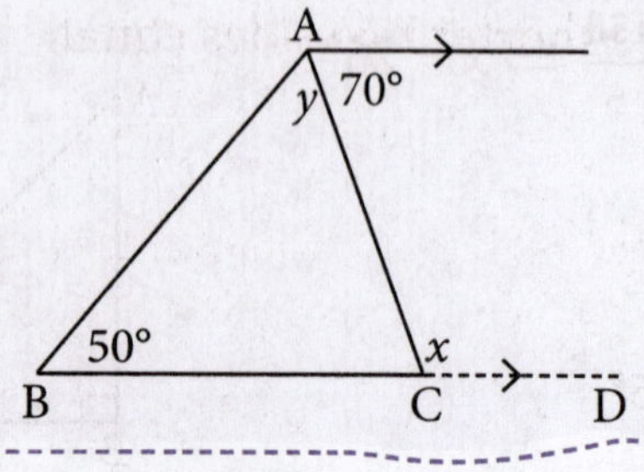

b.

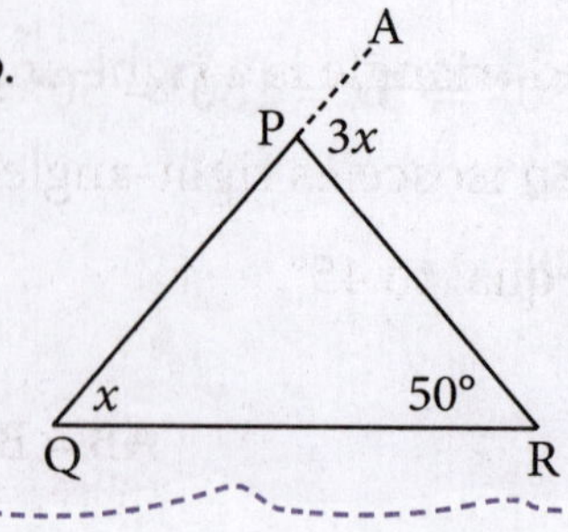

TYPES OF TRIANGLES

Triangles can be classified according to the lengths of their sides or the measure of their angles.

Table 10.1 Types of triangles based on the lengths of sides

Scalene triangle	Isosceles triangle	Equilateral triangle
A triangle in which none of the sides are equal.	A triangle in which two of the sides are equal.	A triangle in which all the three sides are equal.
The three angles of a scalene triangle are not equal.	Angles opposite to equal sides of an isosceles triangle are equal. We can also say: Base angles of an isosceles triangle are equal. Base refers to the unequal side of an isosceles triangle.	All three angles of an equilateral triangle are equal. Each angle is equal to 60°.
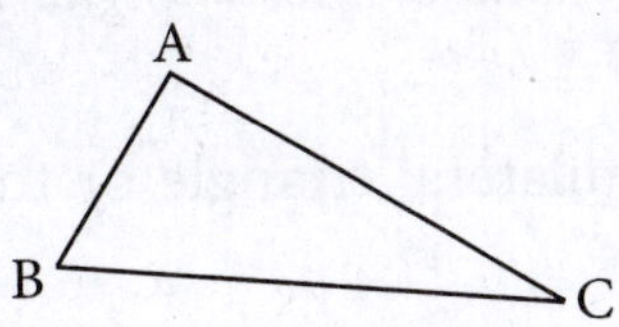 $AB \neq AC \neq BC$	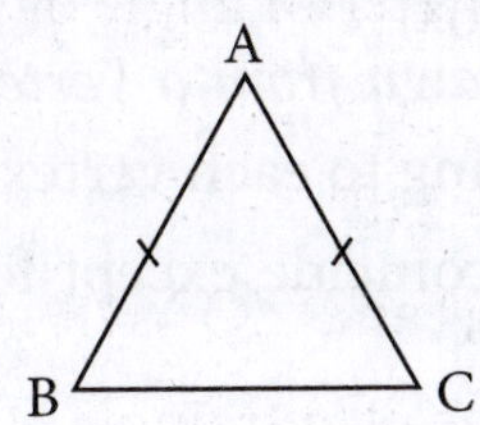 $AB = AC$	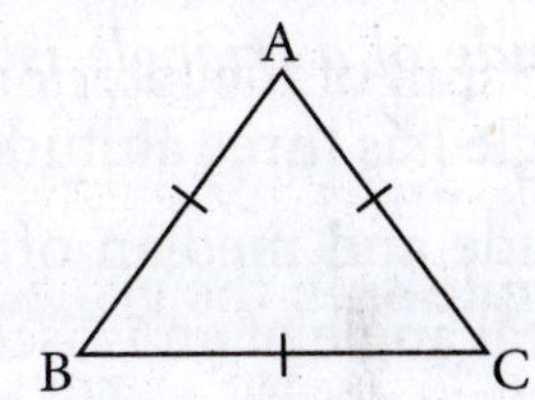 $AB = AC = BC$

Table 10.2 Types of triangles based on the measure of angles

Acute-angled triangle	Right-angled triangle	Obtuse-angled triangle
Acute-angled triangle or acute triangle is a triangle with all three angles less than 90°.	Right-angled triangle or right triangle is a triangle with one angle equal to 90°. A triangle can have only one right angle. Hypotenuse is the longest side of a right-angled triangle and is opposite to the 90° angle. Sum of the acute angles of a right-angled triangle is 90°.	Obtuse-angled triangle or obtuse triangle is a triangle with one angle greater than 90°. An obtuse triangle can have only one obtuse angle.
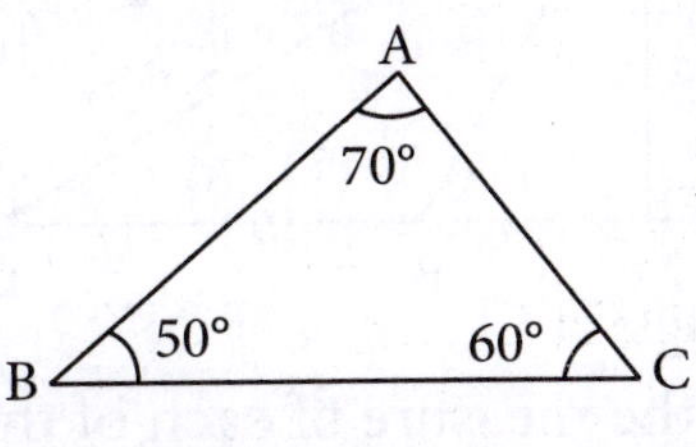	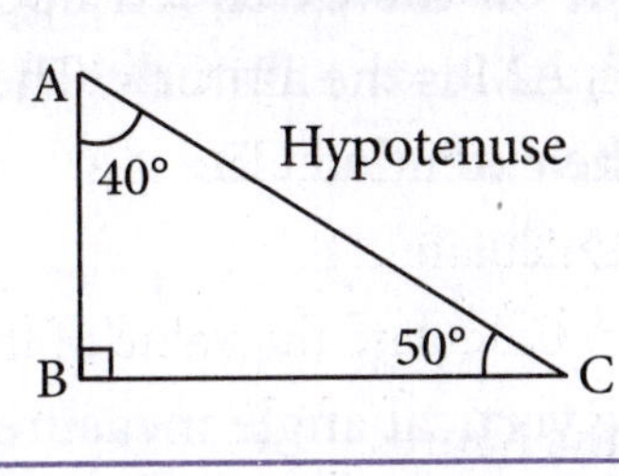	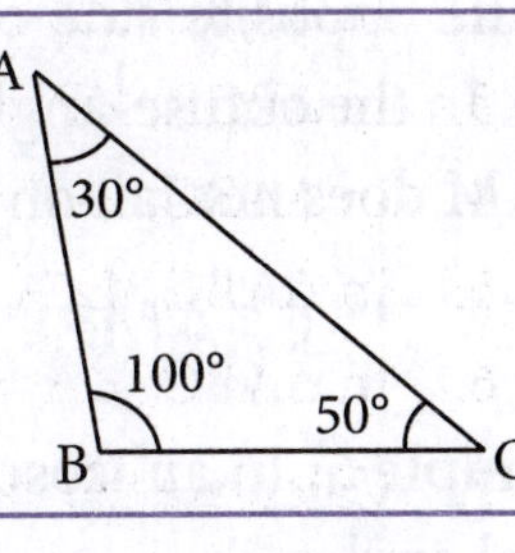

Isosceles right-angled triangle is a right-angled triangle with the shorter two sides equal.

The acute angles of an isosceles right-angled triangle are equal.

Each acute angle is equal to 45°.

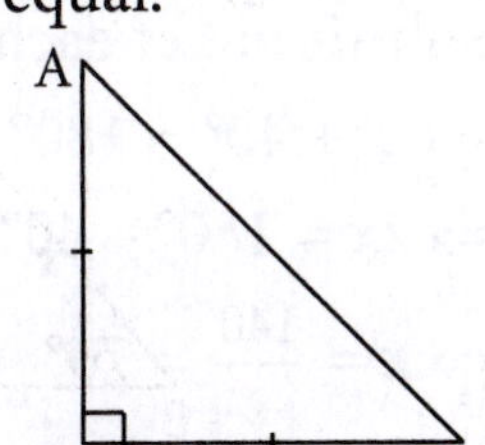

$AB = BC$ and $\angle A = \angle C = 45°$

MEDIAN AND ALTITUDE OF A TRIANGLE

***Median** of a triangle is a line segment drawn from a vertex to the mid-point of the opposite side.* A triangle has three medians, one corresponding to each vertex.

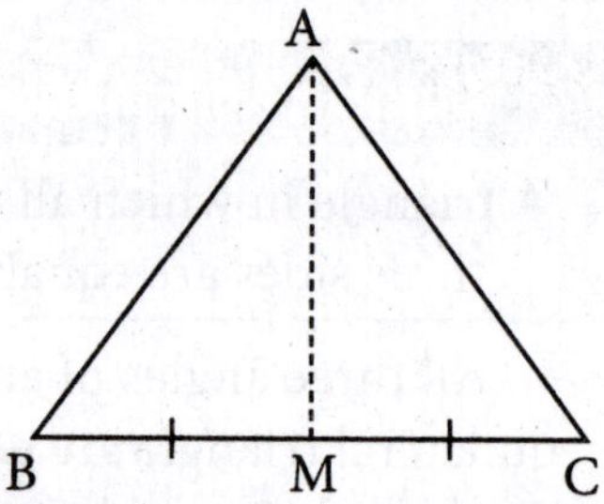

M is the mid-point of BC. AM is the median corresponding to vertex A.

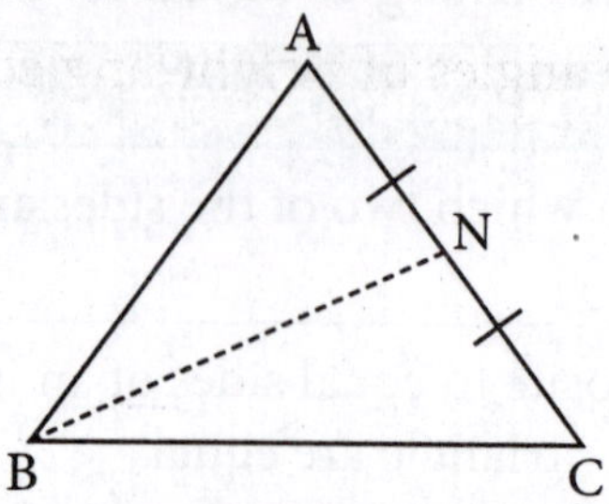

N is the mid-point of AC. BN is the median corresponding to vertex B.

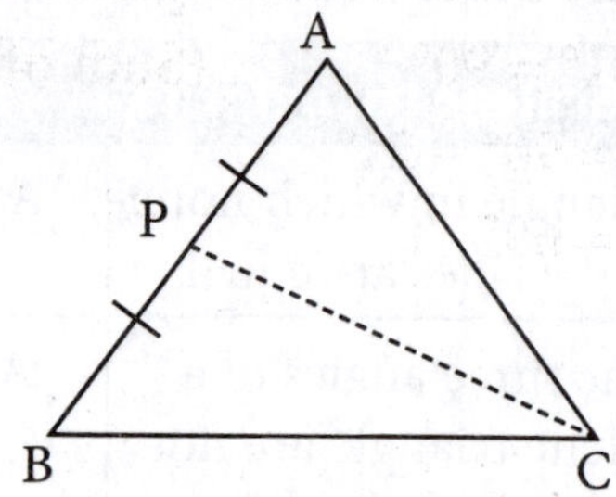

P is the mid-point of AB. CP is the median corresponding to vertex C.

***Altitude** of a triangle is a perpendicular drawn from a vertex to the opposite side of the triangle.* A triangle has three altitudes, one corresponding to each vertex.

Altitude and median of a triangle do not coincide except for that of an equilateral triangle or the vertical angle of an isosceles triangle.

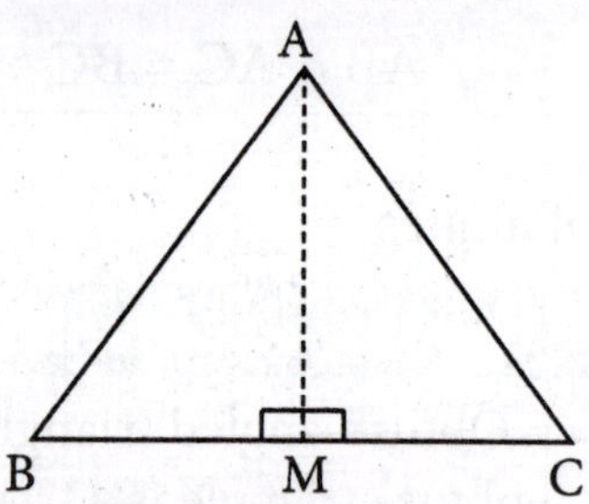

AM is the altitude of the triangle corresponding to vertex A.

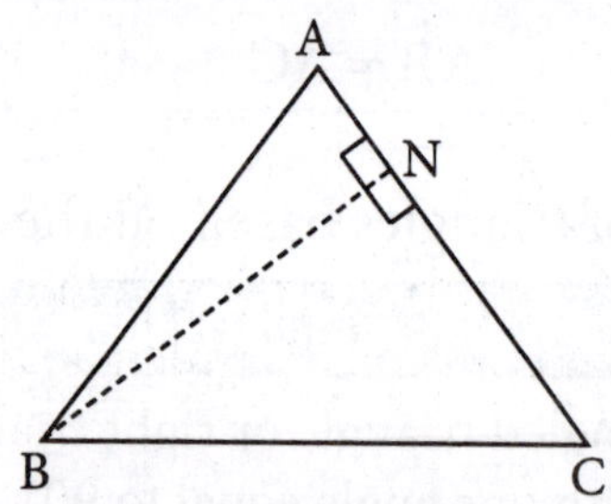

BN is the altitude of the triangle corresponding to vertex B.

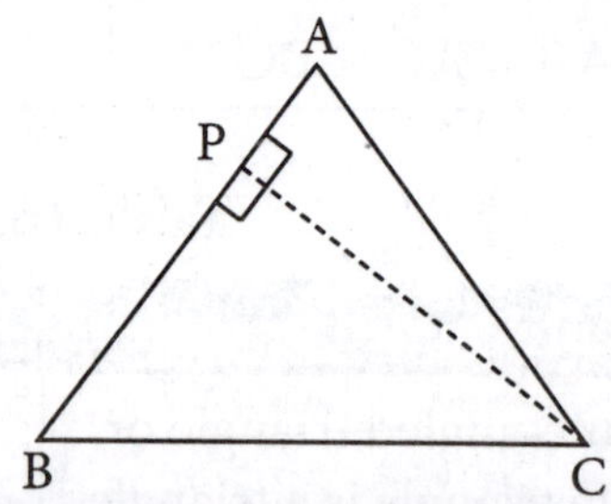

CP is the altitude of the triangle corresponding to vertex C.

In obtuse triangles, the foot of the altitude of a triangle may not fall on the opposite side of the triangle but on the extended opposite side. In the obtuse-angled triangle ABC, AM is the altitude. The foot of AM does not fall on BC. It falls on the extended CB.

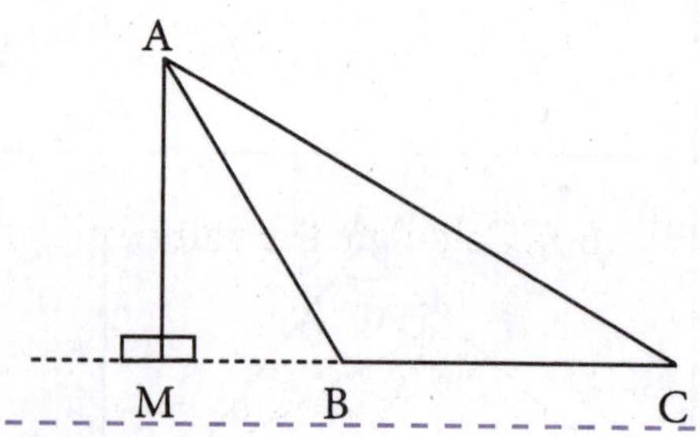

SOLVED EXAMPLES

Example 5: In an isosceles triangle, the vertical angle measures 40°. Find the measure of each of the equal angles.

Solution: Let each of the equal angles be x.

$x + x + 40° = 180°$ (Sum of the angles of a triangle)

$\Rightarrow 2x = 180° - 40° = 140°$

$\Rightarrow x = \frac{140}{2} = 70°$ Each of the equal angles measures 70°.

Example 6: An acute angle of a right-angled triangle measures 21°. Find the measure of the other acute angle.

Solution:

Let the other acute angle be x.

$x + 21° = 90°$ (Sum of the acute angles of a right-angled triangle is 90°)

$\Rightarrow x = 90° - 21°$

$\Rightarrow x = 69°$

EXERCISE 10B

Answer the following questions.

1. An acute angle of a right-angled triangle measures 37°. Find the measure of the other acute angle.
2. In an isosceles triangle, each of the equal angles measures 45°. Find the measure of the vertical angle.
3. In an isosceles triangle, the vertical angle measures 75°. Find the measure of each of the equal angles.
4. In ΔABC, BC = 7.4 cm. Calculate BM. Assign a special name to the line segment AM.

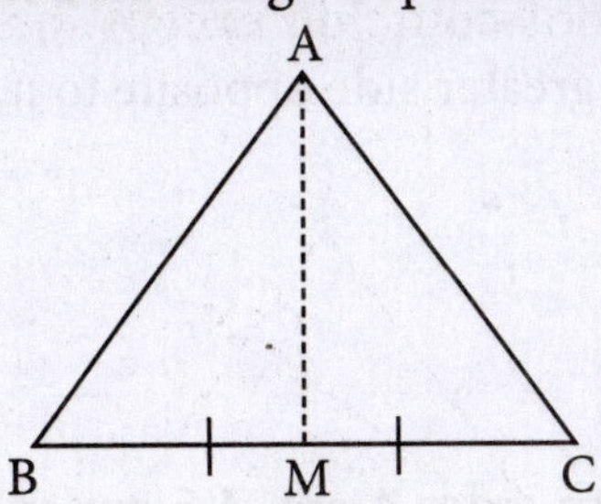

5. In ΔABC, $\angle A = 54°$ and $\angle NBC = 25°$. Calculate $\angle C$. Assign a special name to the line segment BN.

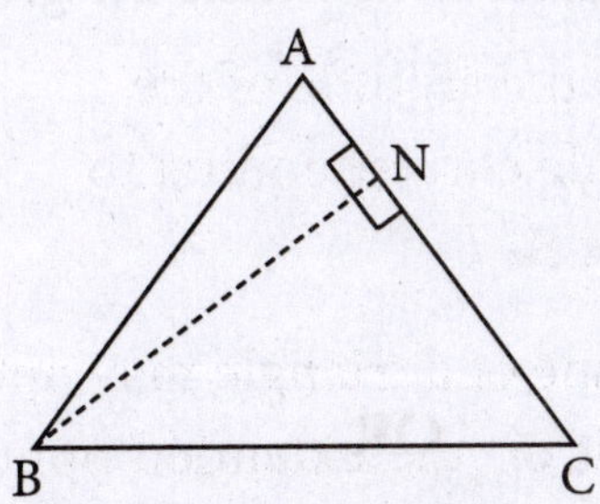

6. Calculate the value of x and y in the following figures.

a.

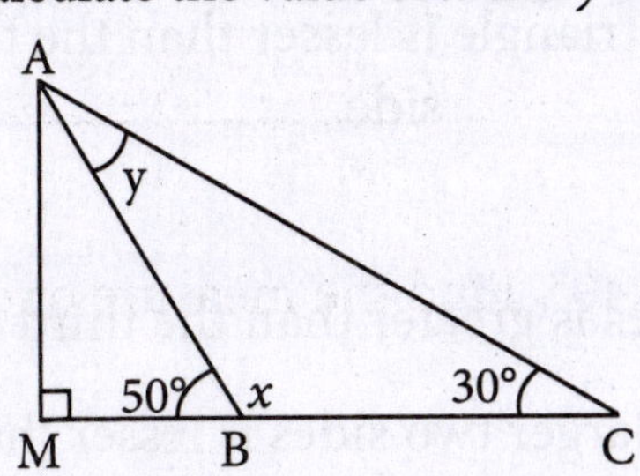

b.

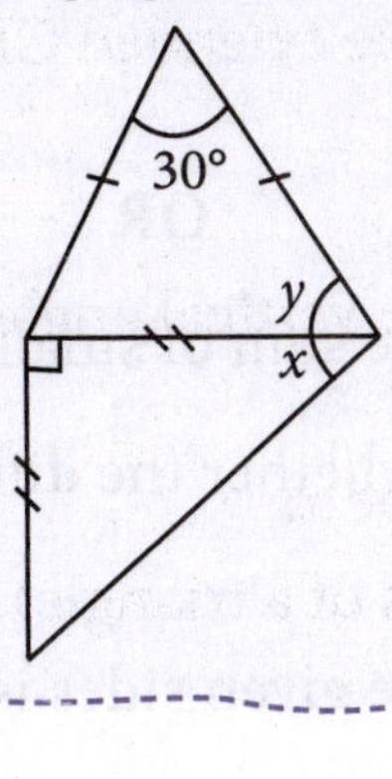

c.

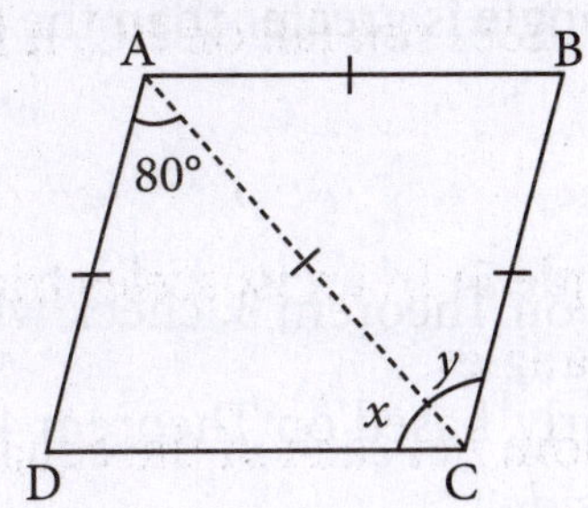

INEQUALITY THEOREM OF TRIANGLES

Theorem 3: *The sum of any two sides of a triangle is greater than the third side.*

Proof: If AB, BC and AC are straight paths of similar kinds and you need to go from B to C, which path would you choose as the shortest?

It will be BC because the shortest distance between any two points is the line segment joining them. So if you go from B to A and then to C, the distance covered will be more than the distance BC.

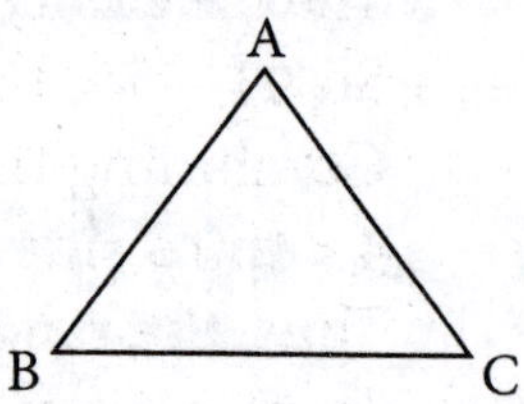

This proves that $AB + AC > BC$.

Theorem 4: *The difference of any two sides of a triangle is lesser than the third side.*

That is, $AB - AC < BC$.

Go Easy!

Greater angle of a triangle has the greater side opposite to it. Smaller angle of a triangle has the smaller side opposite to it.

SOLVED EXAMPLES

Example 7: Can a triangle be drawn with sides 4 cm, 4.5 cm and 6 cm?

Solution: The different possible combinations in which the given sides of the triangle can be added or subtracted are given below.

$4 + 4.5 > 6$

$4 + 6 > 4.5$

$4.5 + 6 > 4$

We see that the sum of any two sides of a triangle is greater than the third side.

OR

$6 - 4.5 < 4$

$6 - 4 < 4.5$

$4.5 - 4 < 6$

We see that the difference of any two sides of a triangle is lesser than the third side.

OR

Based on Theorem 3, check whether the sum of smaller two sides is greater than the third side.

Similarly, based on Theorem 4, check whether the difference of larger two sides is lesser than the third side.

- $4 + 4.5 > 6$. So, a triangle with the given sides is possible.
- $6 - 4.5 < 4$. So, a triangle with the given sides is possible.

Example 8: Two sides of a triangle have lengths 7 cm and 11 cm. What is the range of values that the third side can have?

Solution:

- The sum of any two sides of a triangle is greater than the third side.
  So, 11 + 7 > third side ⇒ 18 > third side.
- The difference of any two sides of a triangle is lesser than the third side.
  So, 11 – 7 < third side ⇒ 4 < third side.
  Combining the above two results, we can say
  4 < third side < 18.
  Thus, the range of values of the third side can be between 4 cm and 18 cm.

Example 9: ABCD is a quadrilateral. Prove that:

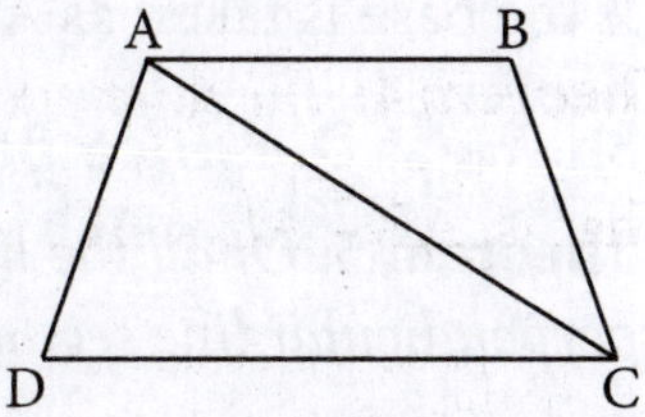

a. AB + BC > AC

b. AD + CD > AC

c. AB + BC + AD + CD > 2AC

Proof:

The sum of any two sides of a triangle is greater than the third side. Therefore,

a. AB + BC > AC.

Similarly,

b. AD + CD > AC

Adding a and b, we get

c. AB + BC + AD + CD > 2AC

EXERCISE 10C

1. **Can a triangle be drawn with lengths of sides given below? Give reasons.**

   a. 3 cm, 5.5 cm and 6 cm b. 2.1 cm, 3 cm and 5.2 cm

   c. 4.2 cm, 4.3 cm and 8.5 cm d. 6.5 cm, 7 cm and 13 cm

2. **Two sides of a triangle have lengths 7 cm and 11 cm. What is the range of values that the third side can have?**

3. **AD is the altitude of the triangle corresponding to side BC. Prove that AB + AC + BC > 2AD.**

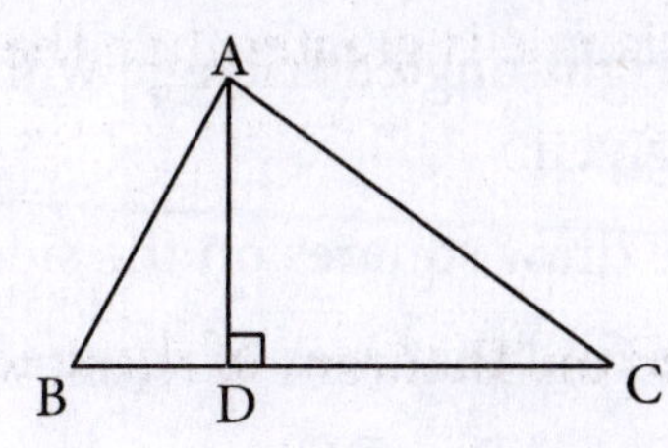

4. **P is a point in the interior of ΔABC. AP, BP and CP are joined. Prove that 2(AP + BP + CP) > AB + AC + BC.**

5. **ABCD is a quadrilateral. Prove that:**

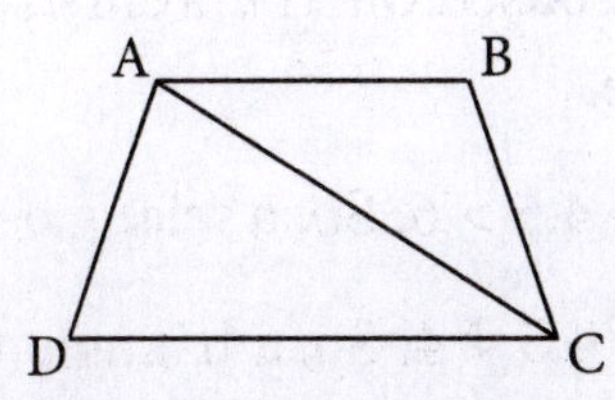

   a. AC – BC < AB

   b. AC – AD < CD

   c. AB + BC + AD + CD > 2AC

PYTHAGORAS THEOREM

In a right-angled triangle, the side opposite to the 90° angle is the longest side of the triangle and is called the **hypotenuse** of the triangle. (Greater angle of a triangle has the greater side opposite to it.) The other two sides are called the **legs** of the triangle or the **perpendicular** and the **base**.

In ΔABC right angled at B, the side opposite to the 90° angle is AC and is called the hypotenuse of the right-angled ΔABC.

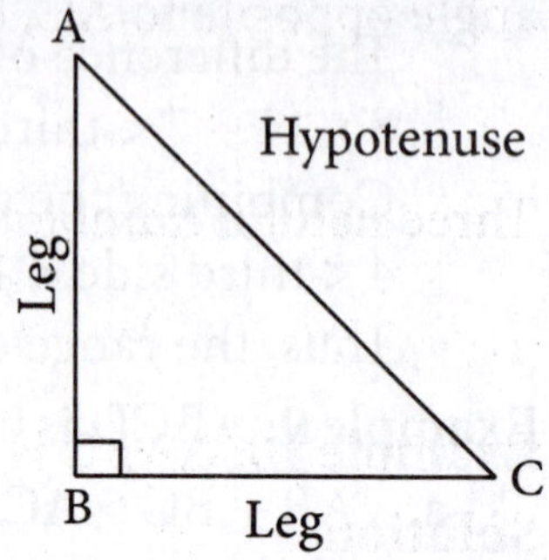

AB and BC are legs of the triangle.

If the base is taken as BC, the perpendicular is AB.

If the base is taken as AB, the perpendicular is BC.

Shortest Distance Between a Point and a Line

Theorem 5: *Of all the line segments that can be drawn to a given line from a given point outside it, the perpendicular line segment is the shortest.*

Given: A line l and a point P outside it. PA is the perpendicular drawn from P to l.

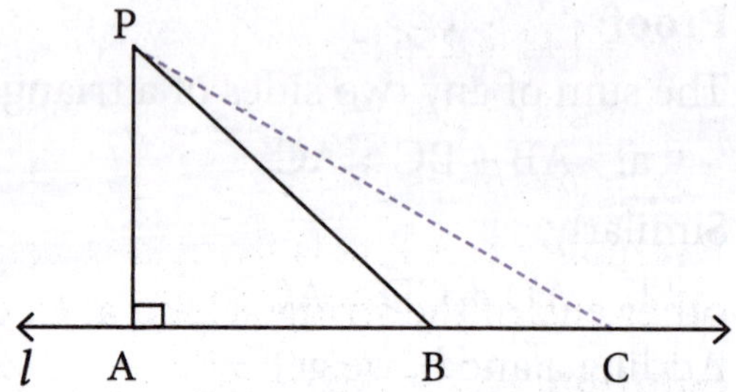

To prove: PA is the shortest distance between P and the line l.

Construction: We take any points B and C on l. We join P with B and C.

Proof:

(i) PB > PA (∠PAB is the greatest angle of ΔABC)

Similarly

(ii) PC > PA

So, PA is the shortest distance between P and the line l.

Pythagoras was a renowned Greek philosopher of the 6th century BC. He discovered a very useful relation between the sides of a right-angled triangle. The relation is called **Pythagoras theorem**.

Theorem 6: *In a right-angled triangle, the square of the hypotenuse equals the sum of the squares of the other two sides.*

A right-angled triangle with AB and BC as its legs and AC as the hypotenuse is given.

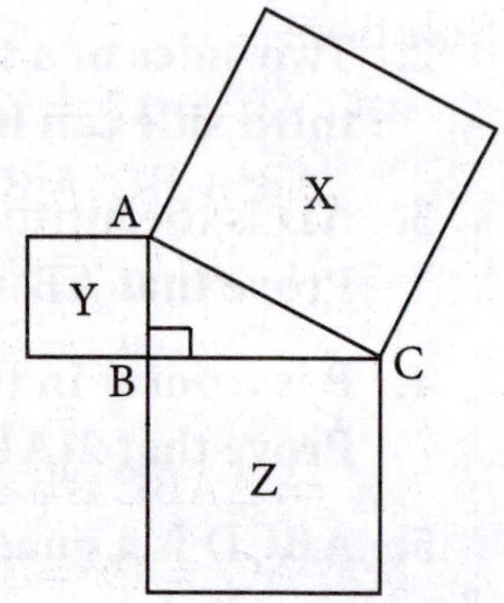

We draw squares on the sides AB, AC and BC.

We find that area of square X = area of square Y + area of square Z.

$AC^2 = AB^2 + BC^2$.

Converse of Pythagoras Theorem

Theorem 7: *In a triangle, if square of one side is equal to the sum of the squares of the other two sides, then the triangle is a right-angled triangle with the longest side as hypotenuse.*

If $AC^2 = AB^2 + BC^2$, the triangle ABC is a right-angled triangle with AC as the hypotenuse and the angle opposite to AC, that is, $\angle B$ as the right angle.

Pythagorean Triplets

Three natural numbers *a*, *b* and *c* (*c* being the greatest) form a Pythagorean triplet if $c^2 = a^2 + b^2$.

SOLVED EXAMPLES

Example 10: ΔABC is a right-angled triangle with AB = 12 cm and BC = 16 cm. Calculate AC.

Solution:

$AC^2 = AB^2 + BC^2$ (By Pythagoras theorem)

$= 12^2 + 16^2$

$= 144 + 256$

$= 400 = 20^2$

AC = 20 cm

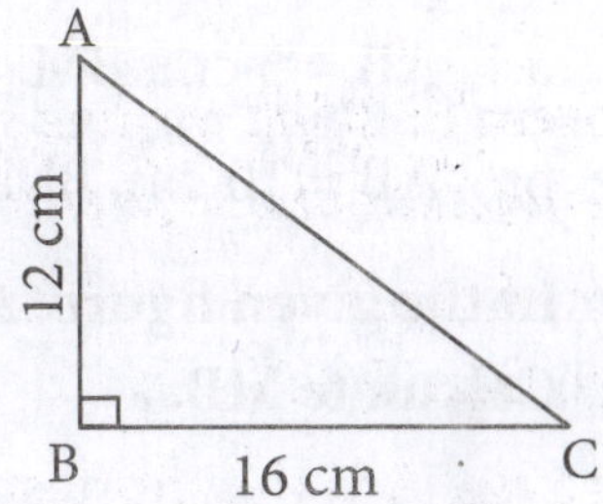

Example 11: A kite is flying at a height of 6 m above the ground. The length of its string is 10 m. The other end of the string is held at C. Find the length of BC.

Solution: $AC^2 = AB^2 + BC^2$ (By Pythagoras theorem)

$10^2 = 6^2 + BC^2$

$100 = 36 + BC^2$

$100 - 36 = BC^2$

$BC^2 = 64$

BC = 8 m

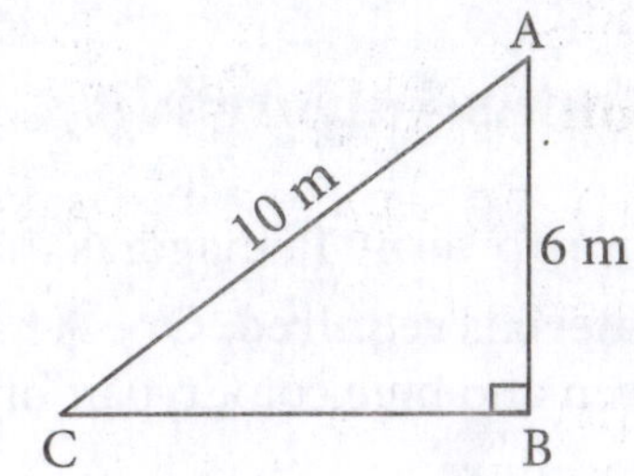

Example 12: Can a right-angled triangle be drawn with lengths of sides as given below?

a. 8 cm, 15 cm and 17 cm b. 9 cm, 16 cm and 19 cm

Solution:

a. $AC^2 = 17^2 = 289$

$AB^2 + BC^2 = 8^2 + 15^2$

$= 64 + 225$

$= 289$

$= AC^2$

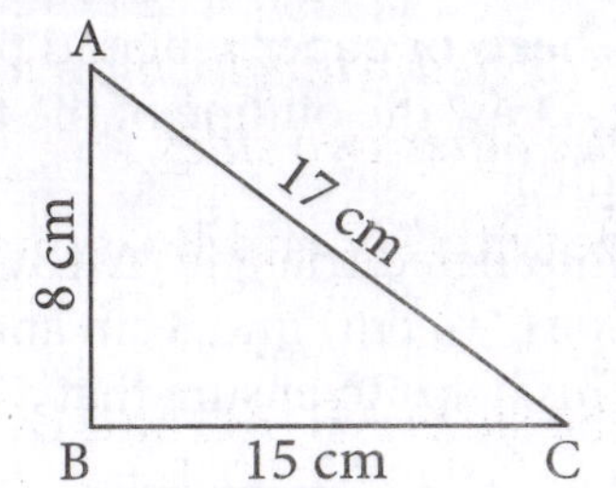

$\Rightarrow \Delta ABC$ is a right-angled triangle. (By converse of Pythagoras theorem)

b. $AC^2 = 19^2 = 361$

$AB^2 + BC^2 = 9^2 + 16^2$

$= 81 + 256$

$= 337$

$\neq AC^2$

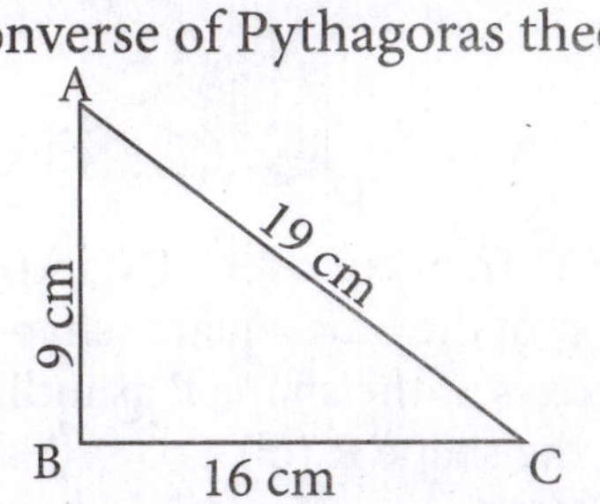

$\Rightarrow \Delta ABC$ is not a right-angled triangle. (By converse of Pythagoras theorem)

EXERCISE 10D

1. **Can a right-angled triangle be drawn with lengths of sides given below? Give reasons.**

   a. 5 cm, 12 cm and 13 cm b. 7 cm, 24 cm and 25 cm

   c. 9 cm, 11 cm and 14 cm c. 6 cm, 9 cm and 12 cm

2. **ΔABC is right angled at B, AB = 6 cm and BC = 8 cm. Calculate AC.**

3. **The foot of a 5 m long ladder placed against a vertical wall is 3 m away from the base of the wall. Find the height at which the top of the ladder reaches the wall.**

4. **In the given figure,**

   a. AB = 5 cm, BM = 3 cm, AC = 12 cm. Calculate MC.

   b. AB = 10 cm, BM = 6 cm, AC = 17 cm. Calculate BC.

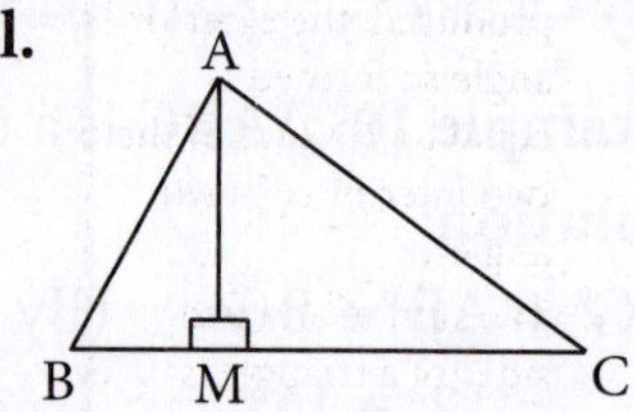

5. **In the given figure, AB = 15 cm, MC = 24 cm, AC = 26 cm. Calculate MB.**

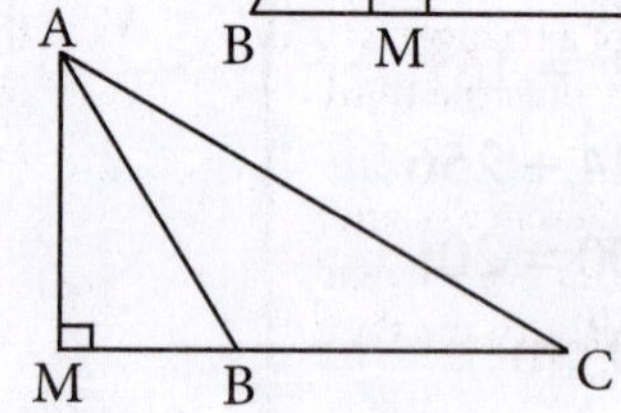

Maths Lab Activity

Aim: To verify Pythagoras theorem

Materials required: One A4 size sheet (or chart paper) each of white, yellow, green and blue colour, pair of scissors, geometry box and pencil

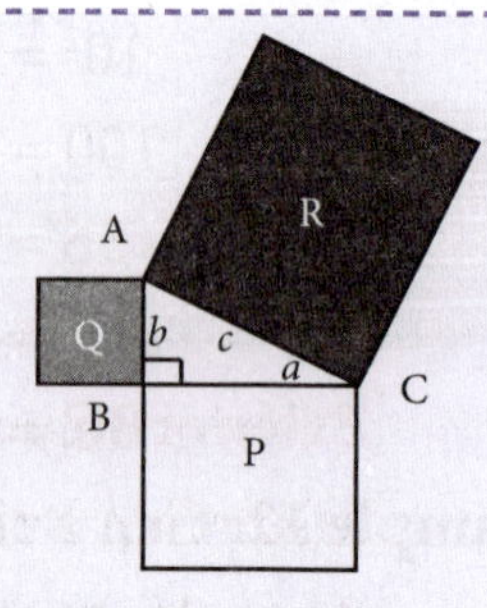

Procedure:

1. On a white sheet of paper, using set-square, draw a right-angled triangle with a = 4 cm, b = 3 cm and c = 5 cm.
2. Draw squares of sides 3 cm (shape P), 4 cm (shape Q) and 5 cm (shape R) respectively on yellow, green and blue sheets of paper. Cut and place the three squares to form a white triangle (ΔABC) as shown above. Draw the outline of the triangle ABC as shown. Now remove the three squares (shapes P, Q and R).
3. Side a of the right-angled triangle (ΔABC) is greater than side b and less than side c. Now divide each side of shape Q (4 cm) into 3 cm and 1 cm. (Starting from O, divide each side clockwise in the ratio 3 : 1. This helps to ensure that a 3 cm side is not adjacent to another 3 cm side.)

4. Join MN and XY. Then cut over MN and XY to get four shapes as shown. Place the yellow square (shape P) on top of the blue square (shape R). Then place the 4 green pieces (shape Q cut into four pieces) at the edges of the shape P as indicated. The square formed by the shapes P and Q ($a^2 + b^2$) coincides with the shape R (c^2).

Conclusion: $c^2 = a^2 + b^2$

Concept Map

Triangles

- **Parts**
  - **3 sides**
    - If a side of a triangle is produced, the exterior angle so formed is equal to the sum of the two interior opposite angles.
    - The sum of any two sides of a triangle is greater than the third side.
    - The difference of any two sides of a triangle is lesser than the third side.
  - **3 angles**
    - The sum of the angles of a triangle is 180°.
    - Exterior angle is equal to sum of the interior opposite angles.
- **Types**
  - **Based on sides**
    - **Scalene triangle** All the sides are of different lengths.
    - **Equilateral triangle** All the sides are of same length.
    - **Isosceles triangle** Only two sides are of same length.
  - **Based on angles**
    - **Acute-angled triangle** All the angles are less than 90°.
    - **Right-angled triangle** One of the angles is 90°.
    - **Obtuse-angled triangle** One of the angles is more than 90°.

Key Concepts

- **Triangle:** A triangle is a closed figure made of three line segments
- **Exterior angle:** An angle formed by extending a side of the triangle
- **Median:** A line segment drawn from a vertex to the mid-point of the opposite side of a triangle
- **Altitude:** A perpendicular drawn from a vertex to the opposite side of a triangle
- **Isosceles right-angled triangle:** A right-angled triangle with the shorter two sides equal
- **Pythagoras theorem:** In a right-angled triangle, the square of the hypotenuse equals the sum of the squares of the other two sides
- **Converse of Pythagoras theorem:** In a triangle, if square of one side is equal to the sum of the squares of the other two sides, then the triangle is a right-angled triangle with the longest side as hypotenuse

CHAPTER REVISION

A. Choose the correct option.

1. Which of the following set of sides will not form a triangle?
   a. 4 cm, 6 cm, 10 cm
   b. 4.2 cm, 6.8 cm, 10.5 cm
   c. 4.2 cm, 6.8 cm, 10 cm
   d. 4.2 cm, 6.5 cm, 10.5 cm
2. Which of the following will not be true for an isosceles triangle ABC with AB = AC?
   a. Altitude for BC < AB
   b. Median for BC < AB
   c. Altitude for BC < AC
   d. Altitude for BC < median for BC
3. In a triangle ABC right angled at A, which of the following is true?
   a. AB > BC
   b. AC > BC
   c. AB – AC > BC
   d. AB + AC > BC

B. Fill in the blanks.

1. To prove that a triangle can be drawn with the sides 4 cm, 6.5 cm and 8 cm, it is sufficient to prove that _____ + _____ > _____.
2. To prove that a triangle can be drawn with the sides 4.5 cm, 6 cm and 10 cm, it is sufficient to prove that _____ – _____ < _____.
3. The greatest angle in a triangle has the _______ side opposite to it.
4. The sum of the acute angles of a right-angled triangle is _____.
5. The sum of the exterior angles of a triangle is ______.
6. In the given triangle, $\_\_\_\_\_^2 + \_\_\_\_\_^2 = \_\_\_\_\_^2$ (by Pythagoras theorem).

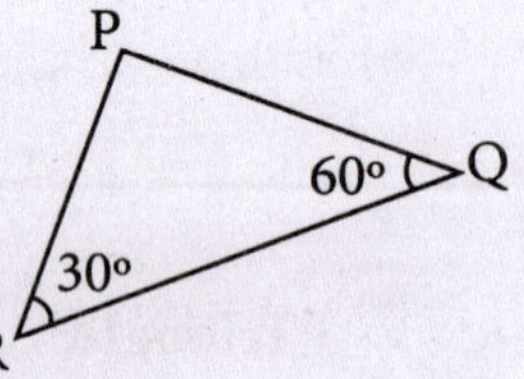

C. Match the following if in ΔABC, BD = DE.

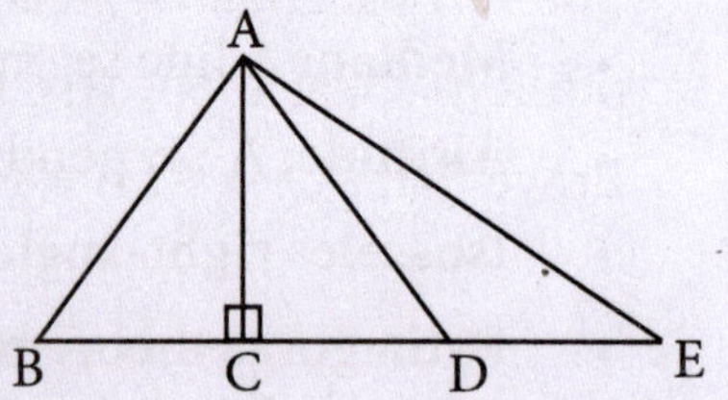

1. Median
2. Altitude
3. Inequality theorem
4. Pythagoras theorem
5. Isosceles triangle
6. Isosceles right-angled triangle

a. $AE^2 = AC^2 + CE^2$
b. AE < AC + CE
c. AB = AD
d. AC = CD
e. AC
f. AD

D. Answer the following questions.

1. ΔABC is right angled at B, AB = 4.5 cm and BC = 6 cm. Calculate AC.
2. ΔABC is right angled at C, AB = 26 cm and BC = 24 cm. Calculate AC.
3. A girl walks 24 m towards the east and then she walks 7 m towards the north. How far is she from her starting point?
4. A tree breaks at a height of 8 m above the ground. Its top touches the ground at 15 m from the foot of the tree. Find the original height of the tree.
5. Prove the following.
   a. If $PR^2 = PQ^2 + QR^2$, the triangle PQR is right angled at Q.
   b. The exterior angle of a triangle is equal to the sum of the interior angles.
   c. 12, 35 and 37 form a Pythagorean triplet.

6. In the given figures, AB || DC and AB = BC.

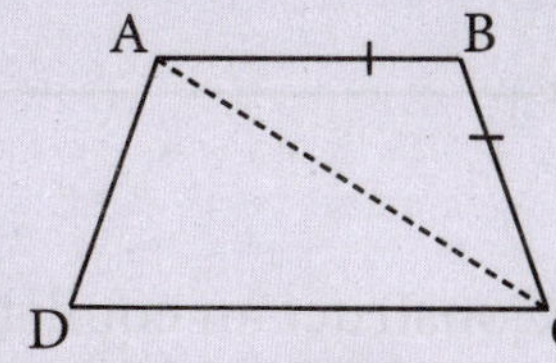

a. Calculate ∠BCD if:

i. ∠BAC = 40° ii. ∠ABC = 50°.

b. Calculate the following:

i. ∠ACE ii. b

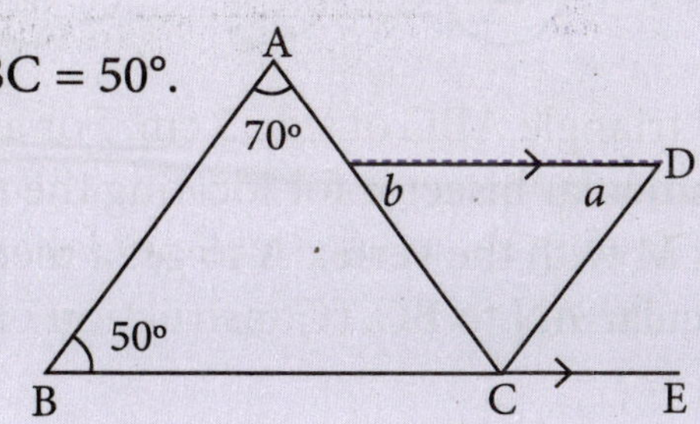

SKILL UP!

Project

Great Pyramids are an example of the use of triangles in architecture. When, where and why were the Great Pyramids built? Find out and make a report on your findings.

Life Skills

Have you seen a cheerleading squad build a human pyramid? To form a structure like a pyramid, which part of the pyramid would have a major role to play? Analyse and discuss.

Mind Buzzer

The vertical angle of an isosceles triangle is twice the sum of its base angles. Find the measure of the vertical angle. In a triangle PQR, PM is perpendicular to QR.
Prove that $PQ^2 + RM^2 = PR^2 + QM^2$.

Teacher's Notes

- Begin the lesson by a recap of the parts of a triangle and the kinds of triangles taught in class VI.
- Through activities and construction, explain the various theorems on triangles.
- Emphasize on drawing figures and on writing statements and reasons correctly for proving theorems.
- Encourage the students to apply the learnt concepts in real-life situations.

WORKSHEET

Construct an equilateral triangle ABC of side 5 cm. For any one of the sides, say BC, draw the perpendicular bisector for locating the mid-point of the side. Join this mid-point M with the vertex A to get a median. Now from A, construct a perpendicular AN to BC. (Construction of a perpendicular from a point to a line.)

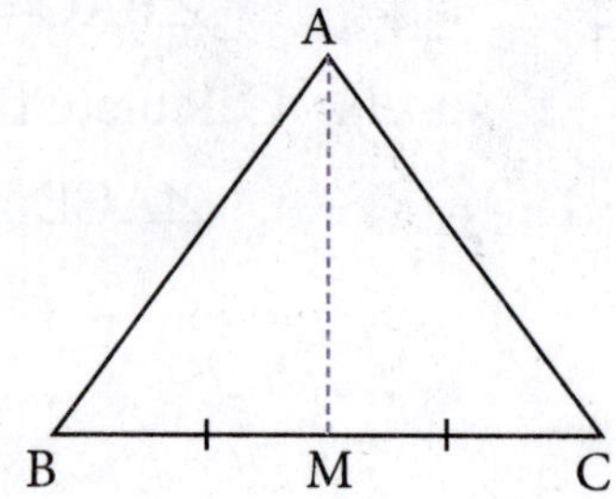

Do the median and the altitude coincide?

Now construct an isosceles triangle ABC with AB = AC = 6 cm and BC = 5 cm.

As above, check whether the median and altitude coincide for AB and for BC.

11

Congruence of Triangles

Learning Objectives

- To identify whether the given plane figures are congruent or not
- To verify the congruency of triangles using the four conditions for congruence of triangles
- To calculate the corresponding parts of congruent triangles

Let's Get Started

Take a few coins (e.g., ₹1, ₹2, ₹5, ₹10) and place the coins with same denominations and of same size one above the other as shown in the first image. Next try to place coins with different denominations one over the other as shown in the second image.

What do you observe? In both cases, do the coins cover each other completely?

You will notice that the coins with same denominations cover each other exactly, as they are of the same shape and size. But the coins with different denominations do not cover each other completely as each coin of a different denomination has a different size.

So, objects or figures or shapes that are of the same shape and same size are said to be congruent to one another. In other words, **congruent** objects are exact copies of each other.

Now, look at the given objects. Put a tick mark (✓) for congruent objects and a cross mark (✗) for non-congruent objects.

The property of any two objects or figures/shapes being congruent is called **congruence.** In this chapter, we will learn about congruence of plane figures and mainly deal with congruence of triangles.

CONGRUENT FIGURES

Figures which have exactly the same shape and the same size are called **congruent figures**. The symbol used for congruence is ≅.

We can identify congruent figures by the method of superimposition. Consider the two figures given alongside. To verify whether these are congruent, we can trace a copy of one of them on a patty paper and cut it out. Then place this cut-out over the other (i.e., superimpose them) and see if they cover one another exactly. If the figures cover each other completely, then they are congruent.

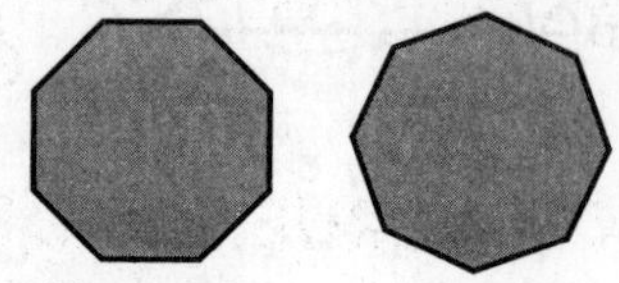

Figure 1 Figure 2

Here, Figure 1 is congruent to Figure 2, which can be written as Figure 1 ≅ Figure 2.

Congruency of Plane Figures

- Two **line segments** are said to be congruent if they have the same length.

  Suppose $\overline{AB}$ = 3 cm, $\overline{CD}$ = 3 cm and $\overline{PQ}$ = 4 cm.

  We have $\overline{AB} = \overline{CD}$. So, $\overline{AB}$ is congruent to $\overline{CD}$, that is, $\overline{AB} \cong \overline{CD}$.

  But $\overline{AB} \neq \overline{PQ}$. So, $\overline{AB}$ and $\overline{PQ}$ are not congruent.

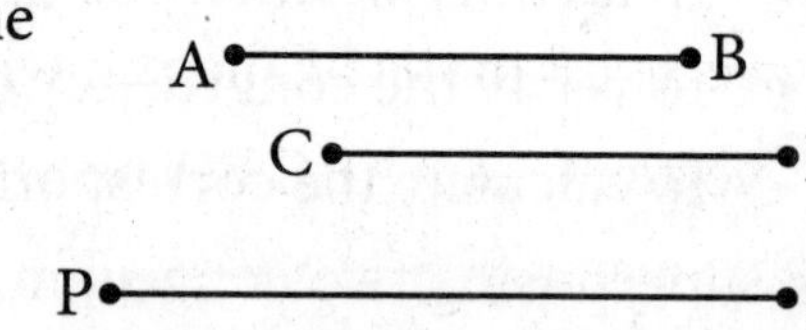

- Two **angles** are said to be congruent if they have the same measure.

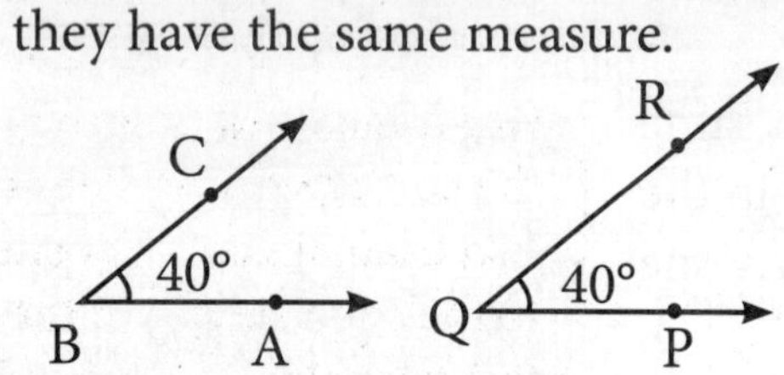

- Two **equilateral triangles** are said to be congruent if the lengths of their sides are the same.

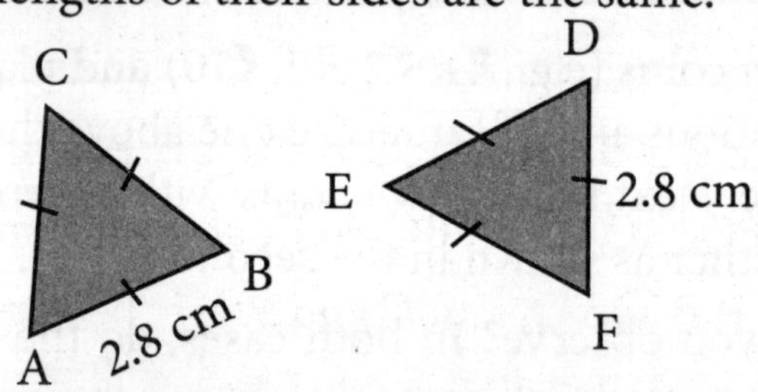

- Two **squares** are said to be congruent if the lengths of their sides are the same.

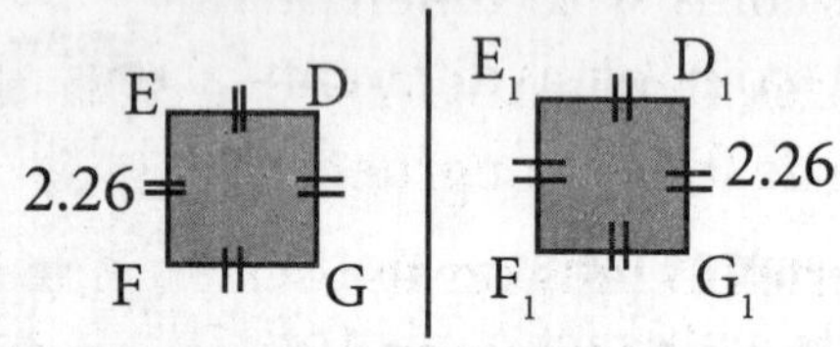

- Two **rectangles** are said to be congruent if their length and breadth are the same.

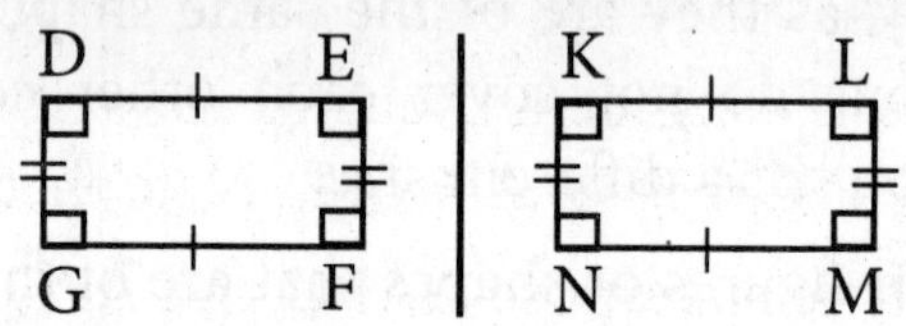

- Two **regular polygons** are said to be congruent if the lengths of all their sides are the same.

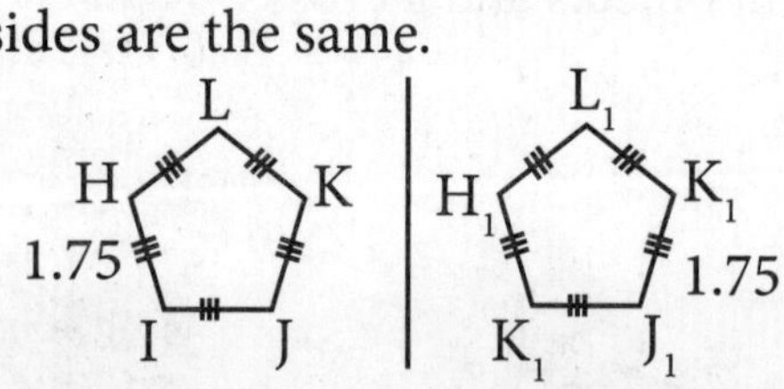

- Two **circles** are said to be congruent if they have the same radius.

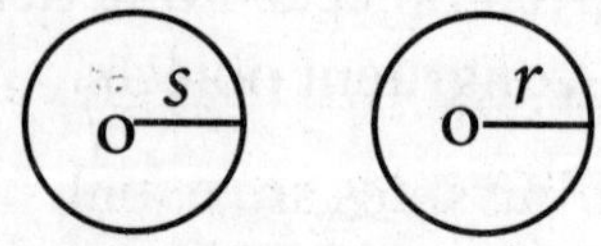

All congruent figures are equal (in area) but all equal figures are not congruent.

A triangle may be equal in area to a circle or a square. However, as these shapes are different, a triangle, a circle and a square cannot be congruent.

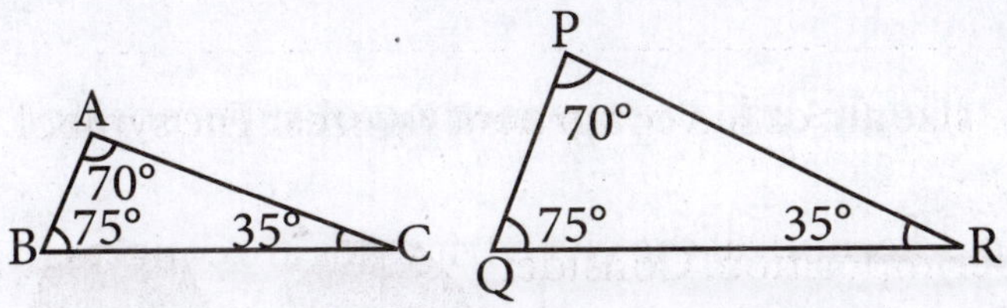

In the given triangles, the three angles of ΔABC are respectively equal to the three angles of ΔPQR. Although the shape of both the triangles is the same, their sizes are different. That is, ΔABC is smaller in size to ΔPQR. So, the two triangles are not congruent.

CONGRUENCE OF TRIANGLES

Trace the given triangles on a patty paper and cut them. Try to superpose the two triangles by placing the cut-out of one triangle on top of the cut-out of other.

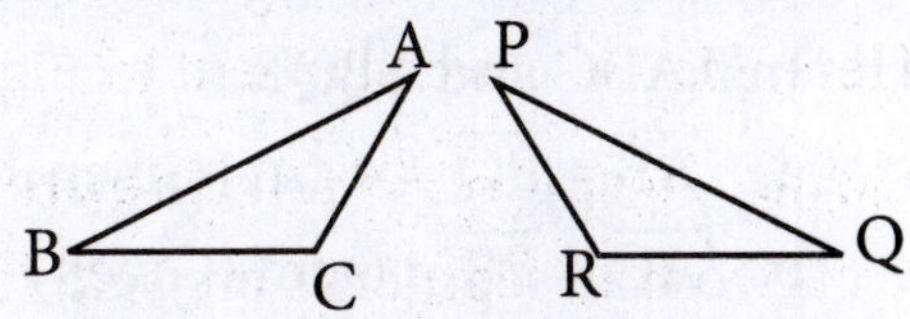

After superposing, find out the following:

- vertex A of ΔABC lies on which vertex of ΔPQR ?
- vertex B of ΔABC lies on which vertex of ΔPQR ?
- vertex C of ΔABC lies on which vertex of ΔPQR ?

On superposing two congruent triangles, the sides and angles which match one another (or coincide) are called their **corresponding parts.**

⟷ symbol is used to denote the corresponding parts.

Thus, for the triangles ΔABC and ΔPQR ,

- $\angle A = \angle P, \angle B = \angle Q, \angle C = \angle R$ are the corresponding angles.
- $\overline{AB} = \overline{PQ}, \overline{AC} = \overline{PR}, \overline{BC} = \overline{QR}$ are the corresponding sides.
- A and P, B and Q, and C and R are the corresponding vertices.

  That is, A ⟷ P, B ⟷ Q, C ⟷ R .

  ΔABC ⟷ ΔPQR means that the first vertex A is the corresponding vertex for P, the second vertex B is the corresponding vertex for Q and the third vertex C is the corresponding vertex for R.

Note

In congruent triangles, the corresponding angles of two triangles are opposite to the equal sides of the two triangles. Similarly, the corresponding sides of two triangles are opposite to the equal angles of the two triangles.

If the vertices of congruent triangles are written in a different order, that is ΔBCA ⟷ ΔPQR, then it means B ⟷ P, C ⟷ Q, A ⟷ R. Note that this need not be true for all congruent triangles.

Suppose that we superpose ΔABC and ΔPQR such that the vertex B falls on the vertex P. It is not always necessary that the other two vertices of the two triangles will correspond or match exactly. This implies that for congruence of triangles, not only the measures of angles and the lengths of sides matter, but also matching of vertices is important.

So, we can conclude that two triangles are congruent when:

- the corresponding sides are equal.
- the corresponding angles are equal.
- the corresponding vertices match exactly with each other.
- There are 3 pairs of corresponding sides, 3 pairs of corresponding angles, and 3 pairs of matching vertices in two congruent triangles.
- c.p.c.t.c stands for corresponding parts of congruent triangles are congruent or equal.

Conditions For Congruence of Triangles

It is not always possible to cut out any one of the given triangles and use the method of superposition to verify if the given triangles are congruent or not.

There are a few criteria or conditions using which we can determine if the given triangles are congruent or not. Let us learn about them.

1. **SSS Criterion for Congruence: SSS** stands for side-side-side.

   If the three sides of one triangle are equal to the corresponding three sides of another triangle, then the two triangles are congruent by SSS criterion.

   In ΔABC and ΔPQR,

   a. $\overline{AB} = \overline{PQ} = 4$ cm (Given)

   b. $\overline{AC} = \overline{PR} = 6$ cm (Given)

   c. $\overline{BC} = \overline{QR} = 5$ cm (Given)

   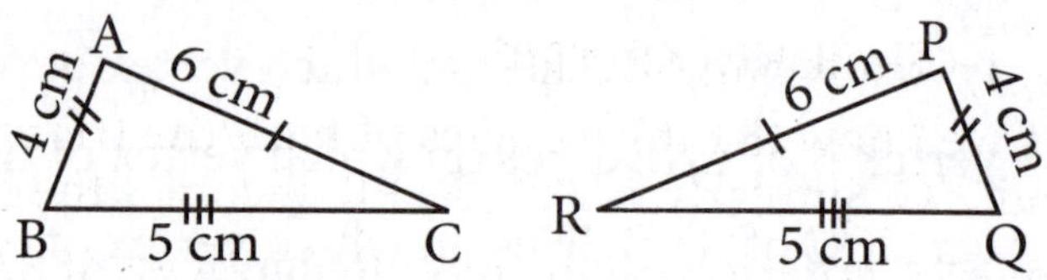

   Thus, $\Delta ABC \cong \Delta PQR$ by SSS criterion.

2. **SAS Criterion for Congruence: SAS** stands for side-angle-side.

   If two sides and the included angle of one triangle are equal to the corresponding two sides and the included angle of another triangle, then the two triangles are congruent by SAS criterion.

   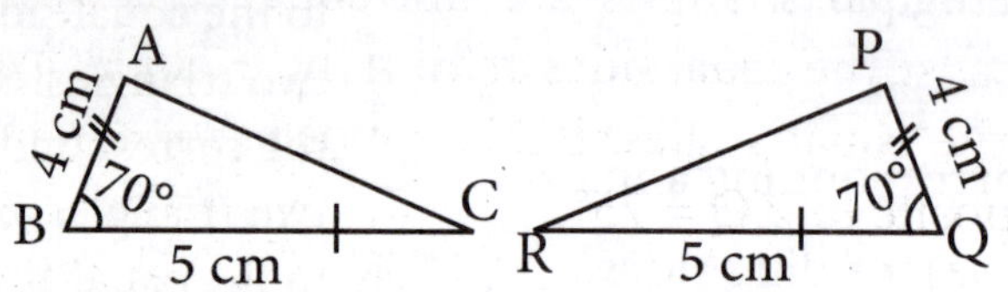

   > **Note**
   >
   > Included angle is the angle between the two intersecting sides.

   Here, in ΔABC and ΔPQR, $\angle B$ and $\angle Q$ are included between the equal sides AB, BC and PQ, QR, respectively. So, $\angle B$ and $\angle Q$ are the included angles for both the triangles.

   So, we have:

   a. $\overline{AB} = \overline{PQ} = 4$ cm (Given)

   b. $\angle B = \angle Q = 70°$ (Given)

   c. $\overline{BC} = \overline{QR} = 5$ cm (Given)

   Thus, $\Delta ABC \cong \Delta PQR$. by SAS criterion.

   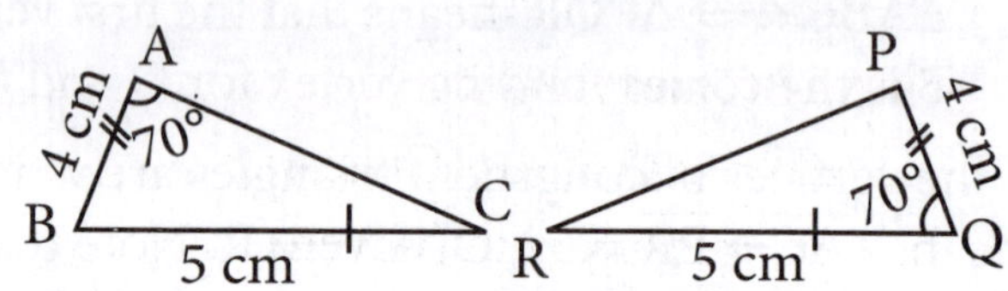

   Figure 1

Now look at these two triangles (Figure 1). Here, $\overline{AB} = \overline{PQ}$ and $\overline{BC} = \overline{QR}$ but $\angle A = 70°$ is not the included angle between the sides AB and BC, whereas $\angle Q = 70°$ is the included angle between the sides PQ and QR. So, the two triangles are not congruent by SAS criterion.

3. **ASA Criterion for Congruence: ASA** (or AAS or SAA) stands for angle-side-angle.

   If two angles and the included side of one triangle are equal to the corresponding two angles and the included side of another triangle, then the two triangles are congruent by ASA criterion.

   The **included side** is the base on which the two equal angles of the two triangles are formed.

   In ΔABC and ΔPQR,

   a. $\angle C = \angle R = 35°$ (Given)

   b. $\overline{BC} = \overline{QR} = 5$ cm (Given)

   c. $\angle B = \angle Q = 75°$ (Given)

   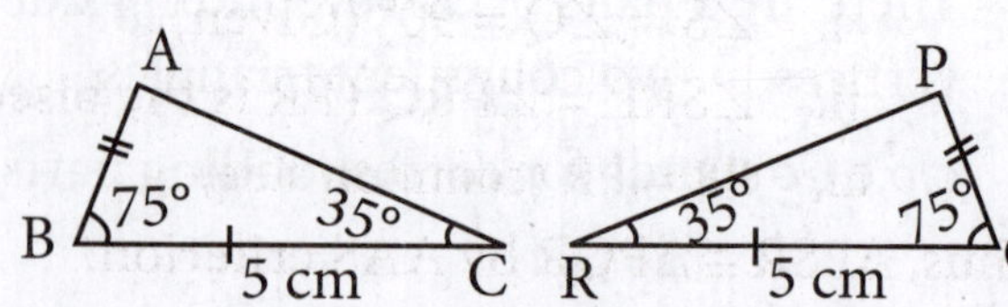

   Thus, $\Delta ABC \cong \Delta PQR$ by ASA criterion.

If the side given is not the included side, then can we apply ASA criterion? For example, consider the two triangles given alongside. This time, two angles each from both the triangles and the lengths of sides AC and PR are same, which are not the included sides. Now, if two angles of a triangle are equal to the corresponding two angles of another triangle, then the third angle of both the triangles will also be equal by the angle sum property. That is,

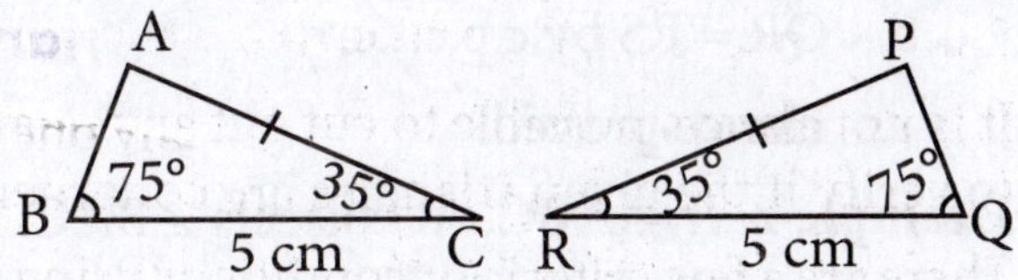

$\angle A + \angle B + \angle C = 180°$ (Sum of the angles of a triangle)

$\angle A + 75° + 35° = 180°$

$\angle A = 180° - 110° = 70°$

Similarly, $\angle P = 70°$

As we know the third angles of both the triangles, in ΔABC, AC becomes the included side for $\angle A$ and $\angle C$. Similarly, in ΔPQR, PR becomes the included side for $\angle P$ and $\angle R$.

So, ASA criterion can be modified to AAS or SAA criterion, provided the corresponding sides of both the triangles are equal.

The above two triangles ΔABC and ΔPQR are congruent by SAA criterion because the equal sides of both the triangles are opposite to the equal angles $\angle B = \angle Q$.

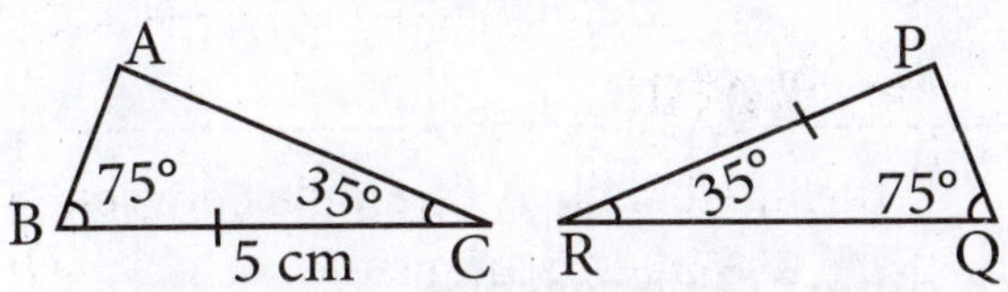

These two triangles are not congruent by SAA criterion because the equal sides of both the triangles are not opposite to the equal angles. BC is opposite to $\angle A = 70°$ but PR is opposite to $\angle Q = 75°$.

4. **RHS Criterion for Congruence: RHS** stands for right angle-hypotenuse-side.
   If the hypotenuse and one other side of a right-angled triangle are equal to the corresponding hypotenuse and side of another right-angled triangle, then the two triangles are congruent by RHS criterion.
   In ΔABC and ΔPQR,
   a. $\angle B = \angle Q = 90°$ (Given)
   b. $\overline{AC} = \overline{PR} = 5$ cm (Given)
   c. $\overline{BC} = \overline{QR} = 4$ cm (Given)
   Thus, ΔABC and ΔPQR are congruent by RHS criterion.

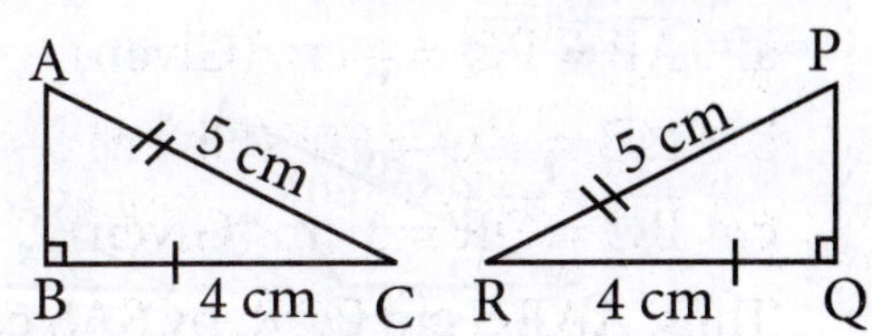

SOLVED EXAMPLES

Example 1: PQRS is a quadrilateral with PR as the bisector of $\angle QRS$. Prove that:

a. PQ = PS
b. QR = RS

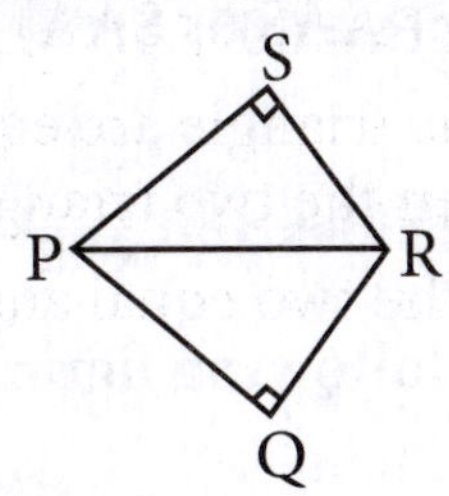

Solution:

a. In ΔPSR and ΔPQR
   i. $\angle S = \angle Q = 90°$ (Given)
   ii. $\angle SRP = \angle PRQ$ (PR is the bisector of $\angle QRS$)
   iii. PR = PR (common side)

Thus, $\Delta PSR \cong \Delta PQR$ by AAS criterion.

So, PQ = PS by c.p.c.t.c.

Common Errors

Students tend to make errors in writing corresponding vertices. To avoid this, in the first step, when we write which triangles we are comparing, write the corresponding vertices in order. In Solved Example 1, it is evident that $P \leftrightarrow P$, $S \leftrightarrow Q$, $R \leftrightarrow R$. So, we should write 'In ΔPSR and ΔPQR'.

b. QR = RS by c.p.c.t.c.

Hence proved.

Example 2: In ΔABC, AO bisects $\angle BAC$. Prove that $\angle AOC = 90°$.

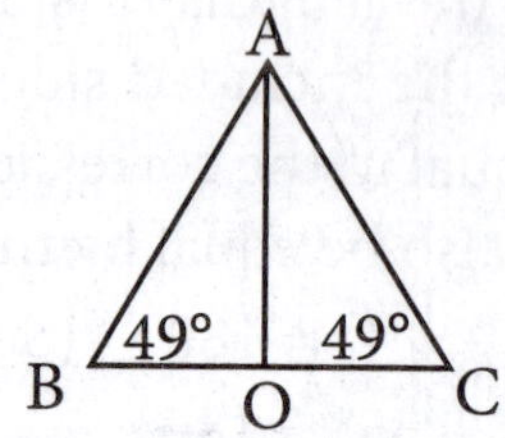

Solution: In ΔAOB and ΔAOC

a. $\angle B = \angle C = 49°$ (Given)

b. $\angle BAO = \angle OAC$ (AO is the bisector of $\angle BAC$.)

c. AO = AO (Common side)

Thus, $\Delta AOB \cong \Delta AOC$ by AAS criterion.

$\angle AOB = \angle AOC$ (by c.p.c.t.c.)

$\angle AOB + \angle AOC = 180°$ (linear pair)

$\angle AOC + \angle AOC = 180°$

$2\angle AOC = 180°$

$\angle AOC = 90°$

Hence proved.

Note

A bisector is a line which divides a line segment or an angle into two equal halves. Bi means 2. Sect means divide. Bisect means divide into two equal halves.

EXERCISE 11

1. **Are the following pairs of triangles congruent to each other? Give reasons.**

a.
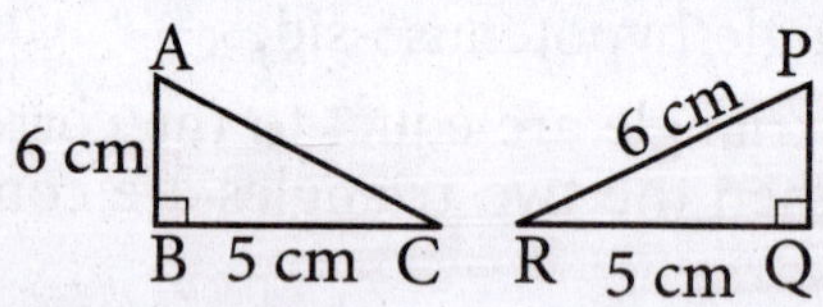

b.
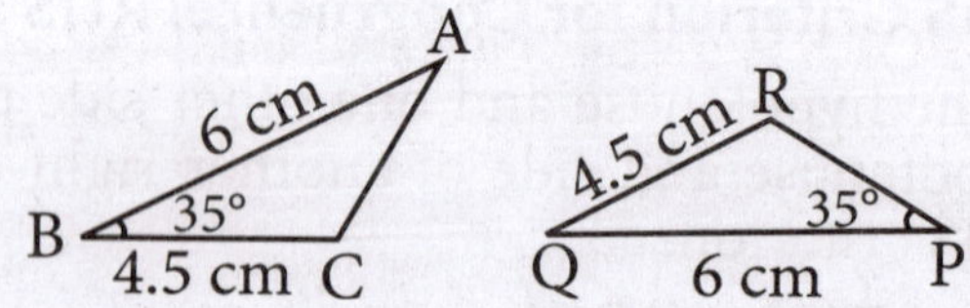

c.
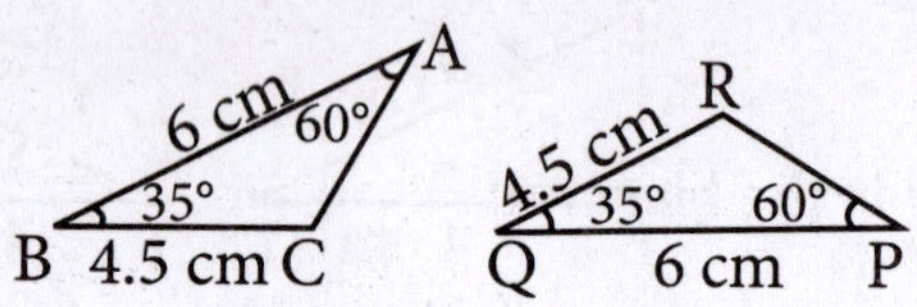

d.
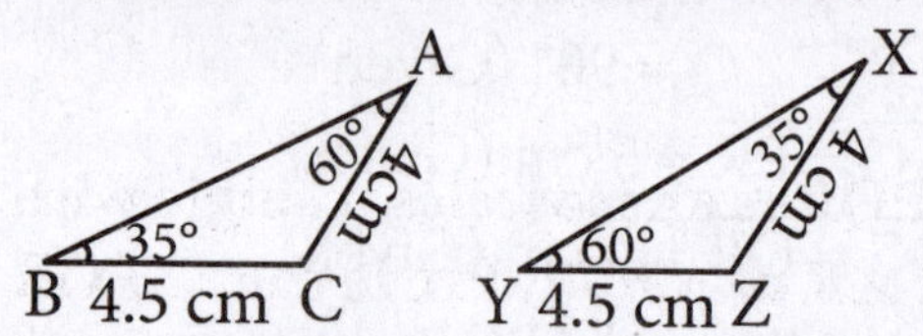

e. In ΔABC and ΔDEF, $\angle A = 70°$, $\angle B = 60°$, BC = 5.5 cm, $\angle D = 70°$, $\angle E = 60°$ and DF = 5.5 cm.

f. In ΔABC and ΔDEF, $\angle A = 90°$, $\angle B = 60°$, AB = 5.5 cm, $\angle D = 90°$, $\angle E = 60°$ and DF = 5.5 cm.

2. **$\Delta XYZ \cong \Delta PQR$. Which are the equal sides and angles of the two triangles?**

3. **Prove that ΔAOC and ΔBOD in the following figures are congruent to each other.**

a.
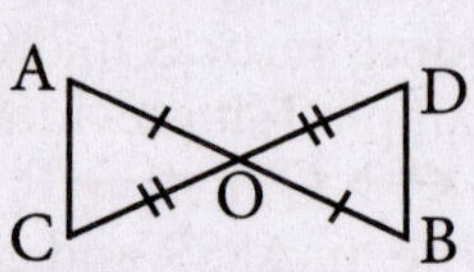

b.
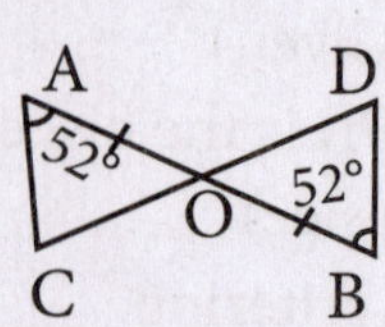

4. **Prove that ΔAOB and ΔAOC in the following figures are congruent to each other.**

a. 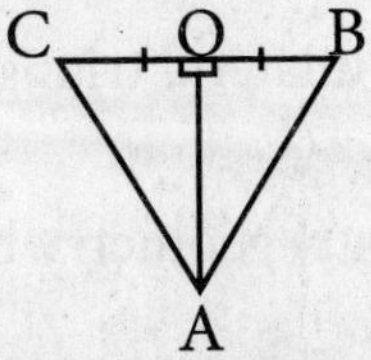

b. 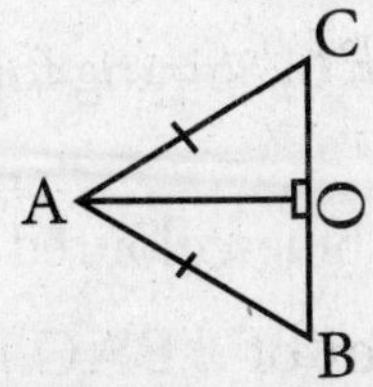

c. 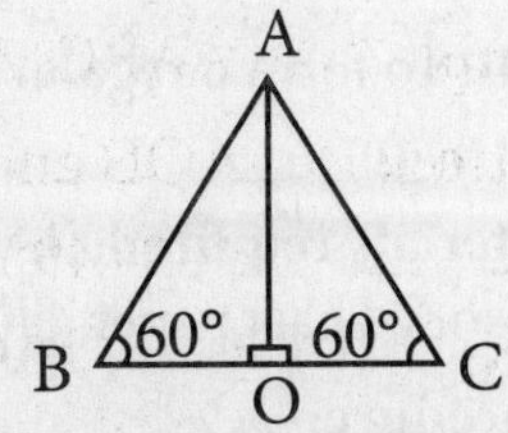

d. 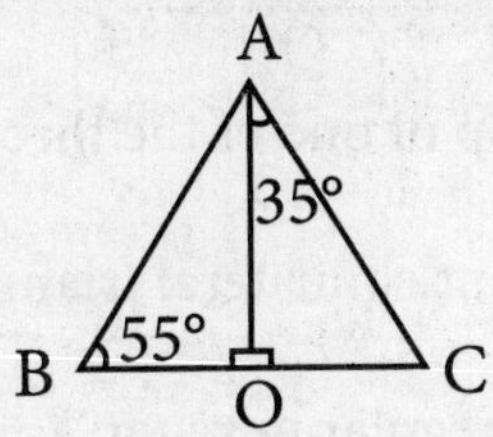

e. 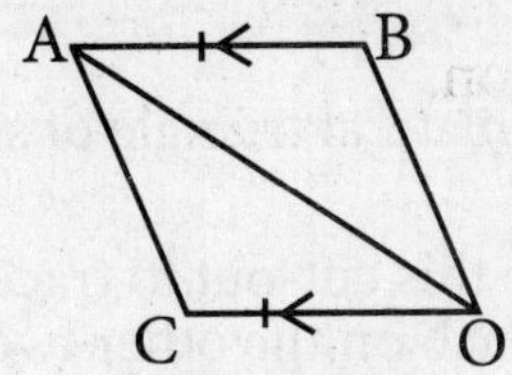

f. 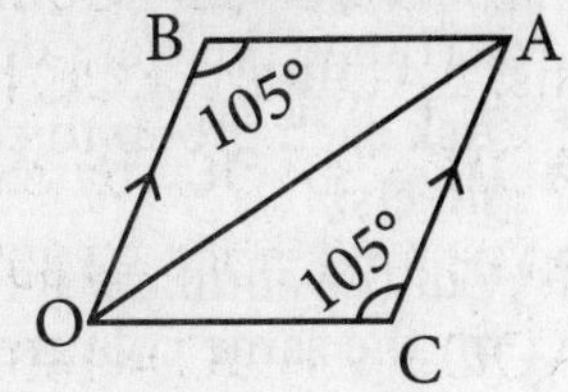

5. **ABCD is an isosceles trapezium with AB || DC. Prove that AC = BD.**

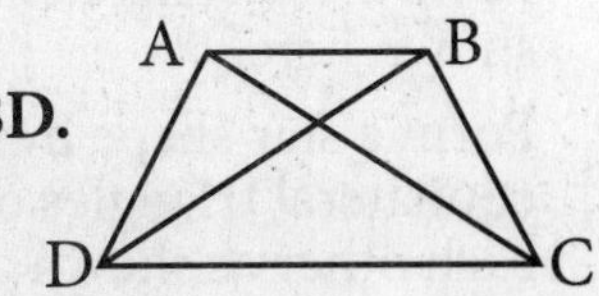

6. **In the following figure, PQ and RS are straight lines intersecting at O.**

a. If PQ and RS bisect each other at O, prove that PS = RQ.

b. If PS = RQ and ∠PQS = ∠RQS, prove that PQ = RS.

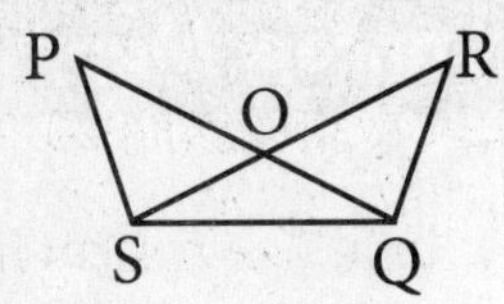

7. **PQRS is a quadrilateral with QR = RS. Prove that**

a. PQ = PS

b. PR is the bisector of ∠QPS

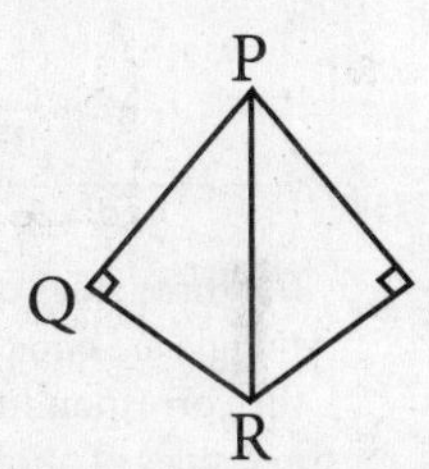

8. **ΔPQR is an isosceles triangle with PR = RQ. RO is the bisector of ∠R of ΔPQR. Prove that ∠POR = 90°.**

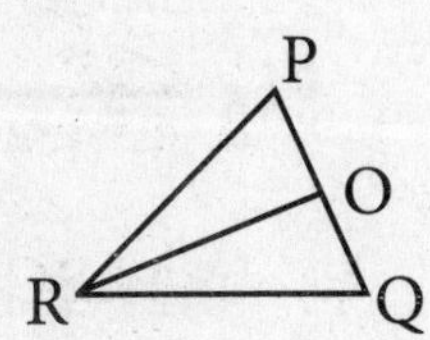

Maths Lab Activity

Aim: To form a regular hexagon of side 4 cm by joining together 6 congruent equilateral triangles of side 4 cm

Materials required: A yellow, a green and a blue-coloured A4 size paper per group, geometry box, scissors, chart paper, glue, pencil and eraser

Procedure:

1. Arrange the class into groups of 4.
2. Ask each group to construct an equilateral triangle of side 4 cm at the top of one of the three paper sheets.
3. Cut the equilateral triangle and use this cut-out to trace 5 more congruent equilateral triangles: one on the same coloured sheet and 2 each on the other two sheets.
4. Paste these congruent equilateral triangles on the chart paper to form a regular hexagon as shown here.

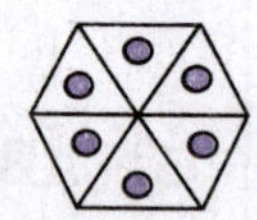

Form a star shape by placing two congruent equilateral triangles of side 4 cm on top of each other as shown alongside. Ask the students to form more shapes using congruent triangles.

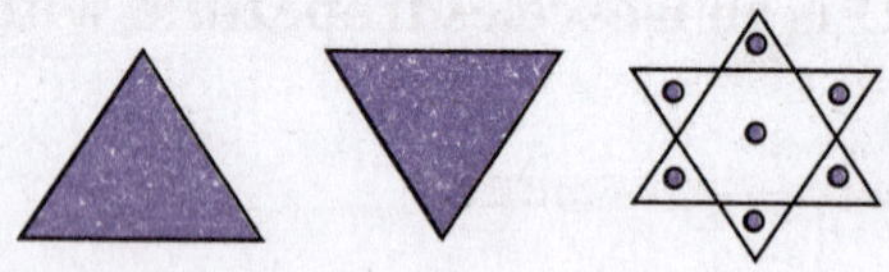

Concept Map

Congruent Triangles
Triangles with same shape and size.
They are equal in area.

- **SSS** — The three sides of a triangle are equal to the corresponding three sides of another triangle
- **SAS** — Two sides and the included angle of a triangle are equal to the corresponding two sides and the included angle of another triangle
- **ASA** — Two angles and the included side of one triangle are equal to the corresponding two angles and the included side of another triangle
  - **AAS/SAA** — Two angles of a triangle are equal to two angles of another triangle; the third angle of both the triangles will also be equal.
- **RHS** — In two right-angled triangles the hypotenuse and one more side of a triangle are equal to the corresponding hypotenuse and side of the other triangle

Key Concepts

- **Congruent figures:** Figures with same shape and same size
- **Superimposition:** Placing one figure on top of the other such that they cover each other exactly
- **Corresponding parts:** A pair of corresponding sides or angles of two triangles
- **Included angle:** The angle formed between two intersecting sides
- **Bisector:** A line which divides a line segment or an angle into two equal halves
- **c.p.c.t.c:** Corresponding parts of congruent triangles are congruent

CHAPTER REVISION

A. Choose the correct option.

1. Pick the odd one out.

   a. SSS b. AAA c. SAS d. ASA

2. Pick the odd one out in the given figure.

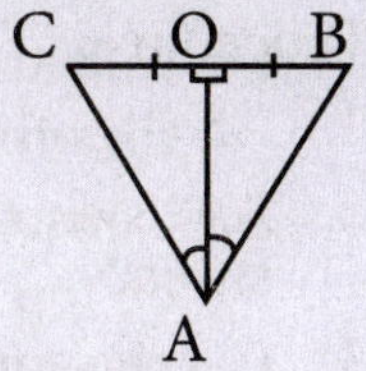

   a. AO is a perpendicular bisector. b. AO is a hypotenuse.

   c. AO is an angle bisector. d. AO is a median.

3. Pick the odd one out.

   a. Equal lines b. Equal angles c. Equal circles d. Equal triangles

4. In two triangles, if two angles of each triangle are equal and one angle is 90°, the triangles may not be

   a. isosceles triangles b. isosceles right-angled triangles

   c. congruent triangles d. right angles

B. Fill in the blanks.

1. Two line segments are congruent if they have the same ________.
2. If two triangles are congruent, their corresponding sides are ________.
3. Congruent circles have the same lengths of their _______.
4. A bisector is a ______ which divides a line segment or an _______ into two equal halves.

C. Write T for true and F for false.

1. All equal figures are congruent.
2. All equilateral triangles are congruent.
3. All squares with same lengths of sides are congruent.
4. Congruent figures are equal in area.

D. Match the following for ΔXYZ and ΔPQR.

1.	XY = PQ, YZ = QR, ∠Y = ∠Q = 90°	a. SSS
2.	XZ = PR, YZ = QR, ∠Y = ∠Q = 90°	b. SAS
3.	XY = PQ, XZ = PR, YZ = QR	c. ASA
4.	XZ = PR, ∠Y = ∠Q = 90°, ∠X = ∠P	d. RHS

E. Prove that ΔABC ≅ ΔDEF if :

1. ∠A = 72°, ∠B = 65°, AB = 5 cm, ∠D = 72°, ∠E = 65° and DE = 5 cm.
2. ∠A = 90°, ∠B = 47°, BC = 6 cm, ∠D = 90°, ∠F = 43° and EF = 6 cm.

SKILL UP!

Project

Perform the following and record the observations and findings in your notebook. Discuss and compare your findings with the rest of the classmates.

1. Construct two circles of radius 5 cm on a sheet of paper. Cut them and place one on top of the other. Do the two circles overlap?
2. Construct two equilateral triangles with each side of length 5 cm. Cut them and place one on top of the other. Do the two equilateral triangles overlap?
3. Place the triangle on top of the circle, do the two figures overlap? If not, why?
4. Construct a circle of radius 3 cm on a sheet of paper. Cut it and place it on top of a circle of radius 5 cm. Are the two circles congruent? If not, why?
5. Trace a copy of both your palms on a sheet and cut them. Place one cut-out on top of the other. Do the cut-outs of palms overlap?

Life Skills

1. The Hawa Mahal or 'Palace of Winds' has 953 intricate windows. This curved palace is considered the tallest building in the world without foundation. It stands firm till now due to its pyramidal shape.
   In which city and state is the Hawa Mahal located? Why was this building created?
   Do the different windows have the same shape and size? Do the windows look congruent?
2. Apply the concept of congruency for drawing rangoli/origami patterns or objects. Write a brief note explaining how you applied the concept.

Mind Buzzer

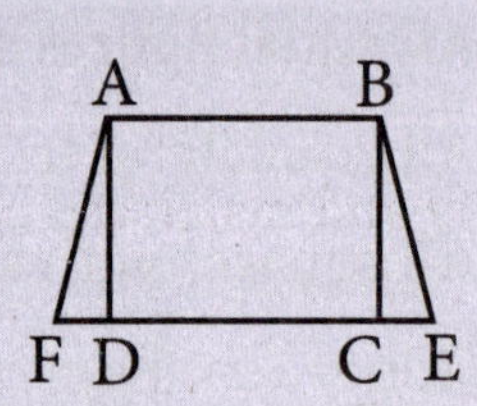

1. ABCD is a rectangle and ABEF is an isosceles trapezium with AB = 10 cm and FE = 16 cm. Prove that FD = CE. Calculate FC.
2. Draw two congruent triangles. Are their areas and perimeters same?

Teacher's Notes

- Ask students to identify pairs of objects like doors, windows, furniture and stationery items in the classroom which have the same shape and the same size.
- Explain the concept of congruency of various triangles, circles, squares and rectangles using paper cut-outs.
- Emphasize on corresponding parts of congruent triangles and explain the conditions for congruency of triangles.
- Encourage the students to prove whether or not given triangles are congruent and to calculate the corresponding parts of congruent triangles.

WORKSHEET

1. Look for the following terms learnt in this chapter in the word grid given.

WORDS					
Congruent	Shape	Area	Corresponding	Size	Angle
Coincide	Side	Right	Hypotenuse	Included	Vertex

C	O	N	G	R	U	E	N	T
O	Q	A	A	X	C	D	V	A
R	W	E	N	E	A	I	R	H
R	E	I	G	T	B	C	E	Y
E	R	O	L	R	D	N	V	P
S	I	D	E	E	Z	I	S	O
P	N	A	A	V	A	O	H	T
O	C	B	E	A	R	C	A	E
N	L	C	I	E	I	S	P	N
D	U	A	O	I	G	I	E	U
I	D	B	U	O	H	A	C	S
N	E	C	A	U	T	R	O	E
G	D	A	B	A	V	H	R	A

2. Identify and match the congruent shapes by colouring each pair with the same colour.

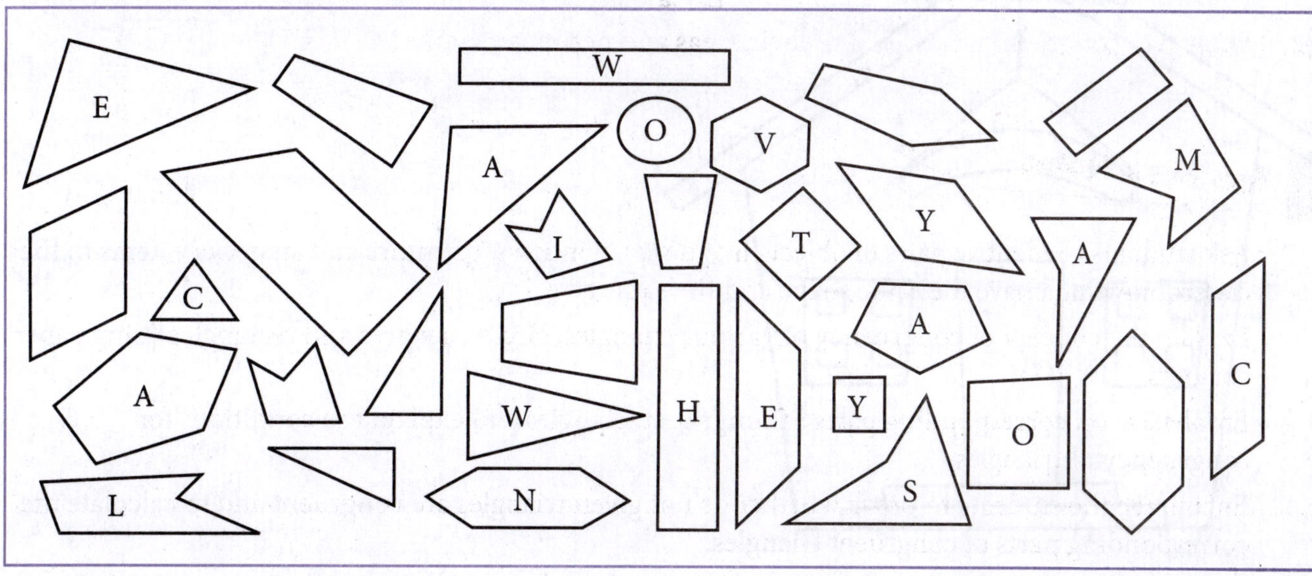

12 Practical Geometry

Learning Objectives

- To construct a line parallel to the given line through a point not on the line
- To construct triangles based on SSS, SAS, ASA and RHS criteria

Let's Get Started

The figure given below consists of parallel lines, perpendiculars and angles. Identify the lines and angles. Also, reconstruct the figure in the space given below.

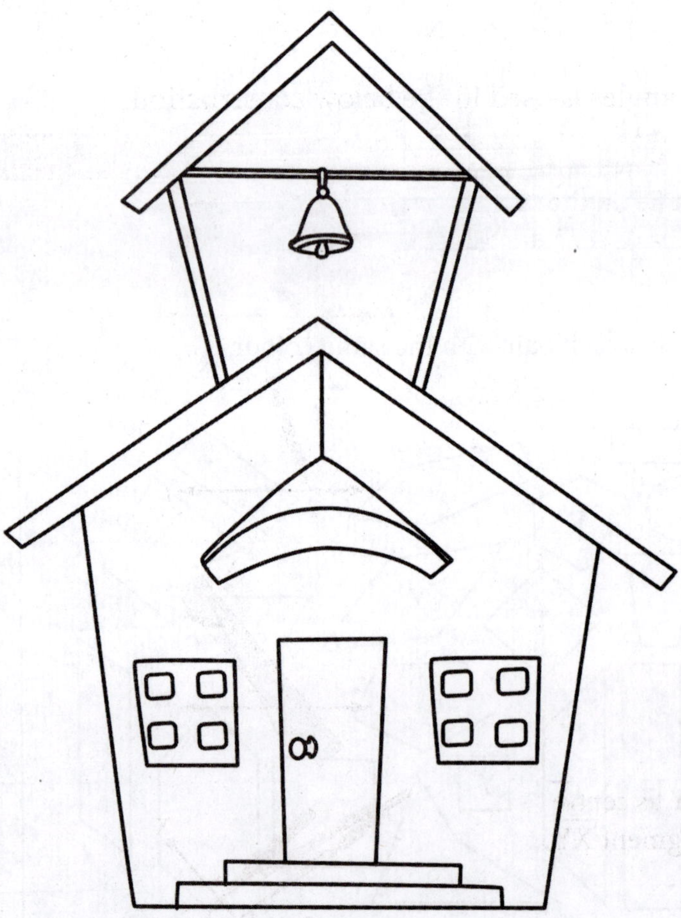

We know that two or more lines in a plane which do not meet at any point are called **parallel lines.**

For examples:  Railway tracks  Lines on a T-shirt

We know that the perpendicular distance between any two points on the parallel lines is the same. Let us recall the properties of a transversal that we have learnt earlier.

PARALLEL LINES AND TRANSVERSAL

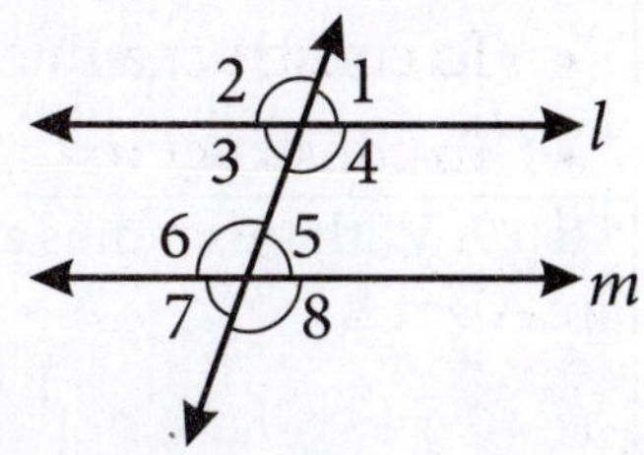

Let l and m be two parallel lines intersected by a transversal. Then,

- pairs of corresponding angles are equal.

That is, $\angle 1 = \angle 5$; $\angle 4 = \angle 8$; $\angle 2 = \angle 6$ and $\angle 3 = \angle 7$

- pairs of alternate interior angles are equal.

That is, $\angle 4 = \angle 6$ and $\angle 3 = \angle 5$

- pairs of interior angles on the same side of the transversal are supplementary.

That is, $\angle 4 + \angle 5 = 180°$ and $\angle 3 + \angle 6 = 180°$

Let us learn to construct a line parallel to a given line by using one of the above properties.

Construction of a line parallel to a given line through a point not on the given line

Instruments used: Ruler, pencil and compass

Note that the property of pair of alternate interior angles is used in the below construction.

Steps of construction	Figure
Step 1: Draw a line l and mark a point X that does not lie on the line l as shown.	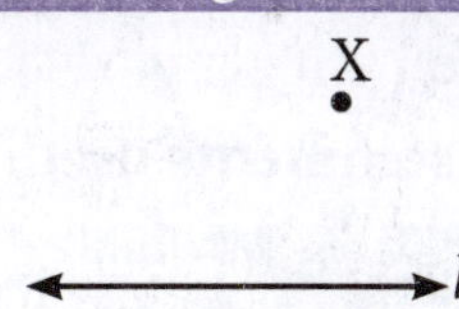
Step 2: Mark a point Y on the line l.	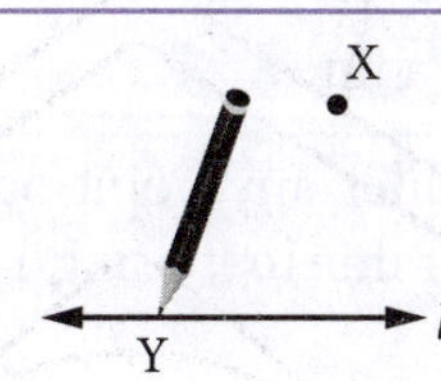
Step 3: Join X and Y using a ruler.	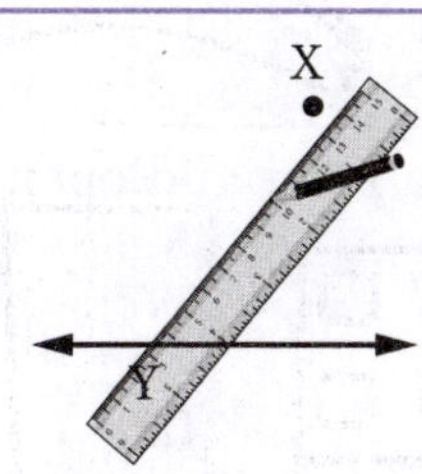
Step 4: With the help of a compass, draw an arc with Y as centre and any radius cutting the line l at M and the line segment $\overline{XY}$ at N.	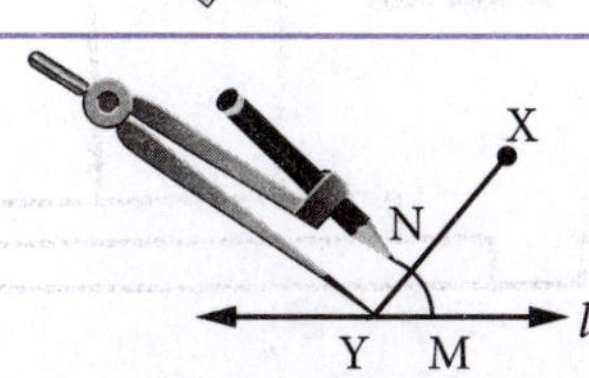

Step 5: With X as centre and with the same radius, draw an arc AB, cutting $\overline{XY}$ at O.	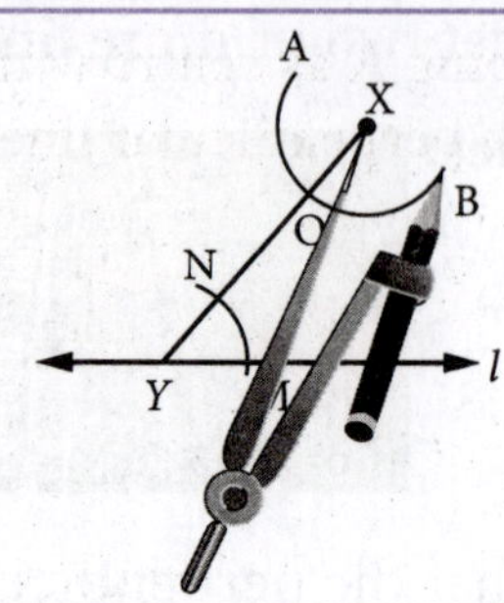
Step 6: Keeping the pointed tip of the compass at N, adjust its width such that the opening (pencil's tip) of the compass is at M.	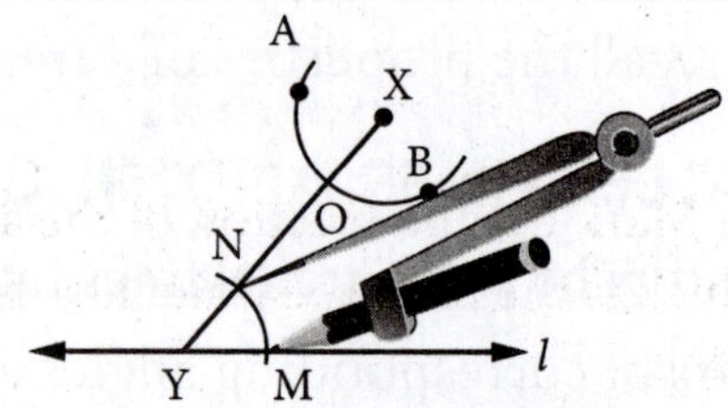
Step 7: With this radius and O as centre, draw an arc, cutting the arc AB at P.	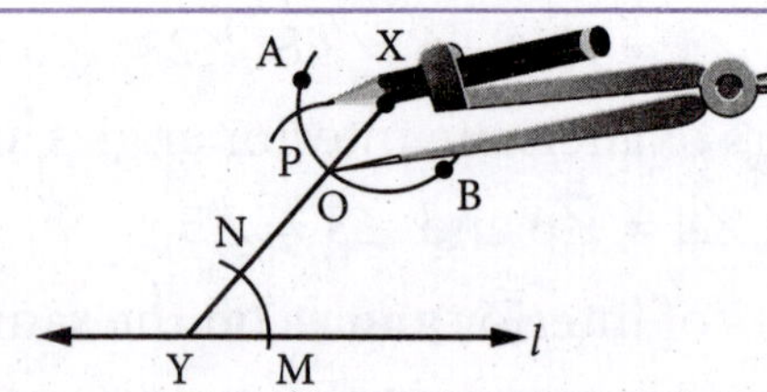
Step 8: Join P and X to get the required parallel line *m*.	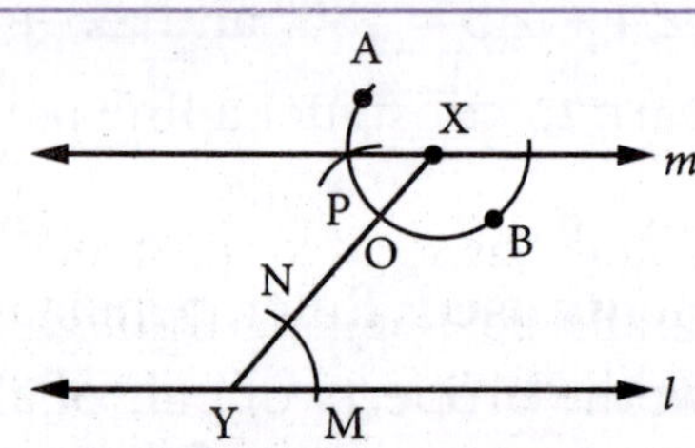

Example 1: Construct a line parallel to the line *l* through a point which is at a distance of 4.6 cm from the given line.

Solution: Instruments used: Ruler, pencil and compass

Steps of construction	Figure
Step 1: Draw a line *l*.	
Step 2: Consider any point outside the line *l* and construct a perpendicular line to it using a compass. Mark point A on line *l*.	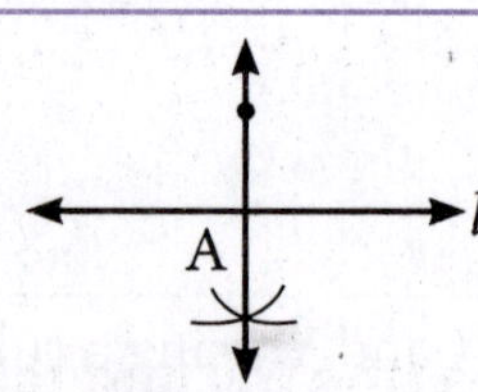
Step 3: Take a ruler and open the compass to measure 4.6 cm on the ruler.	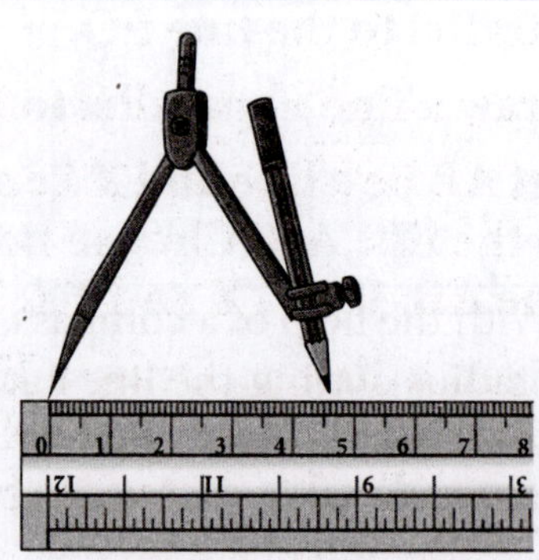

Step 4: Keeping A as centre without changing the radius, draw an arc on the perpendicular line.	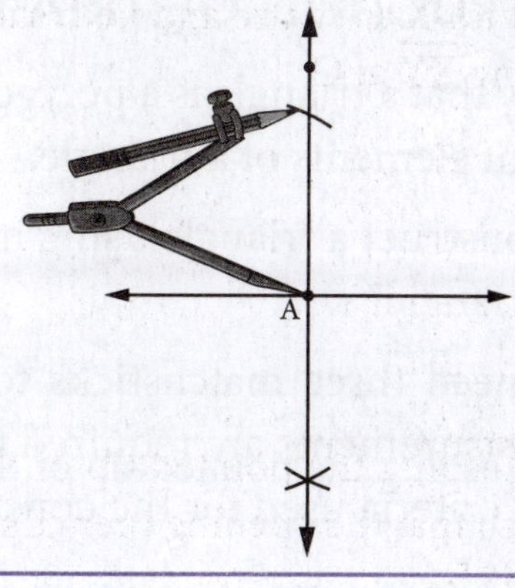
Step 5: Mark the intersection of the arc and perpendicular line as P which is the required point at a distance of 4.6 cm from the given line.	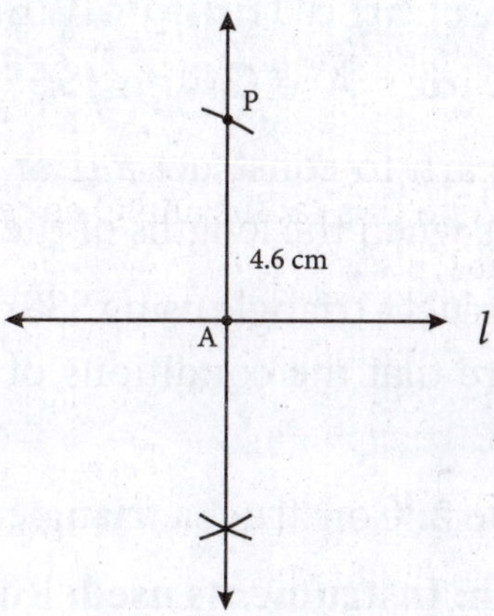
Step 6: Follow the steps to construct a parallel line and construct a line parallel to l passing through the point P. Line m is the required parallel line.	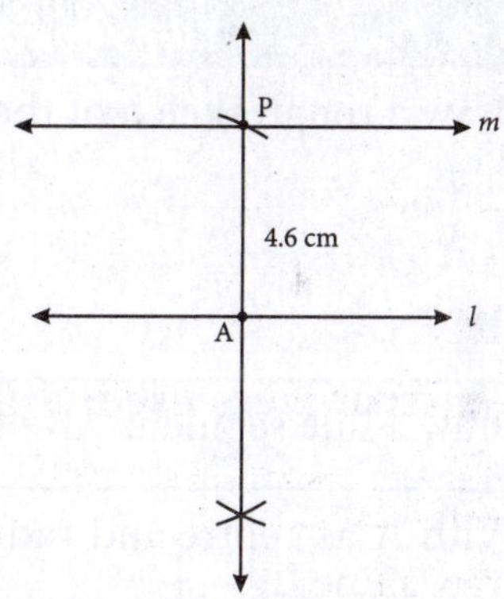

EXERCISE 12A

1. **Draw a line PQ and take a point R not on line PQ. Through the point R, draw a line MN parallel to the line PQ.**
2. **Draw a line *m* parallel to the line CD which is at a distance of 6 cm from the line CD.**
3. **Let AB be a line and X be a point outside it. Through the point X, draw a line PQ parallel to the line AB. Choose two distinct points Y and Z on the line PQ and a point T on the line AB. Join TY and TZ. What do you get?**
4. **Given a line *p*. Draw a line *m* parallel to the line *p* through a point not on the line *m*. Draw a line *r* parallel to line *m* through a point outside the line *m*. Measure the perpendicular distances between all the parallel lines.**

CONSTRUCTION OF TRIANGLES

We know that a triangle is a polygon with three sides. It has three sides and three angles which are the important elements of a triangle.

Let us construct a triangle using matchsticks. Are two matchsticks sufficient to form a triangle?

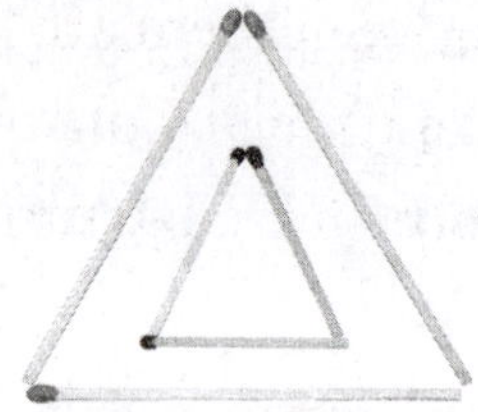

No, we need three matchsticks to form a triangle. Therefore, a minimum of three measurements are required to construct a triangle. Let us learn about the different criteria used for the construction of triangles.

Constructing a Triangle When Lengths of Three Sides Are Given (SSS Criterion)

Let us learn to construct a triangle using a ruler and a compass when the lengths of the three sides are known.

To construct a triangle using SSS criterion, it is important to ensure that the conditions of triangle inequality are satisfied.

> **Note**
>
> The inequalities of a triangle are:
> - The sum of any two sides is always greater than the third side.
> - The difference between any two sides is always less than the third side.

Example 2: Construct a triangle whose side lengths are 6 cm, 4 cm and 3 cm.

Solution: Instruments used: Ruler, pencil and compass

Steps of construction	Figure
Step 1: Draw a rough sketch of the triangle.	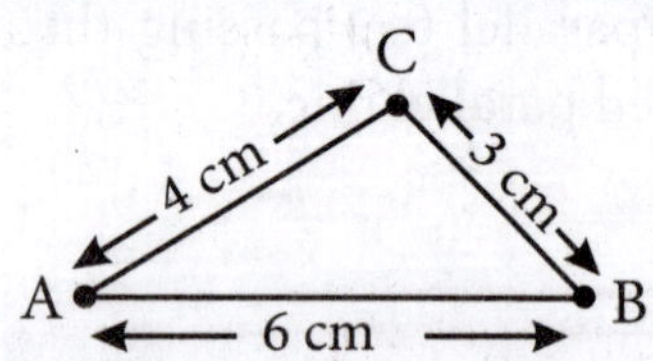
Step 2: Draw a line segment AB of length 6 cm.	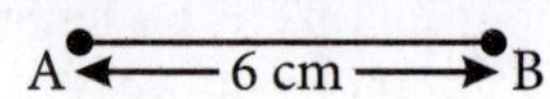
Step 3: With A as centre and radius 4 cm, draw an arc on one side of AB.	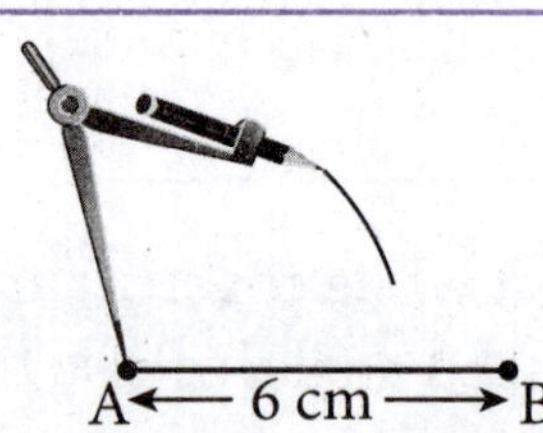
Step 4: With B as centre and radius 3 cm, draw another arc cutting the previous arc at C.	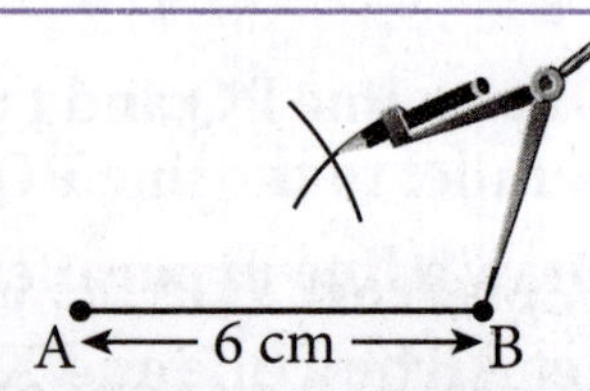
Step 5: Join A and C, and B and C to get the required triangle ABC.	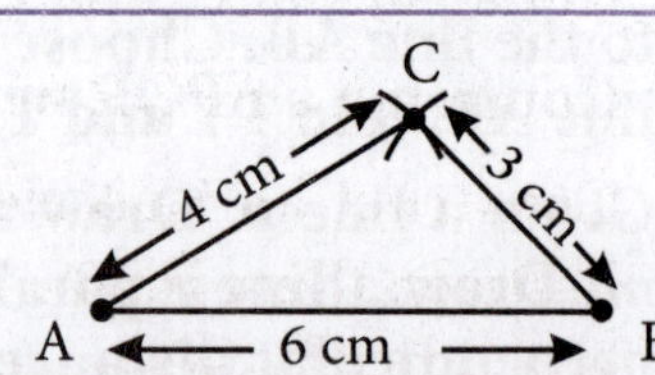

Note that while using the SSS criterion, we start the construction by drawing the longest side first.

Constructing a Triangle When Lengths of Two Sides and the Included Angle Are Given (SAS Criterion)

Let us learn to construct a triangle when the lengths of two of its sides and the measure of the angle between them are known.

Example 3: Construct a triangle ABC with AB = 5 cm, AC = 3 cm and ∠BAC = 60°.

Solution: Instruments used: Ruler, pencil and compass

<table>
<tr><th>Steps of construction</th><th>Figure</th></tr>
<tr><td>Step 1: Draw a rough sketch of the triangle.</td><td>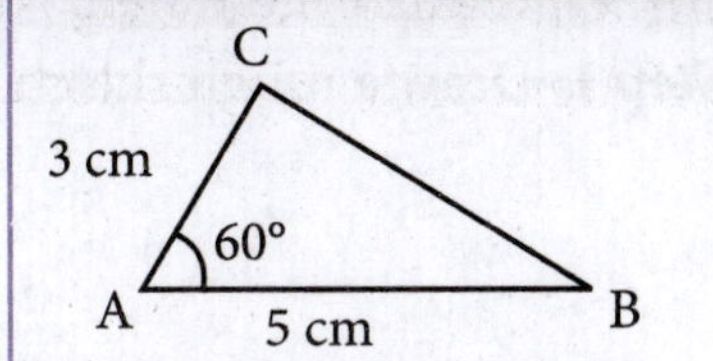
</td></tr>
<tr><td>Step 2: Draw a line segment $\overline{AB}$ of length 5 cm.</td><td>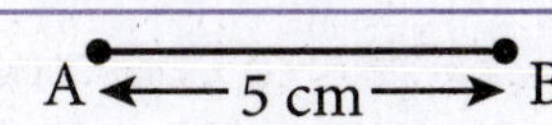
</td></tr>
<tr><td>Step 3: With a compass, construct ∠XAB = 60° (using the method already learnt in Class 6).</td><td>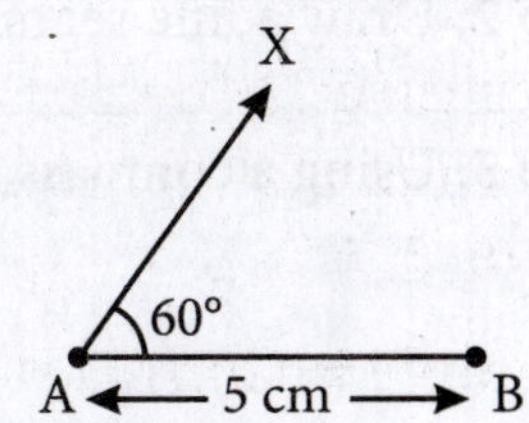
</td></tr>
<tr><td>Step 4: With A as centre and radius 3 cm, draw an arc cutting the ray $\overline{AX}$ at C.</td><td>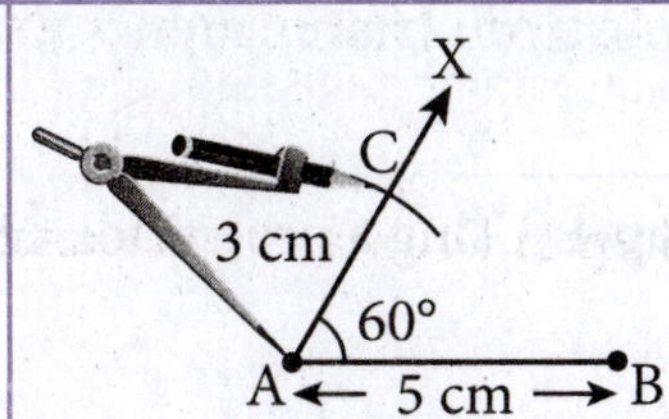
</td></tr>
<tr><td>Step 5: Join B and C to get the required triangle ABC.</td><td>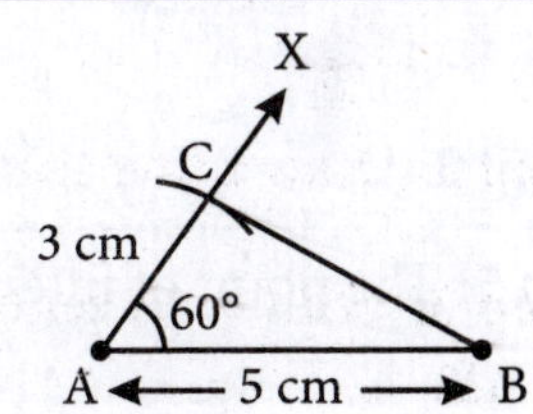
</td></tr>
</table>

Note that while constructing a triangle with two sides and one angle given, the known angle must be an included angle, or else the triangle constructed will not be unique.

EXERCISE 12B

1. **Construct a ΔABC with $\overline{AB}$ = 5.5 cm, $\overline{BC}$ = 3.5 cm and $\overline{AC}$ = 4 cm.**
2. **Construct an equilateral triangle with the length of each side equal to 4.5 cm.**
3. **Construct a ΔPQR with $\overline{PQ}$ = 7 cm, $\overline{QR}$ = 5 cm and $\overline{PR}$ = 6 cm.**
4. **Construct an isosceles triangle with equal sides measuring 6 cm each and the angle between them is 50°.**
5. **Construct a ΔXYZ with $\overline{YZ}$ = 5 cm, ∠XZY = 105° and $\overline{XZ}$ = 4.7 cm.**

Constructing a Triangle When Two Angles and the Included Side Are Given (ASA Criterion)

Let us learn to construct a triangle when the measures of two of its angles and the length of the side included between them are known.

Example 4: Construct a triangle PQR with QR = 4 cm, ∠Q = 60° and ∠R = 70°.

Solution: Instruments used: Ruler, pencil, protractor and compass

Steps of construction	Figure
Step 1: Draw a rough sketch of the triangle.	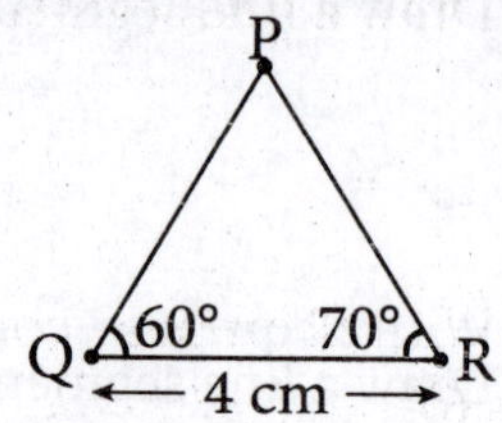
Step 2: Draw a line segment of length 4 cm.	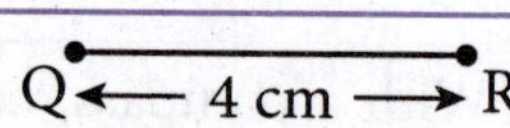
Step 3: Using a compass, construct ∠Q = 60°.	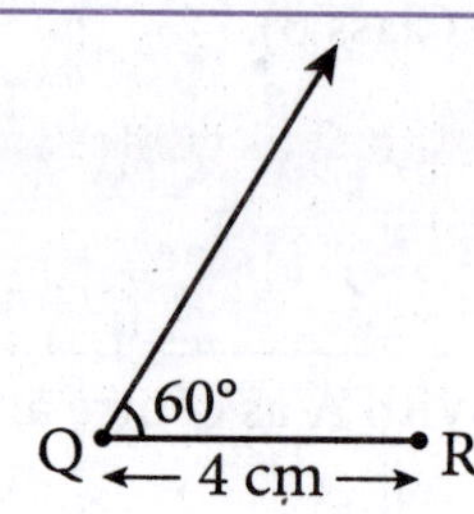
Step 4: Using a protractor, construct ∠R of measure 70° at point R.	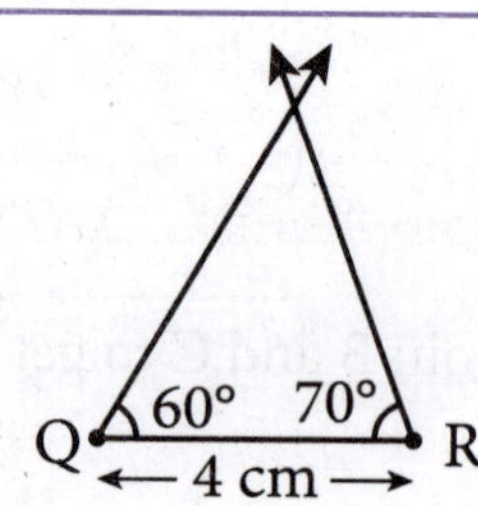
Step 5: The point of intersection is P. ΔPQR is the required triangle.	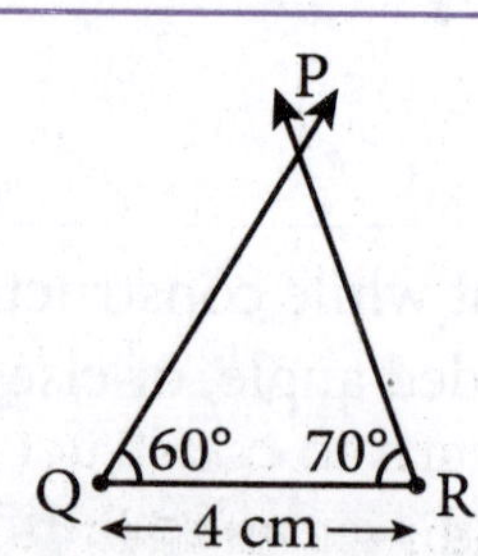

Constructing a Right-Angled Triangle (RHS Criterion)

As the name suggests, a right-angled triangle has one angle measuring 90°. The remaining two angles measure less than 90° (as the sum of the angles in a triangle is 180°).

Construction of a right-angled triangle using SAS criterion

Let us learn to construct a right-angled triangle when the lengths of one side and the hypotenuse that make a right angle are known.

Example 5: Construct a right-angled triangle ABC, right angled at B with $\overline{BC}$ = 4 cm and $\overline{AC}$ = 5 cm.

Solution: Instruments used: Ruler, pencil and compass

Steps of construction	Figure
Step 1: Draw a rough sketch of the triangle.	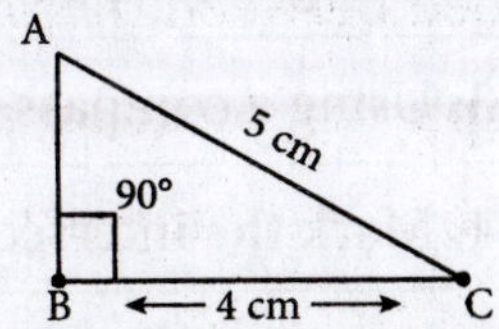
Step 2: Draw a line segment $\overline{BC}$ of length 4 cm.	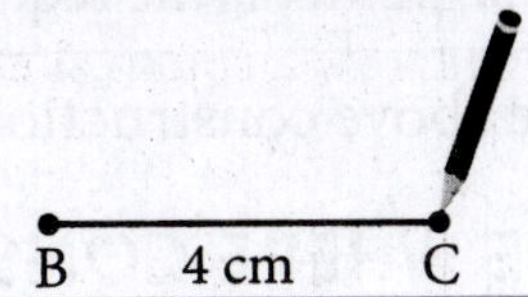
Step 3: With a compass, construct ∠B = 90° (using the method already learnt in Class 6).	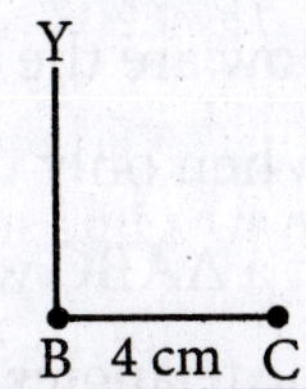
Step 4: With C as centre and radius 5 cm, draw an arc cutting BY at A.	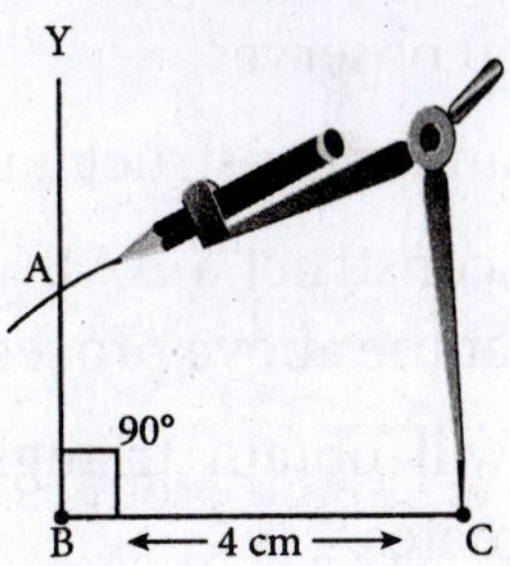
Step 5: Join A and C. ΔABC is the required right-angled triangle.	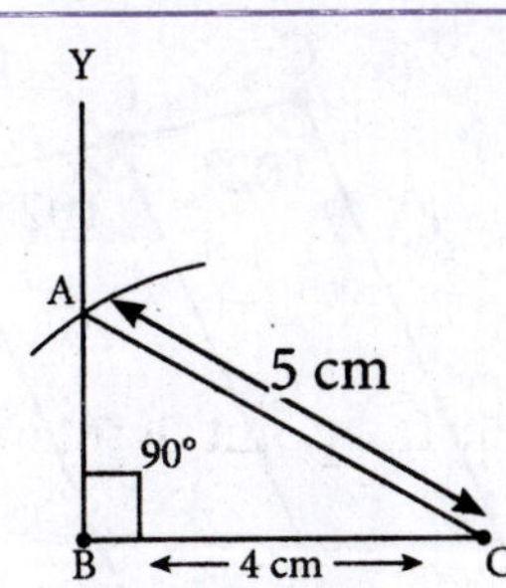

Construction of a right-angled triangle using ASA criterion

Let us learn to construct a right-angled triangle when the length of one of the sides making a right angle and measure of the angle adjacent to this side are known.

Example 6: Construct a right-angled triangle LMN with $\overline{MN}$ = 5 cm, ∠L = 60° and right angled at M.

Solution: We know that the sum of the angles in a triangle = 180°

So, ∠L + ∠M + ∠N = 180°

∠N = 180° – (90° + 60°) = 180° – 150° = 30°

Thus, we have the three measurements, that is, ∠M, the included side MN and ∠N. Using ASA criterion, ΔLMN is constructed as follows:

Steps of construction	Figure
Step 1: Draw a line segment $\overline{MN}$ of length 5 cm.	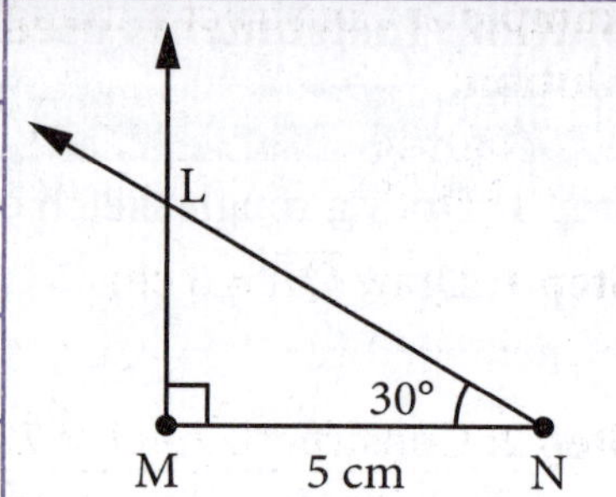
Step 2: Using a compass, construct $\angle M = 90°$.	
Step 3: Using a compass, construct $\angle N = 30°$.	
Step 4: Mark the intersection point of the two rays as L.	
Step 5: ΔLMN is the required right-angled triangle.	

In the above construction, measure $\angle L$ and verify whether it is 60°.

CASE WHERE CONSTRUCTION OF UNIQUE TRIANGLES IS NOT POSSIBLE

Given below are the two cases where the construction of a unique triangle is not possible.

Case 1: When only the measures of the three angles are given.

Construct a ΔABC with $\angle A = 50°$, $\angle B = 70°$ and $\angle C = 60°$ on a patty paper with suitable side lengths. Look at the triangles constructed by your classmates and try to superimpose with your triangle. What do you observe?

We cannot construct a unique triangle even if we know all the three angles of the triangle.

Now construct a ΔABC with $\angle A = 56°$ and $\angle C = 102°$ on a patty paper with suitable side lengths. Repeat the above procedure again.

You will obtain triangles as shown below on superimposing the triangles constructed by your classmates.

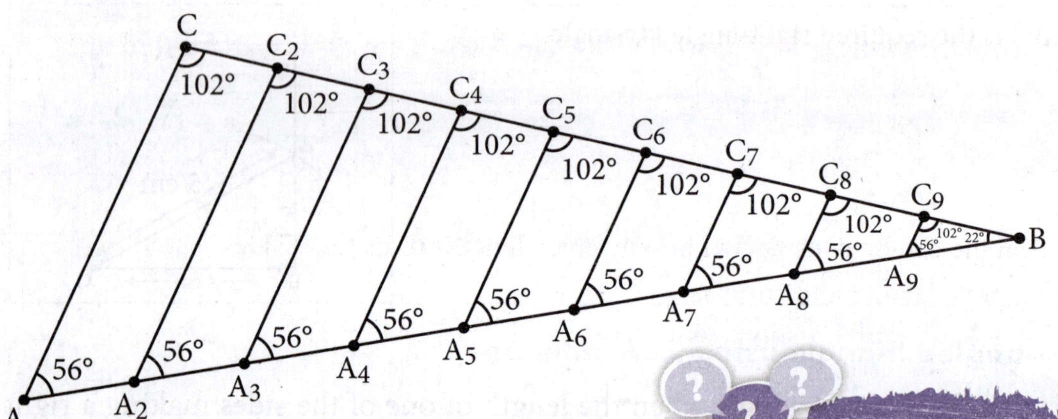

Why is it not possible to construct a unique triangle in this case?

As we can calculate the third angle using the angle sum property, it means that it is the same as knowing only two independent measurements. But we need a minimum of three independent measurements to construct a unique triangle.

Mental Maths

1. Give the measurements of a triangle that can be constructed by SSS criterion.
2. Give any five real-life examples of parallel lines.
3. The construction of a triangle is not unique by AAA criterion. Justify.
4. Give the measurements of a right-angled triangle that can be constructed by RHS criterion.
5. Which criterion can be used to draw a scalene triangle?

Case 2: When only two sides and an angle other than the included angle are given.

Example 7: Construct a triangle PQR with $\overline{PQ}$ = 4.7 cm, $\overline{QR}$ = 5 cm and ∠QRP = 70°.

Solution:

Steps	Figure
Step 1: Draw $\overline{QR}$ = 5 cm.	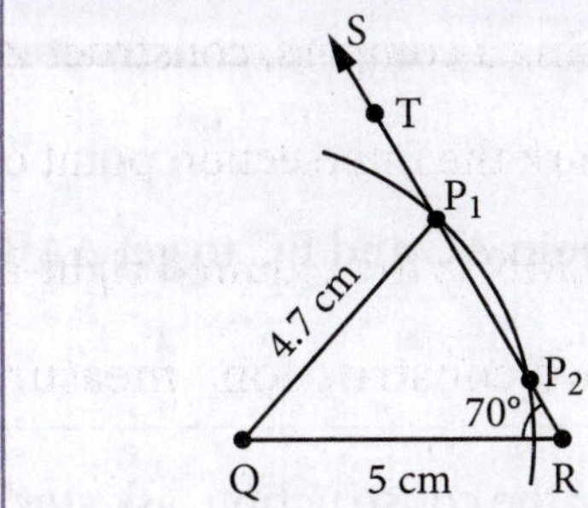
Step 2: Construct ∠QRT = 70°.	
Step 3: Draw an arc with Q as centre and a radius of 4.7 cm.	

We find that the arc intersects the ray RS at two points, both of which can be point P. Thus, we got two different triangles P_1QR and P_2QR for the same information given. Hence, a unique triangle cannot be constructed in this case.

EXERCISE 12C

1. **Construct a ΔXYZ with $\overline{XY}$ = 4 cm, ∠Y = 75° and ∠Z = 45°.**
2. **Construct a ΔABC with $\overline{AB}$ = 6.2 cm, ∠A = 100° and ∠B = 50°.**
3. **Construct a ΔPQR with $\overline{PQ}$ = 5 cm, ∠P = 45° and ∠R = 60°.**
4. **Construct a right ΔMNP right angled at M with $\overline{MN}$ = 4 cm and $\overline{MP}$ = 3 cm. Measure the hypotenuse.**
5. **Construct a right-angled triangle DEF with $\overline{DE}$ = 6 cm, $\overline{EF}$ = 8 cm and right angled at D.**

Maths Lab Activity

Aim: To find whether a triangle can be constructed for any given lengths of its three sides

Materials required: Paper, pencil, ruler and compass

Procedure:

1. Arrange the class into pairs.
2. Distribute paper, pencil, ruler and a compass to each group.
3. Direct each group to follow the steps of construction as given below.
   To check whether ΔABC with sides 8 cm, 9 cm and 5 cm can be constructed:

Steps of construction	Figure
Step 1: Draw a line segment $\overline{AB}$ = 8 cm.	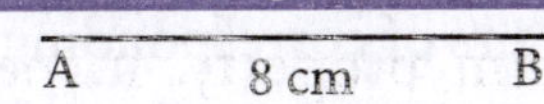
Step 2: With A as centre, draw an arc of radius 9 cm.	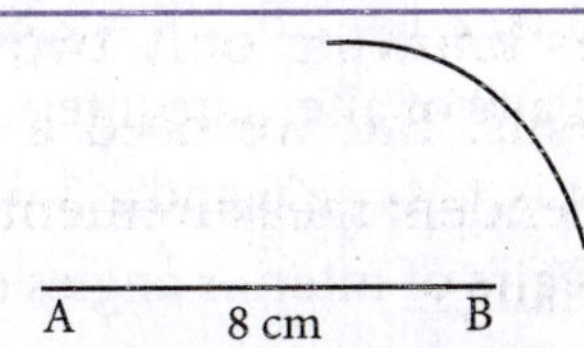

Step 3: With B as centre, draw an arc of radius 5 cm to cut the previously drawn arc at C.	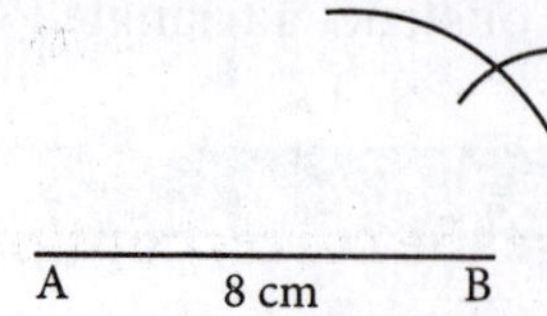
Step 4: Join AC and BC to get ΔABC with the given sides.	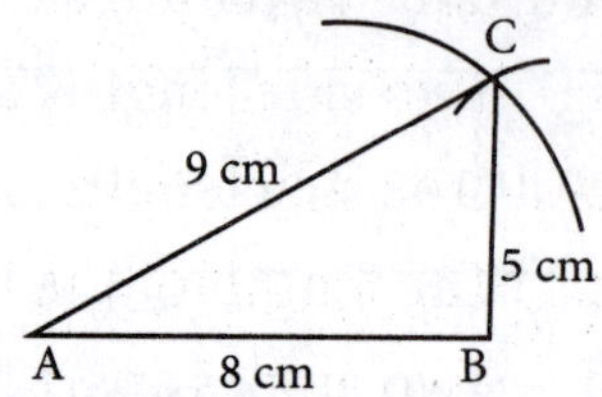

4. After the construction, ask students to measure the length of AC and BC.
5. Give different lengths of the sides to each group and ask them to find whether the triangle can be constructed using the same procedure as discussed above. Let each group compare their findings.

Concept Map

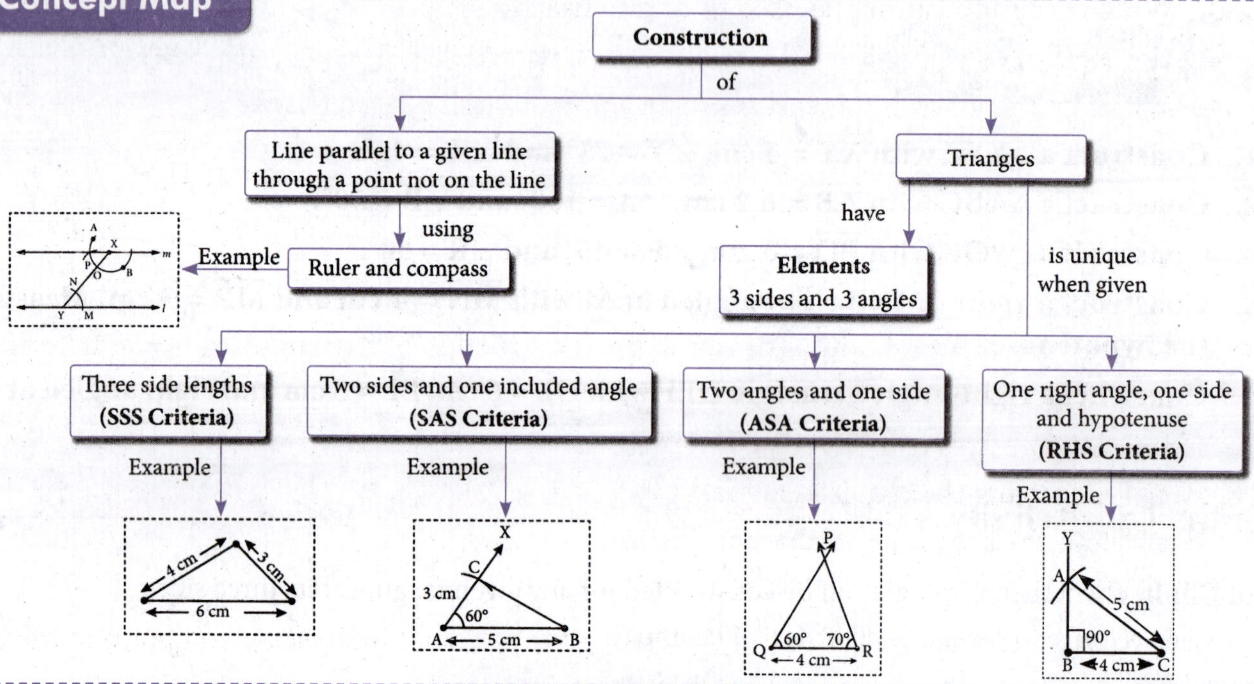

Key Concepts

- **Parallel lines:** Two or more lines in a plane which do not meet at any point
- **Triangle:** A polygon with three sides
- **Parallel lines and transversal:** Let *l* and *m* be two parallel lines intersected by a transversal. Then,

  i. Pairs of corresponding angles are equal.

  That is, $\angle 1 = \angle 5$; $\angle 4 = \angle 8$; $\angle 2 = \angle 6$; $\angle 3 = \angle 7$

  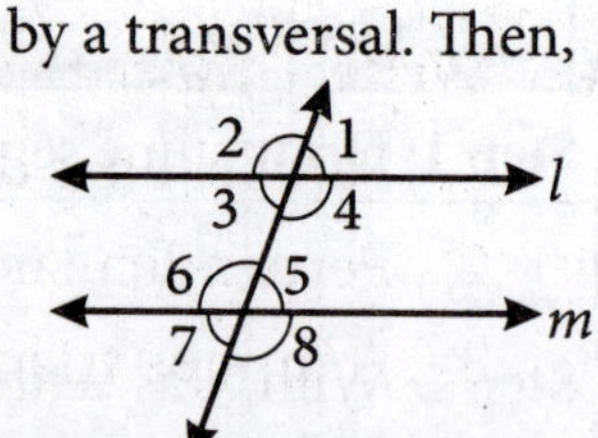

  ii. Pairs of alternate interior angles are equal.

  That is, $\angle 4 = \angle 6$ and $\angle 3 = \angle 5$

  iii. Pairs of interior angles on the same side of the transversal are supplementary.

  That is, $\angle 4 + \angle 5 = 180°$ and $\angle 3 + \angle 6 = 180°$

CHAPTER REVISION

A. Choose the correct option.

1. A unique right-angled triangle cannot be constructed when
   a. Two side lengths are given
   b. One side length and hypotenuse are given
   c. The length of the base having right angle and the other base angle are given
   d. Two angles apart from the right angle are given
2. Which triangle with the following given lengths of sides can be constructed using SSS criterion?
   a. 5 cm, 6 cm, 4 cm b. 6 cm, 2 cm, 3 cm
   c. 4.5 cm, 4 cm, 8.5 cm d. 3 cm, 7 cm, 2.5 cm
3. Which criterion cannot be used to draw a triangle?
   a. RHS b. SSA c. ASA d. SAA
4. Which of the following measures form a unique right-angled triangle?
   (i) ΔABC with $\angle B = 90°$, BC = 5 cm and CA = 8 cm
   (ii) ΔABC with $\angle B = 90°$ and CA = 7 cm
   (iii) ΔABC with $\angle B = 90°$, BC = 5 cm and $\angle C = 60°$
   a. Only (i) b. Both (i) and (ii) c. Only (iii) d. Both (i) and (iii)
5. Choose the incorrect option based on the construction of a triangle using SSS criterion.
   a. Draw a line of required length.
   b. Cut two arcs with the required length of the other lines.
   c. Construct the required angle.
   d. Join the arc to the vertices of the line.

B. Fill in the blanks.

1. Two or more lines are called ____________ if they do not intersect at any point in the plane.
2. Interior angles on the same side of the transversal are ____________.
3. We cannot construct a ____________ triangle when three angles are given.
4. A triangle constructed would not be unique if the angle is not ____________ between the lines given.
5. Parallel lines can be constructed using ruler and ____________.

C. Write T for true and F for false.

1. Parallel lines do not intersect.
2. Perpendicular lines do not intersect.
3. A unique triangle is possible with three angles.
4. A unique triangle is possible with three sides.
5. To construct an equilateral triangle, the measure of one side is enough.

D. Match the steps to construct a line parallel to the line *l* through a point at a distance of 7 cm from the given line.

1. **Step 1**	a. Construct a parallel line to *l* passing through the point P. Line *m* is the required parallel line.
2. **Step 2**	b. Keeping A as centre without changing the radius, draw an arc on the perpendicular line.
3. **Step 3**	c. Consider any point outside the line *l* and construct a perpendicular line to it.
4. **Step 4**	d. Mark the intersection of the arc and perpendicular line as P which is the required point which is at a distance of 7 cm from the given line.
5. **Step 5**	e. A line *l* is given.
6. **Step 6**	f. Take a ruler and compass and open the compass to measure 7 cm.

E. Show the actual construction for the steps matched in Question D.

F. Construct ΔABC for the below-given measurements.

1. AB = 4.8 cm, BC = 5.4 cm and AC = 6 cm
2. AC = 5 cm, BC = 6 cm and ∠C = 75°
3. ∠A = 100°, ∠B = 45° and AB = 7 cm
4. Right angled at B with AB = 6 cm and ∠C = 50°
5. AB = BC = AC = 6.5 cm

G. Construct the following.

1. Construct an isosceles triangle in which each equal side is 6.5 cm and the included angle is 110°.
2. Draw a line AB. Take a point C outside it and draw a line parallel to AB from C.
3. Construct a triangle ABC such that AC = BC = 4 cm and ∠B = 45°. Is this triangle right angled?

H. Find whether unique triangles can be constructed with each of the following measurements. If yes, identify the criterion to be used and construct them in your notebook.

1. Equilateral triangle with side 7.2 cm
2. AB = 5.5 cm, BC = 4.4 cm and CA = 2.8 cm
3. Isosceles triangle with equal sides as 5 cm and included angle as 45°
4. LM = 3.1 cm, MN = 4.2 cm and ∠N = 50°

SKILL UP!

Project

1 Computer Aided Design (CAD) is software used by architects, engineers, construction managers to create precise drawings. It was first released in December 1982 as a desktop app that ran on microcomputers. Find out how drawings are made using CAD.

2. Congruent triangles are used in construction of bridges. Congruent triangles help to spread out the weight of vehicles crossing the bridge. Equilateral triangles are most commonly used in construction of bridges.

   Try to build your own bridge out of triangles with the help of straws. Experiment with bridges made from different kinds of triangles. Which bridge holds the most weight?

Life Skills

Carpenters use the concept of triangles in designing cabinets for office space, houses, etc. The carpenters ensure that the walls are straight and the corners are perpendicular. Find out the instruments that are used by them for the design.

If you had to design a small cabinet for your room, how would you do it?

Mind Buzzer

1. While constructing a triangle with two angles and one side, should the known side be the included side? Is it not possible to get a unique triangle?
2. For constructing an equilateral triangle, it is sufficient to know the length of a side. Justify.
3. To construct an isosceles triangle, it is sufficient to know the length of the equal sides and the angle between them. Give reasons.

Teacher's Notes

- Before starting with the actual construction, draw a rough sketch and discuss the steps of construction.
- Discuss the various criteria where the construction of unique triangles is possible. In the cases where construction of unique triangles is not possible, discuss the reasons.
- Use teacher's geometry box for demonstrating all the constructions.

WORKSHEET

Complete the following table.

Triangle	Equilateral	Isosceles	Right-angled
Definition			
Criteria used			
Steps of construction			
Figure			

13 Symmetry

Learning Objectives

- To identify the line of symmetry for regular polygons
- To understand relation between reflection and symmetry
- To define rotational symmetry
- To find the order of rotation and angle of rotation for the given figures
- To identify figures with both line symmetry and rotational symmetry

Let's Get Started

Janhvi wants to participate in a rangoli competition that will be held as part of pongal celebrations in her apartment complex. She collected the following rangoli designs. She started identifying the symmetrical patterns among them. Help Janhvi identify the lines of symmetries in each of these designs and write the number of lines of symmetries in the boxes provided below.

LINE SYMMETRY

In the previous class, we learnt about line symmetry. Let us recall it and learn further. A figure is said to have **line symmetry**, if one half of it exactly matches with the other half when it is folded along a dotted line. The dotted line along which the figure is folded is called the **line of symmetry**. We can observe line symmetry everywhere around us. Some examples are given below.

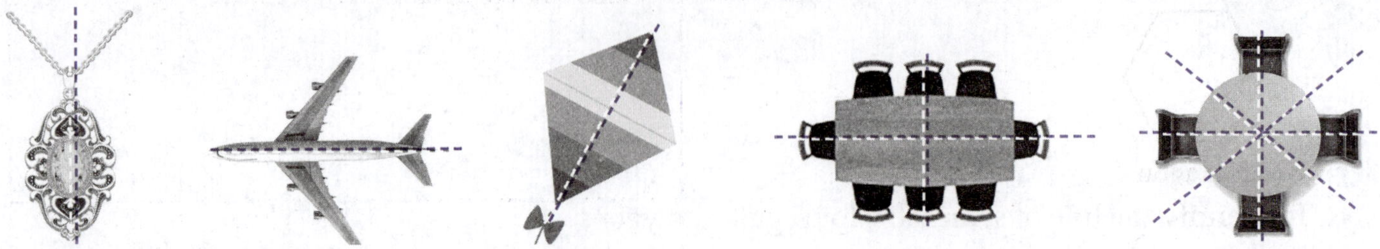

(a) (b) (c) (d) (e)

In the above figures, figure (a) has **vertical** line of symmetry, figure (b) has **horizontal** line of symmetry and figure (c) has **diagonal** line of symmetry. Figure (d) has both **vertical** and **horizontal** lines of symmetry and figure (e) has **vertical, horizontal** and **diagonal** lines of symmetry.

Lines of Symmetry for Regular Polygons

Look at the following shapes. What are these shapes called?

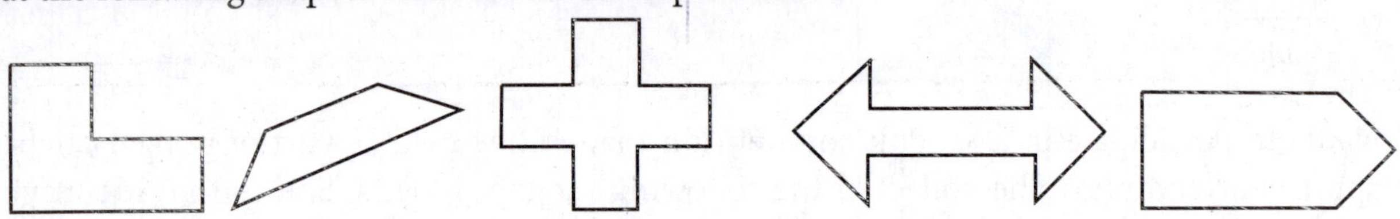

These are all polygons. A **polygon** is a closed figure made up of only line segments. Look at the polygon shown aside. How is it different from the above polygons?

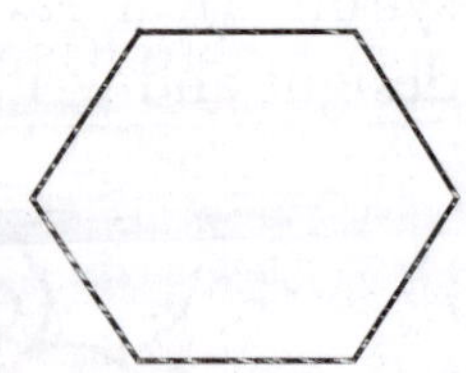

By measuring its sides and angles, we can see that all sides are of equal length and all its angles are also of equal measure. Such polygons are known as **regular polygons**. They are named based on the number of sides.

All regular polygons exhibit interesting patterns with respect to line symmetry.

Now look at the following table, observe and try to complete it. Use a mirror to find the lines of symmetry for each polygon.

Regular polygon	Number of sides	Number of lines of symmetry
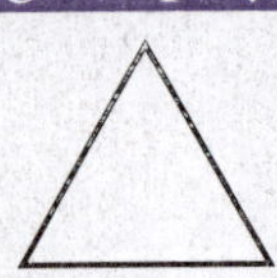 Equilateral triangle	3	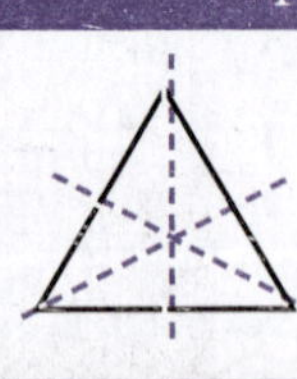 3 lines of symmetry
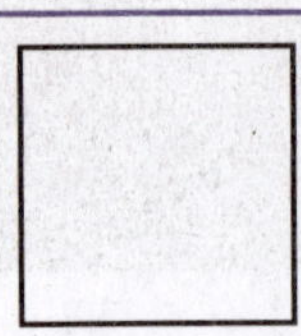 Square	4	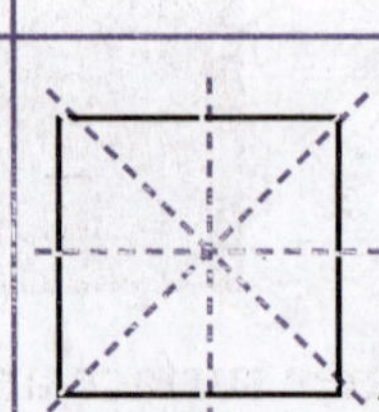 4 lines of symmetry

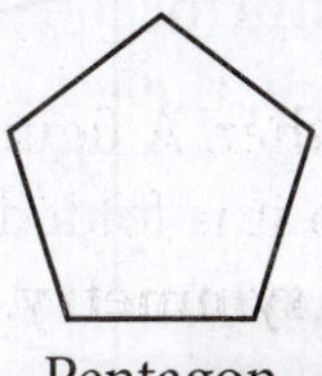 Pentagon	5	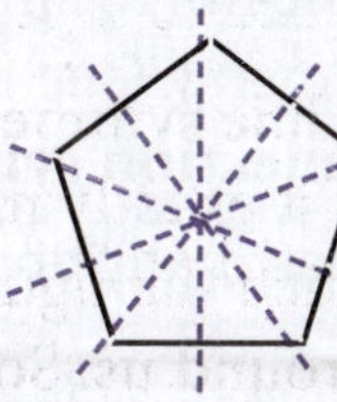 5 lines of symmetry
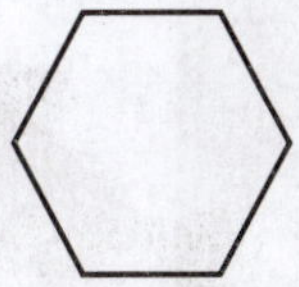 Hexagon	6	
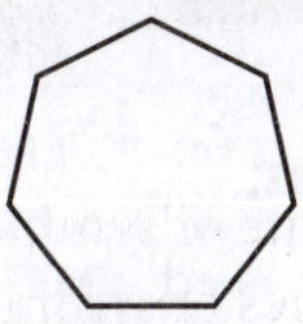 Heptagon	7	
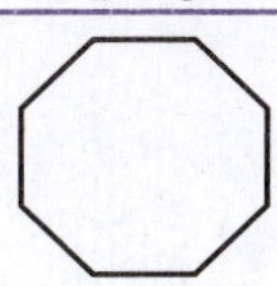 Octagon		
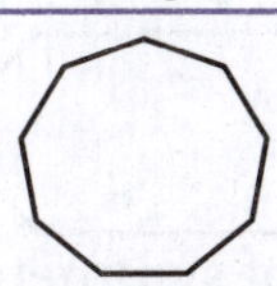 Nonagon		
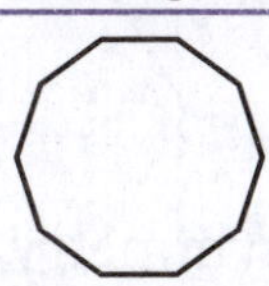 Decagon		

From the above table, we can observe that **a regular polygon with *n* sides has *n* lines of symmetry**.

REFLECTION AND SYMMETRY

Observe the following figures. What can you see?

The objects are reflected over the water surface and their images are formed. The images formed are of the same size and shape as that of the original object, but its direction is reversed. The object and its reflected image together form a beautiful symmetrical figure. So, we can say that a shape or figure has line symmetry when one half of it is the mirror image of the other half. Here, the mirror line helps to visualise the line of symmetry (see the figure given alongside). Hence, the line symmetry is also referred to as **reflection symmetry** or **mirror symmetry**.

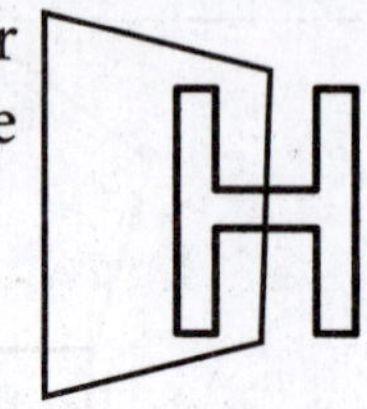

The concept of reflection symmetry has many applications.

- It is used for decoration in temples, palaces, etc.
- In building kaleidoscope

You would have seen the magic mirror galleries in science exhibitions. They have been built upon this concept of mirror reflection.

SOLVED EXAMPLES

Example 1: Find the number of lines of symmetry for each of the following figures.

a. 

b. 

c. 

d. 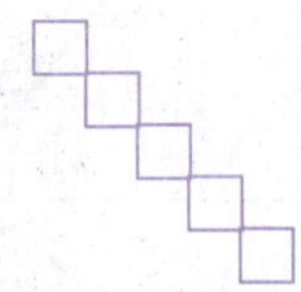

Solution:

a. 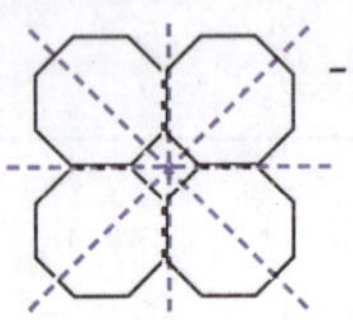 - 4 lines of symmetry

b. 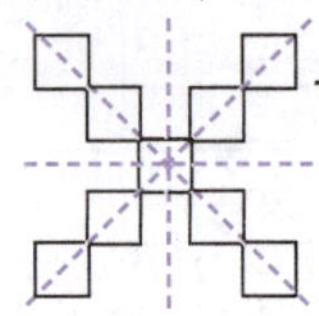 - 4 lines of symmetry

c. 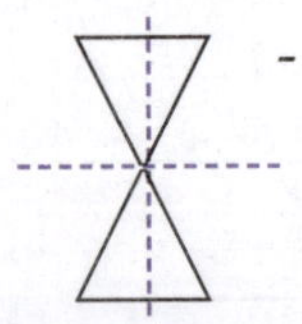 - 2 lines of symmetry

d. 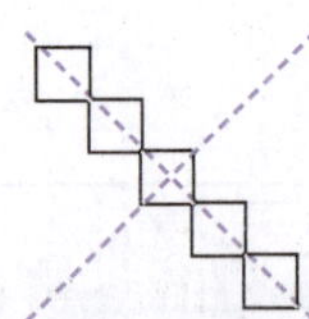 - 2 lines of symmetry

Example 2: Complete the following figures such that the dotted line is the line of symmetry.

a. 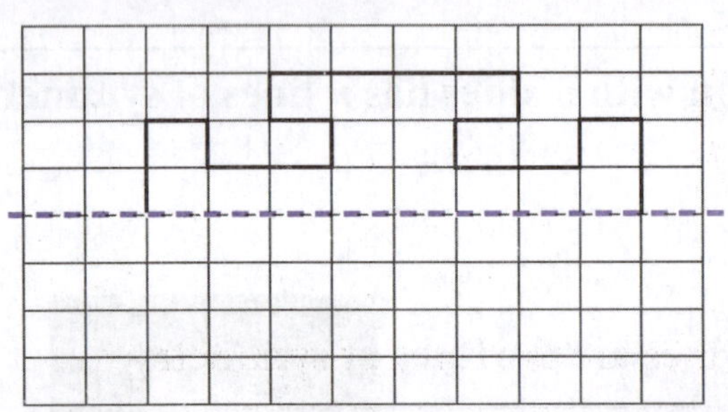

b. 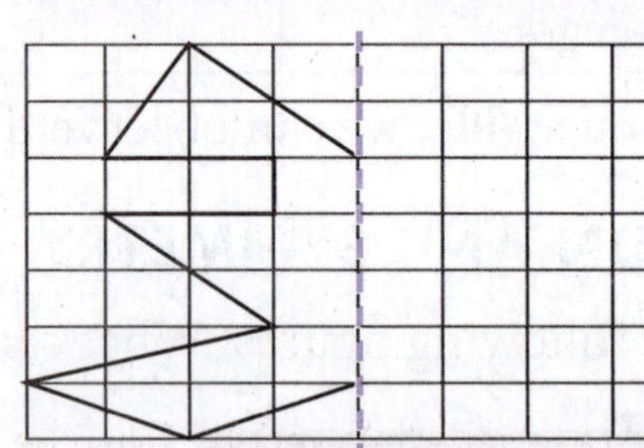

Solution:

a. 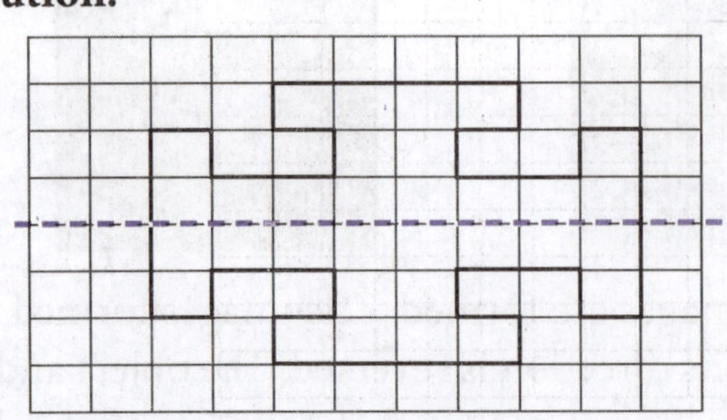

b. 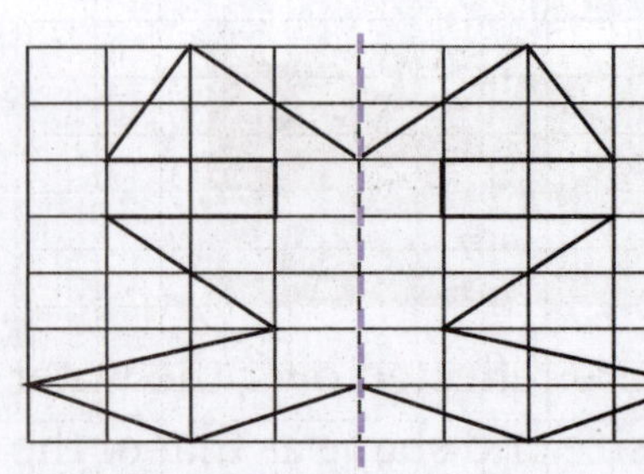

EXERCISE 13A

1. **Draw the line(s) of symmetry for the following figures.**

a. 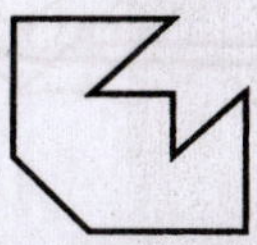 b. 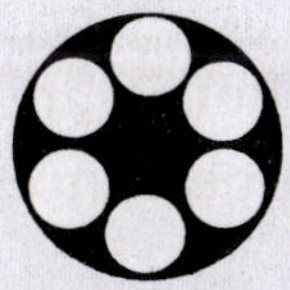 c. 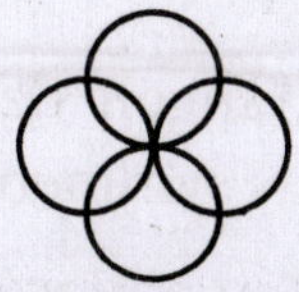 d. 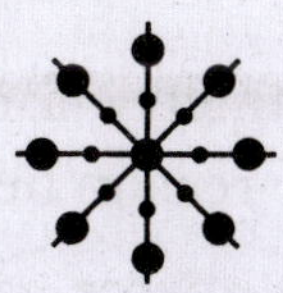 e. 

2. **Match the figures with their lines of symmetry.**

a.  i. 2

b.  ii. 6

c.  iii. 5

d. 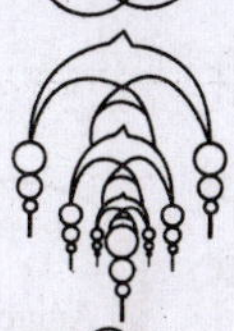 iv. 4

e. 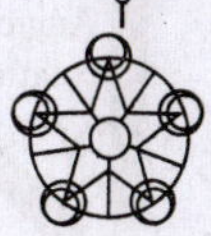 v. 1

3. **Identify the number of lines of symmetry for the given figure.**

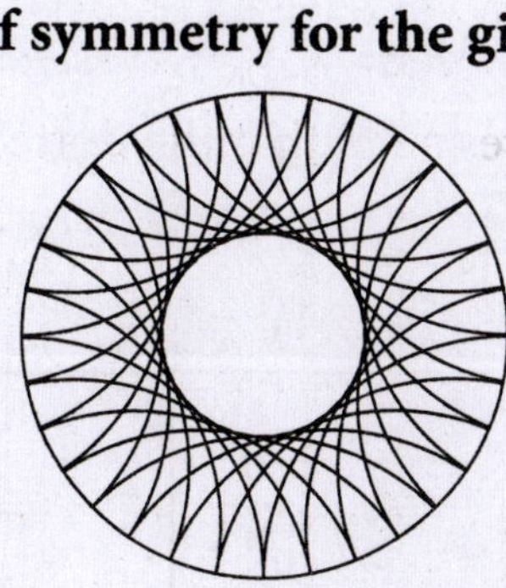

4. **Complete the following figures so that the dotted lines are the lines of symmetry.**

a. 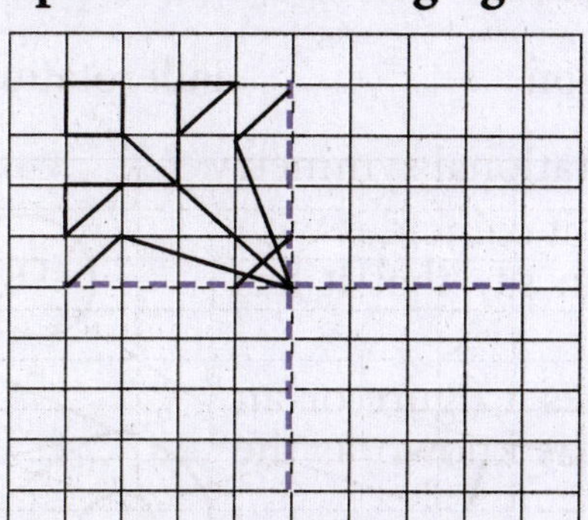

b. 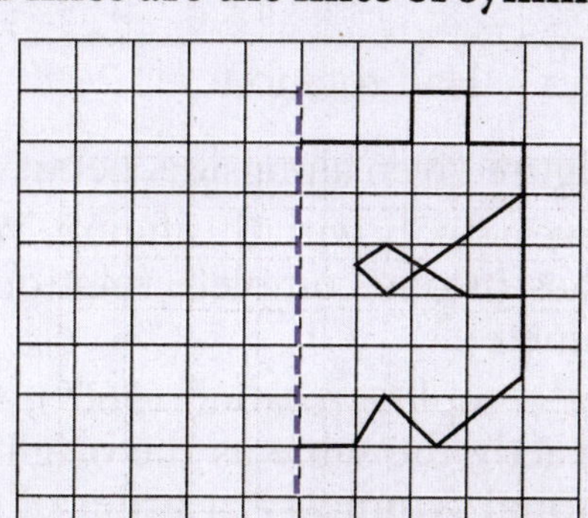

ROTATIONAL SYMMETRY

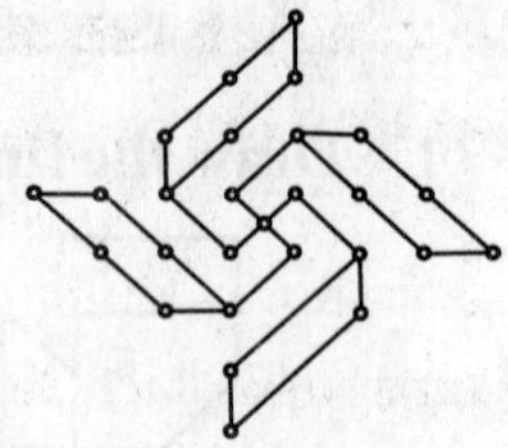

We have seen many rangoli designs and explored the lines of symmetry in them. Look at the rangoli design shown alongside. Can you find the line(s) of symmetry for it?

No, there are no lines of symmetry for this rangoli design. But it appears symmetrical. Let us find out the reason behind its symmetrical appearance.

ACTIVITY

Take two patty papers and copy this rangoli design on both. Place them one above the other such that they exactly coincide and pin them at the centre. Now, rotate the top design and observe if it coincides with the bottom design at least once before one complete rotation.

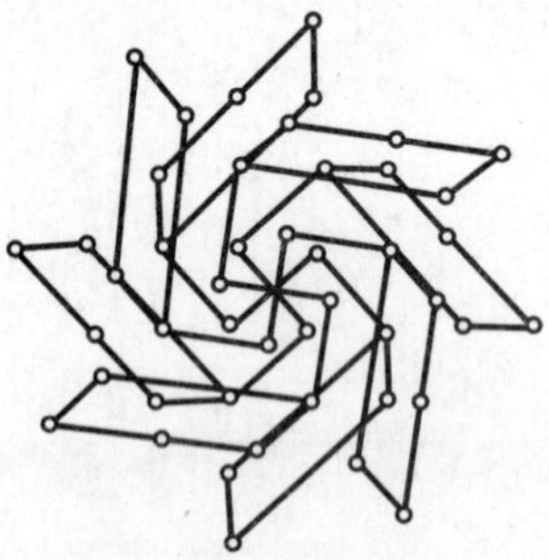

> We will observe that the design coincides or matches exactly with itself four times in one complete rotation. Such figures are said to have **rotational symmetry**.
>
> **A figure has rotational symmetry if it looks exactly the same in one complete rotation**. When a figure or an object rotates, its shape and size do not change.

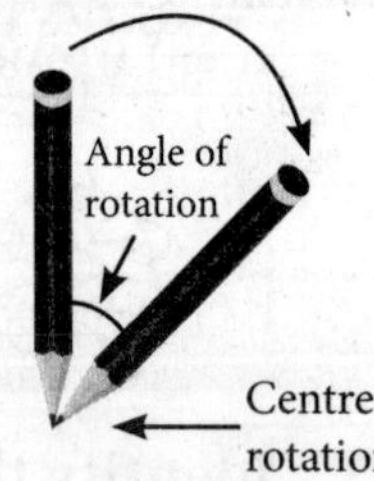

When an object or figure is rotated about a fixed point completely, it covers one full rotation. The fixed point is called the **centre of rotation**. The angle by which the object is turned or rotated is known as the **angle of rotation**.

In one complete rotation, the angle covered is 360°. Similarly, in half rotation, it is 180°; in quarter rotation, it is 90° and in three-fourths rotation, it is 270°, all of which are illustrated below.

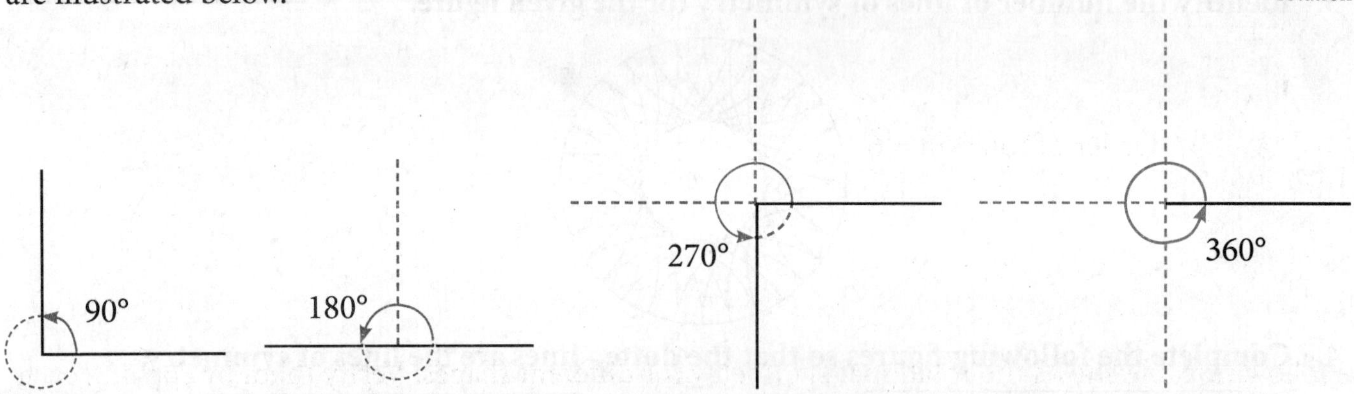

Quarter rotation   Half rotation   Three-fourth rotation   Full rotation

Consider the figure given alongside. Let us find out if it has rotational symmetry. Repeat the above activity with this figure. We will observe that it coincides with itself three times in one complete rotation. Therefore, we can say that it has rotational symmetry.

Further, in one complete rotation (360°), the number of times a figure or an object looks exactly the same as the original figure or object is known as the **order of rotational symmetry** or **order of rotation.**

Hence, the order of rotational symmetry of this figure is 3.

The order of rotational symmetry of the figure given alongside is 4.

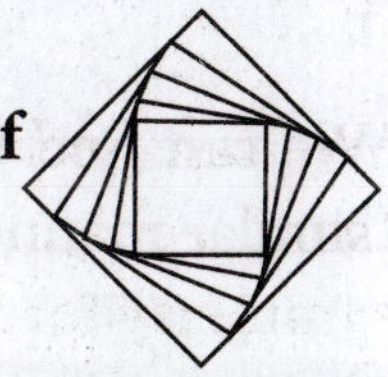

We can find the angle of rotation if we know the order of rotation. If the order of rotation of a figure is n, then the angle of rotation is given by $\frac{360°}{n}$.

SOLVED EXAMPLES

Example 3: Tick the objects that have rotational symmetry of order more than 1. Also find their order of rotational symmetry.

> **Note**
>
> By default, all figures or objects have a rotational symmetry of order 1 as they look the same after a complete rotation (of 360°).

a. 

b. 

c. 

d. 

e. 

Solution:

a.  Order of rotation = 7

b.  Order of rotation = 10

c.  Not more than 1

d. 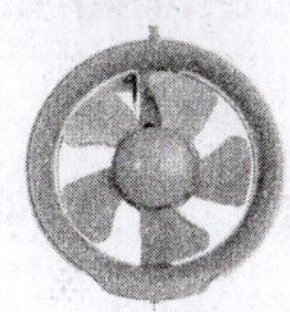 Order of rotation = 5

e.  Order of rotation = 6

Rotational Symmetry in General Shapes

The following table shows the rotational symmetry for different shapes. Verify them by copying each shape on a patty paper and rotating them.

Figure	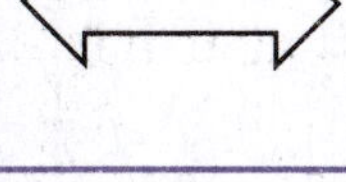	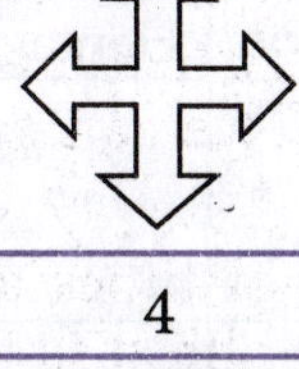		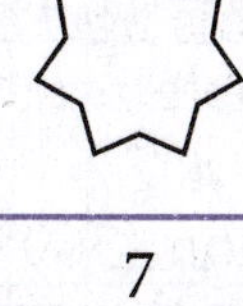	
Order of rotation	2	4	8	7	1
Angle of rotation	180°	90°	45°	51.4°	360° (does not have rotational symmetry)

Rotational Symmetry in Geometrical Shapes

We can find the rotational symmetry of different polygons like triangles, quadrilaterals etc. in the similar manner as done above. Some of them are given below.

Shape	Order of rotation	Angle of rotation	Remarks
Scalene triangle	1	360°	Does not have rotational symmetry
Isosceles triangle	1	360°	Does not have rotational symmetry
Rectangle	2	180°	
Rhombus	2	180°	
Parallelogram	2	180°	
Trapezium	1	360°	Does not have rotational symmetry
Kite	1	360°	Does not have rotational symmetry
Circle	Infinite	Every angle	Has rotational symmetry of infinite order

ROTATIONAL SYMMETRY IN REGULAR POLYGONS

We learnt that regular polygons exhibit a pattern in line symmetry. Do they also exhibit a similar pattern in rotational symmetry? Let us explore it.

Copy the regular polygons given below on a patty paper and find the order and angle of rotational symmetry for each.

Regular polygon	Equilateral	Square	Pentagon	Hexagon	Heptagon	Octagon	Nonagon	Decagon
Order of rotational symmetry	3	4	5	6	7	8	9	10
Angle of rotational symmetry	120°	90°	72°	60°	51.42°	45°	40°	36°

From the table on previous page, we can observe that **a regular polygon with *n* sides has a rotational symmetry of order *n* and the angle of rotation is given by $\frac{360^\circ}{n}$.**

LINE SYMMETRY AND ROTATIONAL SYMMETRY

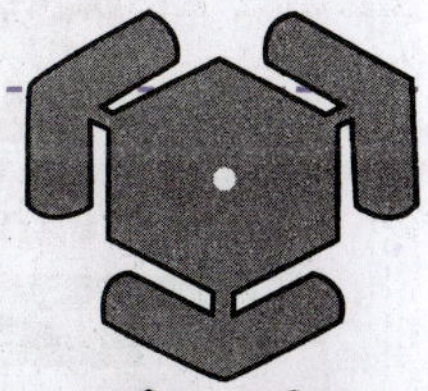

Look at the figure shown alongside. Does it have line symmetry or rotational or both? Take a mirror and identify the lines of symmetry. We will find that it has 3 lines of symmetry.

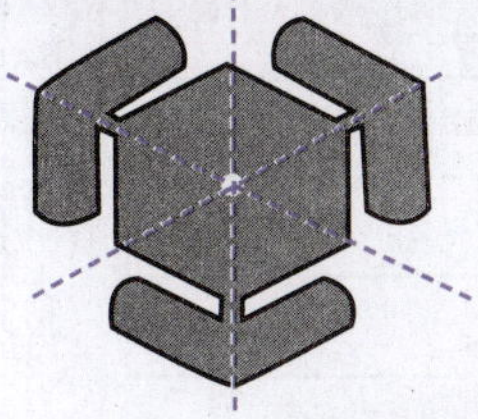

Let us find out whether it has rotational symmetry. Copy the figure on a patty paper and rotate it. We will notice that it has rotational symmetry of order 3 and its angle of rotation is 120°.

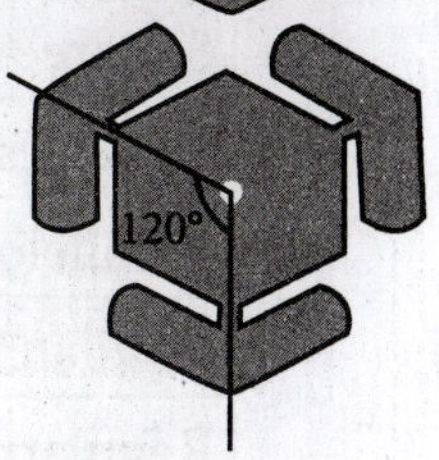

Therefore, the given figure has both line symmetry and rotational symmetry.

Let us consider a few more examples to explore it further.

This has only line symmetry with 1 line of symmetry. It has no rotational symmetry.

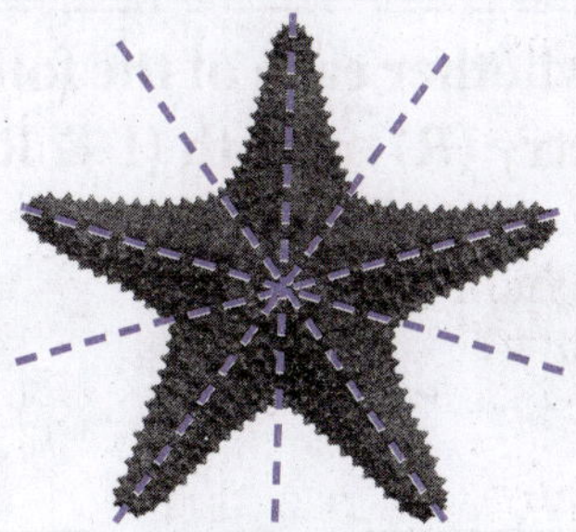

This has 5 lines of symmetry. It has a rotational symmetry of order 5 and the angle of rotation is 72°.

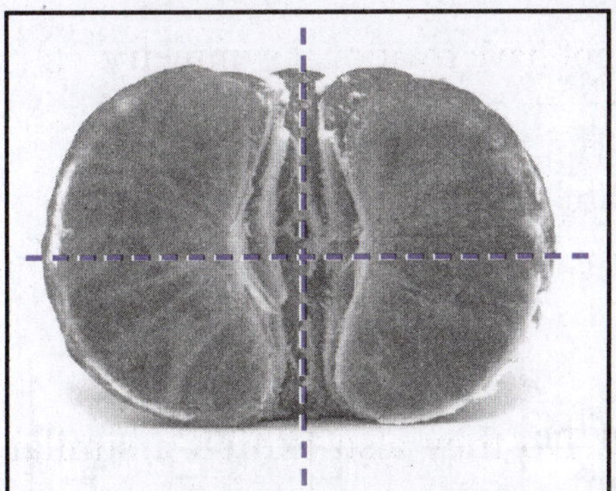

This has 2 lines of symmetry. It has a rotational symmetry of order 2 and the angle of rotation is 180°.

This has only rotational symmetry of order 5 and the angle of rotation is 72°. It has no line symmetry.

Mental Maths

1. Name the letters that have rotational symmetry of order 2.
2. Name the numbers that have rotational symmetry of order 2.
3. Name at least three real-life objects that exhibit rotational symmetry.
4. Name category of shapes that have same number of lines of symmetry and the order of rotation.
5. What can you say about rotational symmetry of circle?

EXERCISE 13B

1. **Which of the following images have rotational symmetry of order more than 1?**

a. 

b. 

c. 

2. **Write the order of rotational symmetry for the following figures.**

a. 

b. 

c. 

3. **Write the order and the angle of rotational symmetry for the following shapes.**

Shape	Order of rotational symmetry	Angle of rotational symmetry
Square		
Isosceles trapezium		
Parallelogram		
Equilateral triangle		
Regular nonagon		

4. **Write whether each of the following figures has only line symmetry (L) or only rotational symmetry (R) or both (L & R) or none (N).**

a. 

b. 

c. 

d. 

e. 

Maths Lab Activity

Aim: To identify the line symmetry and rotational symmetry in the nets of a cube

Materials required: Patty paper cut-outs of the nets of cubes given here, cardboard and board pin, plane mirror

Procedure:

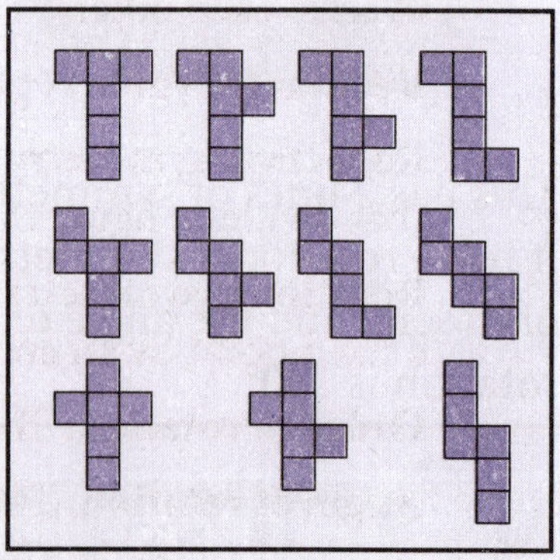

1. Arrange the students into groups and provide two sets of cut-outs of the nets of cube; a cardboard and board pins; and a mirror to each group.

To find the lines of symmetry

2. Ask each group to use the mirror and mark the line of symmetry for each of the nets if any and write their observations in the table format given below.

To find the rotational symmetry

3. Then ask each group to fix the two cut-outs of the same net on the cardboard using a board pin.
4. Instruct them to rotate the top net and check if it coincides with the bottom net before one complete rotation. And if it coincides, how many times does it coincide.
5. Ask each group to note down their observations in the following format and compare their findings.

Net of the cube	Has line symmetry? (Yes/No)	Number of lines of symmetry	Has rotational symmetry? (Yes/No)	Order of rotational symmetry

Concept Map

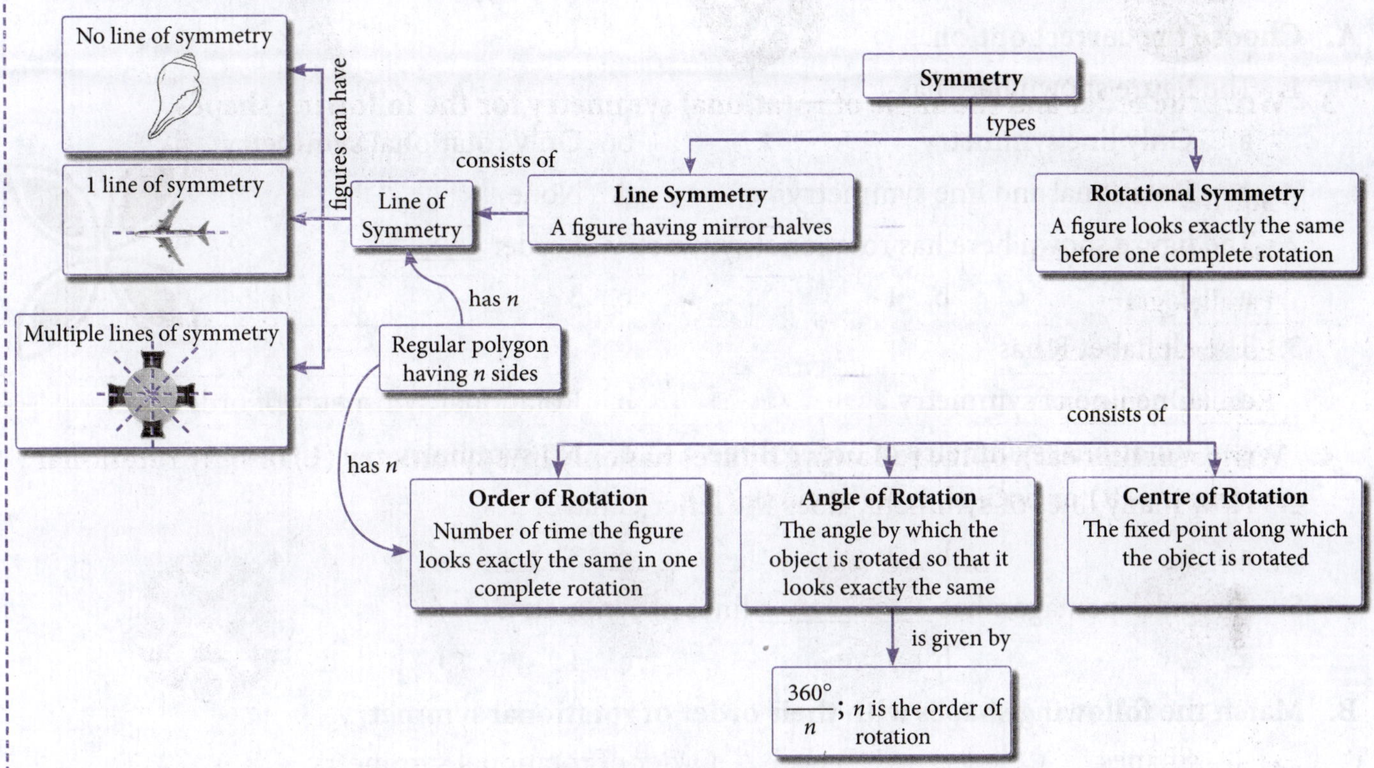

Key Concepts

- **Symmetry:** The property of any object or figure being made up of exactly identical parts or halves
- **Line of symmetry:** The line along which a figure can be folded so that the two halves exactly overlap each other
- **Regular polygon:** A polygon whose sides are of equal length and whose angles are of equal measure
- **Reflection symmetry:** A figure is said to have reflection symmetry if there exists at least one line that divides a figure into two mirror halves
- **Rotational symmetry:** The property of a figure to look exactly the same when it is rotated around a fixed point by an angle
- **Order of rotation:** The number of times an object looks exactly the same in one complete rotation
- **Angle of rotation:** The angle by which the object is rotated to look exactly the same
- **Centre of rotation:** The fixed point along which the object is rotated

CHAPTER REVISION

A. Choose the correct option.

1. The figure shown here has________.
   a. Only line symmetry   b. Only rotational symmetry
   c. Rotational and line symmetry   d. None
2. The figure shown here has rotational symmetry of order _______.
   a. 2   b. 1   c. 3   d. 4
3. The alphabet R has
   a. One line of symmetry   b. Rotational symmetry of order two
   c. Rotational symmetry of order three   d. No symmetry
4. How many lines of symmetry does the letter O have?
   a. 1   b. 2   c. 3   d. 4
5. A regular pentagon has ___________ lines of symmetry.
   a. 2   b. 3   c. 4   d. 5

B. Match the following shapes with their order of rotational symmetry.

Shapes	Order of rotational symmetry
1. Equilateral triangle	a. Infinite
2. Parallelogram	b. 2
3. Circle	c. 4
4. Kite	d. 1
5. Square	e. 3

C. Fill in the blanks.

1. Figures that do not have any lines of symmetry are called ___________ figures.
2. Figure has___________ symmetry if it can be rotated about a fixed point about a certain angle.
3. A regular polygon with 15 sides will have ___________ lines of symmetry.
4.  has only ___________ symmetry.
5. The angle of rotation of a figure whose order of rotation is r is ___________.

D. Write T for true and F for false.

1. The letter Q has rotational symmetry.
2. Everything in nature is symmetrical.
3. Every triangle has 3 lines of symmetry.
4. The letter E has one line of symmetry.
5. For every regular polygon, the number of lines of symmetry and the order of rotation are same.

E. Answer the following questions.

1. State the types of symmetries found in a circle. Also, mention the number of lines of symmetry, order of rotational symmetry.
2. Draw the lines of symmetry of the following polygon and fill in the blanks.

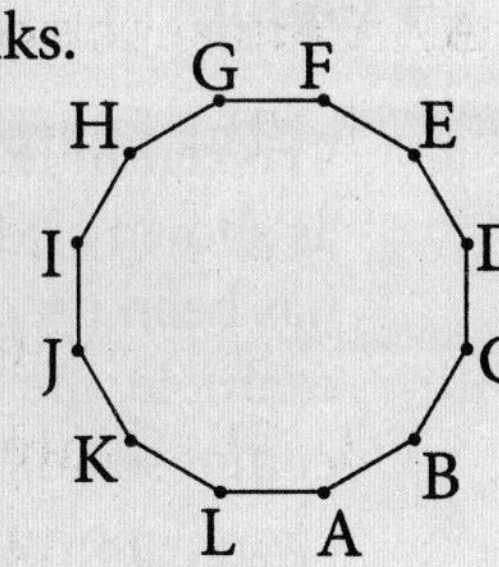

   a. Number of sides is ____________.
   b. Number of lines of symmetry is ____________.
   c. Order of rotational symmetry is ____________.
   d. Name of the regular polygon is ____________.
3. Draw all possible lines of symmetry for the figures shown below.

a. 

b. 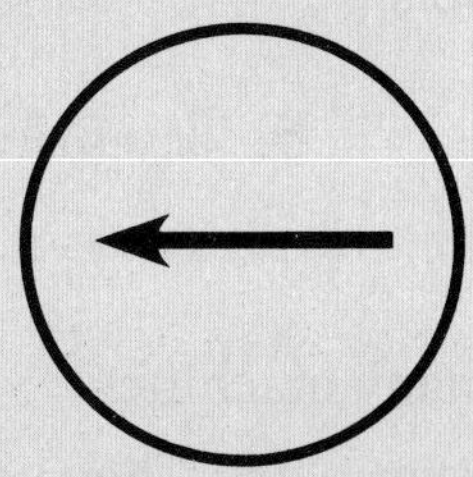

c. 

d. 

4. Find the number of lines of symmetry as well as order and angle of rotational symmetry for the following figure.

5. Draw lines of symmetry and write the order of rotation for the following polygons.
   a. Regular hexagon
   b. Regular pentagon
   c. Rectangle
   d. Regular nonagon
   e. Regular heptagon

SKILL UP!

Project

Triskelion is an image consisting of a triple spiral as shown aside. It exhibits rotational symmetry. It has been used in many art works, logos, etc. For example, the flag of the Isle of Man is a triskelion, composed of three armoured legs with golden spurs, upon a red background. Does it have a line symmetry? Also, find some more logos, symbols and pictures where it has been used.

Triskelion

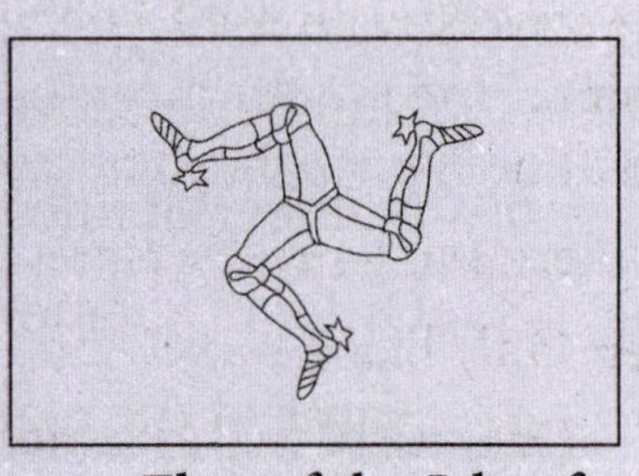

Flag of the Isle of Man

Life Skills

1. Rotational symmetry is very essential to run many machines.

   For example, the windmills exhibit rotational symmetry. They use the wind's motion to turn their symmetric turbines. Find out the role of rotational symmetry in it. Also, find out how electricity is generated.
2. We come across various logos/symbols in our everyday lives. Look for these logos and symbols in magazines and newspapers and paste their cut-outs in a chart paper. Identify the line symmetry and rotational symmetry for each of them.

Mind Buzzer

All of you would have visited a fair and enjoyed many rides there. The most common and the famous ride is the giant wheel. Look at the giant wheel and analyze the symmetry that it exhibits.

Teacher's Notes

- Bring regular polygons to the class and distribute them to students and investigate their line symmetry and rotational symmetry.
- Explain clearly the difference between the line symmetry and rotational symmetry.
- Give sufficient practice of finding the order and angle of rotation for different objects.
- Build a kaleidoscope in the class and let each student explore its design.

WORKSHEET

While travelling on road, you would have come across different signals. Each signal conveys a specific meaning. Find out the meaning of each signal. Given below are some of the traffic signals. Some of them exhibit line symmetry, some exhibit rotational symmetry; some exhibit both and some none.

Find them and write the codes given for each in the space provided.

Codes: Only line symmetry: L

Only rotational symmetry: R

Both line symmetry and rotational symmetry: L & R

None: N

Road Close

Overtaking Prohibited

No Entry for Motor Vehicles

Roundabout

Y-junction

No parking

Police checkpoint

Audible Warning Device prohibited

Keep To the Right

Keep To the left

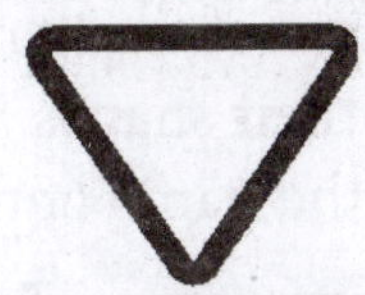
Give way Sign

Hump/Speed Breaker

Uneven Road

Road Dips

Pedestrian crossing

No Entry

Stop Sign

Steep Ascent

Carrtageway Narrows

Cattle Crossing

Slippery Road

One Way Road

Dangerous Descent

Road Works

14 Visualising Solid Shapes

Learning Objectives

- To differentiate between the plane or 2-D shapes and solid or 3-D shapes
- To identify faces, edges and vertices of different solid shapes
- To draw nets of different solid shapes
- To draw oblique sketches and isometric sketches of solid shapes
- To illustrate various ways of viewing different sections of a solid

Let's Get Started

Eva is arranging some of the items in her room. She requests her brother to help her in arranging the items according to their shapes. Help them in identifying the shapes of the items and arranging them accordingly. Write the name of the shape and the corresponding item in the space provided.

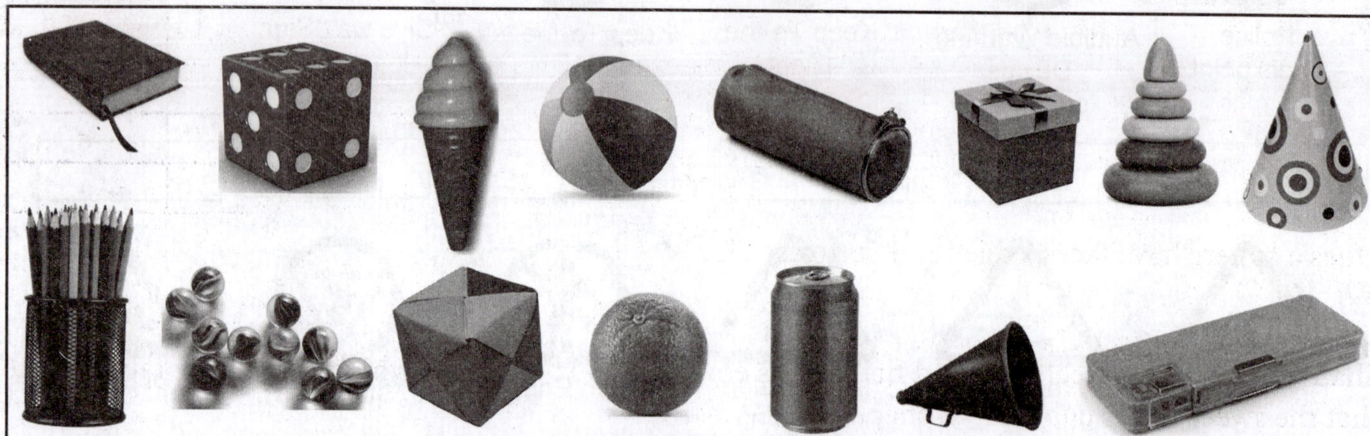

PLANE FIGURES AND SOLID SHAPES

We can classify figures based on their dimensions. All the objects given in the previous section are called solid shapes or three-dimensional shapes (3-D shapes).

A solid shape has length, breadth and height (or depth). It also has surface area and volume. Look at the figures shown below.

They are called plane figures or two-dimensional shapes (2-D shapes). A plane figure has only length and breadth. It has only area. Plane figures can be drawn on paper (i.e., a flat surface).

Prisms and pyramids are also examples of 3-D shapes. Do you remember how a prism is different from a pyramid?

Let us study more about 3-D shapes in this chapter.

FACES, EDGES AND VERTICES OF A SOLID

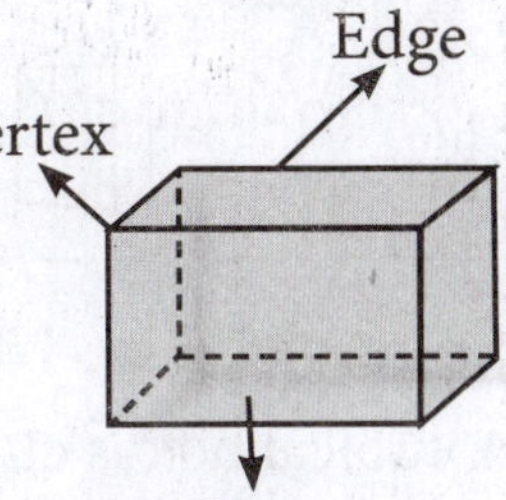

Consider a solid shape (e.g., a cuboid) shown alongside.

The surface of a solid is called its **face**. It may be flat or curved. The line where two faces meet is called an **edge**. The point where two or more edges meet is called a **vertex.**

The number of faces, edges and vertices of different solids is given in the following table:

Solid	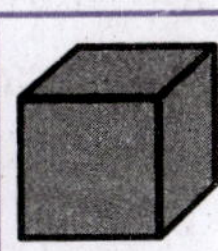 Cube	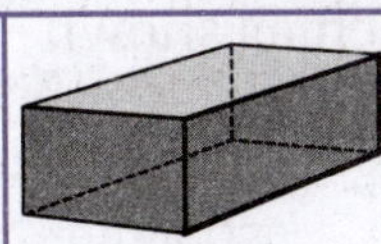 Cuboid	 Cone	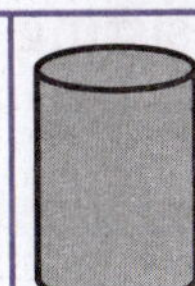 Cylinder	 Triangular prism	 Triangular pyramid
Faces	6	6	2	3	5	4
Edges	12	12	1	2	9	6
Vertices	8	8	1	0	6	4

Does a sphere have faces, edges and vertices? Think!

NETS OF 3-D SHAPES

Shaurya is fond of sweets. He and his friends emptied a box of sweets which was on the table. (Note that the sweet box is cuboidal in shape.)

Before throwing the box into the bin, he opened the box and it looked like as shown below.

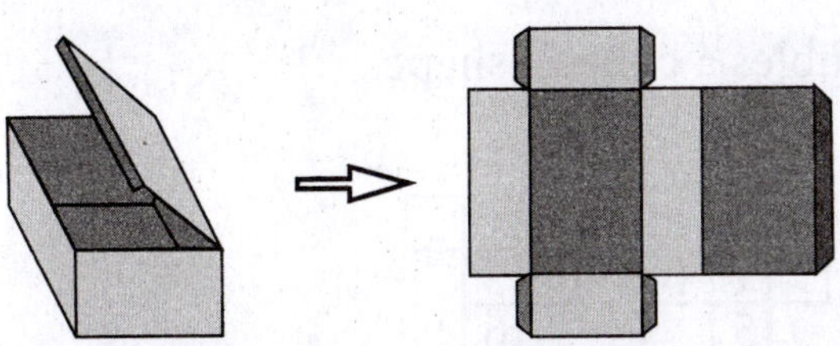

We can see three pairs of rectangles of different sizes, each pair being identical.
In other words, a 2-D shape is obtained when a 3-D solid is opened. It is the net for that sweet box.
So, a **net** is a 2-D shape that can be folded to form a 3-D solid.

Net is obtained when the surface of a 3-D shape is laid flat showing each face of the shape.

Now use glue and try to stick the edges together to get back the box. Is it possible?

The nets of some common 3-D shapes are shown below:

Net of a cube: It has 6 squares. 	**Net of a cuboid:** It has 3 pairs of rectangles of different sizes, each pair being identical. 
Net of a cone: It has 1 circle and 1 sector of another circle. 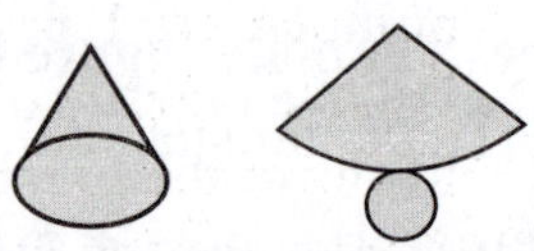	**Net of a cylinder:** It has 2 circles and 1 rectangle. 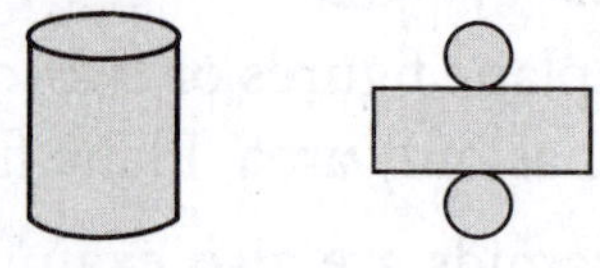
Net of a triangular prism: It has 2 triangles and 3 rectangles. 	**Net of a triangular pyramid:** It has 4 equilateral triangles. 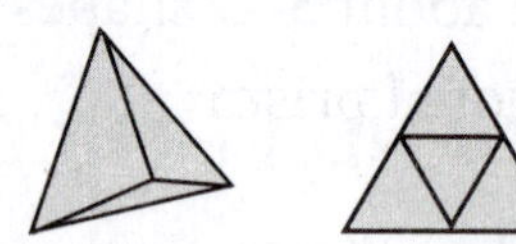

Special Case: Net of a Cube

A cubical box is cut open and its net is shown alongside.

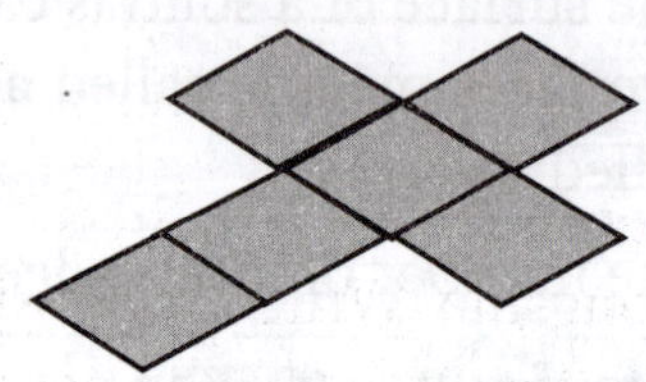

Take objects (such as sweet boxes of different sizes) that resemble a cube and cut them open. Try to draw all possible nets for each of them.

We will find that a cube has 11 nets consisting of 6 squares each as shown here.

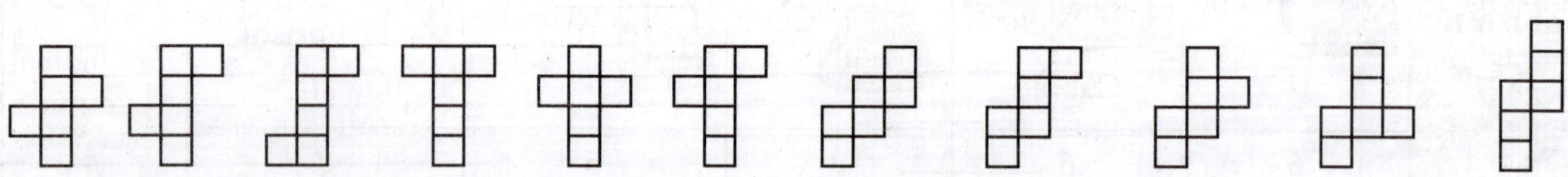

We know that a dice is an example of a cube. Take a dice, roll it and record your observations in the format given below.

Number on the dice	Number on the opposite side of the dice	Sum

We can infer from the above activity that **the opposite faces of a dice sum up to 7.**

The net of a dice is the same as the net of a cube as a dice resembles a cube in shape.

Given below are the nets of a dice with numbers.

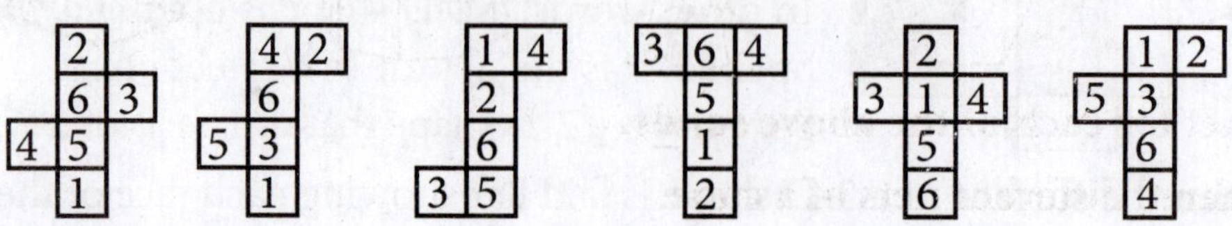

SOLVED EXAMPLES

Example 1: Name the solids and identify the number of faces, edges and vertices. Also, draw the nets of the given solids.

a. 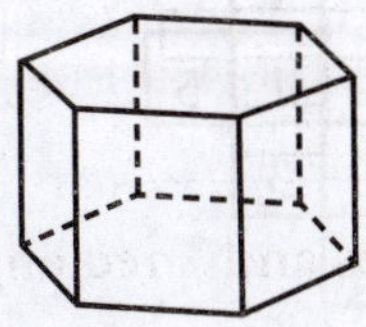

b. 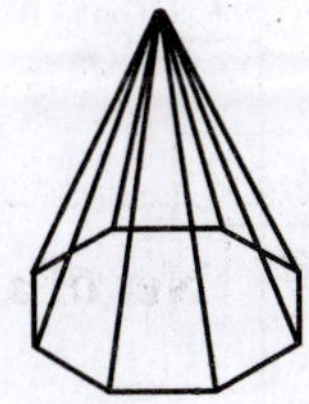

> **Go Easy!**
>
> There is an easy way of filling the numbers in the net of the numbered dice. Basic rule is that the sum of the numbers on the opposite faces is 7. The pairs of numbers are 1, 6; 2, 5 and 3, 4. Fill one number of any pair, say 2, in any of the squares. Then put a cross over each line of that square to the neighbouring squares. Fill the other number in the pair in the square that is not reached. Similarly, fill the other two pairs.

Solution:

a. Hexagonal prism

F = 8, E = 18, V = 12

Net of a hexagonal prism

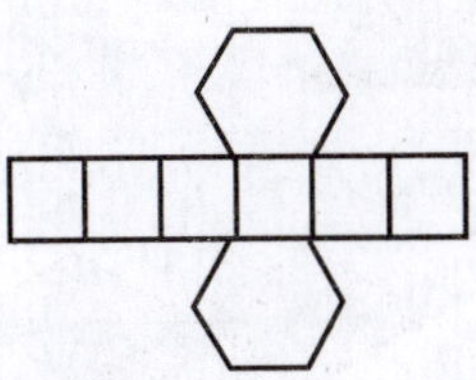

b. Octagonal pyramid

F = 9, E = 16, V = 9

Net of an octagonal pyramid

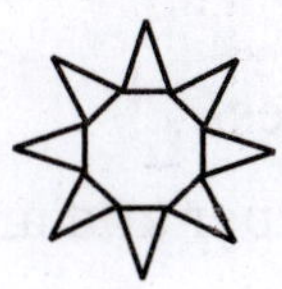

Example 2: The nets of a cube are given alongside. Write the missing numbers from 1 to 6 so that it forms the net of a dice.

a. 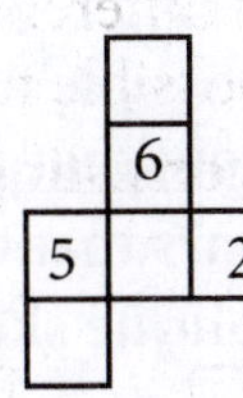

b. 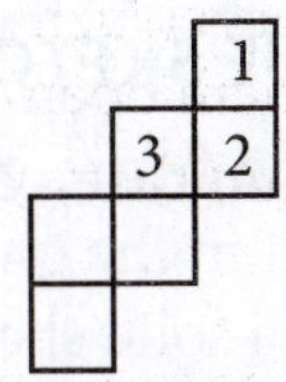

Solution:

a. 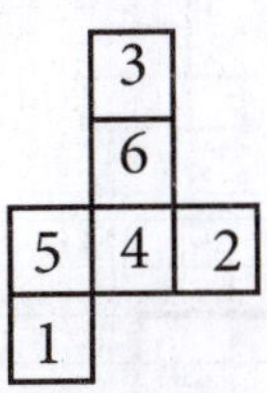

b. 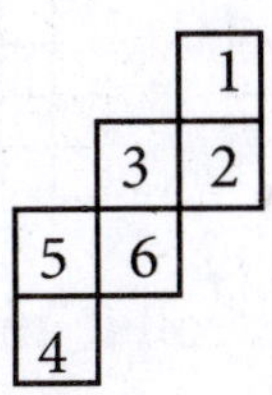

EXERCISE 14A

1. **Give three examples each for plane figures and solid shapes.**
2. **Name any two real-life objects that resemble a cylinder and a cone.**
3. **Write the name, number of faces, edges and vertices for each of the following solids.**

a. 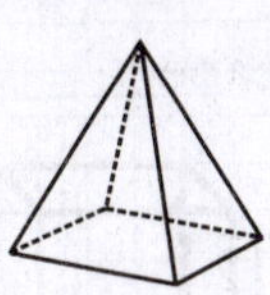

b. 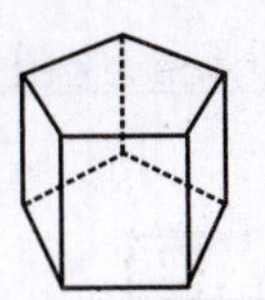

c. 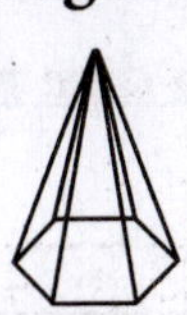

d. 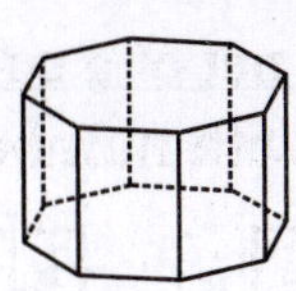

e. 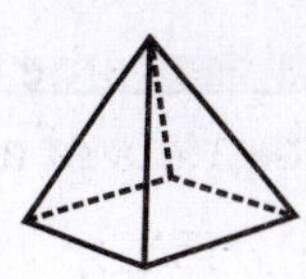

f. 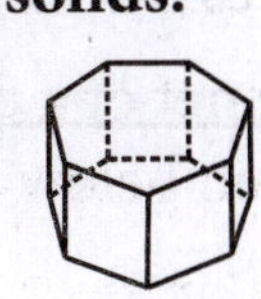

4. **Draw the net for each of the above solids.**
5. **Draw any three different nets of a cube.**

6. Which among the following is not a net of a dice? Justify your answer. Rewrite the numbers so that it becomes the net of a dice.

a. 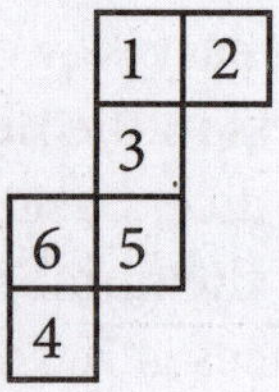

b. 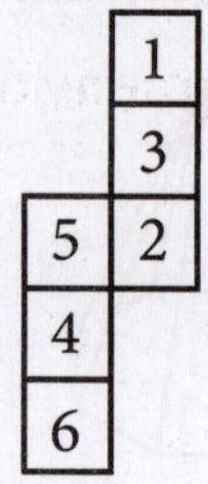

c. 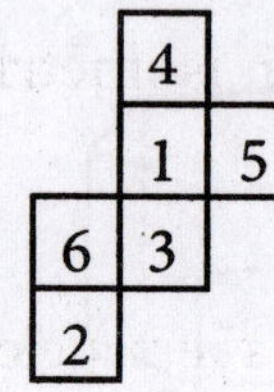

DRAWING SOLID SHAPES ON FLAT SURFACES

We all know that plane figures can be drawn on a sheet of paper. Is it possible to draw a 3-D shape on paper?

Solid shapes like cubes, cuboids, etc. can be drawn on the following:

- A square grid paper—Gives oblique sketches
- Isometric dot paper—Gives isometric sketches

Find out what is the difference between a grid paper and an isometric dot paper.

Let us learn how to draw solid shapes on flat surfaces.

OBLIQUE SKETCHES

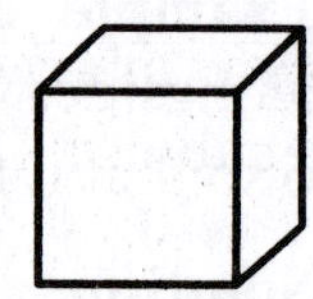

This is the figure of a cube. We know that the lengths of all the edges in a cube are equal. But in the given figure, it appears that the length of each edge is not equal. Such a sketch of a solid shape is called an **oblique sketch.** To draw an oblique sketch, we need a squared paper (with lines or dots).

Let us draw an oblique sketch of a cube.

<table>
<tr><td>Step 1: Draw the front face of the cube.</td><td>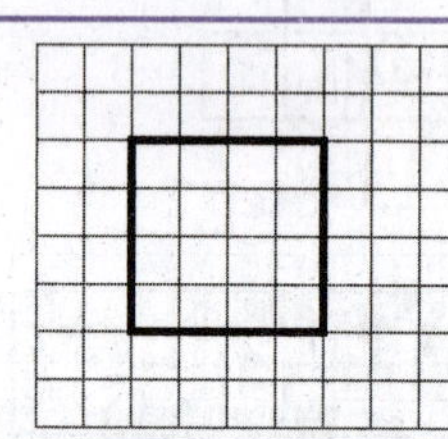</td></tr>
<tr><td>Step 2: Draw the back face (opposite face) one division above and one division to the side of the front face. The size of both the faces should be the same.</td><td>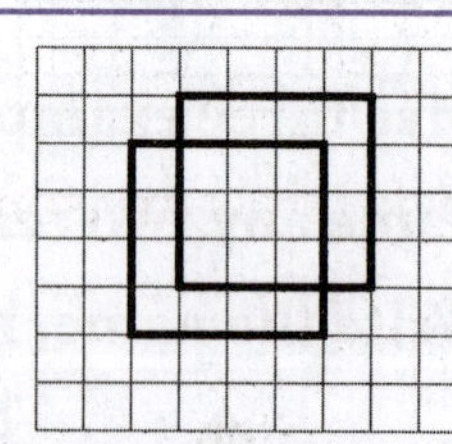</td></tr>
<tr><td>Step 3: Join the corresponding vertices. Use dotted lines for hidden edges.</td><td>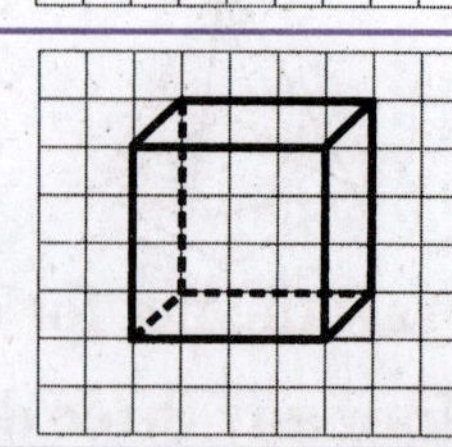</td></tr>
</table>

Observe that in the above oblique sketch drawn, the edges of the cube and the sketch appear to be the same although the exact measures of those edges are not taken into account.

ISOMETRIC SKETCHES

An isometric dot paper divides the paper into small equilateral triangles consisting of dots or lines. It is used to draw sketches with the same measurements as those of the original solid.

Let us draw an isometric sketch of a cuboid of dimensions (4 × 3 × 2) units.

Step 1: Draw a rectangle of (4 × 3) units.	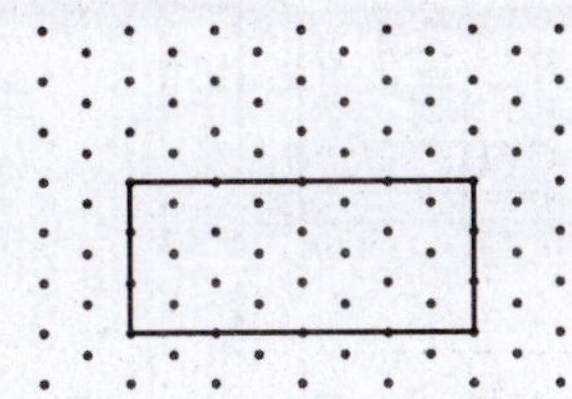
Step 2: From all the four corners of the rectangle, draw slanting lines of 2 units.	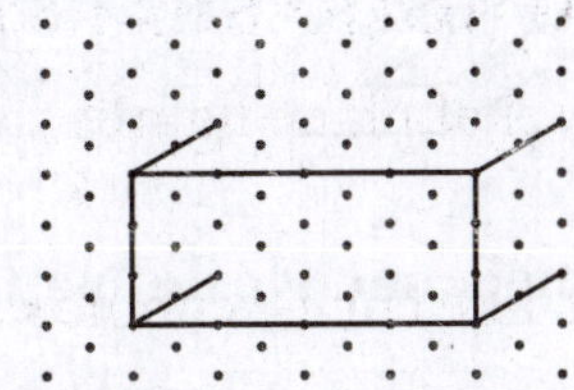
Step 3: Draw another rectangle of (4 × 3) units touching the corners of all the slanting lines drawn. We get the isometric sketch of a cuboid of dimensions (4 × 3 × 2) units.	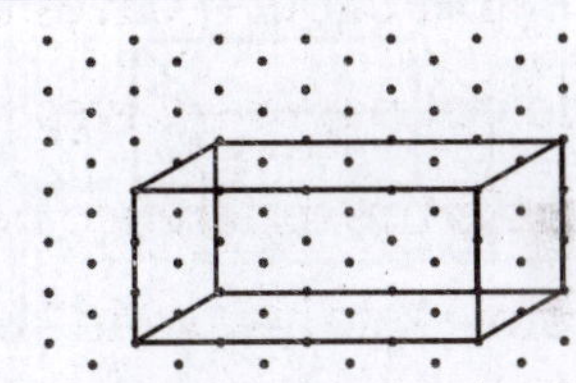

How many different isometric and oblique sketches can be drawn for a cuboid? Think!

Note

Measurements agree with those of the solid in the case of an isometric sketch unlike an oblique sketch.

SOLVED EXAMPLES

Example 3: Complete the steps of drawing an oblique sketch of a cuboid.

Solution:

Step 1	Step 2	Step 3
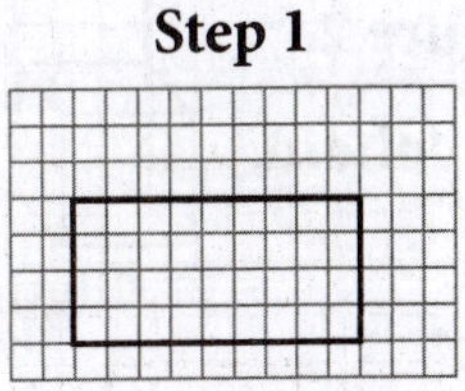	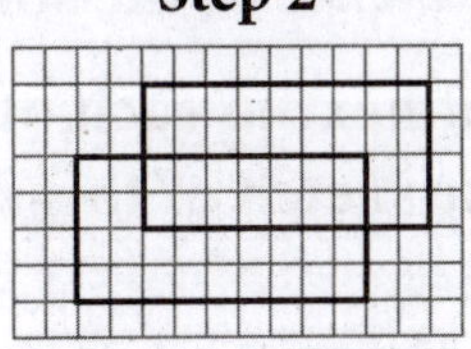	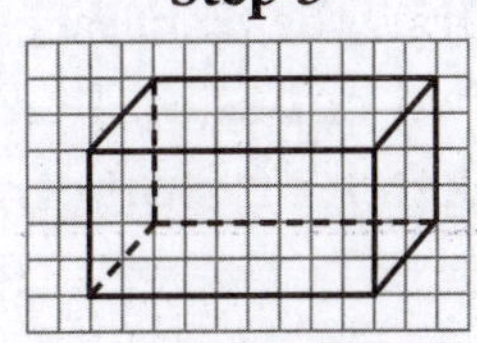

Example 4: Draw an isometric sketch of a cube of side 3 units.

Solution:

Step 1	Step 2	Step 3
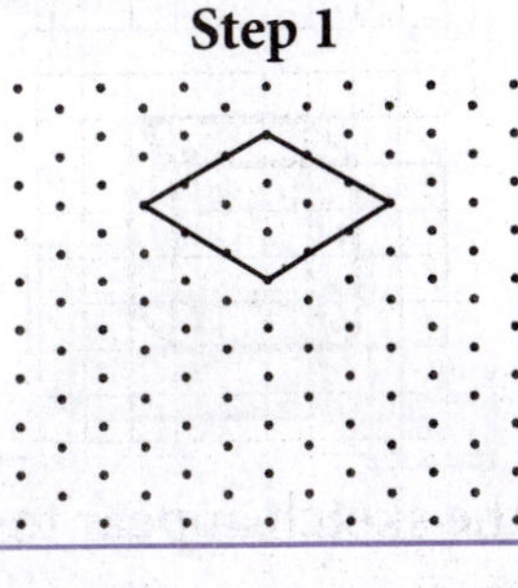	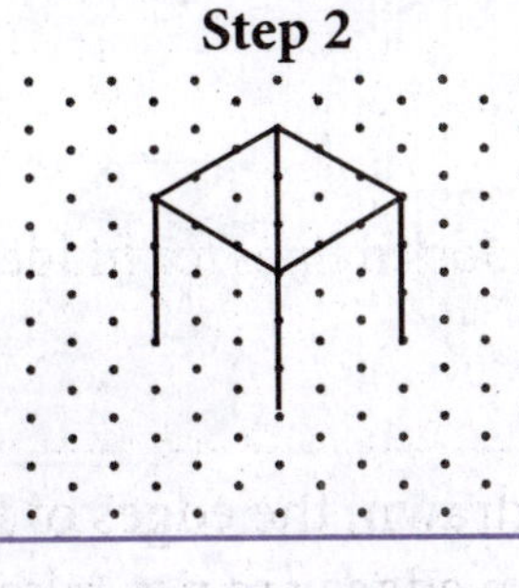	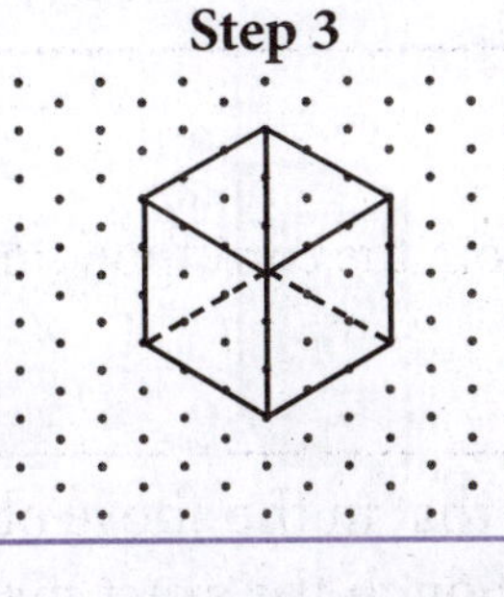

EXERCISE 14B

1. **Make an oblique sketch for the isometric shapes shown below.**

a. 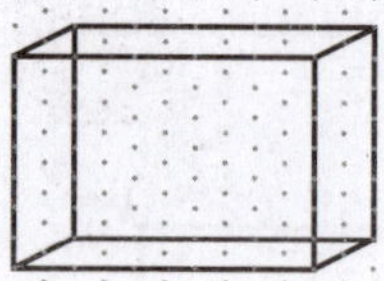

b. 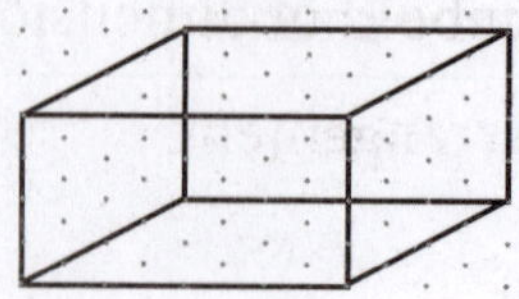

c. 

d. 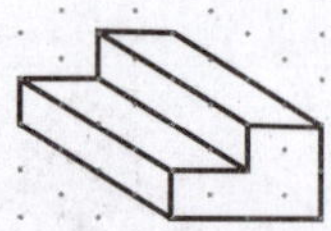

e. 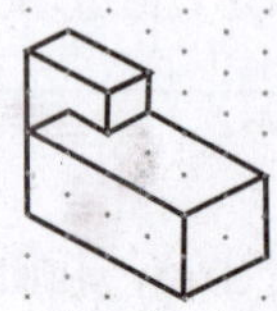

f. 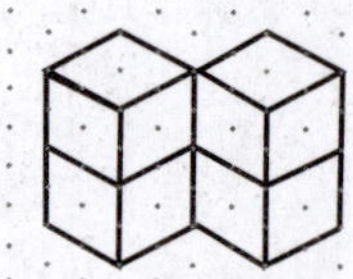

2. **Using isometric dot paper, draw an isometric sketch for each of the following solids.**

a. 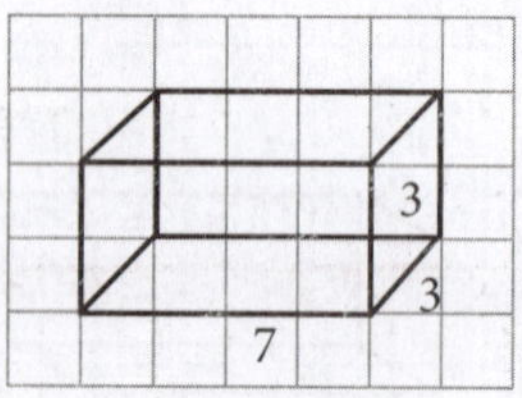

b. 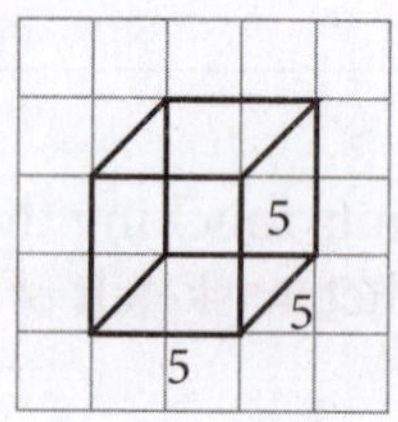

c. 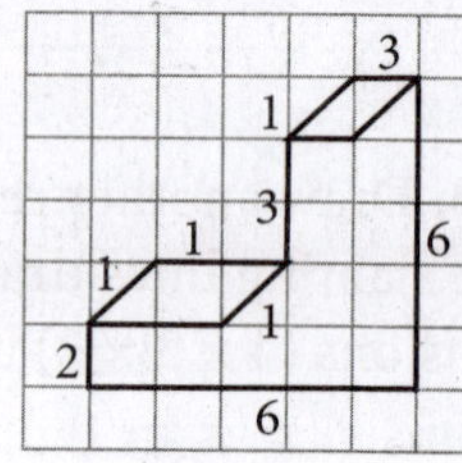

d. 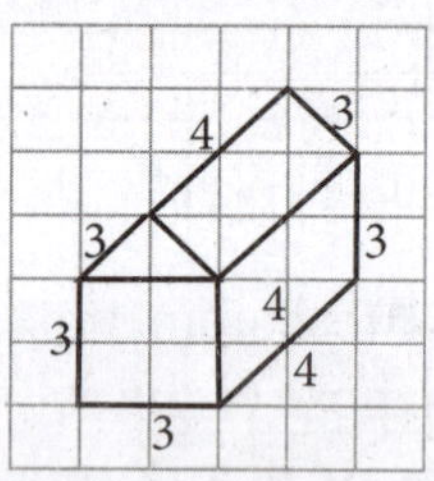

e. 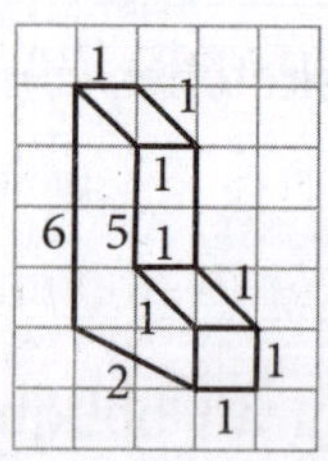

f. 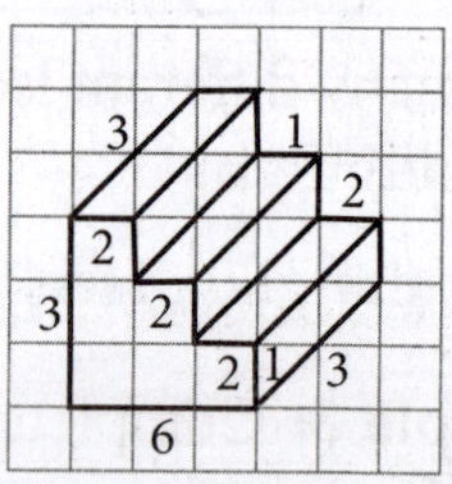

3. **The dimensions of a cuboid are 2 × 3 × 4 cm. Draw all possible isometric sketches of the cuboid.**
4. **Draw the oblique and isometric sketches of the solid shown in Figure 2.**
5. **Two cubes of 4 cm edge are placed next to each other to obtain a cuboid. Sketch an isometric and an oblique sketch of this cuboid.**

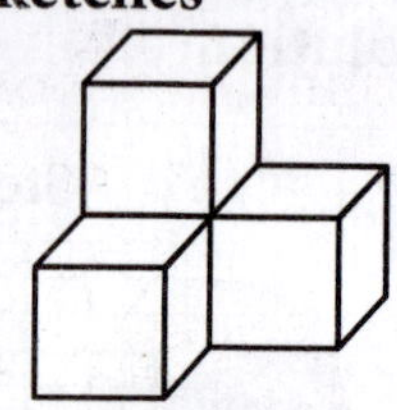

Figure 2

VISUALISING SOLID SHAPES

Jia made the following solids by connecting cubes. Can you guess the number of cubes in each arrangement?

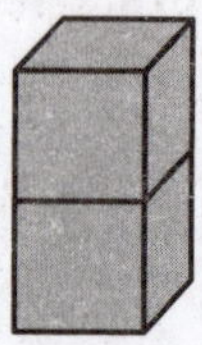

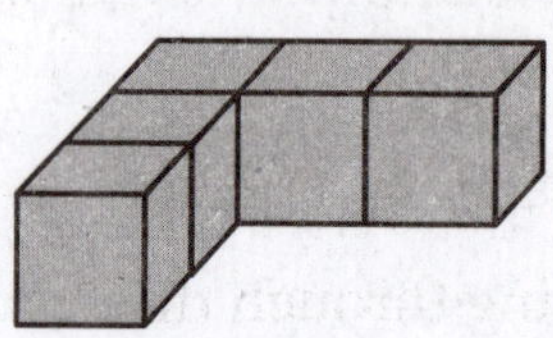

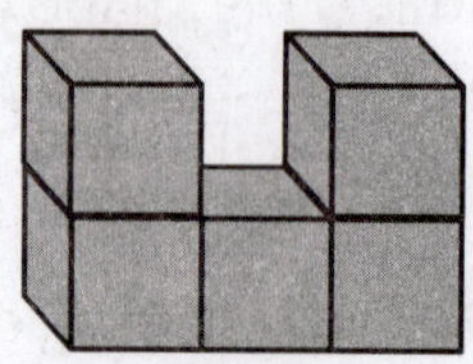

It is difficult to guess the number of cubes in the fourth solid as all the cubes are not clearly visible. Only 5 cubes are visible.

The figure given alongside represents the arrangement of cubes in the fourth solid with each layer separated so that it can be counted.

Thus, there are 6 cubes in the fourth arrangement.

SOLVED EXAMPLES

Example 5: Find the number of cubes in each of the following arrangements.

a. 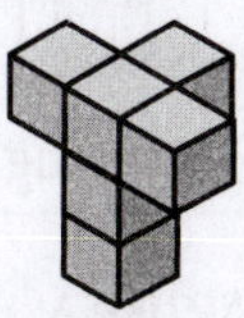

b. 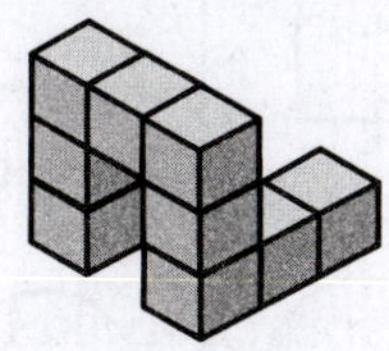

c. 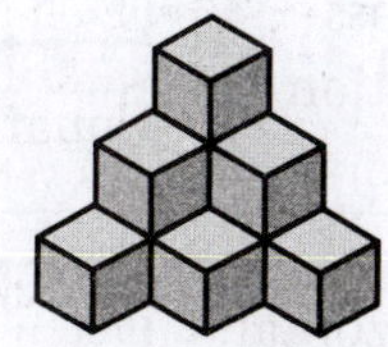

Solution:

a. 7 cubes

b. 9 cubes

c. 10 cubes

Example 6: Anurag placed four cubes of side 3 cm each side by side as shown alongside. What are the dimensions of the resulting solid?

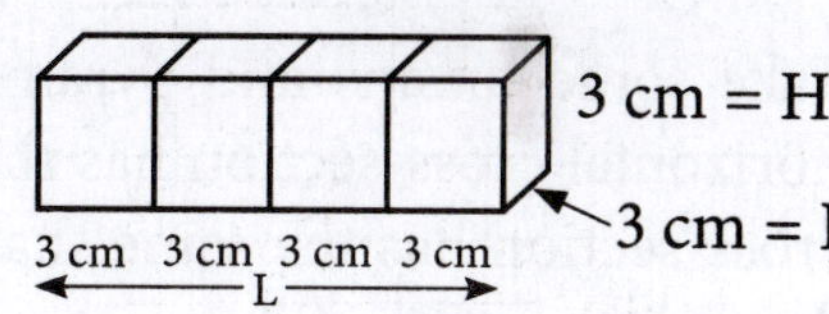

Solution: When four cubes are placed side by side, the length of the cube increases while the breadth and height remain the same.

The new length = 3 + 3 + 3 + 3 = 12 cm.

The resulting solid has a length of 12 cm, breadth of 3 cm and height of 3 cm.

We can view different sections of a solid in various ways. Let us see how we can do so.

Viewing the Cross-Section by Cutting or Slicing

Roshni likes cooking and had attended cooking classes during her vacation. She baked a cake for her mother's birthday.

(i)

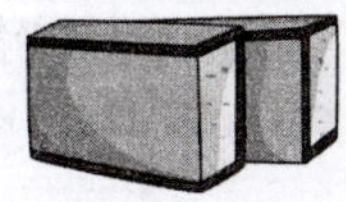

(ii)

(iii)

We can see that the baked cake (first image) is in the shape of a cuboid. Roshni cut half of the cake vertically and obtained the pieces as shown in the second image. She cut the remaining half of the cake horizontally to apply cream between those pieces and obtained the pieces as shown in the third image.

Note that in both the ways of cutting, the shape of the cake pieces obtained is rectangle. They are called the cross-sections of a cake.

So, a **cross-section** of an object is the shape obtained when it is cut through.

The cross-section of a solid can be seen by slicing or cutting through the solid.

The cross-sections of some common 3-D shapes are shown below.

Solid	Cube	Cuboid	Cylinder	Cone	Sphere	Square pyramid	Triangular prism
Vertical cross-section	Square	Rectangle	Rectangle	Triangle	Circle	Triangle	Rectangle
Horizontal cross-section	Square	Rectangle	Circle	Circle	Circle	Square	Triangle

Take some prisms and pyramids. Observe their cross-sections. You will find that in prisms, the horizontal cross-section has the same shape and size as that of its base. In pyramids, the horizontal cross-section has the same shape as its base but the size decreases on considering the cross-section towards the apex.

Viewing Solids by Shadow Play

One evening, there was power cut at Farhaan's home. He lit a diya and its shadow appeared on the floor as shown here.

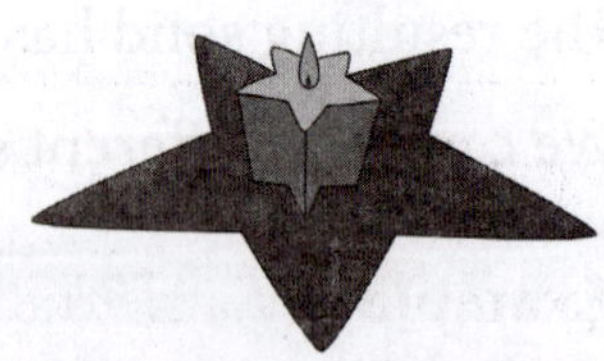

Observe the shape of the shadow obtained. It resembles a star, which is a 2-D shape.

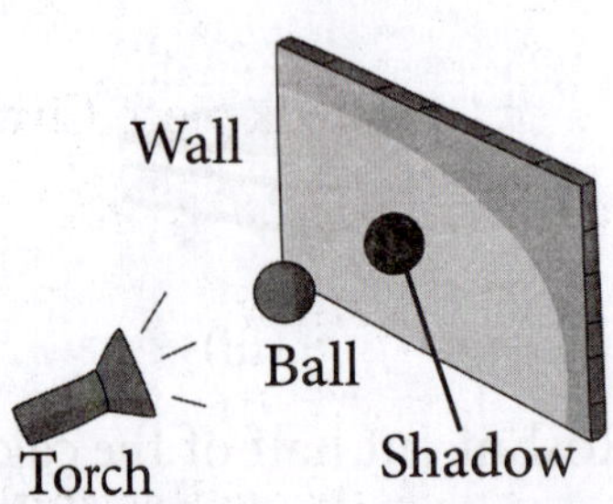

Have you noticed the shadow of a ball cast on the wall when it is held in front of a torchlight? As shown in the adjacent figure, you will notice that a ball resembles a sphere which is a 3-D shape, but its shadow cast on the wall is a circle, which is a 2-D shape.

Now take objects resembling a cube, cuboid, cylinder and cone. Hold a source of light and observe their shadows. Change the position of the source of light and observe the size and position of the shadows formed.

Viewing Solids From Different Angles

We can get different views of a solid when viewed from different angles. Let us see how they look from different angles.

Sophia's father purchased a brand-new car. She saw the car parked at the gate from the top floor of her building. It appeared as shown in Figure (i). She ran down and stood in front of it. Now, the car appeared to be as shown in Figure (ii). She went to the car's side to put her bag inside and it appeared to her as shown in Figure (iii).

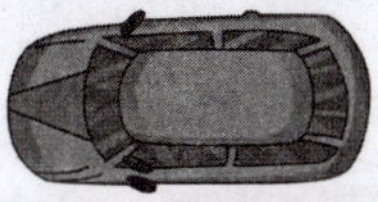
(i)

(ii)

(iii)

The view of the car changes with respect to the positions from where it is being looked at.

Figure (i) shows the top view of the car, Figure (ii) is the front view of the car and Figure (iii) is the side view of the same car.

Similarly, a solid can also have different views. Look at the following solids and their views.

Solid	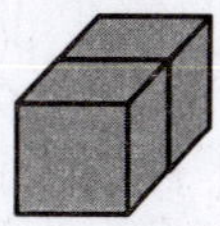	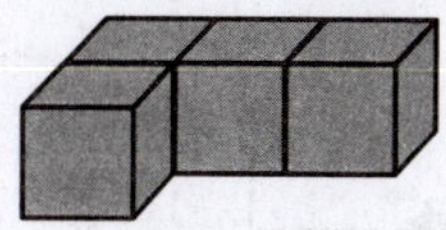	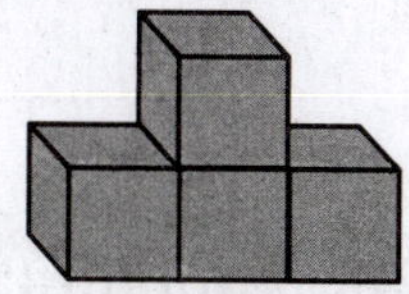
Front view	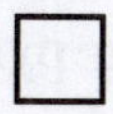	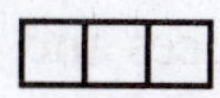	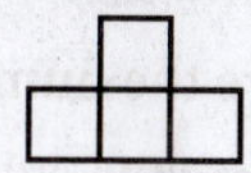
Top view	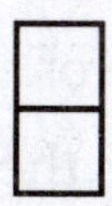	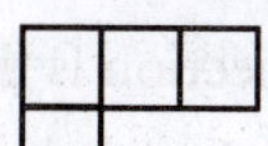	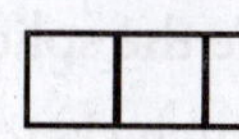
Side view	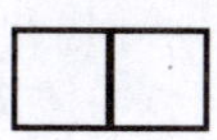	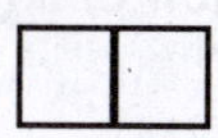	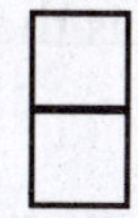

SOLVED EXAMPLES

Example 7: Name the cross-sections obtained when the following solids are cut horizontally.

a. A pencil box b. An orange c. A chalk piece

Solution:

a. A pencil box: Rectangle b. An orange: Circle c. A chalk piece: Circle

Example 8: What cross-sections do you get when the following solids are cut vertically?

a. A joker's cap b. A dice c. A straw

Solution:

a. A joker's cap: Triangle b. A dice: Square c. A straw: Rectangle

Example 9: Name at least two solids whose shadows are of the following shapes.

a. Circle b. Triangle c. Rectangle

Solution:

a. Circle: Sphere, cone, cylinder b. Triangle: Cone, square pyramid

c. Rectangle: Cylinder, cuboid

Example 10: Draw the views of the objects given below.

a.

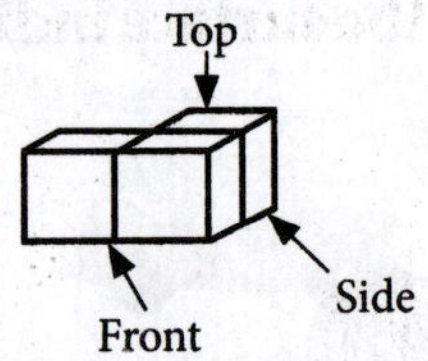

b.

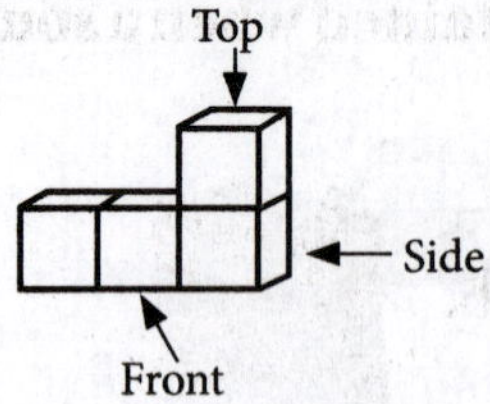

Solution:

a.

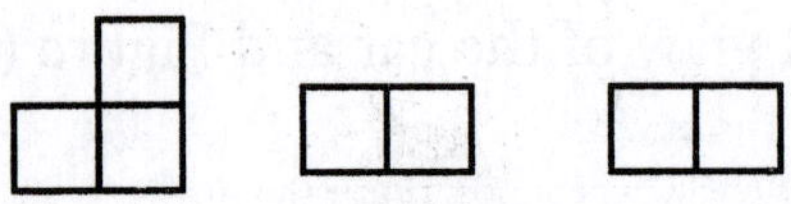

Top view Side view Front view

b.

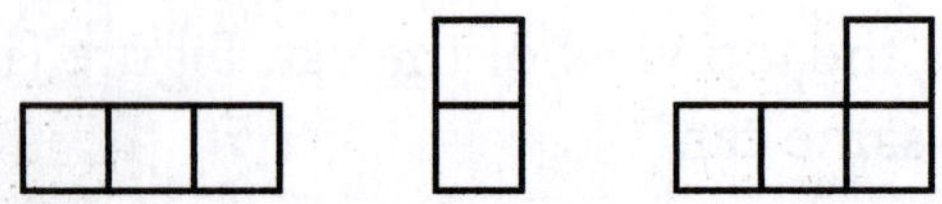

Top view Side view Front view

Mental Maths

1. Give the number of faces, vertices and edges of a rectangular pyramid.
2. Name the solid whose net consists of four equilateral triangles.
3. Name the solid whose cross-section is the same irrespective of a vertical or a horizontal cut.
4. In which sketch of a solid are the measurements the same as the original?
5. What is the shape of the top view of a marker pen?

EXERCISE 14C

1. Count and write the number of cubes in each of the following arrangements.

a.

b.

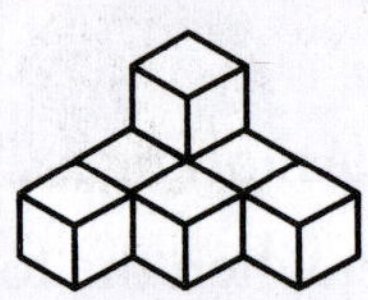

c.

d.

e.

f.

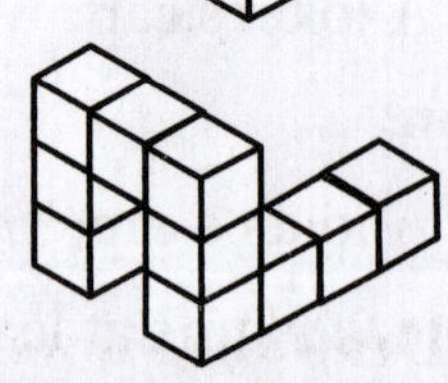

2. Name the cross-sections obtained when the following solids are cut vertically as well as horizontally.

a. Straw b. Brick c. Clown's cap d. Apple

e. Geometry box f. Ice cube g. Juice can h. Rubik's cube

3. **Write the shape of the shadow obtained when a source of light falls on the surface indicated by the arrows.**

a. 

b. 

c. 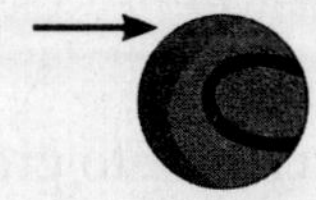

d. 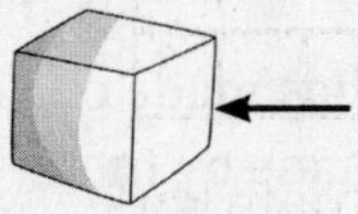

e. 

f. 

4. **Name the views of the following objects.**

a. A hat

 ________  ________  ________

b. A sofa

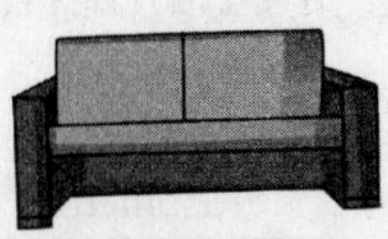 ________ 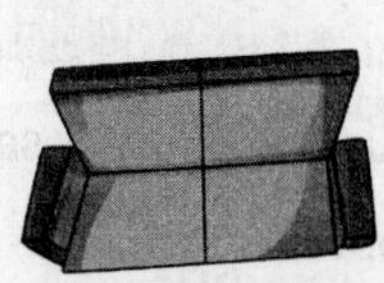 ________  ________

c. A table

 ________  ________  ________

d. A house

 ________  ________  ________

e. A water bottle

 ________  ________  ________

5. **Draw the views of the following solids.**

a. 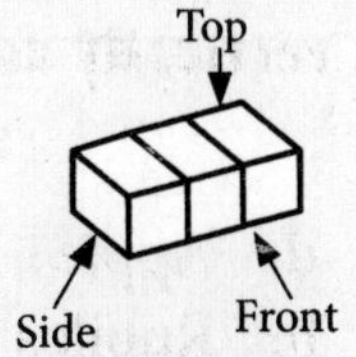

b. 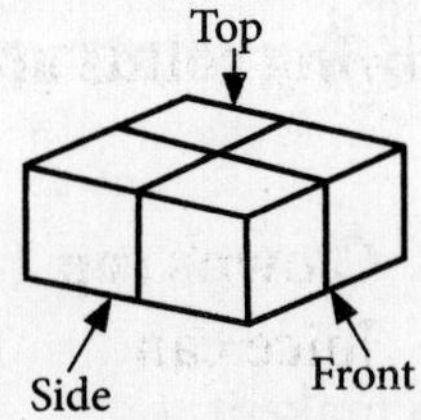

c. 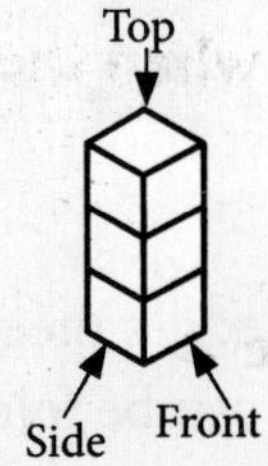

d. 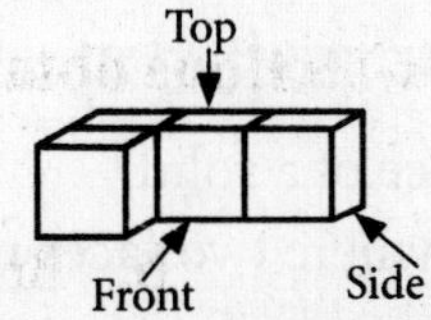

e. 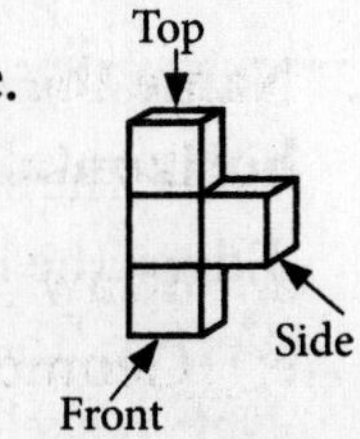

Maths Lab Activity

Aim: To identify different views of a solid

Materials required: Connecting cubes, sheets of paper, pencil and ruler

Procedure:

1. Arrange the class into groups.
2. Provide each group with a few paper sheets, pencil, ruler and the same number of connecting cubes.
3. Direct them to make a solid using those cubes.
4. Ask them to draw the top, side and front views of the solid that each group has made on the paper.
5. Ask each group to come forward and show the sheets along with the solid made by them. The teacher will check their drawings and award them points.
6. The group which has identified and drawn the views correctly gets 10 points. The group with the maximum points will be the winner.

Concept Map

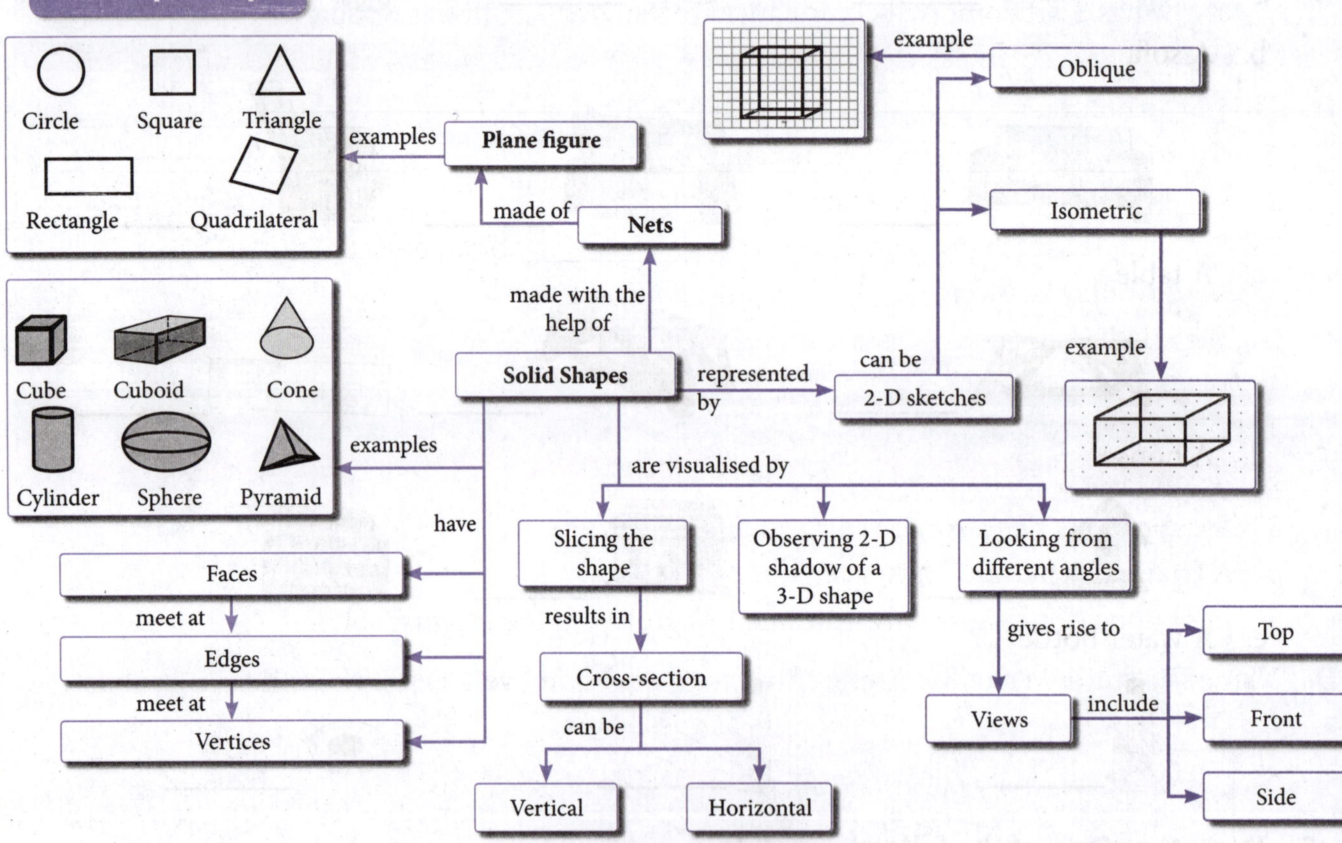

Key Concepts

- **Face:** The surface of a solid
- **Edge:** The line where two faces meet
- **Vertex:** The point where two or more edges meet
- **Net:** A skeleton outline of a solid that can be folded to make it
- **Cross-section:** The shape obtained when an object is cut through

CHAPTER REVISION

A. Choose the correct option.

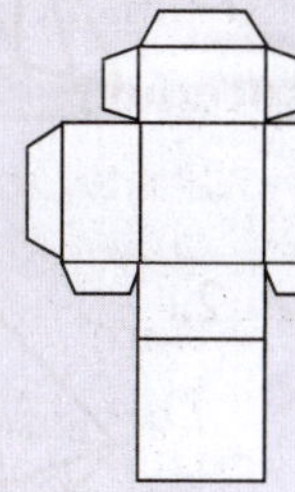

1. Which solid is formed by folding the figure shown?
   a. Circle b. Cuboid
   c. Prism d. Cylinder
2. How many edges are there in a triangular prism?
   a. 3 b. 5 c. 6 d. 9
3. Which of the following solids has a rectangular shadow?
   a. Cylinder b. Cuboid c. Prism d. All of the above
4. The number of cubes in the arrangement is
   a. 11 b 9 c. 15 d. 13

5. Which of the following is true for the net of a cuboid?
   a. It has 3 different pairs of identical rectangles b. It has 6 squares
   c. It has 6 rectangles of different size d. It has 4 rectangles of same size

B. Fill in the blanks.

1. The line where two faces meet is called a ____________.
2. A ____________ has no vertices.
3. An oblique sketch gives an image in ____________ for an object.
4. Shadow play is a way of ____________ solid shapes.
5. The solid whose every cross section is a circle is a ____________.

C. Write T for true and F for false.

1. The surface of a solid is called a face.
2. A solid is a 2-D shape.
3. A cube looks like a square from all angles.
4. A triangular pyramid has 4 vertices.
5. In oblique drawing, the measurements agree with the original solid.

D. Name the solid. Write the number of faces, edges and vertices of the following solids.

1. 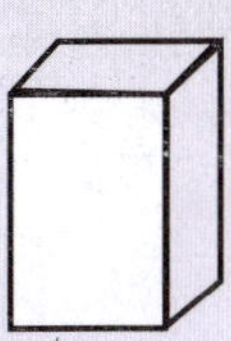
2. 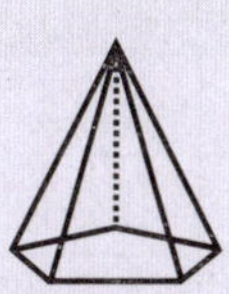
3. 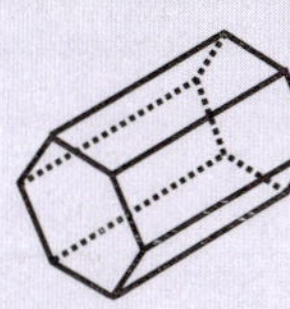
4. 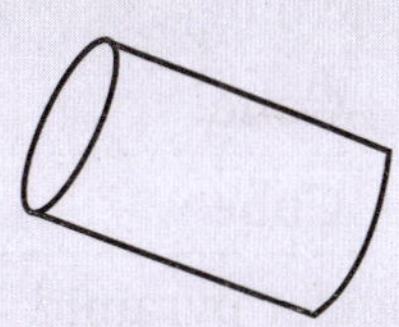
5. 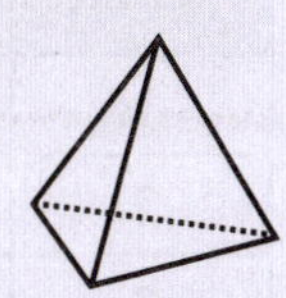

E. Draw isometric sketches for the following.

1. 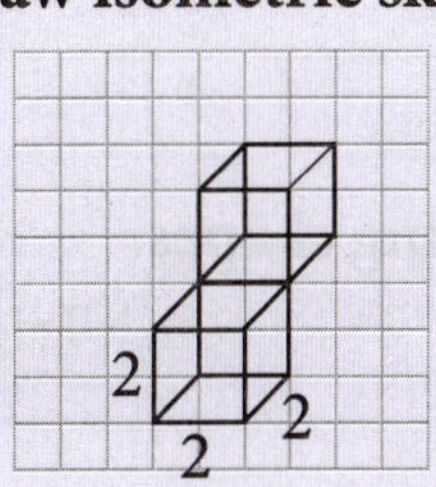

2. 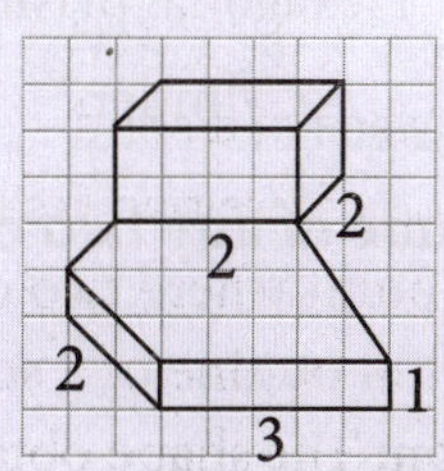

F. Match the solids with their nets.

Solid | Net for the solid

1. 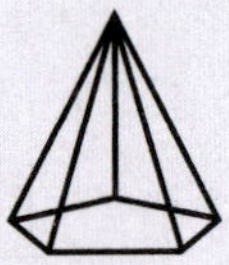

2. 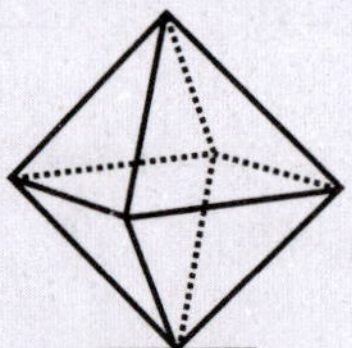

3. 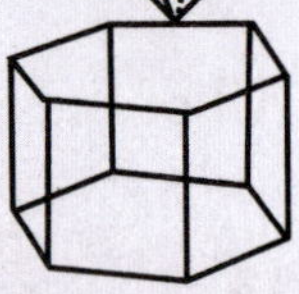

4. 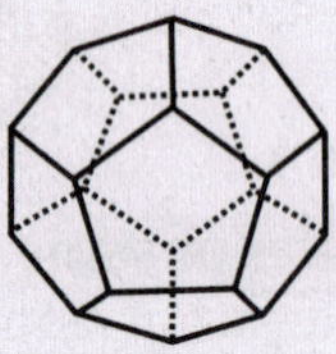

5. 

a. 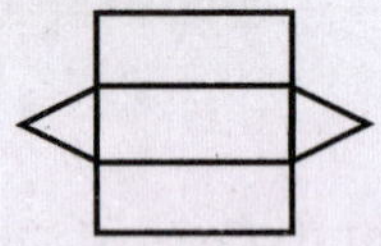

b. 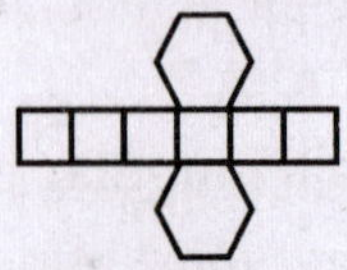

c. 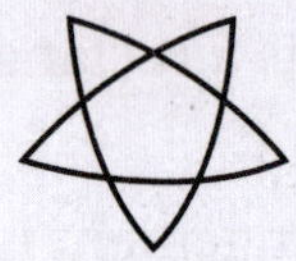

d. 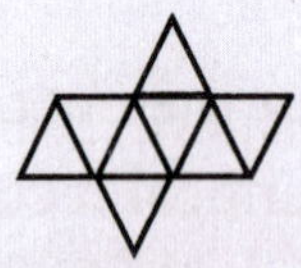

e. 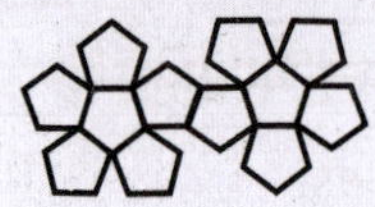

G. Draw an oblique sketch of a triangular prism whose isometric sketch is given alongside.

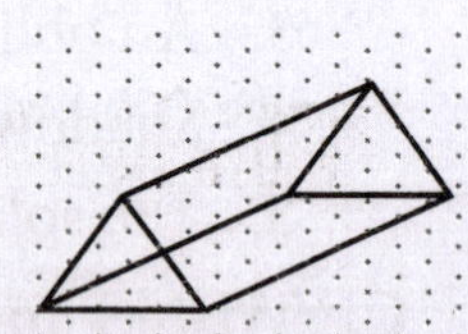

H. Draw the different views of the following solids.

1. 

2. 

3. 

I. Complete the following table.

	Solid	Vertical cross-section	Horizontal cross-section
1.	Cone		
2.	Cube		
3.	Triangular pyramid		
4.	Hexagonal prism		
5.	Cylinder		

J. Write the name of any two objects whose shadows are of the following shapes.

1. Square 2. Circle 3. Rectangle 4. Triangle

SKILL UP!

Project

1. Cut different fruits and vegetables and observe their cross-sections (under an elder's supervision). Prepare a scrapbook based on your observations. Draw or paste or make colour prints (using water colours or acrylic paints) of cross-sections obtained for each fruit and vegetable that you chose.
2. Cube is a 3-D solid whose faces are flat polygons, that is, a square. What is the name of solids whose faces are flat polygons? Find out more about them and make a presentation.

Life Skills

1. The isometric drawing of an object is shown. Name the object. Also, identify its different views.
2. A study room is an area or a room in a house which is meant for activities like paperwork, computer work, or reading. Design a bookshelf, a study table and a chair using 3-D shapes.

Mind Buzzer

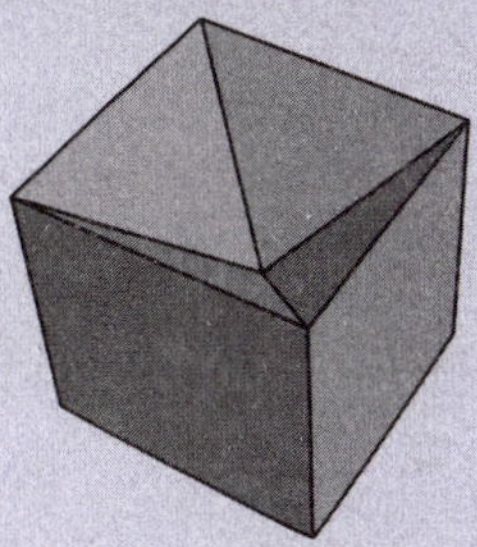

1. Circle is a plane figure. Justify.
2. Find the number of faces, edges and vertices of the solid given here.

Teacher's Notes

- Bring foam solids of a cube, cuboid, cylinder, cone, sphere, pyramid and a prism to discuss the number of faces, edges and vertices of the solids.
- While teaching cross-section by cutting or slicing, bring any five fruits or vegetables to the classroom. Cut them both vertically and horizontally and ask the students to name the shapes obtained.

WORKSHEET

There are a few terms (about 22) hidden in the following word search grid which are related to the concepts learnt in this chapter. Identify and mark them in the grid. Also write them in the box provided.

T	R	I	A	N	G	L	E	A	I	W	E	C	P	K
D	O	I	F	A	C	X	B	M	U	Z	D	U	Y	O
I	E	W	W	A	W	E	S	S	W	L	G	B	R	B
M	T	E	X	Z	C	W	O	Z	H	V	E	E	A	L
E	O	F	D	O	Y	E	O	K	M	A	S	B	M	I
N	P	I	S	O	M	E	T	R	I	C	D	Z	I	Q
S	C	I	R	C	L	E	R	N	P	K	Q	O	D	U
I	V	C	H	S	C	Y	L	I	N	D	E	R	W	E
O	C	R	O	S	S	S	E	C	T	I	O	N	X	S
N	T	O	Q	X	T	D	I	C	U	B	O	I	D	P
X	Z	P	V	E	R	T	I	C	E	S	F	Q	S	H
V	E	R	T	I	C	A	L	G	O	B	F	N	I	E
X	J	I	M	F	R	O	N	T	V	M	Z	E	D	R
B	T	S	F	N	F	L	S	O	L	I	D	T	E	E
E	X	M	N	S	Q	U	A	R	E	C	O	N	E	J

15 Perimeter and Area

Learning Objectives

- To find perimeter and area of squares and rectangles
- To calculate area of triangles and parallelograms
- To solve problems on circumference and area of circles
- To learn conversion of units of area
- To solve questions based on the applications of area and perimeter in real life

Let's Get Started

Kiran designed the following post cards and named them as A, B, C and D. She wants to decorate their boundaries with beadings. Find the length of beading required for each post card.

A

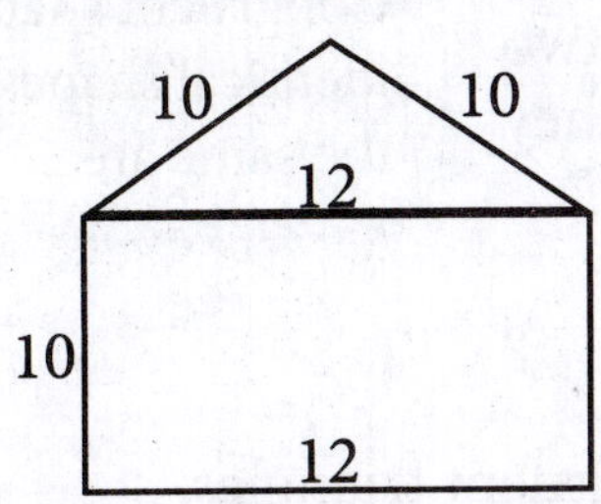

B

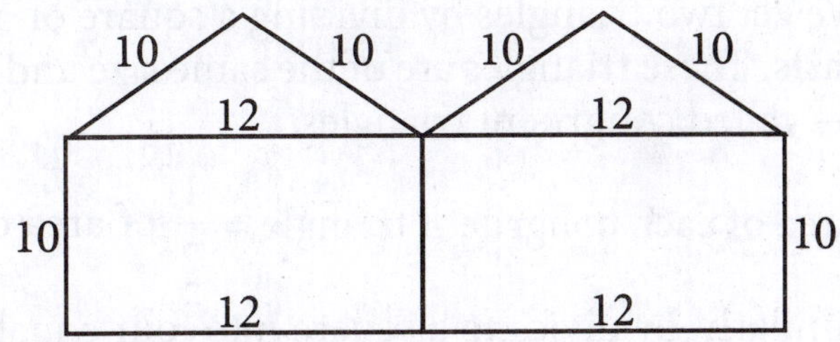

C

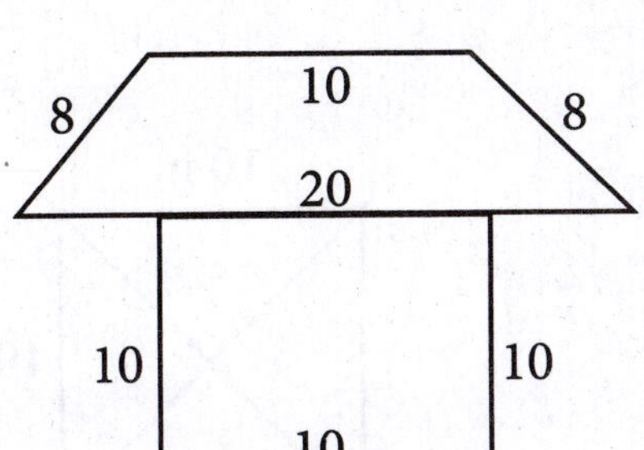

D

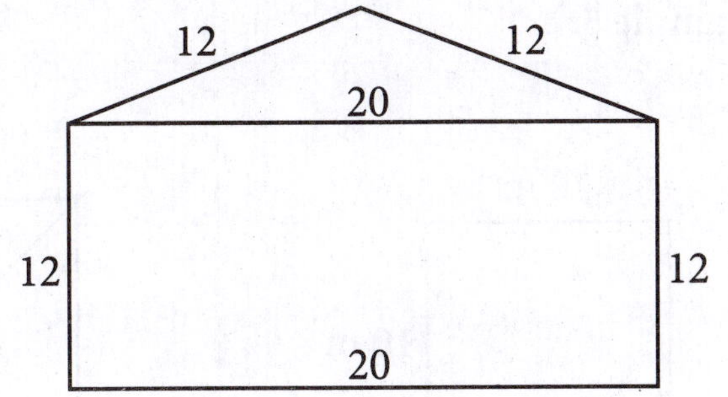

Answer the following questions.

a. Which post card needs the maximum length of beading?

____

b. Which post card needs the minimum length of beading?

____

PERIMETER AND AREA OF SQUARES AND RECTANGLES

Perimeter is the length of the boundary of a closed shape or figure. It is calculated by adding the lengths of all the sides of a closed figure.

Perimeter of a regular polygon = number of sides × length of one side

- **Perimeter of a square = 4 × side**

  Example 1: Measurement of each side of a square is 5 cm.
  Perimeter of the square = 4 × 5 = 20 cm

- **Perimeter of a rectangle = 2 × (*l* + *b*)**

  Example 2: The length and breadth of a rectangle are 6 and 8 cm, respectively.
  Perimeter of the rectangle = 2 × (6 + 8) = 28 cm

Area is the amount of space or region enclosed within a closed shape or figure.

- **Area of a square = side × side**

  Example 3: Measurement of each side of a square is 5 cm.
  Area of a square = 5 × 5 = 25 cm^2

- **Area of a rectangle = *l* × *b***

  Example 4: The length and breadth of a rectangle are 6 and 8 cm, respectively.
  Area of a rectangle = 6 × 8 = 48 cm^2

Congruent Triangles in Squares and Rectangles

We get two triangles by dividing a square or a rectangle equally into two parts. These triangles are of the same size and have equal area. Thus, they are called congruent triangles.

Note

Congruent shapes are identical shapes having the same area.

Area of each congruent triangle = $\frac{1}{2}$ of area of square/rectangle

Similarly, by dividing a square into four equal parts, we get four congruent triangles.

Area of each congruent triangle = $\frac{1}{4}$ of area of square

Example 5:

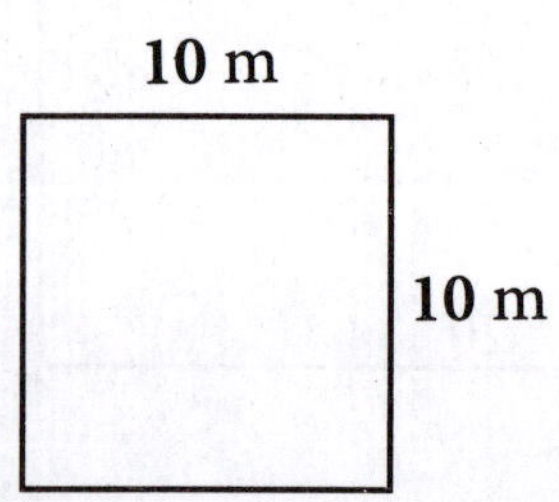

Area of a square = 10 × 10
= 100 m^2

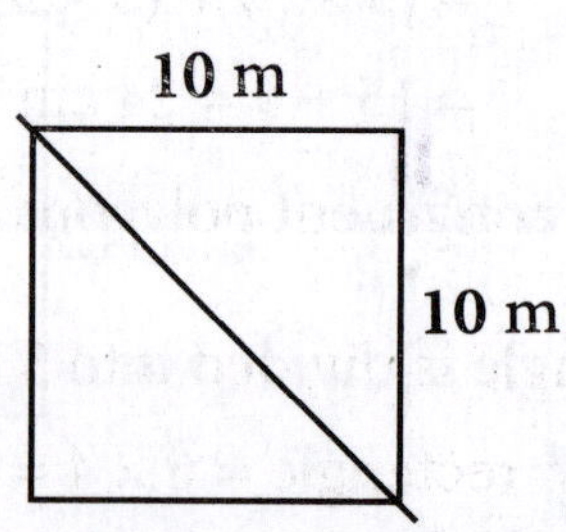

Area of each triangle = $\frac{1}{2}$ × 100
= 50 m^2

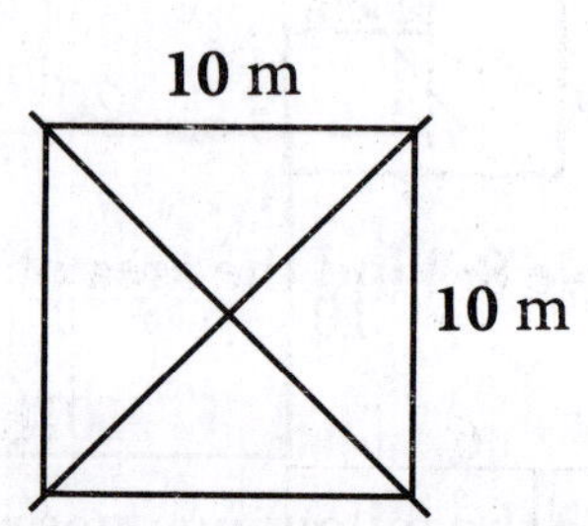

Area of each triangle = $\frac{1}{4}$ × 100
= 25 m^2

Congruent Polygons in Squares and Rectangles

We learnt about the congruent triangles formed in rectangles and squares. Similarly, other shapes can be formed in rectangles and squares by dividing them equally. Area of each congruent shape depends on the number of equal parts.

Example 6:

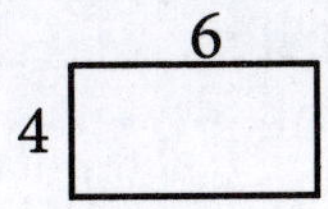

Area of a rectangle = 6×4

$= 24 \text{ cm}^2$

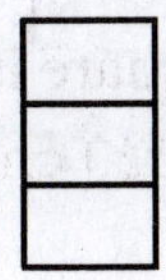

Area of each polygon $= \frac{1}{3} \times 24$

$= 8 \text{ cm}^2$

or

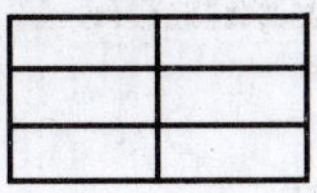

Area of each polygon $= \frac{1}{4} \times 36$

$= 4 \text{ cm}^2$

SOLVED EXAMPLES

Example 7: Find the perimeter and area of the following.

a.

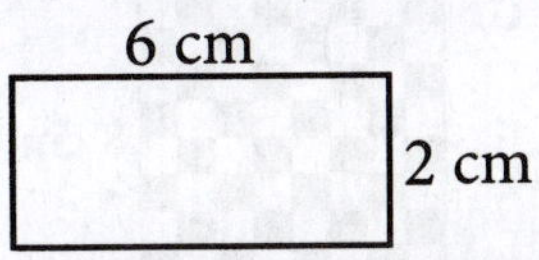

Perimeter of a rectangle $= 2 \times (l + b)$

$= 2 \times (6 + 2) = 16 \text{ cm}$

Area of a rectangle $= l \times b$

$= 6 \times 2 = 12 \text{ cm}^2$

b.

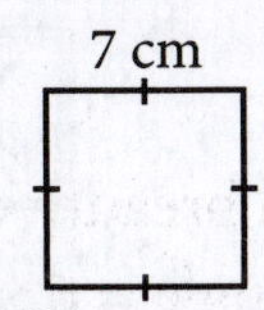

Perimeter of a square = $4 \times$ side

$= 4 \times 7 = 28 \text{ cm}$

Area of a square = side $\times$ side

$= 7 \times 7 = 49 \text{ cm}^2$

c.

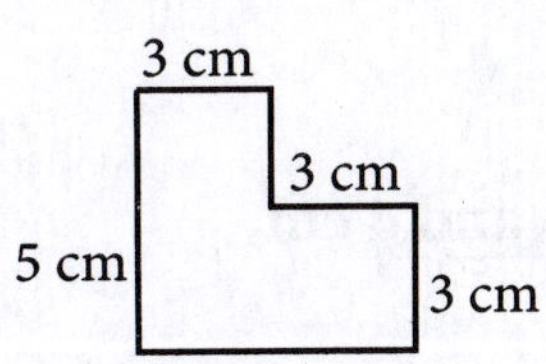

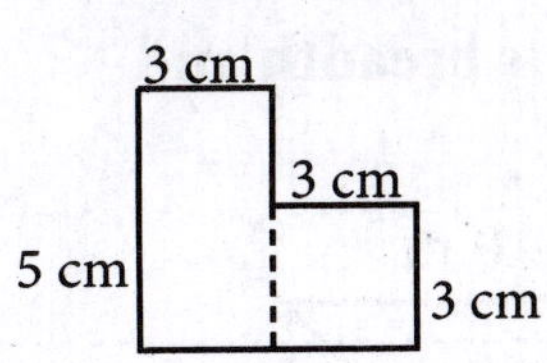

Perimeter of the shape = Sum of all the sides

$= (5 + 3 + 2 + 3 + 3 + 6)$ cm

$= 22$ cm

Area of the shape = Area of rectangle + Area of square

$= (l \times b) + (\text{side} \times \text{side})$

$= (5 \times 3) + (3 \times 3)$

$= 15 + 9 = 24 \text{ cm}^2$

Example 8: Find the area of the following congruent polygons.

a.

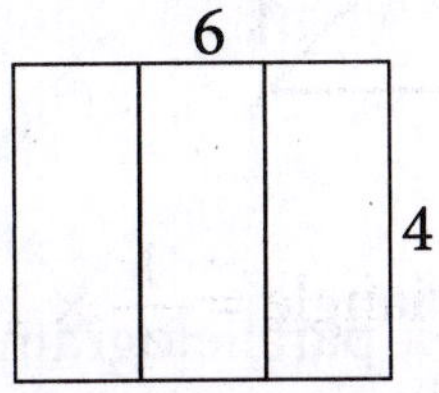

The given rectangle is divided into 3 equal parts.

Area of the given rectangle $= 6 \times 4 = 24$ sq. units

Area of each polygon $= \frac{1}{3} \times 24 = 8$ sq. units

b. 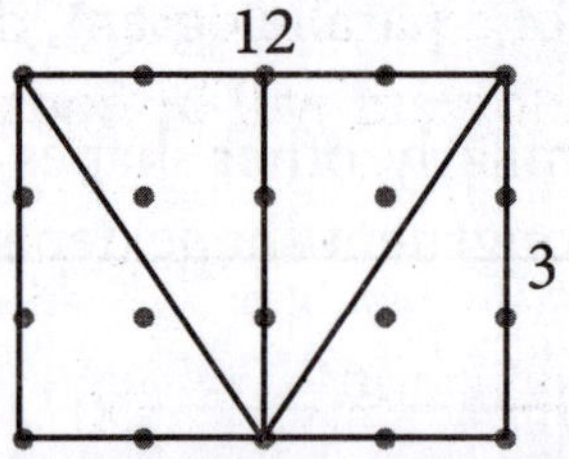

The given rectangle is divided into 4 equal parts.

Area of the given rectangle = $12 \times 3 = 36$ sq. units

Area of each polygon = $\frac{1}{4} \times 36 = 9$ sq. units

EXERCISE 15A

1. Find the perimeter of the following figures.

a. 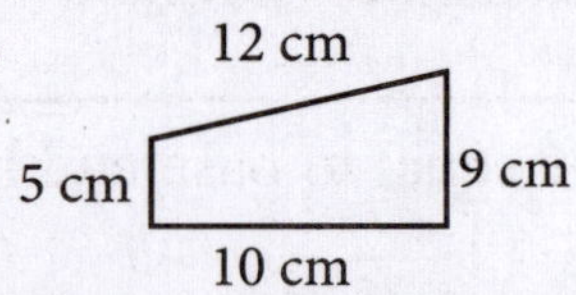

b. 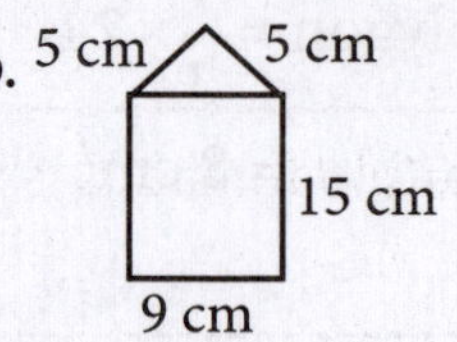

c. 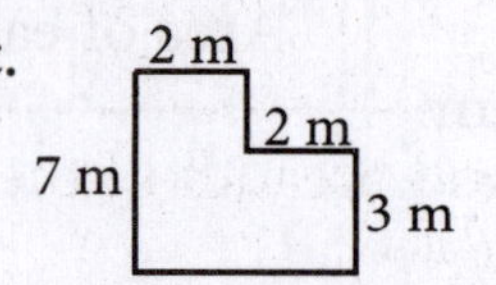

d. 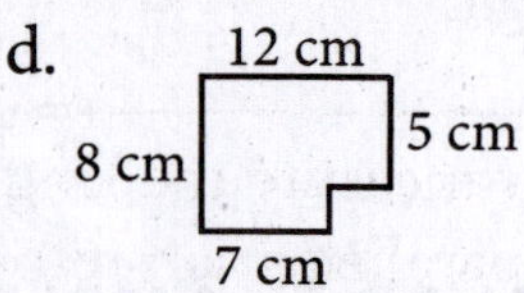

2. Find the area of the following figures.

a. 

b. 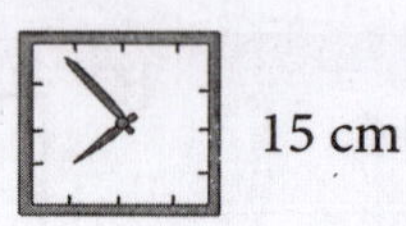

c. 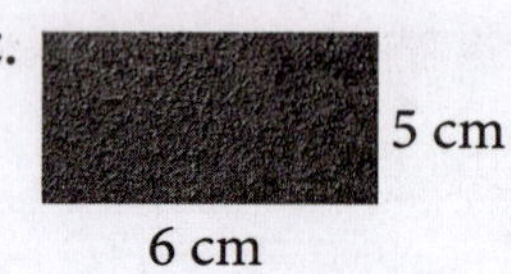

d. 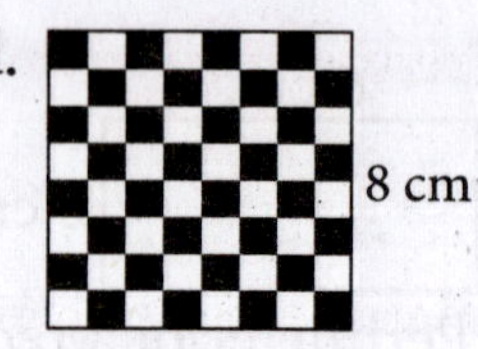

3. Find the area of each congruent part in the following figures.

a. 

b. 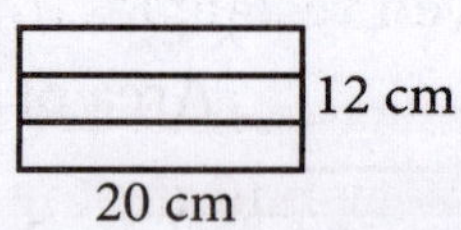

c. 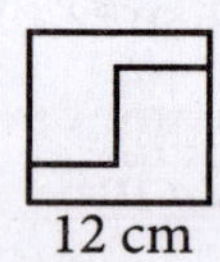

d. 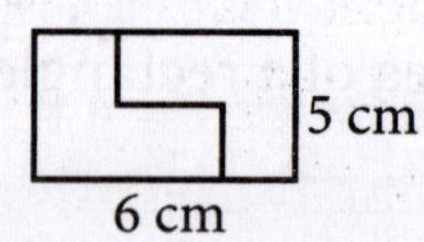

4. Find the perimeter and area of a square of side 15 cm.

5. Find the perimeter of a rectangle whose length and breadth are 3 cm and 4 cm, respectively.

6. The perimeter of a rectangle is 260 cm and its length is 80 cm. Find its breadth and area.

AREA OF PARALLELOGRAMS

Look at both the given figures ABCD and WXYZ. Do they look the same?

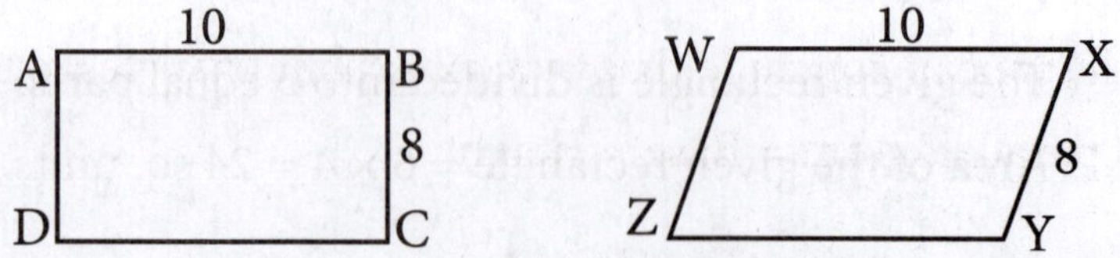

Yes, they appear to be the same. However, ABCD is a rectangle and WXYZ is a parallelogram. A **parallelogram** is a polygon with two pairs of parallel sides. The opposite sides and the opposite angles of a parallelogram are equal.

If the length and breadth of a rectangle are the same as the base and height of a parallelogram, then the parallelogram can be converted into a rectangle. So, the area of a parallelogram will be equal to the area of a rectangle. Let us see how this can be done.

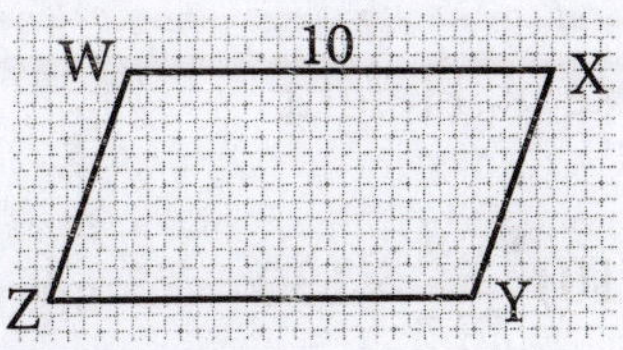	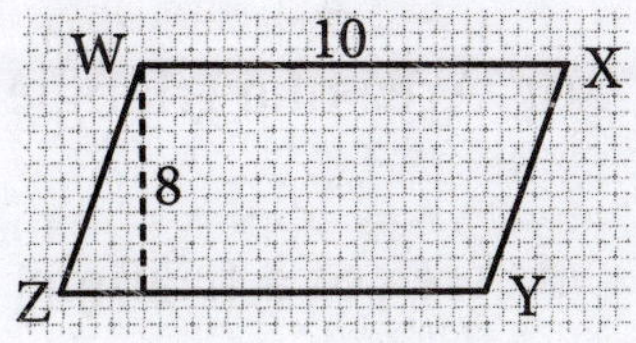	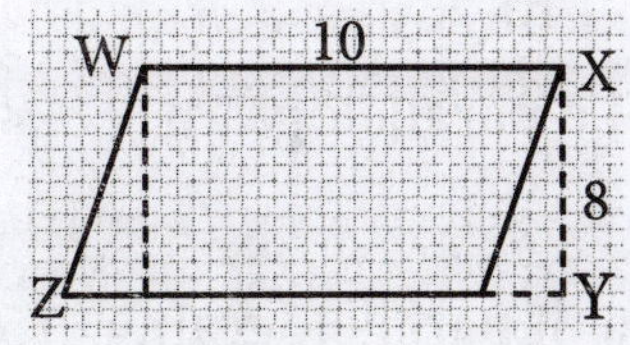
Draw a parallelogram on a graph sheet and measure its base and height.	Draw a perpendicular line from one vertex as shown. Cut out the triangle so formed.	Move the triangle to the other side of the parallelogram to form a rectangle as shown.

Now measure the length and breadth of the rectangle formed; it will be equal to base and height of the parallelogram respectively.

Area of a rectangle = Area of a parallelogram = $b \times h$ (where b is the base and h is the height of the parallelogram)

Therefore, area of the rectangle formed = area of the given parallelogram = $10 \times 8 = 80$ sq. units.

AREA OF TRIANGLES

A **triangle** is a polygon with three sides and three vertices. We know that congruent triangles can be formed by dividing a rectangle or square into two or four equal parts. We also found the area of such congruent triangles by dividing the area of the given rectangles by the number of equal parts.

Suppose we draw a triangle by joining 3 non-collinear points. We can find the perimeter of a triangle by adding the length of all the three sides, but how to find the area of triangles without knowing the area of the rectangle?

Look at this example.

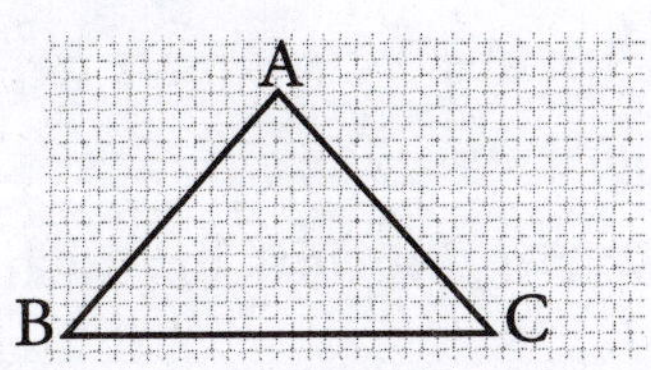

Draw a triangle on a graph sheet. Take the cut-out of the triangle. Make one more cut-out of the triangle such that both triangles are congruent to each other.

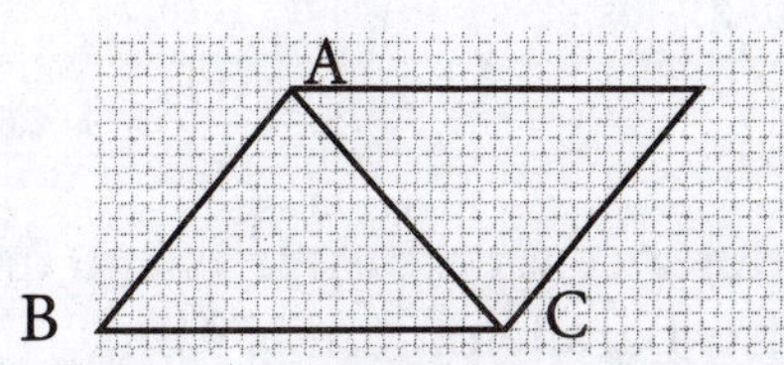

Now, place the congruent triangles one beside the other by rotating them in such a way that a parallelogram is obtained.

From the above example, we can conclude that two congruent triangles form a parallelogram.

We know that area of a parallelogram = Base × Height

Therefore, area of a triangle $= \frac{1}{2} \times \text{Base} \times \text{Height}$

Now consider the following example.

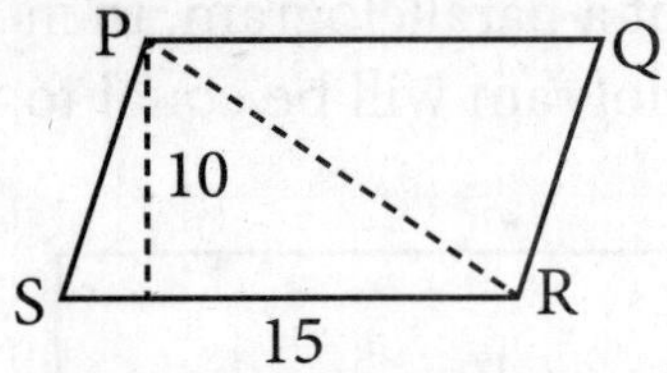

There are two congruent triangles PQR and RSP in the parallelogram PQRS.

Area of each triangle is $\frac{1}{2}$ of the area of parallelogram

or Area of a triangle $= \frac{1}{2} \times$ Base $\times$ Height

$\therefore$ Area of a triangle $= \frac{1}{2}(15 \times 10) = \frac{1}{2} \times 150 = 75$ sq. units

Area of a parallelogram $= b \times h$

$= 10 \times 15$

$\therefore$ Area of parallelogram = 150 sq. units

SOLVED EXAMPLES

Example 9: Find the area of each of the following parallelograms.

a.

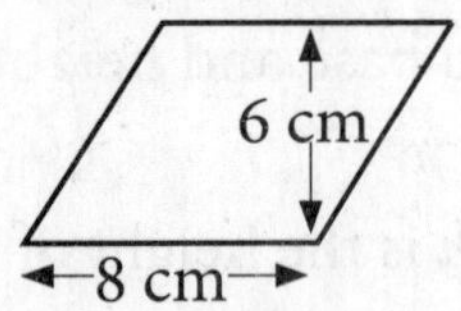

Area of parallelogram $= b \times h$

$h = 6$ cm and $b = 8$ cm

$\therefore$ Area of parallelogram $= 6 \times 8 = 48$ cm^2

b.

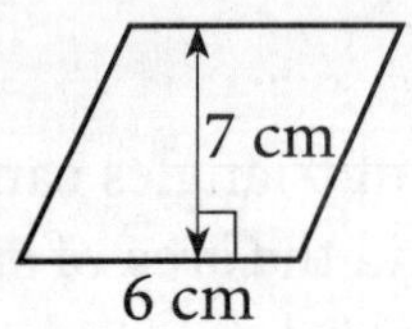

Area of parallelogram $= b \times h$

$h = 7$ cm and $b = 6$ cm

$\therefore$ Area of parallelogram $= 7 \times 6 = 42$ cm^2

Example 10: The area of a parallelogram is 54 cm^2. Find its height if the base is 6 cm.

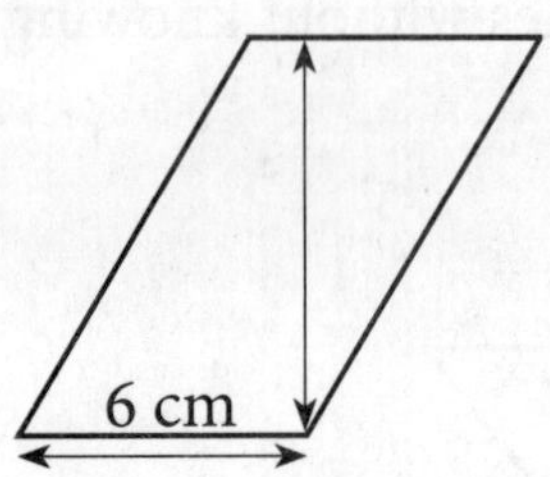

Area of parallelogram $= b \times h$

Area of parallelogram = 54 cm^2 and $b = 6$ cm

$54 = 6 \times h$

$\therefore h = \frac{54}{6} = 9$ cm

$\therefore$ The height of the parallelogram is 9 cm.

Example 11: Find the area of the following triangles.

a.

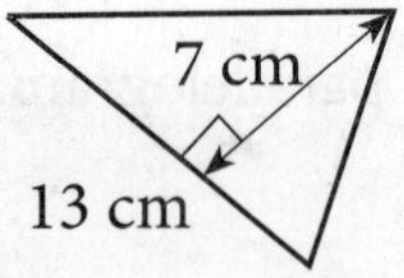

Given: $b = 13$ cm and $h = 7$ cm

Area of a triangle $= \frac{1}{2} \times$ Base $\times$ Height

Area of a triangle $= \frac{1}{2}(13 \times 7) = \frac{1}{2} \times 91 = 45.5$

$\therefore$ The area of the triangle is 45.5 cm^2.

b. 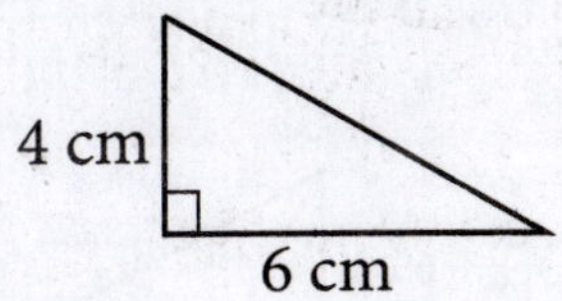

Given: $b = 6$ cm and $h = 4$ cm

$$\text{Area of a triangle} = \frac{1}{2} \times \text{Base} \times \text{Height}$$

$$\text{Area of a triangle} = \frac{1}{2}(6 \times 4) = \frac{1}{2} \times 24 = 12$$

$\therefore$ The area of the triangle is 12 cm^2.

Example 12: Find the area of the shaded part in the given figure.

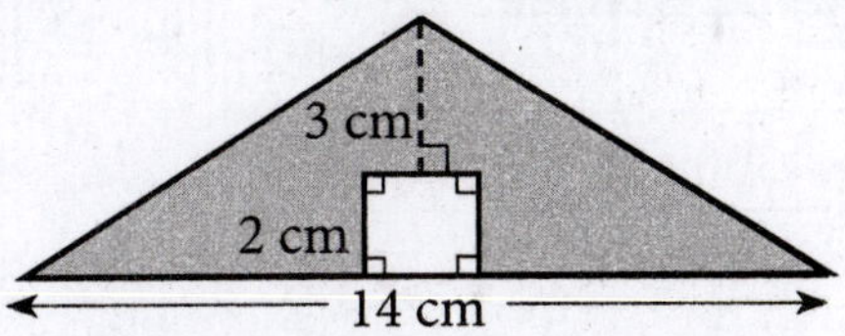

Area of shaded part = Area of triangle – Area of square

$$\text{Area of a triangle} = \frac{1}{2}(14 \times 5) = \frac{1}{2} \times 70 = 35\ cm^2$$

Area of the square = $2 \times 2 = 4\ cm^2$

Area of the shaded part = $35 - 4 = 31\ cm^2$

EXERCISE 15B

1. Match the following triangles with their perimeter.

	Triangles		Perimeter
a.	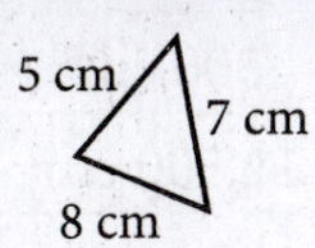	i.	30 cm
b.	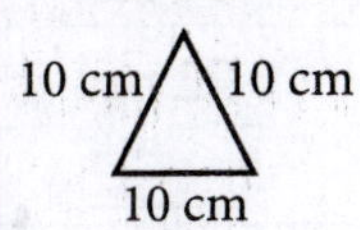	ii.	34 cm
c.	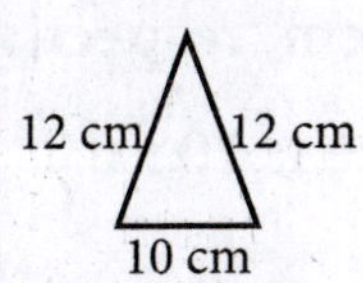	iii.	21 cm
d.	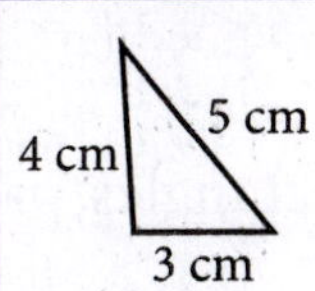	iv.	20 cm
e.	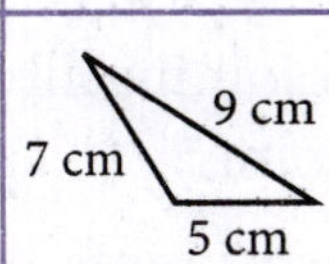	v.	32 cm
f.	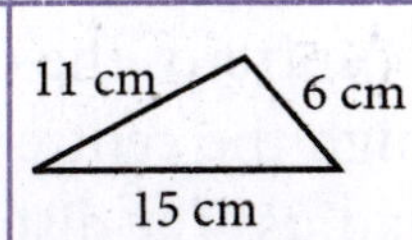	vi.	12 cm

2. **Find the area of the following figures.**

a. 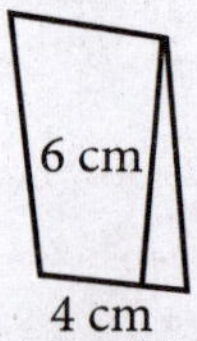

b. 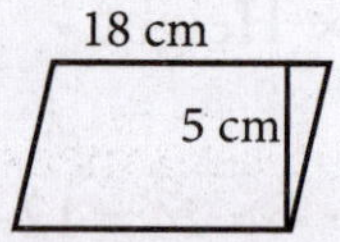

c. 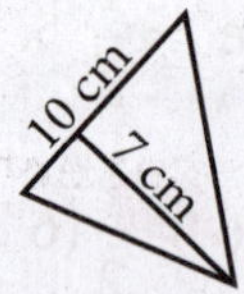

d. 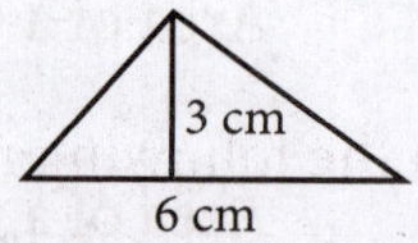

e. 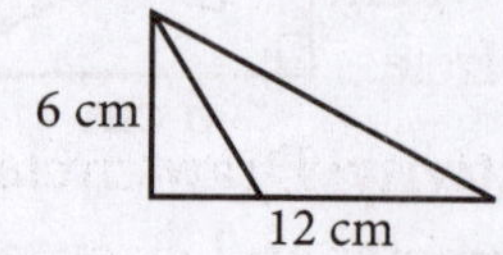

3. **Complete the following table by finding the missing values.**

	Base of the triangle	Height of the triangle	Area of the triangle
a.	12 cm	15 cm	
b.	120 cm		300 cm^2
c.		60 m	1650 m^2
d.	12.5 ft	7.25 ft	
e.		1200 m	75000 m^2
f.	1.5 cm		3.6 cm^2

4. **Complete the following table by finding the missing values.**

	Base of the parallelogram	Height of the parallelogram	Area of the parallelogram
a.	7 cm	8 cm	____
b.	____	20 cm	300 cm^2
c.	125 cm	____	12,500 cm^2
d.	12 m	____	84 m^2
e.	____	8 cm	52 m^2
f.	14.5 cm	5 cm	____

5. **Find the area of a triangle if its base and height are 45 cm and 50 cm, respectively.**
6. **What is the area of a parallelogram whose height is 7.5 m and base is 10 m?**

CIRCLES

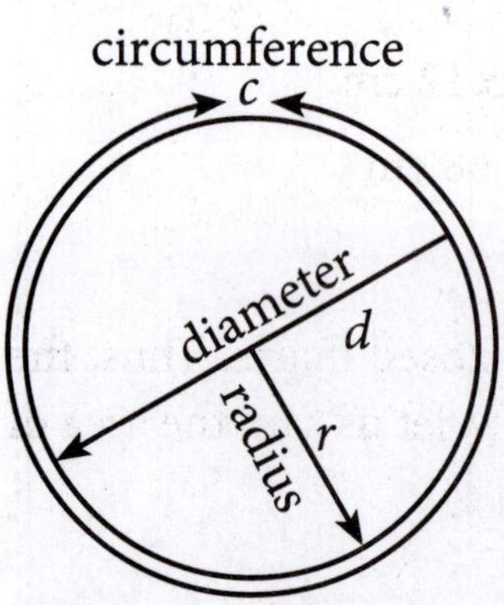

We learnt to find the perimeter and area of squares, rectangles, parallelograms and triangles. Now let us know more about circles.

A **circle** is a simple closed shape or figure formed by joining all the points in a plane that are at equal distances from the centre point.

Chord of a circle is a line segment joining any two points on the circle. **Radius** of a circle is a line segment joining the centre of the circle to any point on the circle. The chord which passes through the centre of the circle is called the **diameter**. The diameter is twice the radius. The distance around the circle (or any circular region) is called its **circumference**.

Relationship Between Circumference and Diameter of a Circle

The following activity will help us arrive at the relationship between circumference and diameter of a circle.

Activity: Draw circles with the following radii in your notebook. Using measuring tools, measure the diameter and circumference of each circle.

Radius (r)	Diameter ($d = 2r$)	Circumference	Ratio of circumference and diameter
2	4	12.57	$\frac{12.57}{4} = 3.1428$
3.5	7	22	$\frac{22}{7} = 3.1428$
5	10	31.4	$\frac{31.4}{10} = 3.14$

Now, observe the ratio of the circumference to the diameter of each circle. The ratio of circumference to the diameter of the circle is the same in all the cases or is always constant. This constant is denoted by the Greek letter 'π'. It is read as 'pi'. Its approximate value is 3.14.

Note

For calculation purposes, the value of π is approximately taken as $\frac{22}{7}$.

Circumference of a Circle

We know that perimeter is the distance covered along the boundary of any object or shape. The perimeter of a circular object is called its circumference. The circumference of some objects like coins, circular plates, bangles, CD, etc. can be found by measuring their circular boundary. Can we find the circumference of a circle without measuring the circular boundary? Yes, we can.

From the above activity, it is clear that the ratio of circumference to the diameter of the circle is constant. That is, $\frac{\text{Circumference}}{\text{Diameter}} = \pi = 3.14$

Therefore, circumference of a circle = $\pi \times d$, where d is the diameter of the circle.

or circumference of a circle = $2\pi r$, where r is the radius of the circle.

For example: If $r = 4$ cm, then the circumference of a circle = 2 (3.14 × 4) = 25.12 cm

If $d = 12$ cm, then the circumference of a circle = 3.14 × 12 = 37.68 cm

Area of a Circle

We know that area is the space or region covered inside the boundary of a closed figure. Thus, the area of a circle is the space covered inside the circumference of the circle. Now, let us find the area of a circle through the following activity.

Activity:

Make a cut-out of a circle. Measure the radius of the circle.	Fold the circle and divide it into even number of congruent parts. Colour each congruent part as shown.	Cut and arrange all the congruent parts in such a way that they form a parallelogram.
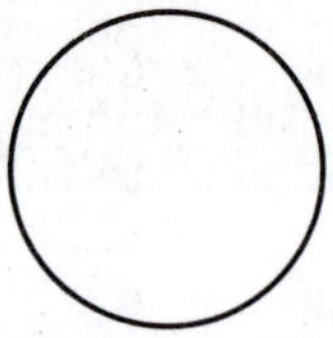	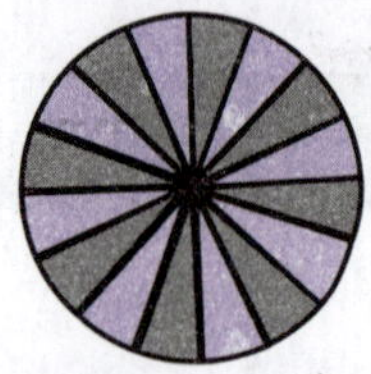	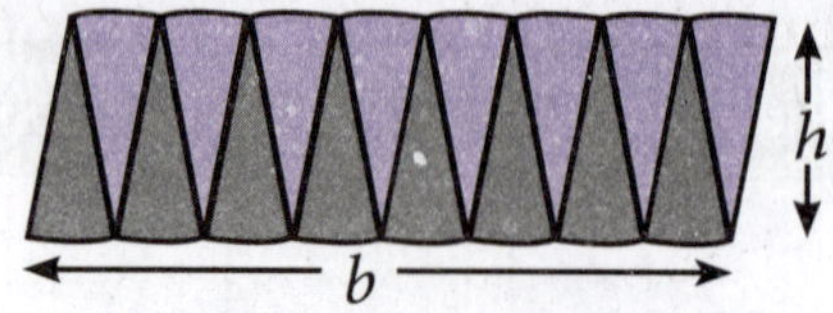

In the above activity, we find that the area of a circle is equal to the area of a parallelogram.

Area of a parallelogram = $b \times h$

Here, b is half the circumference of the circle (πr) as half of the congruent triangles cut out from the circle form the base of the parallelogram and h is the radius of the circle (r).

So, area of the circle = area of the parallelogram = $b \times h = \pi r \times r = \pi r^2$

$\therefore$ Area of the circle (A) = πr^2

For example: If $r = 5$ m, then A = $(3.14 \times 5^2) = 3.14 \times 25 = 78.5$ m^2

If $d = 20$ cm, then $r = 10$ cm and A = $(3.14 \times 10^2) = 3.14 \times 100 = 314$ cm^2

SOLVED EXAMPLES

Example 13: Find the circumference of the following circles.

a. $d = 10$ cm

Circumference of circle = $\pi \times d$

$\therefore$ Circumference = 3.14×10

= 31.4 cm

b. $r = 8$ m

Circumference of circle = $2\pi r$

$\therefore$ Circumference = $2(3.14 \times 8)$

= 50.24 m

Example 14: Find the area of the following circles.

a. $r = 3$ m

Area of the circle (A) = πr^2

$= (3.14 \times 3^2)$

$= 3.14 \times 9$

= 28.26 m^2

b. $d = 14$ cm

Area of the circle (A) = πr^2

$r = \frac{d}{2} = \frac{14}{2} = 7$ cm

$\therefore$ A = $\pi r^2 = (3.14 \times 7^2)$

$= 3.14 \times 49 = 153.86$ cm^2

Example 15: Find the radius and diameter of the following circles.

a. Circumference of the circle = 188.4 m

Circumference of circle = $2\pi r$

$r = \frac{\text{Circumference}}{2\pi} = \frac{188.4}{2 \times 3.14} = \frac{188.4}{6.28} = 30$

$d = 2r = 2 \times 30 = 60$ m

b. Area of the circle = 706.5 cm^2

Area of the circle (A) = πr^2

$r^2 = \frac{A}{\pi} = \frac{706.5}{3.14} = 225$

$r = \sqrt{225} = 15$

$d = 2r = 2 \times 15 = 30$ cm

Example 16: Complete the following table.

	Radius (mm)	Diameter (mm)	Circumference (mm)	Area (mm^2)
a.	6	12	37.68	______
b.	12	24	______	452.16

Solution: a. Area = $\pi r^2 = 3.14 \times 6 \times 6 = 113.04 \text{ mm}^2$

b. Circumference = $2\pi r = 2 \times 3.14 \times 12 = 75.36$ mm

EXERCISE 15C

1. **Find the circumference of the circles with the following radius/diameter.**

   a. $r = 7$ cm b. $d = 10$ cm c. $r = 8$ m d. $r = 4$ cm e. $d = 22$ m

2. **Find the area of the circles for the following radii.**

   a. 3 cm b. 8.5 m c. 120 cm d. 14 cm e. 12.7 m

3. **Find the diameter of the circles with the following circumferences.**

   a. 31.4 cm b. 6 m c. 63 cm d. 25.12 cm e. 132 cm

4. **Find the radius of the circles with the following areas.**

   a. 28.3 cm^2 b. 102 cm^2 c. 3.14 cm^2 d. 50.3 cm^2 e. 452.16 cm^2

5. **Complete the following table.**

	Diameter (m)	Radius (m)	Circumference (m)	Area (m^2)
a.	30			707
b.		60		
c.	15. 6		49	
d.	220		691	
e.	88	44		6080
f.		9.25	58.1	

6. **If the circumference of a circle is 31.4 cm, then find its radius.**
7. **Calculate the area of a circle whose radius is 0.8 cm.**

CONVERSION OF UNITS OF AREA

We know that area is the amount of space or region enclosed by a closed figure and the units of area are given in square units. We have also learnt conversions of units of length. Let us now learn how to convert units while measuring the area.

If the length of the side of a unit square is 1 cm, then its area is 1 cm^2.

We know that 1 cm = 10 mm. Therefore, 1 cm^2 = 10 mm × 10 mm = 100 mm^2.

Similarly, the other basic conversions can also be done.

The following table gives all the unit conversions in a hierarchical order.

Unit of length	Unit of area	Relationship
Millimetre (mm)	mm^2	
Centimetre (cm)	cm^2	$1\ cm^2 = (10\ mm)^2 = 100\ mm^2$
Decimetre (dm)	dm^2	$1\ dm^2 = (10\ cm)^2 = 100\ cm^2$
Metre (m)	m^2	$1\ m^2 = (100\ cm)^2 = 10{,}000\ cm^2$
Decametre (dam)	dam^2	$1\ dam^2 = (10\ m)^2 = 100\ m^2$
Hectometre (hm)	hm^2	$1\ hm^2 = (10\ dam)^2 = 100\ dam^2$
Kilometre (km)	km^2	$1\ km^2 = (1000\ m)^2 = 10{,}00{,}000\ m^2$

Example 17: Convert 5 m^2 to mm^2.

1 m = 100 cm = 1000 mm

$5\ m^2 = 5 \times (1000)^2 = 50{,}00{,}000\ mm^2$

Example 18: Convert 3 km^2 to m^2.

1 km = 1000 m

$3\ km^2 = 3 \times (1000)^2 = 30{,}00{,}000\ m^2$

Example 19: Convert the following units as directed.

a. 18 m^2 to cm^2

$1\ m^2 = (100\ cm)^2$

$= 10{,}000\ cm^2$

$\therefore\ 18\ m^2 = 18 \times 10{,}000\ cm^2$

$= 18 \times 10^4\ cm^2$

b. 2,50,00,000 m^2 to km^2

$1000\ m = 1\ km \Rightarrow 1\ m = \left(\frac{1}{1000}\right) km$

$\therefore$ 2,50,00,000 m^2

$= 2{,}50{,}00{,}000 \times \left(\frac{1}{1000} \times \frac{1}{1000}\right) km^2 = 25\ km^2$

REAL-LIFE APPLICATIONS OF PERIMETER AND AREA

The concepts of perimeter and area are used in many real-life situations like construction and design of farms, houses, buildings or any other structures. Let us understand this with the help of the following examples.

SOLVED EXAMPLES

Example 20: Solve the following word problems.

a. The height of a triangle is 3 times its base and its area is 54 cm^2. Find the height and base of the triangle.

b. Find the number of rotations made by a circular wheel of radius 42 cm to cover a distance of 1056 cm.

c. A carpet is laid on the floor of a rectangular room whose dimensions are 20 m by 15 m, by leaving a margin of 2 m around it. Find the area of the floor which is not covered by the carpet.

Solution: a. Given: Height of the triangle = 3 times the base, Area of the triangle = 54 cm^2

To find: Value of height and base

Let the base of the triangle be k cm. Then its height will be $3k$ cm.

Area of a triangle $= \frac{1}{2} \times$ Base $\times$ Height

$54 = \frac{1}{2} k \times 3k$

$108 = 3k^2 \Rightarrow k^2 = \frac{108}{3} = 36 \Rightarrow k = \sqrt{36} = 6$

$\therefore$ Base of the triangle is 6 cm and its height is $3k = 3 \times 6 = 18$ cm

b. Given: Radius of wheel = 42 cm, Distance covered by wheel = 1056 cm

To find: Circumference of the wheel and number of rotations made by the wheel

Let the number of rotations made by the wheel be k.

Circumference of the wheel = $2\pi r = 2 \times 3.14 \times 42 = 263.76$ cm

Number of rotation of the wheel = $\dfrac{\text{Total distance covered}}{\text{Circumference of the wheel}} = \dfrac{1056}{263.76} = 4$

$\therefore$ The number of rotations made by the wheel is 4.

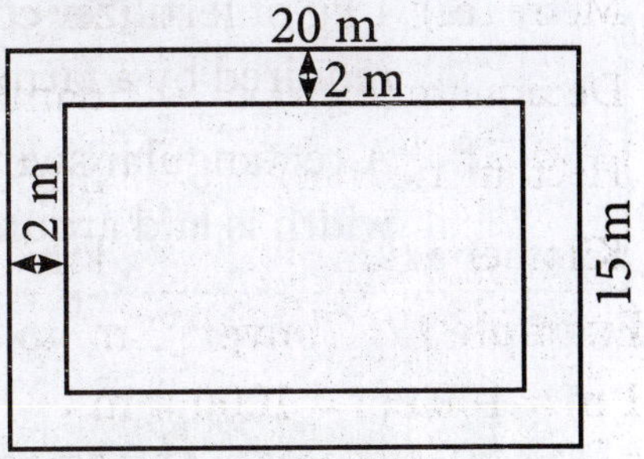

c. Given: Length of the carpet = 20 m and width of the carpet = 15 m

Margin left around the carpet = 2 m

To find: Area of the floor which is not covered by the carpet

Area of rectangle = $l \times b$

Length of the carpet = 20 m – (2 m + 2 m) = 16 m

Breadth of the carpet = 15 m – (2 m + 2 m) = 11 m

Area of the floor not covered by the carpet = Area of the floor – Area of the carpet

Area of the floor = 20 m × 15 m = 300 m^2

Area of the carpet = 16 m × 11 m = 176 m^2

$\therefore$ Area of the floor not covered by the carpet = 300 m^2 – 176 m^2 = 124 m^2

Example 21: In the given figure, the two circles have the same centre. The radius of the larger circle is 6 cm and that of the smaller circle is 4 cm. Find the area of the shaded region between the two circles.

Solution: Given: Radius of larger circle = 6 cm, Radius of the smaller circle = 4 cm

To find: Area between the two circles

Area of the shaded region = Area of the larger circle – Area of the smaller circle

Area of the larger circle = $\pi r^2 = 3.14 \times 6 \times 6 = 113.04$ cm^2

Area of the smaller circle = $\pi r^2 = 3.14 \times 4 \times 4 = 50.24$ cm^2

So, area of the shaded region = 113.04 – 50.24 = 62.80 cm^2

EXERCISE 15D

1. Fill in the blanks.

a. 1 cm^2 = ______ mm^2 b. 10 cm^2 = ______ m^2 c. 1 km^2 = ______ hectare

d. 1 km^2 = ______ m^2 e. 10 km^2 = ______ m^2 f. 100 cm^2 = ______ m^2

2. Solve the following word problems.

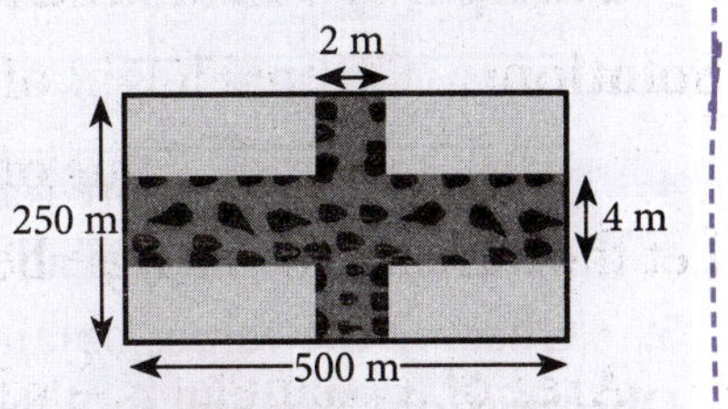

a. Two paths are crossing each other at right angles in a rectangular park as shown. Find the area of the path and that of the park not covered by the paths.

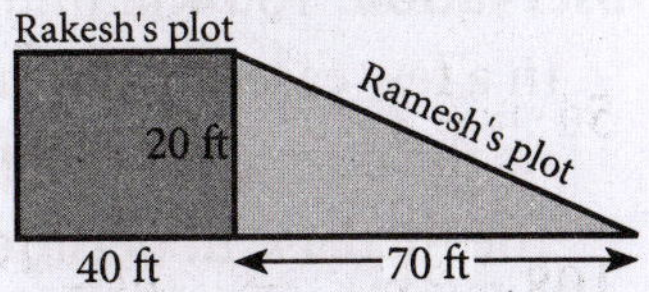

b. Rakesh bought a rectangular plot of dimension 20 ft by 40 ft. Ramesh bought a triangular plot adjacent to Rakesh's plot, at the same cost. Whose plot is bigger and by how many feet?

c. The area of triangle ABC in the figure shown here is 52.5 cm². Find the area of the triangle BDC.

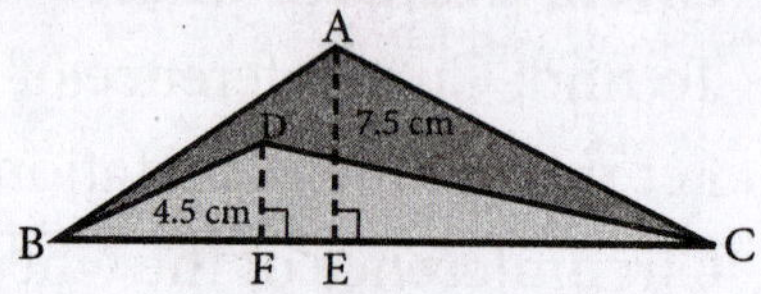

d. Julie built a kennel whose base is in the shape of a rectangle of dimensions 100 cm by 40 cm. She wants to put a fence around it. Find the length of fence required in metres.

e. 1 kg of fertilizer covers an area of half-square metre. Find the amount of fertilizer required by a farmer for his circular field whose radius is 14 m.

f. A rectangular swimming pool has dimensions 45 m by 20 m. A concrete path of 3.5 m width is laid around it. Find the cost of laying the path at a rate of ₹25 per m².

Mental Maths

1. What is the perimeter of a square whose side is 100 m?
2. What is the area of a circle whose radius is 9 cm?
3. Find the area of a parallelogram whose base is 20 cm and height is 7 cm.
4. What is the radius of a circle whose area and perimeter are equal to 12.5 units?
5. What is the formula of the perimeter of a rectangle?

Maths Lab Activity

Aim: To generalize that an increase in the perimeter of a rectangle may not lead to an increase in its area

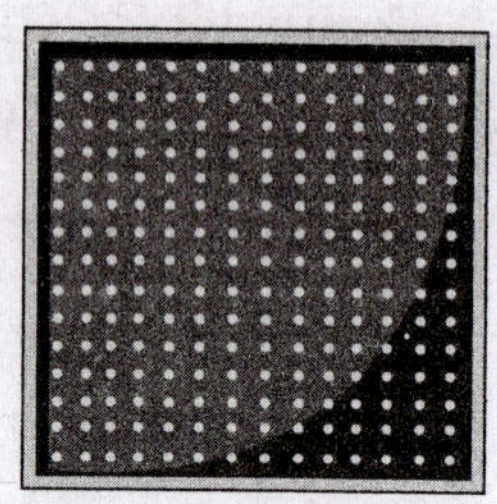

Materials required: Geoboard, rubber band and observation sheets

Procedure:

1. Take a geoboard and a rubber band.
2. Form a rectangle of dimensions 8 units by 3 units using rubber bands.
3. Find the area and perimeter of the rectangle formed. Note down the values in the format given below.

Rectangle	Length	Breadth	Perimeter	Area
1.				
2.				

4. Now form some more rectangles which have greater dimensions than the previous one. Find the perimeter and area of all the rectangles formed.
5. Observe the values obtained for the perimeter and area of all the rectangles.

Observation: You will find that

- In a few cases, the area increases and in some other cases, the area decreases.
- As the perimeter increases, the area need not increase.
- The increase in perimeter need not lead to increase in area.

Concept Map

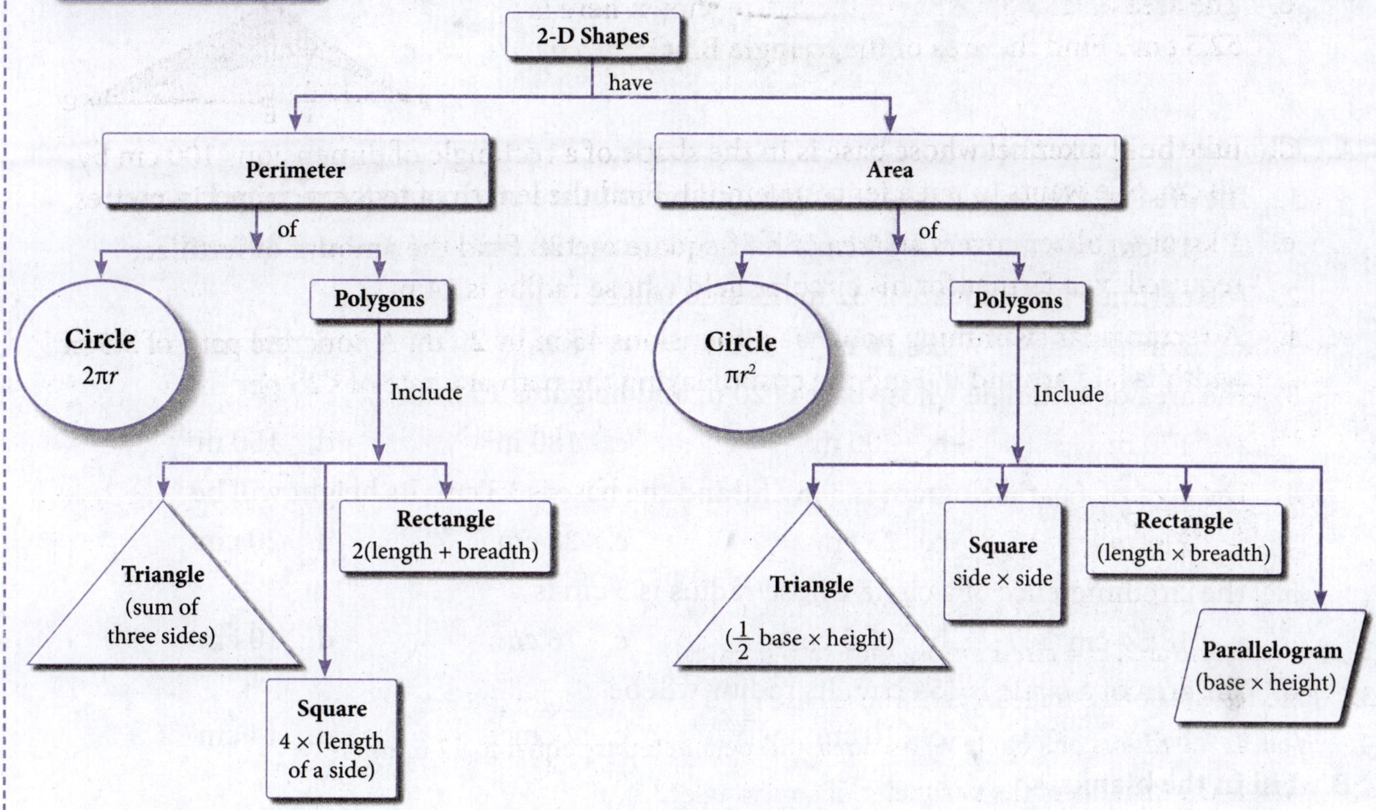

Key Concepts

- **Perimeter:** It is the distance covered along the boundary of a closed shape
- **Area:** It is the amount of space enclosed within a closed shape
- **Parallelograms:** A polygon with two pairs of parallel sides
- **Triangle:** A polygon with three sides and three vertices
- **Congruent:** Identical shapes having same area
- **Radius:** A line segment joining the centre of the circle to any point on the circle
- **Diameter:** The chord which passes through the centre of the circle
- **Circumference:** Perimeter of the circle

CHAPTER REVISION

A. Choose the correct option.

1. The area of a rectangle whose length and breadth are 10 cm and 8 cm, respectively, is
   a. 18 cm b. 80 cm^2 c. 120 cm^2 d. 200 cm^2
2. The perimeter of a square is 32 m. Its side will be
   a. 2 m b. 16 m c. 8 m d. 64 m
3. The area of a triangle whose base is 20 m and height is 15 m is
   a. 120 m^2 b. 200 m^2 c. 180 m^2 d. 150 m^2
4. The area of a parallelogram is 345 cm^2 and the base is 15 cm. Its height will be
   a. 21 cm b. 23 cm c. 28 cm d. 20 cm
5. The circumference of a circle whose radius is 3 cm is
   a. 18.84 cm b. 12.5 cm c. 16 cm d. 10 cm
6. The area of a circle is 154 cm^2. Its radius will be
   a. 8 cm c. 10 cm c. 7 cm d. 14 cm

B. Fill in the blanks.

1. The area of a triangle is given by ___________.
2. The side of a square whose area and perimeter are the same is __________ units.
3. If the length and breadth of a rectangle is 20 cm and 10 cm, respectively, then the perimeter is ___________.
4. 1 m^2 = ___________ cm^2.
5. The area of a circle whose radius is 8 m is ___________.
6. The distance around a circle is called ___________.

C. Write T for true and F for false.

1. If the side of a square is 12 cm, its perimeter is 48 cm.
2. The area of a parallelogram is $\frac{1}{2} \times$ base $\times$ height.
3. The diameter of a circle is twice the radius.
4. 1 cm^2 = 1000 mm
5. If the perimeter of an equilateral triangle is 120 cm, then each side will be 40 cm.
6. The area of a rectangle is length × breadth.

D. Find the perimeter of the following figures.

1. 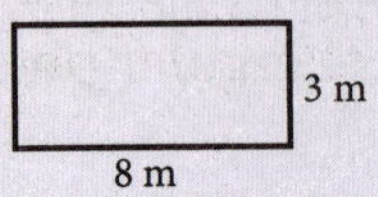

2. 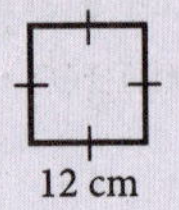

3. 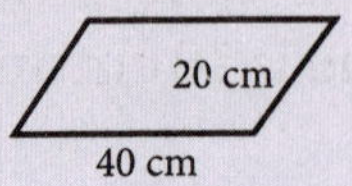

4. 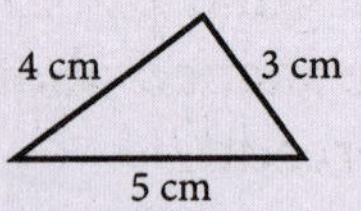

5. 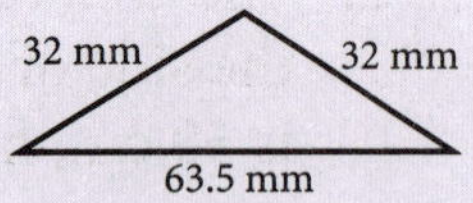

E. Match the following.

1. 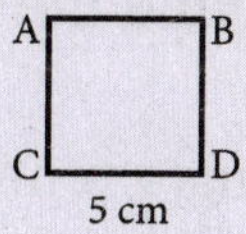

a. 154 cm^2

2. 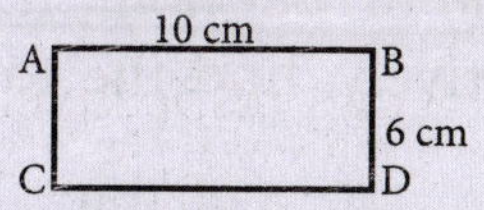

b. 30 cm^2

3. 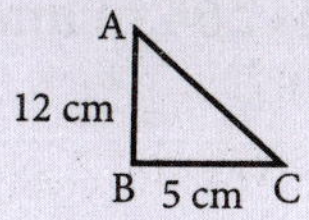

c. 84 cm^2

4. 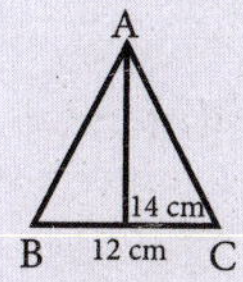

d. 60 cm^2

5. 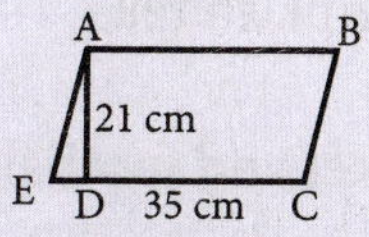

e. 25 cm^2

6. 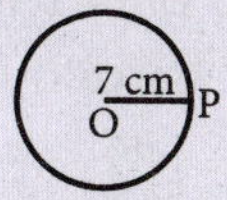

f. 735 cm^2

F. Complete the following table.

	Base	Height	Area of parallelogram
1.	7 cm	6 cm	
2.	9 cm	6 cm	
3.	12 cm	5 cm	
4.	12 cm	10 cm	
5.	34 cm	16 cm	

G. Complete the following table.

	Radius (r)	Diameter (d)	Circumference of circle	Area of circle
1.	5 cm	10 cm		
2.	7 m	______		
3.	8.5 cm	16 cm		
4.	______	20 m		
5.	35 cm	70 cm		

H. Solve the following word problems.

1. Shreya has a square-shaped garden whose side length is 15 m. What is the cost of fencing the garden at the rate of ₹100 per metre?
2. The area of a rectangular photo frame is same as the area of a square-shaped photo frame. If the side of a square shaped photo frame is 10 cm and the length of a rectangular photo frame is 50 cm, find its breadth.
3. Find the height of a triangular plate, if its area is 1225 cm^2 and base is 35 cm.

4. Find the height, if the area of parallelogram-shaped mat is 100 m^2 and base is 10 m.
5. The base of a triangular tile is 2 times the height and its area is 100 sq. ft. Find the height and base of the tile.
6. A field is in the shape of a parallelogram that needs to be ploughed using a rented plough. The charge for one hour is ₹300 and it can plough an area of 400 m^2 per hour. If the length and corresponding height of field are 80 m and 50 m, respectively, find the total cost of ploughing the field.
7. A garden is surrounded by a circular path whose inner circumference is 264 m and the outer circumference is 308 m. Find the width of the path.

SKILL UP!

Project

1. Find the dimensions of the field required for the following and also the total play area required for having these under one roof.
   a. 1 swimming pool b. 1 skating rink c. Playground to play cricket and football
2. Taj Mahal, a world famous structure, is located in Agra in Uttar Pradesh on the banks of Yamuna River. It is one of the famous tourist attractions in India. The Taj Mahal garden is popularly known as Charbagh.
   Using the Internet, find more about the garden (such as its dimensions, number of equal parts in the garden, flowerbeds, etc.) and then answer the following questions based on your findings.
   a. Calculate the perimeter and area of Charbagh.
   b. What is the area of each flowerbed in Charbagh?

Life Skills

The standard parking area required for a car is 2.5 m × 5 m. We can park 5 motor bikes in one car parking space. Find the total area required to park 10 cars and 25 bikes.

Mind Buzzer

The side of a square is 4 cm. If its side is doubled, then how many times would be the area of the new square greater than the area of the old square?

Teacher's Notes

- Use graph sheets while teaching perimeter and area so that the students can verify their answers by counting the number of squares.
- Conduct hands-on activities for finding congruent shapes in rectangles and squares.
- Conduct paper-folding activities in the class to teach finding the area of a circle.
- Use real-life examples to explain how to solve problems on area and perimeter.

WORKSHEET

This is the floor plan of a house. The dimensions of different rooms of the house are provided. Based on these measurements, find out the area and perimeter of the hall.

Do all your calculations in the space provided below.

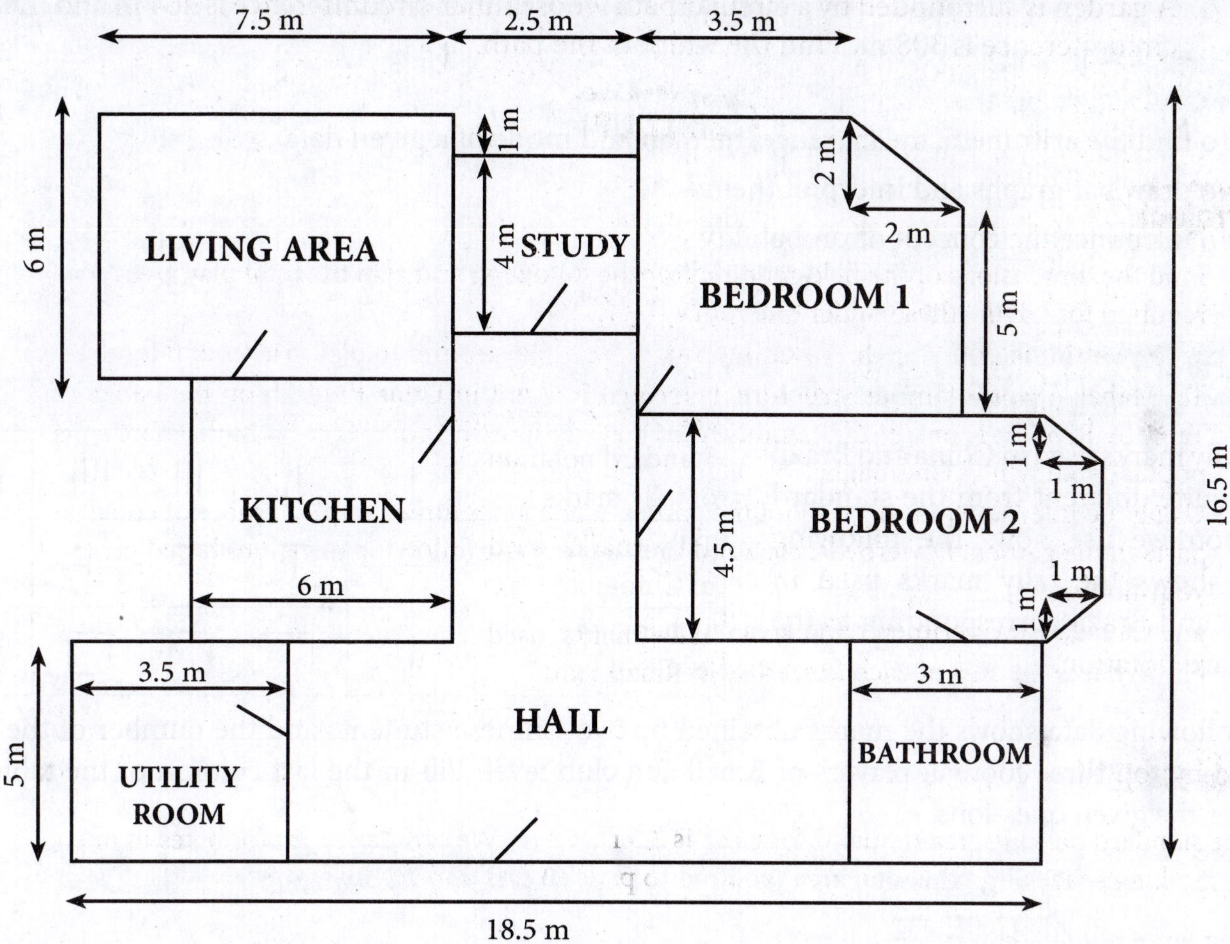

16 Data Handling and Probability

Learning Objectives

- To find the arithmetic mean, range, median and mode of a given data
- To draw bar graphs and interpret them
- To introduce the concept of probability

Let's Get Started

The tally marks used in China and Brazil were quite different from the standard notation we use now. The following table shows the tally marks used in China and Brazil corresponding to the standard notation.

Standard notation of tally marks	|	||	|||	||||	卌
Tally marks used in China	一	丅	下	止	正
Tally marks used in Brazil					

The following data shows the marks obtained by two Chinese students and the number of the goals scored by top three football players of Brazil at a club level. Fill in the last column of the table and answer the given questions.

Name	Tally marks	Total
Huang Fu	正 正 下	
Cheng	正 正 正 一	
Pele	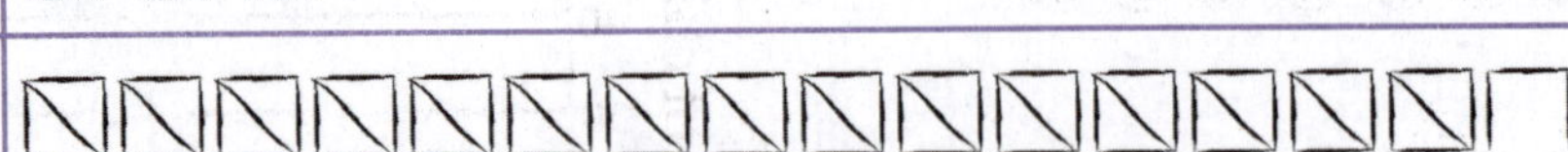	
Ronaldo	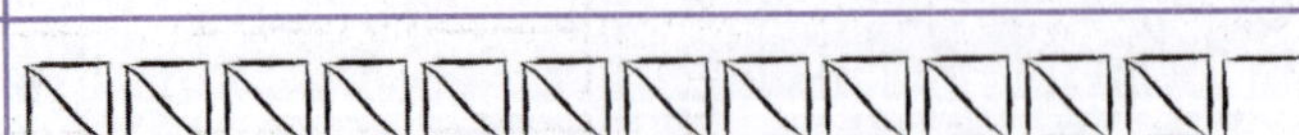	
Rivaldo	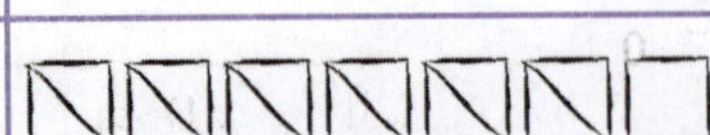	

a. Who scored more marks: Cheng or Huang Fu?

____

b. What is the difference in the number of goals scored by Rivaldo and Pele?

____

COLLECTION AND ORGANIZATION OF DATA

We have learnt to collect, tabulate and represent data using pictographs and bar graphs. Let us first recall some of the terms we have learnt so far.

- **Data** is a group of numerical values collected and recorded for a specific purpose.
- **Raw data** is the data obtained in the original form.
- **Array** is the arrangement of numerical data in increasing or decreasing order.
- **Observations** are the individual numerical values in data.
- **Frequency** is the number of times a particular observation occurs in data.
- **Tabulation of data** is the arrangement of data in a systematic form in a table.
- **Pictograph:** It is a method of representing information using pictures and symbols.
- **Tally marks** help in counting objects in groups of five. The first four counts are represented by four vertical lines and the fifth by a diagonal line across the four vertical lines.
- **Bar graph:** It is a graphical representation of numerical data in the form of rectangles of equal width and different heights that represent the frequency of the given data.

Do you know?

Statistics is the field of study that deals with the collection, organization, presentation, analysis and interpretation of data.

Example 1: The following data can be represented using both pictograph and bar graph as shown below.

Favourite breakfast	Number of children
Idli	30
Dosa	40
Parantha	15
Poori	50

Solution:

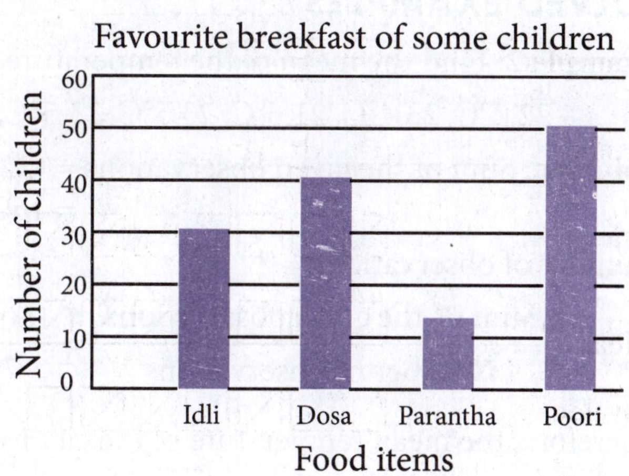

REPRESENTATIVE VALUES

While dealing with data, small or large, we use representative values. A representative value is an indication of the central value (or average value) of a data sample. It gives the closest value to a series of measurements. Different types of representative values are the following:

- Arithmetic mean (Average)
- Range
- Median
- Mode

Of these, mean, median and mode are types of average. Let us learn more about each of these terms.

Note

Average is the calculated central value of a set of data.

To calculate it, we add up all the observations (values) in the given set and divide the sum by the total number of observations in the set.

Arithmetic Mean (Average) of Ungrouped Data

Read the following statements. Have you come across such statements in daily lives?

- Somu rides 12 km on an average in a day.
- She uses 5 m of cloth on an average for a garment.
- The train travels at an average speed of 80 km per hour.

The values in the given statements are not exact, but convey that the actual amounts could be around these values. Such values represent or give us an average value (arithmetic mean) of a group of observations or data.

The arithmetic mean (or simply mean) for a given data is given by the following expression:

$$\textbf{Mean} = \frac{\textbf{Sum of the given observations}}{\textbf{Number of observations}}$$

Note

While finding the mean, ensure all the quantities are in the same units.

Range

Range is defined as the difference between the highest and the lowest value (observation) in a given data. It gives an approximate idea of the spread of the data (observations). Range is calculated by subtracting the lowest value from the highest value in the given data.

SOLVED EXAMPLES

Example 2: Find the mean of the temperatures of a city during one week.

22.2°C, 23.4°C, 21.6°C, 23.5°C, 23.5°C, 23.6°C, 22.5°C

Solution: Sum of the given observations = (22.2 + 23.4 + 21.6 + 23.5 + 23.5 + 23.6 + 22.5)°C
= 160.3°C

Number of observations = 7

$$\text{Mean} = \frac{\text{Sum of the given observations}}{\text{Number of observations}} = \frac{160.3}{7} = 22.9^\circ\text{C}$$

Therefore, the mean temperature of the city for that week is 22.9°C.

Example 3: Rohan played outdoors for 40 min, 1 h, 25 min, 50 min, 25 min and 40 min, respectively, on consecutive days. Find out his mean playtime per day.

Solution: Sum of the given observations = (40 + 60 + 25 + 50 + 25 + 40)
= 240 minutes (1 hour = 60 minutes)

Number of observations = 6

$$\text{Mean} = \frac{\text{Sum of the given observations}}{\text{Number of observations}} = \frac{240}{6} = 40 \text{ minutes}$$

Therefore, Rohan plays for 40 minutes on an average per day.

Example 4: Find the range of the following data.

9	2	1	2	5	6	8	9	0	5

Solution: Range = Highest value – lowest value = 9 – 0 = 9

Example 5: Given below is the number of baskets weaved by Lata on different days. Observe the data and answer the questions that follow.

45	24	21	38	36	23	20	20	25

a. What is the maximum number of baskets weaved on a particular day? 45

b. What is the minimum number of baskets weaved on a particular day? 20

c. What is the range of the data?

Range = Highest value – lowest value = 45 – 20 = 25

d. What is the average number of baskets Lata weaves?

Sum of the given observations = (45 + 24 + 21 + 38 + 36 + 23 + 20 + 20 + 25) = 252 baskets

Number of observations = 9

$$\text{Mean} = \frac{\text{Sum of the given observations}}{\text{Number of observations}} = \frac{252}{9} = 28 \text{ baskets}$$

Therefore, Lata weaves 28 baskets on an average per day.

EXERCISE 16A

1. **Find the range and the arithmetic mean of the first 10 odd numbers.**
2. **Find the range and the arithmetic mean of the multiples of 6 between 36 and 96.**
3. **The wages of a worker in rupees from Monday to Saturday are given below. Find the mean wage of the worker per day.**

   750, 600, 550, 1000, 850, 900
4. **The ages of 6 girls at a summer camp are as follows: 9, 10, 10, 13, 12, 15. Find the arithmetic mean of their ages.**
5. **Raghav reads the following number of pages of a storybook every day.**

   20, 25, 46, 40, 22, 30, 24, 31, 32, 20

   Find the average number of pages read by him
6. **Given below is the population of 5 villages of a district. Find the arithmetic mean of the population.**

   9000, 7500, 8310, 5505, 6700

Median of Ungrouped Data

Median of a data sample is the value of the middle observation when the given data is arranged in ascending or descending order.

Steps for finding median:

Let the number of observations of any data be n.

1. Arrange the given data in ascending or descending order.
2. Check if the number of observations is odd or even.
3. If n is odd, then

$$\text{Median} = \text{value of } \left[\frac{1}{2}(n+1)\right]^{\text{th}} \text{ observation}$$

If n is even, then

$$\text{Median} = \frac{1}{2}\left[\left(\frac{n}{2}\right)^{\text{th}} \text{observation} + \left(\frac{n}{2}+1\right)^{\text{th}} \text{observation}\right]$$

Mode of Ungrouped Data

Mode of a data sample is the value of the observation that occurs most frequently.

SOLVED EXAMPLES

Example 6: The heights of 9 students (in cm) are given below. Find the median height.

162, 151, 150, 159, 154, 160, 149, 155, 157

Solution: Arranging the heights in the ascending order, we get

149, 150, 151, 154, 155, 157, 159, 160, 162

Here $n = 9$, so n is odd.

$$\text{Median height} = \text{value of } \left[\frac{1}{2}(n+1)\right]^{\text{th}} \text{ observation}$$

$$= \text{value of } \left[\frac{1}{2}(9+1)\right]^{\text{th}} \text{ observation}$$

$$= \text{value of } 5^{\text{th}} \text{ observation} = 155$$

Therefore, the median height is 155 cm.

Example 7: The weights of 12 students (in kg) are given below. Find the median weight.

45, 50, 52, 46, 48, 55, 49, 54, 57, 43, 40, 53

Solution: Arranging the weights in the ascending order, we get

40, 43, 45, 46, 48, 49, 50, 52, 53, 54, 55, 57

Here $n = 12$, so n is even.

$$\text{Median weight} = \frac{1}{2}\left[\left(\frac{12}{2}\right)^{\text{th}} \text{observation} + \left(\frac{12}{2}+1\right)^{\text{th}} \text{observation}\right]$$

$$= \frac{1}{2}(6^{\text{th}} \text{ observation} + 7^{\text{th}} \text{ observation}) = \frac{1}{2}(49 + 50) = \frac{99}{2} = 49.5$$

Therefore, the median weight is 49.5 kg.

Example 8: Given below are the marks obtained by 15 students in a test. Find the modal marks.

15, 20, 16, 10, 24, 20, 18, 17, 20, 11, 14, 9, 21, 20, 23

Solution: Arranging the marks in ascending order, we get

9, 10, 11, 14, 15, 16, 17, 18, 20, 20, 20, 20, 21, 23, 24

20 occurs the maximum number of times, that is, 4 times.

Therefore, modal marks = 20

Example 9: Given below is the number of books borrowed by students of different classes. Find the mode.

Class	4	5	6	7	8	9
Number of books borrowed	13	12	10	20	14	18

Note

A data sample can have more than one mode.

Solution: As the maximum number of books was borrowed by Class 7, the mode of the given data is 20.

EXERCISE 16B

1. **Find the median of the following.**
   a. 3, 6, 7, 4, 5, 9, 8, 9, 7
   b. 51, 53, 55, 57, 59, 61, 63, 65
   c. 80, 82, 84, 86, 88, 90, 92
   d. 12, 20, 22, 30, 32, 40, 42, 50, 62, 70
   e. 33, 75, 35, 48, 47, 50, 55, 58, 60, 70, 72
2. **Find the mode for the following data.**
   a. 3, 6, 6, 7, 8, 9, 5, 4, 6, 7
   b. 45, 50, 50, 48, 46, 47, 45, 48, 50, 48, 48
3. **The cost of different tickets (in rupees) bought by different passengers travelling in a train is given below. Find the median cost.**
   54, 51, 55, 45, 40, 45, 38, 50, 35, 42, 60, 30, 32, 46, 50
4. **The marks of 10 students in a test are given below. Find the median marks.**
   15, 20, 20, 18, 29, 28, 25, 24, 19, 27
5. **The number of idlis eaten at a hostel was recorded. Find the mode of the data.**
   2, 4, 3, 5, 6, 2, 3, 2, 6, 4, 4, 8, 6, 10, 8, 6, 7, 5, 6, 6
6. **At a party, people were found wearing t-shirts of the following types of designs.**

Design	Iconography	Geometric patterns	Bright colours	Foil prints	Monochrome colour palettes
Number of people	18	11	12	20	18

Find the modal design.

BAR GRAPHS

We know that a **bar graph** is a pictorial representation of numerical data in the form of rectangles (or bars) of equal width and varying heights.

The rectangular bars can be drawn either vertically or horizontally, with equal spaces between them. The heights of the bars vary according to the value each bar represents.

A bar graph uses rectangular bars to show comparison among different categories. We can draw conclusions from the data represented on a bar graph. This is called reading or interpreting a bar graph.

Now let us learn how to draw a bar graph for a given data with the help of the following examples.

SOLVED EXAMPLES

Example 10: The population of some towns are given below.

Name of the town	Rampur	Belagur	Hanthi	Digaru	Mempa
Population	2,60,000	3,20,000	4,00,000	1,80,000	2,40,000

Represent this data on a bar graph.

Solution: We can draw a bar graph by following the steps given below.

Step 1: Title and *x*-axis and *y*-axis: On the graph paper, write the title 'Graph showing the population of some towns'. Draw a horizontal line OX and a vertical line OY as shown. These lines represent the *x*-axis and the *y*-axis, respectively.

Step 2: Labelling: Label 'Towns' along the *x*-axis and 'Population' along the *y*-axis. Along the *x*-axis, mark points at equal intervals and write the names of the towns.

Step 3: Scale: Let the scale on the *y*-axis be: 1 small division = 5000.

> **Note**
>
> Choose an appropriate scale such that
> - the graph occupies most of the page,
> - the divisions on the axes make it easy to plot the points accurately.
>
> Take 1 small division as 2, 5, 10, 25, 50, etc.

The heights of the bars would be as follows:

Rampur $= \frac{1}{5000} \times 260000 = 52$ small divisions

Belagur $= \frac{1}{5000} \times 320000 = 64$ small divisions

Hanthi $= \frac{1}{5000} \times 400000 = 80$ small divisions

Digaru $= \frac{1}{5000} \times 180000 = 36$ small divisions

Mempa $= \frac{1}{5000} \times 240000 = 48$ small divisions

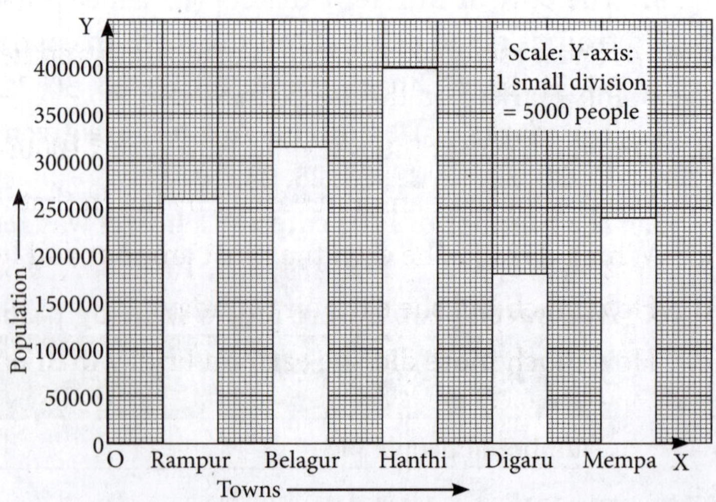

Bar graph showing population of some towns

Step 4: Draw rectangular bars of equal width and heights determined in Step 3. The bars should be centred at the points marked on the x-axis in Step 2. These bars represent the given data.

Example 11: Rini's earnings in a week are given below.

Day	Monday	Tuesday	Wednesday	Thursday	Friday	Saturday
Amount (in rupees)	1200	1000	1500	860	1040	1100

Represent this data on a bar graph. Then answer the questions that follow.

Solution: Draw the bar graph by following the steps given below.

Step 1: Title and x-axis and y-axis: On the graph paper, write the title 'Graph showing Rini's earnings in a week'. Draw a horizontal line OX for the x-axis and a vertical line OY for the y-axis.

Step 2: Labelling: Label Days along the x-axis and 'Amount in rupees' along the y-axis. Along the x-axis, mark points at equal intervals and write the names of the weekdays.

Step 3: Scale: Let the scale on the y-axis be: 1 small division = 20 rupees.

The heights of the bars are as follows:

Monday $= \frac{1}{20} \times 1200 = 60$ small divisions

Tuesday $= \frac{1}{20} \times 1000 = 50$ small divisions

Wednesday $= \frac{1}{20} \times 1500 = 75$ small divisions

Thursday $= \frac{1}{20} \times 860 = 43$ small divisions

Friday $= \frac{1}{20} \times 1040 = 52$ small divisions

Saturday $= \frac{1}{20} \times 1100 = 55$ small divisions

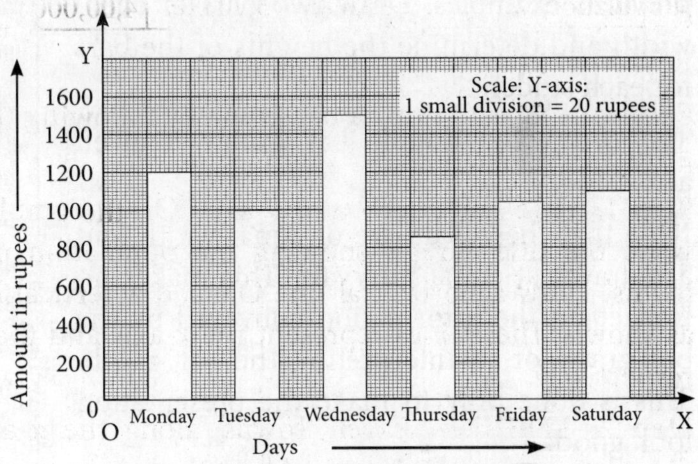

Bar graph showing Rini's earnings in a week

Step 4: Draw rectangular bars of equal width and heights determined in Step 3, and centre the bars at the points marked on the x-axis in Step 2.

a. On which day of the week did Rini earn ₹1000? Tuesday

b. What is the least amount earned by her in that week? ₹860

c. Which day did she earn the most amount and how much? Wednesday, ₹1500

d. How much did she earn on Monday? ₹1200

e. How much more did she earn on Friday than on Tuesday? ₹(1040 – 1000) = ₹40

Double Bar Graphs

Double bar graphs help in comparing or presenting more than one kind of information.

In the following examples, there are two sets of information given. This can be represented in a double bar graph.

Example 12: Marks scored by some students in algebra test without preparation and with preparation are given below. Represent this data on a bar graph.

Names	Hemant	Rishi	Sunita	Nisha	Abhi
Marks scored without preparation	70	68	74	85	60
Marks scored with preparation	85	74	88	97	80

Solution:

Follow the same steps as followed in the previous examples. Draw two bars of equal width and determine the heights of the bars for each student.

The completed double bar graph is given alongside.

Note that these bars are of equal width and are drawn at equal intervals. This makes no impact on the information conveyed by the bar graph or in interpreting the bar graph. This is done only to make the presentation look good.

Bar graph showing the marks scored in algebra test without and with preparation

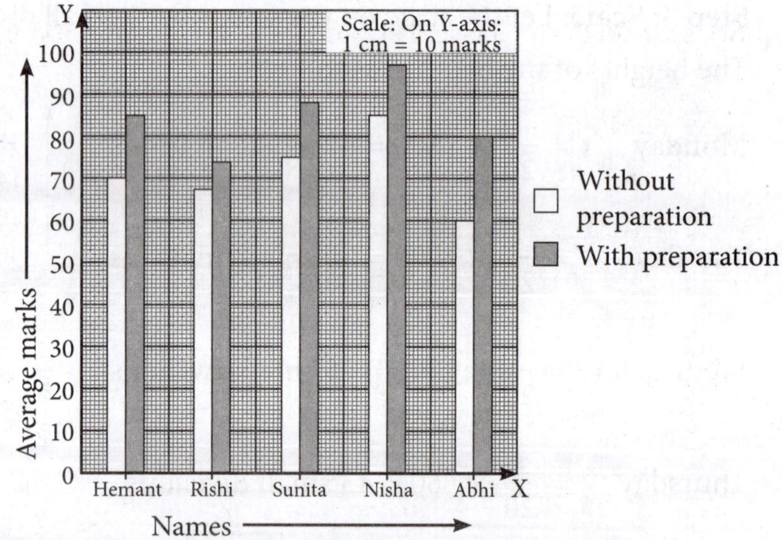

Example 13: Given below is a bar graph showing the amount collected through donations by the students of section A and section B of different classes.

Read the bar graph and answer the following questions.

a. Which section of Class 9 has collected more amount? How much?

b. What is the difference in the amounts collected by Class 6 and Class 9?

c. Have both the sections of any class collected the same amount? If yes, which classes and how much?

d. Which class has collected a total of ₹13,000?

e. How much more should section A of Class 10 have collected to make the same amount as section B?

Bar graph showing the donation amounts collected by two sections of different classes

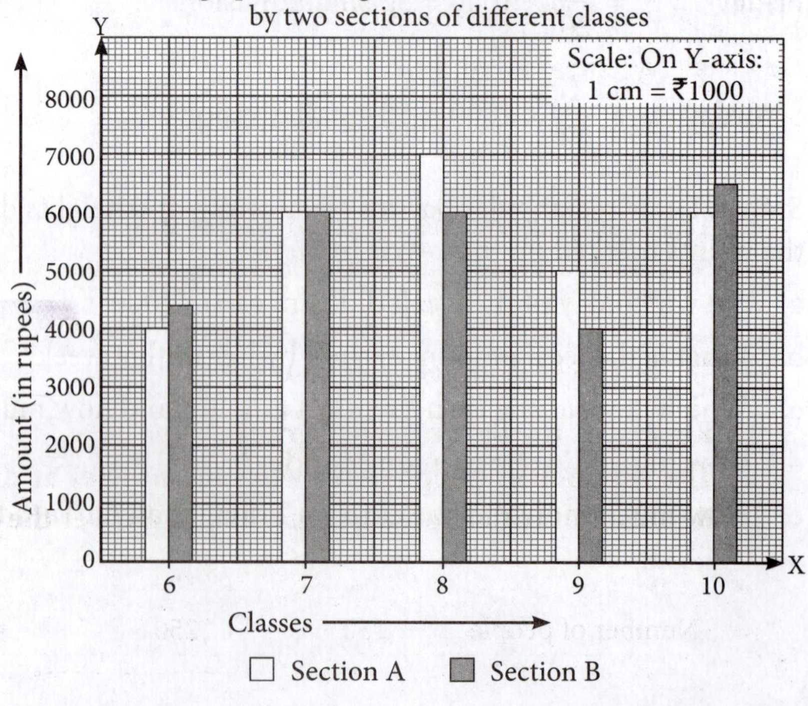

Solution:

a. Section A of Class 9 has collected more amount. They collected ₹5000.

b. Amount collected by Class 6 = ₹4000 + ₹4500 = ₹8500

Amount collected by Class 9 = ₹5000 + ₹4000 = ₹9000

The difference in the amounts = ₹9000 – ₹8500 = ₹500

c. Both the sections of Class 7 have collected ₹6000 each.

d. ₹7000 was collected by section A of class 8. ₹6000 was collected by section B of class 8. So, class 8 has collected a total of ₹13,000.

e. Collection of section A = ₹6000

Collection of section B = ₹6500

Difference = ₹(6500 – 6000) = ₹500

So, section A of Class 10 should have collected ₹500 more.

EXERCISE 16C

1. The math teacher made a list of all the reasons that the students gave for not being prepared for the test. She represented the reasons using a bar graph. Read the bar graph and answer the given questions.

a. What are the different reasons given by the students?

b. Which reason was given by most of the students?

c. How many students said that they had not understood the topic?

d. What reason did four students give?

e. How many students are there in the class?

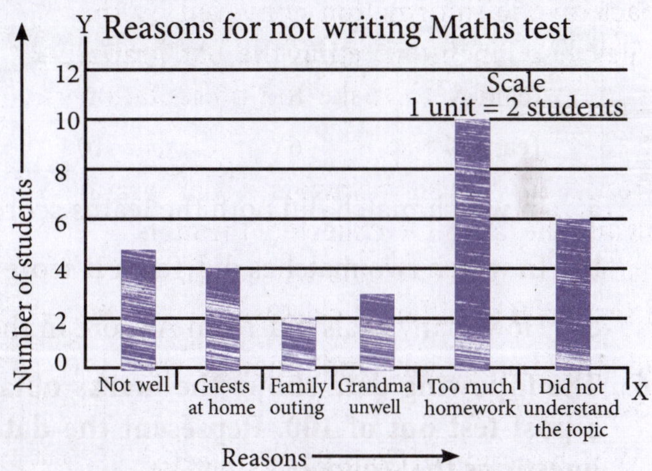

2. The following are the different dishes in the lunch boxes of Class 7 students on a particular day.

Dish	Parantha	Rice item	Sandwich	Dosa	Momos
Number of students	4	10	4	2	5

Represent the data on a bar graph.

3. The number of people who went for movies at different show timings is given below. Represent the data on a bar graph and answer the questions that follow.

Show timings	10:30 a.m.	01:15 p.m.	03:00 p.m.	03:15 p.m.	06:15 p.m.
Number of people	150	250	450	450	500

a Which show timing is preferred by most of the people?

b. How many people went to the 3:00 p.m. show?

c. During which show time did the theatre have exactly 250 people?

4. The list of games played by some boys and girls are represented using the double bar graph as shown here. Answer the following questions.

a. Write the title of the graph.

b. Which game is equally played by both girls and boys?

c. How many boys and girls play kho kho?

d. Which game is played by 6 girls and 10 boys?

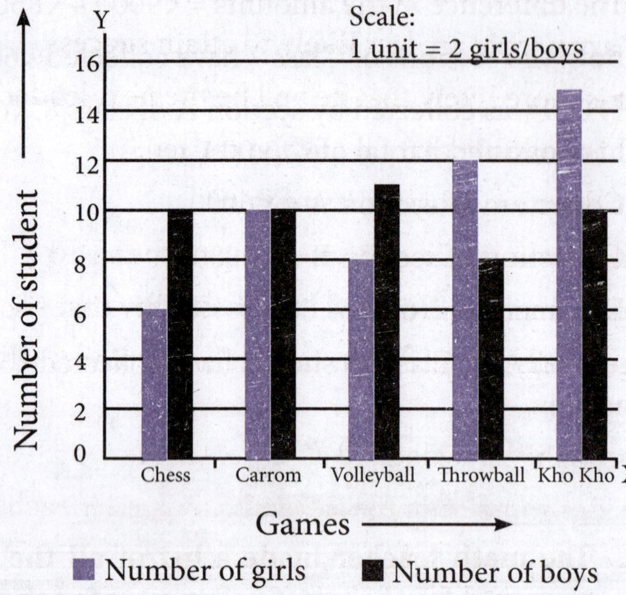

5. The following data shows the number of goals scored by two football teams in different matches. Represent the data using a double bar graph and answer the questions that follow.

Matches	Match 1	Match 2	Match 3	Match 4	Match 5
Team A	8	9	6	9	10
Team B	6	10	8	9	9

a. In which match did both the teams score the same number of goals?

b. In which two matches did Team B score 9 goals?

c. How many goals did Team A score in the first match?

6. The following data shows the marks obtained by different students in a pre-test and a post-test out of 100. Represent the data using a double bar graph and answer the questions that follow.

Students	A	B	C	D	E
Pre-test	85	80	85	80	75
Post-test	90	85	90	80	85

a. Which student scored the same marks in both the tests?

b. Who has scored considerably more in the post-test?

c. Who scored 80 marks in the pre-test and 85 marks in the post-test?

INTRODUCTION TO PROBABILITY

In our day-to-day interactions with friends and family members, we would have heard sentences of the following type.

- He has good **chance** of recovering.
- She went to the park by **chance**.
- Lazy people are less **likely** to attain success.
- It is more **likely** that he will be the next leader.
- It is **possible** that he may be chosen.
- Is there any **possibility** of rain?

What do you think is the meaning of the word 'CHANCE'?

The dictionary meaning is 'the possibility that something will happen'.

We generally use the term 'chance' in instances where we are not sure of things. It may happen or may not happen.

So, **probability** is defined as the extent to which something may happen.

Consider some examples given below under each category.

Certain to happen	Impossible	May or may not happen
The earth rotating on its axis	Going back to past	The train arriving at 8 o' clock
Depletion of oil resources	An escalator to the moon	The quiz team winning every round

Experimental Probability

If we take a one-rupee coin and toss it, we either get a head or a tail. Here, tossing a coin is called the **experiment** or **trial** and the two possibilities (of getting either a head or a tail) are called **outcomes**.

The set of all possible outcomes of an experiment is called the **sample space** of that experiment.

An experiment is said to be a **random experiment** if its outcomes cannot be predicted with certainty. The outcome of a random experiment is independent, and it is not affected by the previous outcome.

Let us consider an experiment of tossing a coin for 10 times and suppose we get the following data.

The sample space of this experiment is given by S = {Head, Tail}.

Number of times heads appeared = 7 times

Number of times tails appeared = 3 times

Total number of times the experiment was repeated = 10

The probability of getting heads is 7 out of 10 times, whereas the probability of getting tails is 3 out of 10 times. We can express probability in fractions as given below:

Probability of heads = $\frac{7}{10}$ Probability of tails = $\frac{3}{10}$

It can also be expressed in terms of percentage as follows:

Probability of heads = $\frac{7}{10} \times 100 = 70\%$ Probability of tails = $\frac{3}{10} \times 100 = 30\%$

In general, probability of an outcome = $\dfrac{\text{Number of times the outcome occurs}}{\text{Total number of times the experiment is repeated}}$

Notation: The capital letter 'P' is used to write the probability in short form. Also, the first letter of outcome is used in a bracket to write the probability. For example, the probability of the occurrence of heads can be written in the short form as **P(H)**. Similarly, the probability of tails can be written as **P(T)**.

SOLVED EXAMPLES

Example 14: Write the sample space for choosing a book from juniors and seniors category and among storybooks, magazines and comics.

Solution: The possible outcomes are: junior storybook (JS), junior magazine (JM), junior comic (JC), senior storybook (SS), senior comic (SC), senior magazine (SM)

Sample space S = {JS, JM, JC, SS, SC, SM}

Example 15: In a bag, there are three different coloured balls, that is, yellow, blue and red.

A student is asked to pick a ball without looking into the bag.

This was repeated 10 times and each time the result was recorded. Find the probability of each outcome.

Solution: Total number of times the experiment is repeated = 10

Blue	Yellow	Red
4	5	1

$\therefore$ P(B) = $\dfrac{4}{10} = \dfrac{2}{5}$ P(Y) = $\dfrac{5}{10} = \dfrac{1}{2}$ P(R) = $\dfrac{1}{10}$

where B, Y and R refer to Blue, Yellow and Red balls, respectively.

EXERCISE 16D

1. **Classify the following into 'certain to happen', 'impossible' and 'may or may not happen'.**
   a. Team A will win the football match today.
   b. The month of February falling after January.
   c. As the length of the side of a square increases, its perimeter also increases.
   d. Water will flow from lower area to higher area without any external force.
   e. A bike without any fuel will run for 100 km.
2. **Write the sample space for the following events.**
   a. Tossing two coins simultaneously.
   b. Selecting a prime number between 5 and 15.
   c. Selecting a vowel from the word 'idea'.
   d. Picking an outfit from 2 T-shirts, 2 jeans and 2 mufflers.
   e. Choosing a pizza combo from large, medium and small and cheese or pepperoni
3. **A coin is tossed 500 times. Heads appeared 275 times and the rest of the times, tails appeared. Find the probability of heads and tails.**

4. **In a survey of 250 people, 175 people favoured political Party A and rest of them favoured political Party B. Find their respective probabilities in terms of percentage.**

5. **In a school of 500 students, a survey was conducted on their favourite language. The results are given below. Find the probability of each language.**

English	Hindi	Sanskrit	German	Japanese	Mandarin
78	90	86	115	36	95

Mental Maths

1. What is the mean of the first 10 natural numbers?
2. What is the range of the data: 3, 9, 2, 2, 10, 18, 10, 3, 3?
3. Find the median of 5, 10, 10, 15.
4. Can a data sample have more than one mode?
5. How is a double bar graph different from a normal bar graph?

Maths Lab Activity

Aim: To find sample space and probability of the sum of two numbers obtained when two dice are thrown

Materials required: 2 dice

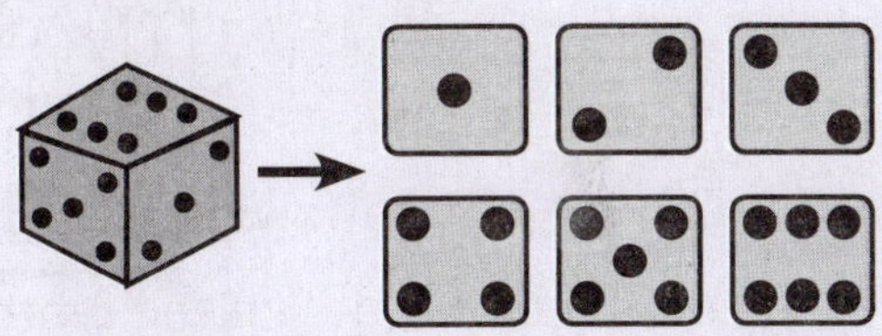

Procedure:

1. Let the students work in groups.
2. Roll the two dice simultaneously. Note the numbers on both the dice and record in a sheet of paper.
3. Repeat Step 2 five times.
4. Tabulate the data and find the sum of the numbers obtained on each dice.

Number of throws	Dice 1	Dice 2	Sum
First time			
Second time			
Third time			
Fourth time			
Fifth time			

5. Find the probability for the following sums:

a. 7 b. 10 c. 12 d. 3 e. 6 f. 8

Compare the results obtained by each group and discuss their findings.

Concept Map

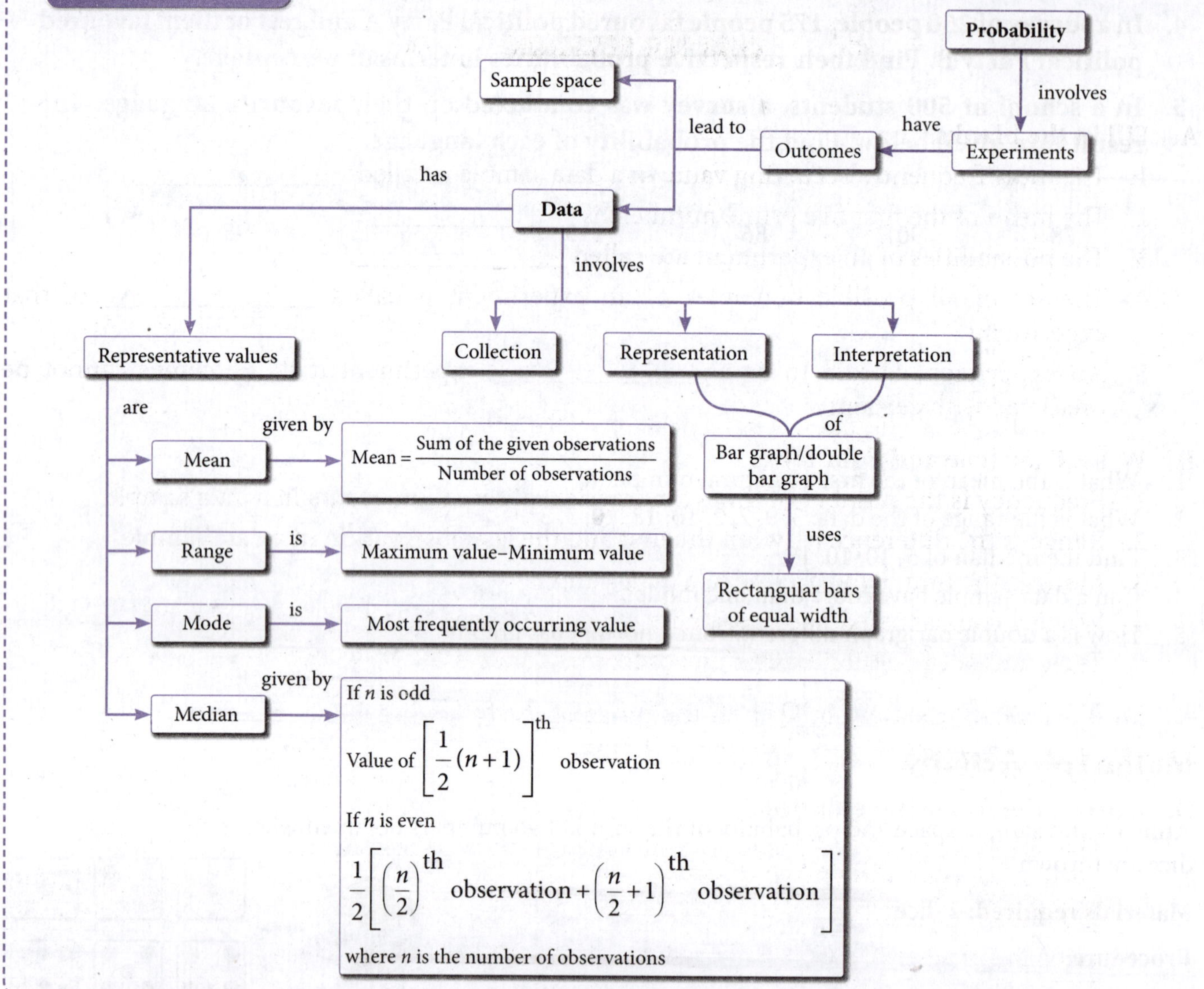

Key Concepts

- **Range:** The difference between the highest and the lowest observation. It gives an approximate idea of the spread of the data.
- **Median:** The value of the middle observation when the given data is arranged in ascending or descending order
- **Mode:** The value of the observation that occurs most frequently
- **Bar graph:** Graphical representation of numerical data in the form of rectangles (bars) of equal width and different heights that represent the frequency of the given data
- **Double bar graphs:** Help in comparing or presenting more than one kind of information
- **Probability:** The extent to which something may happen
- **Outcomes:** The possibilities of an experiment or a trial
- **Sample space:** The set of all possible outcomes of an experiment
- **Random experiment:** An experiment whose outcomes cannot be predicted with certainty

CHAPTER REVISION

A. Fill in the blanks.

1. The most frequently occurring value in a data sample is called ______________.
2. The mean of the first five prime numbers is ______________.
3. The possibilities of an experiment are called ______________.
4. The set of all possible outcomes of an experiment is called ______________ of that experiment.
5. An experiment is said to be a ______________ experiment if its outcomes cannot be predicted with certainty.

B. Write T for true and F for false.

1. Frequency is the number of times a numerical observation occurs in a data sample.
2. Range is the difference between the first and the last observation in a data sample.
3. Mode is the middlemost value of a data sample.
4. When a coin is tossed, the probability of getting a head is 1.
5. The number of possibilities for any outcome is always 2.

C. Find the mean, median, mode and the range of the following data.

125, 152, 512, 215, 412, 214, 125, 152, 125, 125

D. Answer the following questions.

1. The number of national parks in some states of India is listed below.

State	Madhya Pradesh	Kerala	Odisha	Maharashtra	Rajasthan
Number of national parks	9	7	2	4	4

Represent the data on a bar graph and answer the following questions.

a. Which state has the maximum number of national parks?

b. Odisha has how many less national parks than Maharashtra?

c. Which state has 7 national parks?

2. Given below is the data of Prime Ministers of India since 1996 and their tenure in number of days. Represent the data using a bar graph and then answer the questions that follow.

Name of the PM	Tenure (Number of the days)	
Doddegowda Deve Gowda	1 June 1996 to 20 April 1997	324
Inder Kumar Gujral	21 April 1997 to 18 March 1998	332
Atal Bihari Vajpayee	19 March 1998 to 21 May 2004	2272
Manmohan Singh	22 May 2004 to 26 May 2014	3656

a. Which Prime Minister has had the shortest tenure till date?

b. Name the Prime Minister who held the office for 332 days.

3. Represent the following data using a double bar graph and then answer the questions that follow.

Name of the dam	Height (in metres)	Reservoir capacity (in 1 lakh acre-feet)
Tehri	260	32
Bhakra Nangal	226	75
Hirakud	61	48
Nagarjuna Sagar	124	94
Sardar Sarovar	163	77

   a. Which is the tallest dam?
   b. What is the capacity of the shortest dam?
   c. Name the dam whose height is 226 m and the dam whose capacity is 77 lakh acre-ft.

4. A coin is tossed 50 times. Find the probability of heads and tails if they occur 15 times and 35 times, respectively.
5. What is the probability of picking the letter 'A' from the word 'MATHEMATICS'?
6. A number from 1 to 10 is chosen at random. What is the probability of choosing an odd number?
7. Two dice are thrown simultaneously. Find the probabilities for the following events.
   a. The sum of the numbers is even.
   b. The sum of the numbers is odd.
   c. The sum of the numbers is prime.
   d. The product of the numbers is odd.
   e. The product of the numbers is even.

SKILL UP!

Project

Collect data from 50 students and 50 adults in your school on the number of hours spent on texting or calling using a mobile phone.

- Find the mean, median and mode for these data.
- Represent the data using a double bar graph.

Life Skills

Should I wear a jacket today, should I carry an umbrella, what kind of clothes should I wear for the picnic? You may have often asked or heard such questions in your day-to-day life. Sometimes you may wish to know the exact weather conditions to make definite decisions.

Does nature tell you exactly what is going to happen? No, but the weatherman can tell the probabilities of how the weather may behave.

Weather forecasting is the application of current technology and science to predict the conditions of the atmosphere for a given location.

Collect the humidity and temperature data for the last 30 days of your city. Predict the humidity and temperature for the next 3 days. Find out if you were right by cross-checking with actual data.

Mind Buzzer

Write a data sample whose mean, mode and median are the same. Give any five such examples.

Teacher's Notes

- Discuss mean, median and mode in real-life context. Ask students to collect instances where each one is used in real life to bring out the differences among the three values.
- Give the students (individually and in groups) experiences in collecting data, organizing them and interpreting them. Ask them to represent those using bar graphs.
- Ask the students to give examples of real-life instances where double bar graphs can be used. Discuss with them how double bar graphs can be more useful in certain contexts.
- Discuss the applications of probability in real life. Assign different topics to different student groups to find out the use of probability in sports/casinos/weather/lottery, etc., and ask the students to present their information in the class.

WORKSHEET

On the scale shown below, place the given words moving from 'impossible' to 'certain'.

Very likely

Probable

50-50 chance

No chance

Doubtful

Almost Impossible

Very unlikely

Impossible

Certain

Write any two examples of events (either from your surroundings or from real life) in the space provided for each of the following probabilities.

Impossible

Very unlikely

Doubtful

Probable

Very likely

Certain

REASONING WORKSHEET 1

1. Which of the following is not correct with respect to integers *x*, *y* and *z*?

   a. $x - y = z$ b. $x \div y = z$ c. $x + y = z$ d. $x \times y = z$

2. A submarine is situated at a depth of 630 ft below the sea level. If it goes 125 ft further deep into the sea, what is the position of the submarine?

   a. +755 ft b. 505 ft c. –505 ft d. –755 ft

3. The multiplication fact represented by the below given number line is

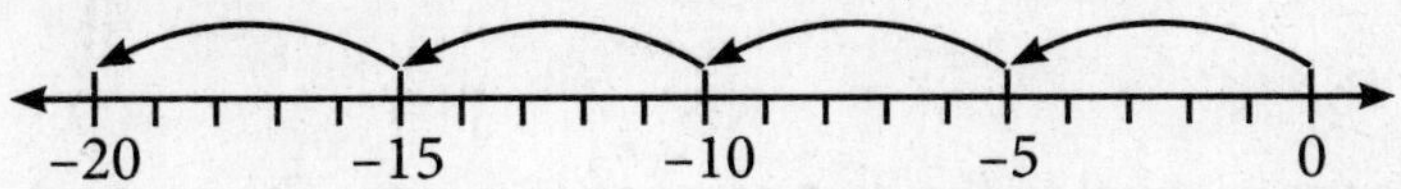

   a. $(-1) \times 20$ b. $5 \times (-4)$ c. $4 \times (-5)$ d. $2 \times (-10)$

4. Pick the odd one out.

   a. London metro train runs in the underground.

   b. James's kite is flying high in the sky.

   c. Sophia's body temperature dropped by few degrees.

   d. My pet lost some weight.

5. $\frac{2}{3} \times \square = \frac{2}{21}$. The missing fraction in this product is

   a. $\frac{1}{2}$ b. $\frac{3}{2}$ c. $\frac{1}{7}$ d. $\frac{1}{10}$

6. The number of 0.2 in 1.4 is

   a. 6 b. 2 c. 7 d. 8

7. Which of the following decimals is multiplied with 0.009 to get 0.009027?

   a. 1.003 b. 1.0027 c. 1.009 d. 1.00279

8. Which of the following rational numbers is positive?

   a. $\frac{-3}{7}$ b. $\frac{3}{-7}$ c. $\frac{-3}{-7}$ d. $-\frac{3}{7}$

9. Identify the rational number which is equal to its reciprocal?

   a. 0 b. 1 c. –2 d. 2

10. Which of the following is not a rational number?

    a. $\frac{1}{0}$ b. $\frac{0}{1}$ c. $\frac{1}{1}$ d. $\frac{-1}{1}$

11. A: Every fraction is a rational number. B: Every rational number is a fraction.

    a. B is true but A is false. b. Both A and B are not true.

    c. Both A and B are true. d. A is true but B is not true.

12. If $\frac{p}{q}$ is a rational number and *m* is a common factor of *p* and *q*, then simplest form of $\frac{p}{q}$ is obtained by

    a. $\frac{p}{q} = \frac{p \div m}{q \div m}$ b. $\frac{p}{q} = \frac{p \times m}{q \times m}$ c. Either a or b d. None of these

REASONING WORKSHEET 2

1. 12% of 12 is

   a. 12 b. 1.44 c. 0.44 d. 0.12

2. 2% of 3% of 4000 is

   a. 12 b. 1.2 c. 2.4 d. 40

3. 70% of 20 students are good in mathematics. The number of students who are not good in mathematics is

   a. 14 b. 6 c. 7 d. 18

4. The selling price of 12 soaps is equal to the cost price of 15 soaps. The gain percentage is:

   a. 12% b. 5% c. 25% d. 10%

5. The length of a wooden piece which is 12 m is cut into 8 m. The percentage of decrease is

   a. 20% b. 33.33% c. 22.22% d. 10.10%

6. An increase of 60% on 300 is

   a. 290 b. 480 c. 460 d. 240

7. A sum of money at simple interest amounts to ₹815 in 3 years and ₹854 in 4 years. The sum is

   a. ₹100 b. ₹200 c. ₹715 d. ₹698

8. Identify the measure of the angles that can form a right-angled triangle.

   a. 75°, 90°, 15° b. 37°, 53°, 90° c. 90°, 20°, 70° d. 28°, 90°, 62°

9. Pick the odd one out.

   a. SSA b. ASS c. AAA d. RHS

10. Name the type of triangle having 45°, 45°, 90° measurement.

    a. Isosceles right-angled triangle b. Right-angled triangle
    c. Isosceles triangle d. None of these

11. Which among the following can be the measurements of a right-angled triangle?

    a. 6 cm, 8 cm, 10 cm b. 3 cm, 4 cm, 5 cm c. 13 cm, 12 cm, 5 cm d. All of these

12. Identify the criterion used for constructing the triangle given alongside.

    a. SAS b. RSA c. SSA d. SSS

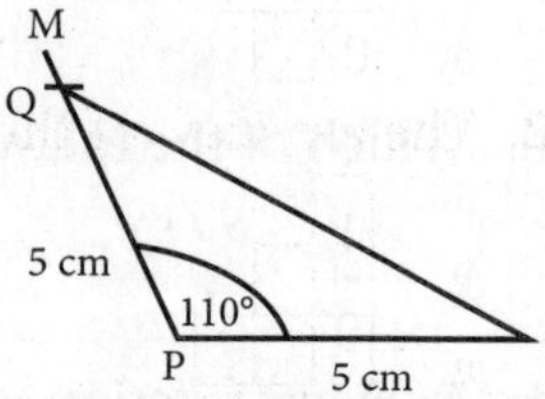

13. Which criterion is used in the construction of an isosceles triangle?

    a. RHS b. ASA c. SAA d. SAS

14. A ΔABC with AB = 8 cm and BC = 7 cm has to be constructed. Identify which measure of ∠B out of those given below makes it a triangle.

    a. ∠B = 90° b. ∠B = 120° c. ∠B = 61° d. None of these

15. Which among the following is different from the rest?

    a. Lines in a notebook b. Railings in a window
    c. Wickets on a cricket pitch d. Steps of a ladder

REASONING WORKSHEET 3

1. Which of the following letters is different with respect to line symmetry?

a. H b. I c. O d. A

2. Which of the following letters does not look the same on mirror reflection when the mirror is placed horizontally?

a. A b. B c. D d. E

3. Pick the odd one out with respect to rotational symmetry.

a.  b.  c.  d. 

4. Identify the traffic signal that has rotational symmetry of different order compared to others.

a.  b.  c.  d. 

5. Which of the following shapes has same lines of symmetry and order of rotation?

a. Square b. Rectangle c. Parallelogram d. Rhombus

6. What is the angle of rotation for a regular octagon to look the same on rotation?

a. 45° b. 90° c. 270° d. All of these

7. An object that repeats itself after every rotation of 60° has a rotational symmetry of order ________.

a. 2 b. 4 c. 6 d. 8

8. Pick the odd one out.

a. Triangle b. Square c. Pentagon d. Pyramid

9. The number of cubes in the solid shown is

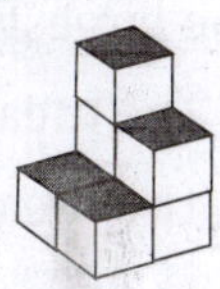

a. 7 b. 8 c. 6 d. 5

10. Name the solid with only one curved face, with no edges and vertices.

a. Cylinder b. Sphere c. Circle d. Cone

11. Which among the following is not a net of a cube?

a. 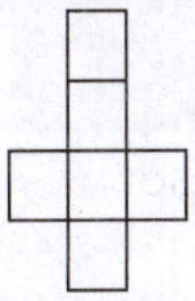 b. 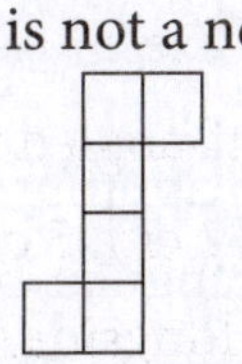 c. 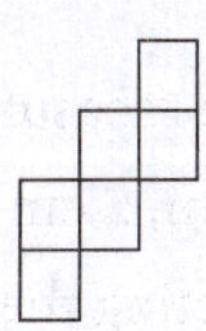 d. 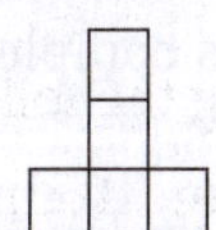

12. The top view of the solid shown aside is

a. 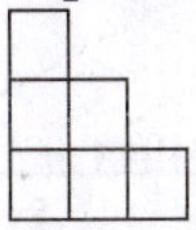 b. 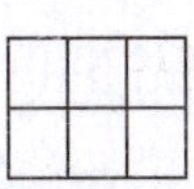 c.  d. 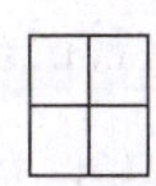

13. Identify the solid that is different from others with respect to cross-section.

a. Sphere b. Cylinder c. Cone d. Cuboid

14. The area of a rectangle is same as the area of a square which is 16 sq. cm. The length of the rectangle is

a. 8 cm b. 13 cm c. 18 cm d. 15 cm

15. How many 1 cm^2 will cover a rectangle of dimensions 12 cm and 24 cm?

a. 128 b. 288 c. 122 d. 200

REASONING WORKSHEET 4

1. The area of a parallelogram is 21 cm² and the breadth is 7 cm. The height is

   a. 3 cm b. 7 cm c. 8 cm d. 5 cm

2. Which of the following figures is odd?

   a. 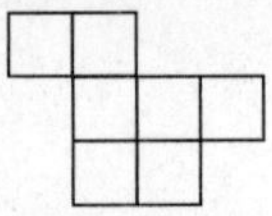 b. 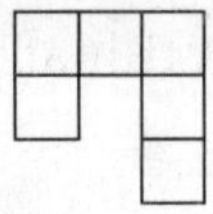 c. 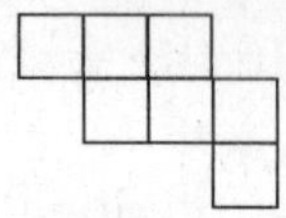 d. 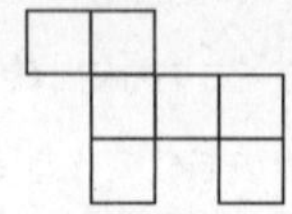

3. The area of the shaded region is

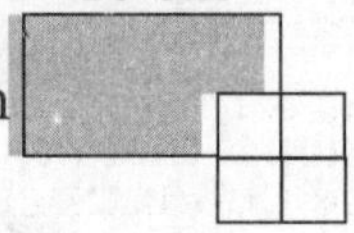

   a. 78 cm² b. 76 cm²
   c. 80 cm² d. 100 cm²

4. If the radius of the circle is doubled, the area becomes

   a. 2 times b. 4 times c. 3 times d. 1 time

5. The average of $\frac{1}{2}, \frac{2}{3}, \frac{1}{4}, \frac{5}{2}, \frac{2}{3}$ is

   a. $\frac{11}{12}$ b. $\frac{11}{6}$ c. $\frac{11}{18}$ d. $\frac{5}{18}$

6. Which of the following is true for the data: 5, 5, 6, 7, 7?

   a. Mean = mode b. Mean = median c. Mean < median d. Mean > median

7. Given below is the average snowfall in inches in Philadelphia for the past 10 years:

   15.6, 0.4, 2.2, 1.0, 4.1, 3.1, 25.2, 2.5, 3.9, 25.9

   If the largest and smallest values are removed, how will the mean, median and mode be affected?

   a. The mean, median and mode are not affected.
   b. The mean and median change, the mode is unaffected.
   c. The mean changes, the median and mode are unaffected.
   d. The mean and mode change, the median is unaffected.

8. A bar graph is complete if:

   a. It has a title. b. It has an appropriate scale.
   c. The axes are labelled. d. The rectangular bars are coloured.

9. Which of the following is a trial?

   a. Tossing a coin
   b. Picking a blue ball from a bag of a certain number of coloured balls
   c. Getting number 6 on a dice when it is rolled
   d. Getting head when a coin is tossed

10. Which of the following is an outcome?

    a. Throwing a dice b. Getting head when a coin is tossed c. Spinning a wheel
    d. Drawing a ball from a bag containing a certain number of coloured balls

11. The probability of 6 as a sum is more than the probability of 5 as a sum, when two dice are rolled.

    a. False b. True c. Cannot say for sure d. Cannot be determined

VEDIC MATHS

ADDITION AND SUBTRACTION OF MIXED FRACTIONS

We can easily add and subtract two mixed fractions using Vedic mathematics. The Vedic sutra used here is ऊर्ध्वतिर्यग्भ्याम् (*Urdhva Tiryagbyham*) which means 'vertically and crosswise'.

In the case of **mixed fractions,** add the whole parts and fractional parts separately.

Method to add two mixed fractions:

Step 1: Add the whole parts and fractional parts separately.

Step 2: For the fractional part, find the sum of cross-products of the given fractions. This will be the numerator of the fraction.

Step 3: Multiply the denominators. This will be the denominator of the fraction. Reduce the fraction obtained to its simplest form, if required.

Step 4: To get the final answer, write the sum obtained for the whole number part and the fraction together.

Method to subtract two mixed fractions:

Step 1: Subtract the whole parts and fractional parts separately.

Step 2: For the fractional part, find the difference between cross-products of the given fractions. This will be the numerator of the fraction.

Step 3: Multiply the denominators. This will be the denominator of the fraction. Reduce the fraction obtained to its simplest form, if required.

Step 4: To get the final answer, write the difference obtained for the whole number part and the fraction together.

SOLVED EXAMPLES

Example 1: Add $2\frac{1}{3}$ and $4\frac{2}{5}$.

Solution: $2\frac{1}{3}+4\frac{2}{5} = (2+4)+\left(\frac{1}{3}+\frac{2}{5}\right)$

$$= 6+\left(\frac{(1\times5)+(2\times3)}{3\times5}\right) = 6+\frac{11}{15} = 6\frac{11}{15}$$

Example 2: Subtract $3\frac{2}{9}$ from $5\frac{4}{15}$.

Solution: $5\frac{4}{15}-3\frac{2}{9} = (5-3)+\left(\frac{4}{15}-\frac{2}{9}\right)$

$$= 2+\left(\frac{(4\times9)-(15\times2)}{15\times9}\right)$$

$$= 2+\frac{36-30}{135} = 2+\frac{6}{135} = 2+\frac{2}{45} = 2\frac{2}{45}$$

INVERSE PROPORTION

We know that the proportion is inverse when one quantity increases in the same ratio as another quantity decreases. The problems which fall under the category of inverse proportion are solved using the sutra '*The first by the first and the last by the last*'.

Let us consider the following examples to understand the application of this sutra.

SOLVED EXAMPLES

Example 1: A fruit seller packs 35 boxes with 40 mangoes in each box. How many boxes are needed if only 25 mangoes are put in each box?

Solution: Let x be the number of boxes needed.

$35 \times 40 = 25 \times x$

$$x = \frac{35 \times 40}{25}$$

$$= 56$$

So, 56 boxes are needed if only 25 mangoes are put in each box.

Example 2: A 4-ton truck removes a mound of earth in 24 journeys. How many journeys would a 6-ton truck have to make?

Solution: Let x be the number of required journeys.

$4 \times 24 = 6 \times x$

$$x = \frac{4 \times 24}{6}$$

$$= 16$$

So, a 6-ton truck would have to make 16 journeys.

Example 3: If 35 boys can arrange chairs in a huge library hall in 12 hours, how long will it take 14 boys to do the same work?

Solution: Let x be the number of hours taken.

$35 \times 12 = 14 \times x$

$$x = \frac{35 \times 12}{14}$$

$$= 30$$

So, 14 boys will take 30 hours to do the same work.

Review 1

REVIEW CORNER

Chapters 1–4

Maximum Marks = 40

A. Choose the correct option. **(1 × 3)**

1. $(3^3 + 3^2)^0 =$

   a. 0 b. 1 c. 3 d. 36

2. $9 + 0.9 + 0.09 + 0.0009 =$

   a. 9.9099 b. 9.099 c. 9.9909 d. 9.999

3. What do you get when –49 is subtracted from 67?

   a. –116 b. 116 c. –18 d. 18

B. Solve the following. **(2 × 3)**

1. A submarine is at a depth of 453 ft below sea level. It further descends by 87 ft. Where is the submarine now?
2. In a school, there are 540 children. If $\frac{2}{3}$ of them are boys, how many girls are there?
3. Represent $-\frac{4}{3}$ on a number line.

C. Answer the following questions. **(3 × 5)**

1. Raj's breakfast costs ₹30 per day at a restaurant. If he deposits an amount of ₹510 in that restaurant, for how many days can he have his breakfast there?
2. Subtract the sum of –1379 and 379 from the product of –20 and –120.
3. Reduce the given rational numbers to the standard form.

   a. $\frac{-63}{108}$ b. $\frac{84}{-98}$

4. Evaluate $\frac{2^{-2}}{4^{-1}} + \frac{1}{37^{-1}}$.
5. Evaluate [95 – (–125)] ÷ [(–13) + 9].

D. Solve the following problems. **(4 × 4)**

1. Find the value of n if $16 \times 2^n = 2^{10}$.
2. A bus travels a distance of 10 km in $\frac{1}{6}$ hours. How much distance will it travel in 5 hours?
3. Evaluate the following:

   a. 4.25 × 0.09 b. 12.5 ÷ 0.25

4. In a class test containing 25 questions, 2 marks are given for every correct answer and 1 mark is deducted for every incorrect answer.

   a. Aryan attempts only 22 questions and gets all of them correct. What is his total score?

   b. Dhruv attempts all questions but gets 15 answers correct. What will be his score?

Review 2

Chapters 5–8

Maximum Marks = 40

A. Fill in the blanks. **(1 × 3)**

1. The degree of the polynomial $3a^2bc + 6ab + 3$ is ________.
2. If a, b, c and d are in proportion, product of means = product of ________.
3. The price of a book is decreased by 10%. Its actual price was ₹290. The new price would be ________.

B. Simply or solve the following. **(2 × 3)**

1. $-7(a - 4) = 14$
2. $-3r(2r - 7)$
3. 3.5% of 350

C. Answer the following questions. **(3 × 5)**

1. The cost of a dress has decreased from ₹1200 to ₹900. Find the percentage of decrease in the cost of the dress.
2. The cost of 25 dark chocolates is ₹225. Find the cost of 20 such chocolates.
3. Find the mean proportion between 18 and 72.
4. Simplify: $5p - (3p + q - 7p) + q$.
5. Solve: $13 - 13(q - 4) = 8q + 6$.

D. Solve the following word problems. **(4 × 4)**

1. Radha is seven times as old as Maya. After 6 years, she will be three times as old as Maya. Find the present age of Radha.
2. By how much does $31a + 11b + c$ exceed the sum of $5a + 11b - c$ and $-3a - 4b$.
3. If A : B = 15 : 16 and B : C = 32 : 25, find A : C and A : B : C.
4. At what rate of simple interest will a sum of money double itself in 8 years?

Comprehensive Review 1

Chapters 1–8

Maximum Marks = 80

A. Fill in the blanks. **(1 × 6)**

1. Multiplicative inverse of 5 is ________.
2. The product of a rational number and its reciprocal is ________.
3. The numerical coefficient of $-18ab$ is ________.
4. $3a$, $15a$, $\frac{a}{2}$ and $-8a$ are ________ terms.
5. If an increase in one quantity brings a corresponding decrease in the other quantity (or vice versa), the two quantities are said to be in ________ variation.
6. The price at which an article is purchased is called its ________ price.

B. Solve the following. **(2 × 6)**

1. Find the fourth proportional to 8, 6, 12.
2. Convert 15.5% to decimal.
3. Evaluate: $21 \times (-29) + (-29) \times 49$.
4. If $a = -1$, evaluate $2a^3 - a^2 + 10$.
5. How much is $4\frac{4}{5}$ of 3280?
6. Add $\frac{13}{-5}$ and $\frac{-33}{-10}$.

C. Answer the following questions. **(3 × 10)**

1. Subtract the sum of 88 and –97 from –205.
2. The cost of $5\frac{1}{4}$ kg of rice is ₹315. What will be the cost price of 1 kg of rice?
3. The profit of a company increases every month in the ratio 5 : 8. If the profit earned in April is ₹1,20,000, find the profit earned in May.
4. Evaluate: $\left(\frac{-4}{5}\right)^2 \div \left(\frac{25}{64}\right)^{-1}$.
5. Express the following numbers in standard form:
   a. 87,000 b. 626.9
6. The sum of two consecutive natural numbers is 85. Find the numbers.
7. The sides of a triangle are in the ratio 5 : 6 : 7. The perimeter of the triangle is 54 cm. Find the sides of the triangle.
8. In what time will ₹2400 amount to ₹3600 at the rate of 5% p.a. simple interest?
9. If 36, x and 81 are in continued proportion, find the value of x.
10. A bike covers a distance of 92.5 km using 2 litres of petrol. How far will it go if it uses 3.5 litres of petrol?

D. Solve the following. **(4 × 8)**

1. The profit obtained on selling a smart phone is ₹2500 per piece and that on selling an old mobile with keypad is ₹900 per piece. During a month, the shopkeeper obtained a net profit of ₹17,900. In this period, he sold 5 smart phones. How many old mobiles did he sell in that period?
2. Evaluate $\left\{9^{-1} + \left(\frac{9}{2}\right)^{-1}\right\}^2$.
3. The number of children who went for a cable car ride in an amusement park was one-fourth of the number of children who went for striking cars. If the total number of children who went for the two rides was 160, find the number of children who went for the cable car ride.
4. Solve: $\frac{x+1}{3} - \frac{x-1}{5} = 18$
5. Simplify: $(0.2a + 3)(a - 5)$
6. Take away $7a - 9b$ from the sum of $4a + 6b - 2c$ and $8a + b - 4c$.
7. A camp had food for 60 people for 75 days. 15 more people came to the camp. How long will the food last?
8. What sum will amount to ₹6000 in 4 years at 5% per annum?

Review 3

Chapters 9–12
Maximum Marks = 40

A. Choose the correct option. (1 × 3)

1. Linear pair of angles forms a straight line and add up to _____.
   a. 90° b. 180° c. 360° d. 270°
2. An acute-angled triangle is a triangle with all three angles less than _____.
   a. 180° b. 45° c. 90° d. 60°
3. If the three sides of a triangle are equal to the corresponding three sides of another triangle, the two triangles are congruent by _____ criterion.
   a. SSS b. SAS c. ASA d. RHS

B. Find the following. (2 × 3)

1. Find the supplement of the following angles:
   a. 89° b. 141°
2. An acute angle of a right-angled triangle measures 35°. Find the measure of the other acute angle.
3. If ΔLMN ≅ ΔABC, write down the corresponding vertices of the congruent triangles.

C. Answer the following questions. (3 × 5)

1. In the given figure, AB || CD and EF || GH. If ∠DKH=115°, calculate the following angles:
   a. ∠AJK b. ∠BJK c. ∠CLF

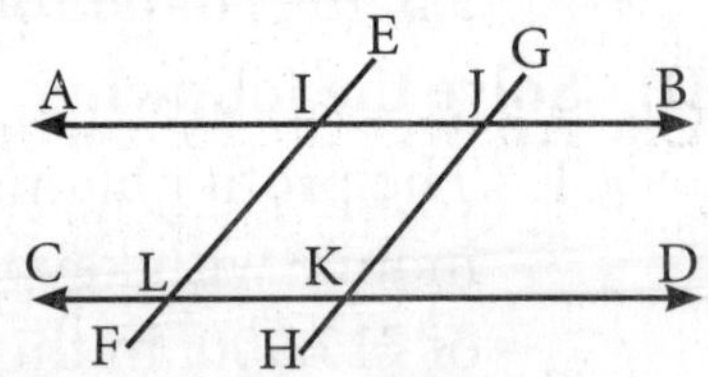

2. In a ΔABC, ∠A = 42° and ∠B = 88°. Calculate the value of the exterior angle at C.
3. Identify the congruence rule followed in the given congruent triangles.
   a.

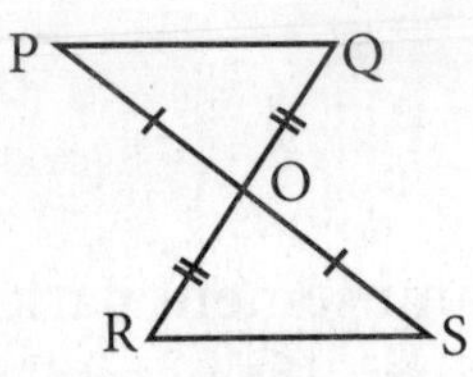

   b.

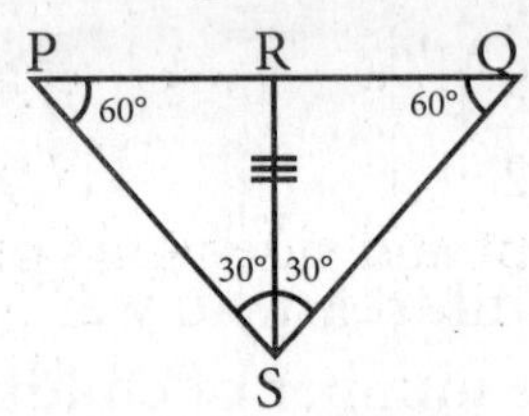

4. Draw a line *l* parallel to the line AB which is at a distance of 8 cm from the line AB.
5. Construct a triangle whose sides are of lengths 8 cm, 6 cm and 10 cm.

D. Solve the following. (4 × 4)

1. A football ground is in the shape of a rectangle that has a length of 105 m and width of 88 m. The coach asked the players to run from one corner to the corner diagonally across the ground. How much distance do the players need to run?
2. Prove that ΔABC ≅ ΔDEF if:
   a. AB = 12 cm, BC = 9 cm, ∠B = 70°, DE = 9 cm, EF = 12 cm, ∠E = 70°
   b. ∠B = 90°, AC = 12 cm, AB = 5 cm, ∠E = 90°, DE = 5 cm, DF = 12 cm
3. Construct a right-angled triangle ABC with AB = 8 cm, ∠B = 45° and right angle at A.
4. Construct a triangle LMN with LN = 5.5 cm, LM = 6 cm and ∠LMN = 65°.

Review 4

Chapters 13–16
Maximum Marks = 40

A. Fill in the blanks. (1 × 3)

1. The number of lines of symmetry in the letter X is ______.
2. The number of vertices in a cylinder is ______.
3. The area of a circle whose radius is 5 cm is ______.

B. Solve the following. (2 × 3)

1. How many lines of symmetry do the following regular polygons have?
   a. Hexagon b. Decagon
2. Find the number of edges, vertices and faces of the solid given alongside.

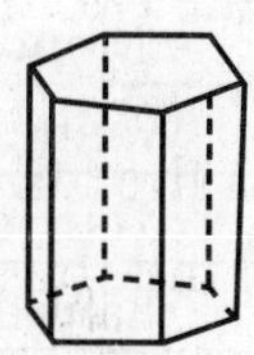

3. Make an oblique sketch for the isometric shapes given below.

a. 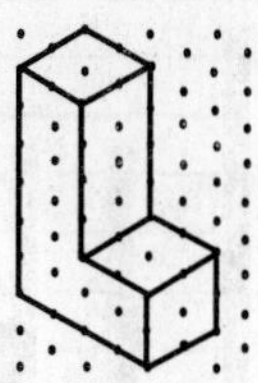

b. 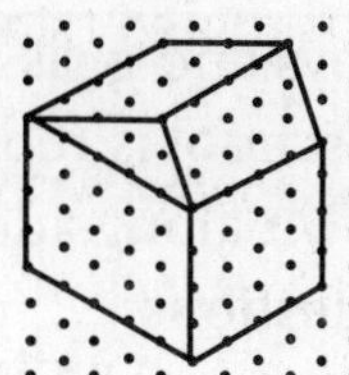

C. Answer the following. (3 × 5)

1. Write the order of rotational symmetry for the given figures.

a. 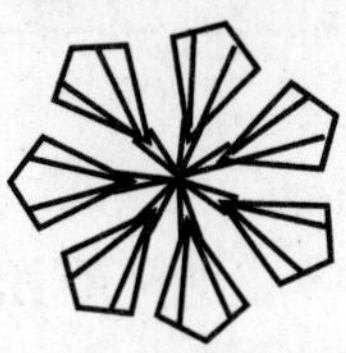

b. 

2. Draw the top, front and side views of the following figures.

a. 

b. 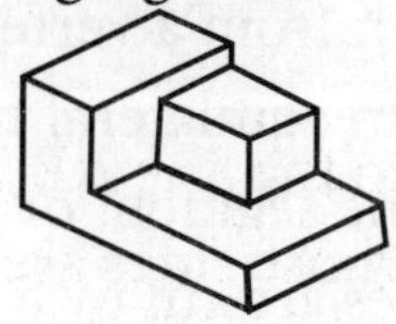

3. Find the area of the following figures.

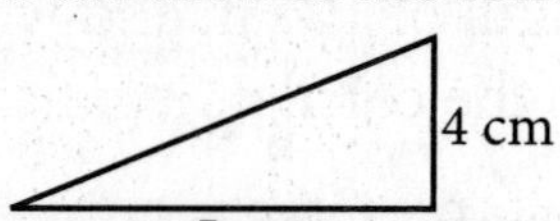

a.

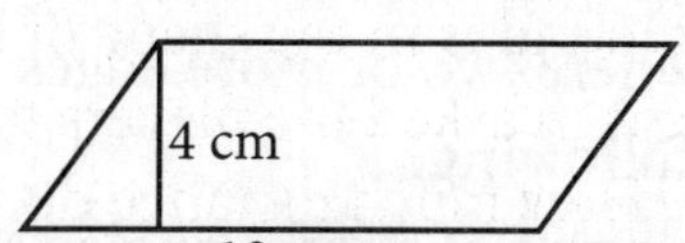

b.

4. A coin is tossed 100 times. Heads appeared 45 times and rest of the times, tails appeared. Find the probability of heads and tails.
5. Find the mean, median and mode for the following data:
   20, 34, 40, 18, 18, 20, 35, 36, 42, 18, 30, 30, 40, 18, 19, 23, 26, 28, 18, 13

D. Solve the following questions. (4 × 4)

1. Find the number of lines of symmetry as well as order and angle of rotational symmetry for the following figure.

2. Two paths are crossing each other at right angles in a rectangular park as shown. Find the area of the path and that of the park not covered by the paths.

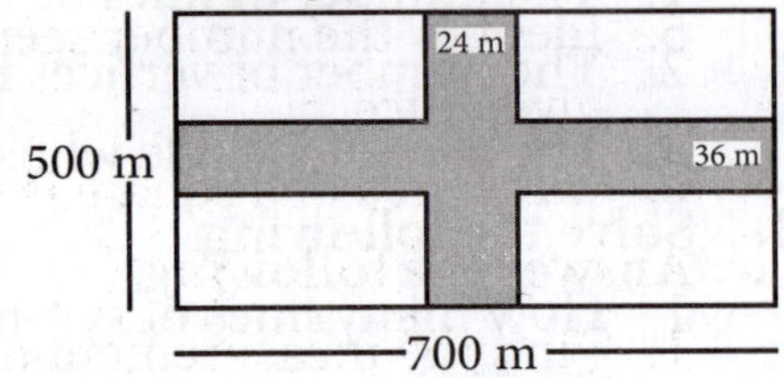

3. Draw a bar graph for the following information.

Day	Number of books sold
Monday	12
Wednesday	10
Thursday	8
Saturday	20
Sunday	40

4. The list of number of boys and girls present on Independence Day in a school is represented using a double bar graph as shown alongside. Observe the graph and answer the given questions.

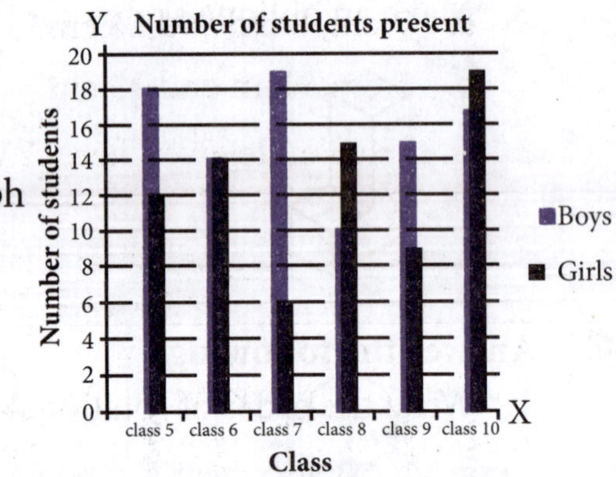

   a. What is the scale of the graph?
   b. How many students of class 10 were present on that day?
   c. How many girls were present on that day?
   d. Which class had the least number of students?

Comprehensive Review 2

Chapters 9–16

Maximum Marks = 80

A. Write T for true and F for false. (1 × 6)

1. A perpendicular drawn from a vertex to the opposite side of the triangle is called a median.
2. All the three sides of an equilateral triangle are equal and each angle measures 60°.
3. A bisector divides a line segment or an angle into two equal halves.
4. When two parallel lines are cut by a transversal, alternate interior angles are equal.
5. A regular polygon with *n* number of sides has infinite lines of symmetry.
6. The point where two or more edges meet is called a face.

B. Calculate the following. (2 × 6)

1. If one acute angle of a right-angled triangle measures 45°, then find the measure of the other acute angle.
2. State the congruence criteria for the following congruent triangles.

a.

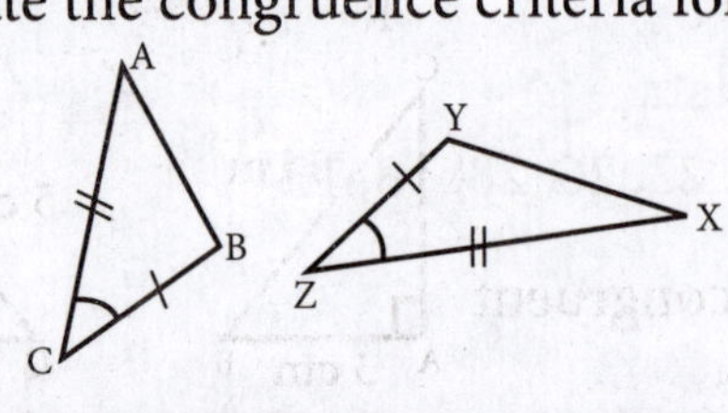

b.

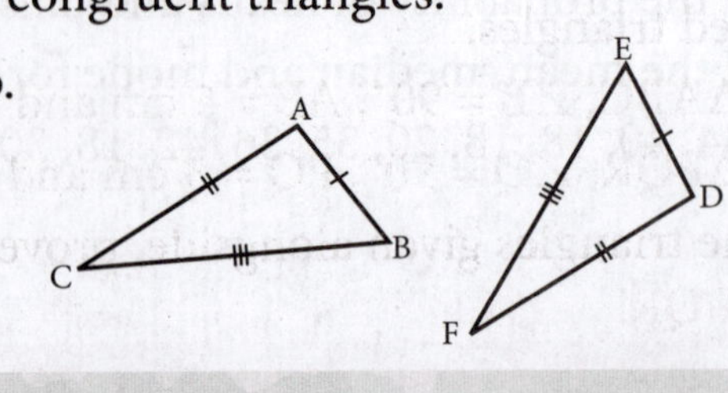

3. Name the type of triangle formed on the basis of the angles and sides given below.
   a. MN = 6 cm, $\angle M = 90^\circ$ and LN = 8 cm
   b. MN = 8 cm, $\angle M = \angle N = 70^\circ$
4. List the numbers between 0 and 9 that have rotational symmetry.
5. Identify the number seen from the top view and the side view of the given dice.

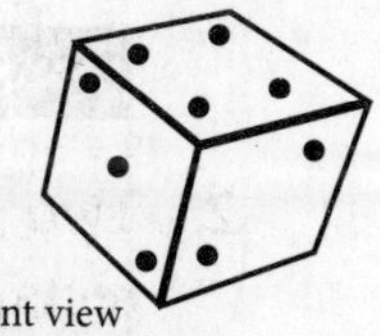

Front view

6. If the area of a square is 49 cm^2, what will be the perimeter of the square?

C. Answer the following. **(3 × 10)**

1. Find the measurement of the following angles in the given figure.

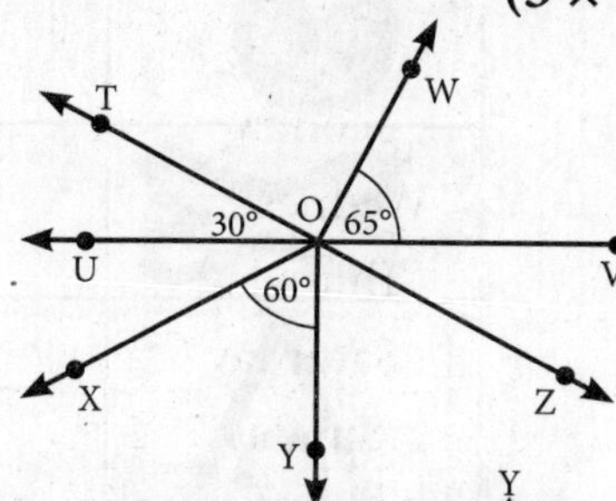

   a. $\angle TOW$ b. $\angle UOX$ c. $\angle YOZ$
2. Which of the following measures forms a triangle?
   a. 7 cm, 8 cm and 12 cm
   b. 5 cm, 6 cm and 13 cm
3. In the triangle given here, YW bisects $\angle XYZ$. Prove that ΔXWY is congruent to ΔZWY.

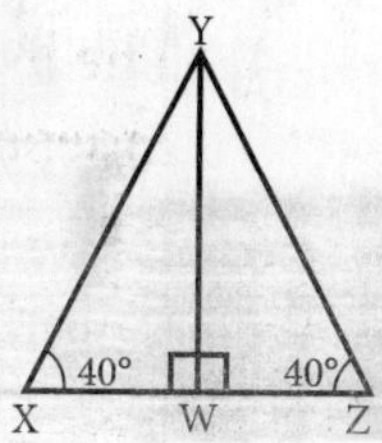

4. Construct an equilateral triangle whose side is 5 cm.
5. Draw the lines of symmetry for the following figures.

a.  b.  c. 

6. Draw the nets for the following solid shapes.
   a. Cuboid b. Square pyramid c. Triangular prism
7. A slab is in the shape of a parallelogram of 10 feet length and 12 feet width. Find the cost of tiling the slab at ₹30 per square feet.
8. Find the circumference and area of a circle of radius 3 cm.
9. Find the mean, median and mode for the following data:
   50, 41, 45, 43, 40, 45, 48, 50, 45, 42, 40, 40, 42, 46, 40
10. There are 5 red, 3 yellow and 2 green balls in a basket. Find the probability of the following:
    a. Picking one ball b. Picking one red ball c. Picking one yellow ball

D. Solve the following questions. **(4 × 8)**

1. Find all the angles formed on either side of the transversal in the figure given alongside.

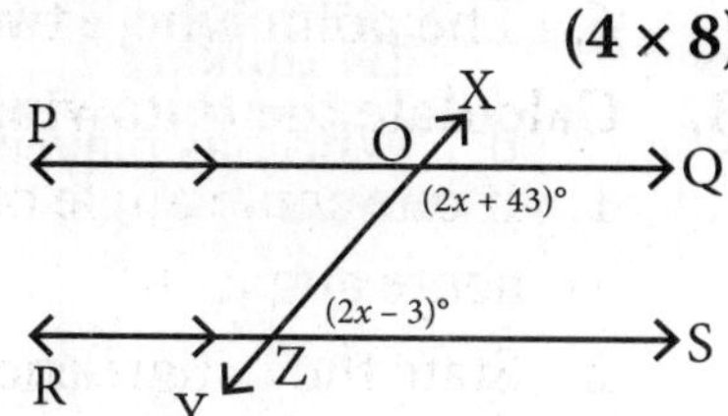

2. Find the measure of the missing sides in the following right-angled triangles.
   a. ΔABC, $\angle B = 90^\circ$, AB = 5 cm and AC = 13 cm
   b. ΔPQR, $\angle Q = 90^\circ$, PQ = 3 cm and RQ = 4 cm
3. In the triangles given alongside, prove that ΔABC is congruent to ΔPQR.

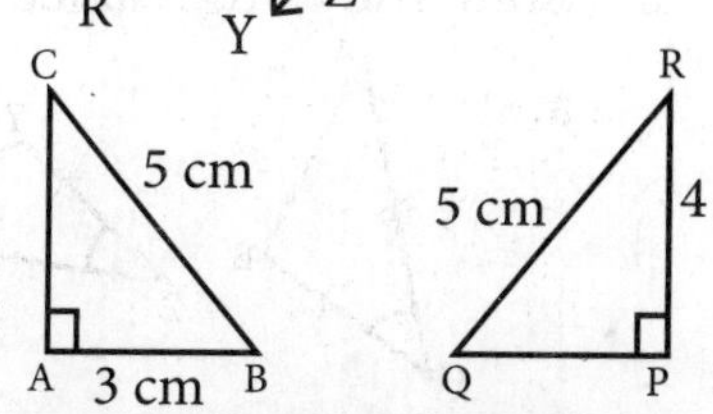

4. Construct a triangle OUP, where OU = 10 cm, UP = 6 cm and OP = 8 cm.
5. Find the order of symmetry and the angle of rotational symmetry for the following symbols.

Symbol	Order of symmetry	Angle of symmetry
a. 		
b. 		
c. 		
d. 		

6. Draw an isometric sketch of a cuboid measuring 5 cm in length, 2 cm in breadth and 3 cm in height in the given grid.

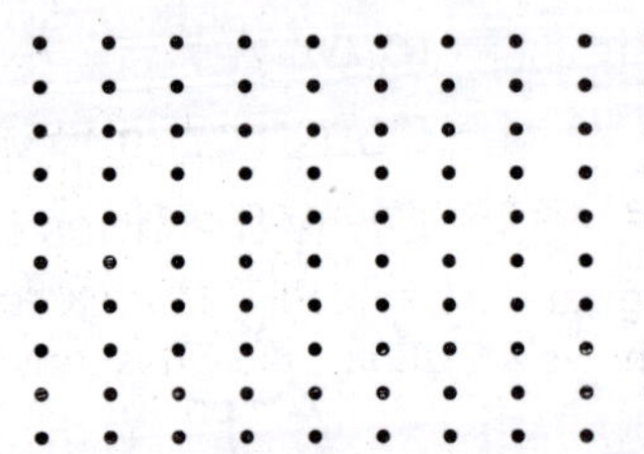

7. A rectangular loop of length 50 cm and width 38 cm is converted into a circular loop. Find the radius of the circular loop.
8. Read the bar graph given and answer the questions that follow.
   a. Which captain has played the most number of matches?
   b. How many less matches has Mohammed Azharuddin played compared to Mahendra Singh Dhoni?
   c. Who played one more match than Sachin Tendulkar?
   d. Who has played 77 matches?

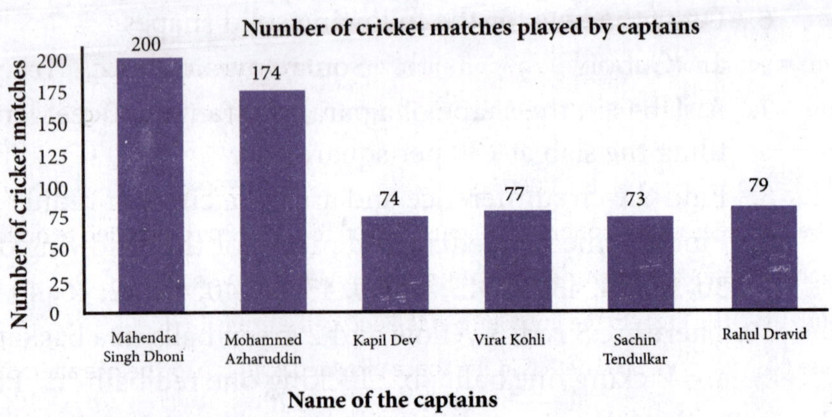

CLASS

7

QUESTION PAPER SET

A

IMO

SOF INTERNATIONAL MATHEMATICS OLYMPIAD 2018-19

DO NOT OPEN THIS BOOKLET UNTIL ASKED TO DO SO

Total Questions: 50 | Time: 1 hr.

Guidelines for the Candidate

1. You will get additional ten minutes to fill up information about yourself on the OMR Sheet, before the start of the exam.
2. Write your Name, School Code, Class, Section, Roll No. and Mobile Number clearly on the OMR Sheet and do not forget to sign it. We will share with you your marks / result on your mobile number.
3. The Question Paper comprises four sections:

   Logical Reasoning (15 Questions), Mathematical Reasoning (20 Questions), Everyday Mathematics (10 Questions) and Achievers Section (5 Questions)

   Each question in Achievers Section carries 3 marks, whereas all other questions carry one mark each.
4. All questions are compulsory. There is no negative marking. Use of calculator is not permitted.
5. There is only ONE correct answer. Choose only ONE option for an answer.
6. To mark your choice of answers by darkening the circles on the OMR Sheet, use HB Pencil or Blue / Black ball point pen only. E.g.

   Q.16: Rahul bought 4 kg 90 g of apples, 2 kg 60 g of grapes and 5 kg 300 g of mangoes. The total weight of all the fruits he bought is_______.

   A. 11.450 kg B. 11.000 kg C. 11.350 kg D. 11.250 kg

   As the correct answer is option A, you must darken the circle corresponding to option A on the OMR Sheet.

   16. ● Ⓑ Ⓒ Ⓓ
7. Rough work should be done in the blank space provided in the booklet.
8. Return the OMR Sheet to the invigilator at the end of the exam.
9. Please fill in your personal details in the space provided on this page before attempting the paper.

SOF

SCIENCE OLYMPIAD FOUNDATION

Inspiring Young Minds Through Knowledge Olympiads

Name:..

Section:.............. SOF Olympiad Roll No.:......................... Contact No.:...

LOGICAL REASONING

1. There is a certain relationship between figures (i) and (ii). Establish a similar relationship between figures (iii) and (iv) by selecting a suitable figure from the options that would replace the (?) in figure (iv).

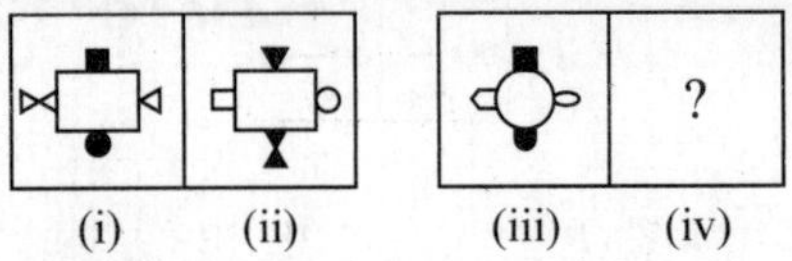

A. 

B. 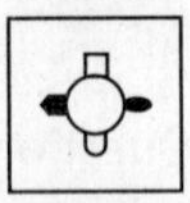

C. 

D. 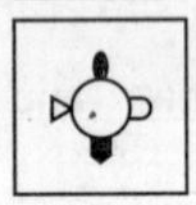

2. How many squares are there in the given figure?

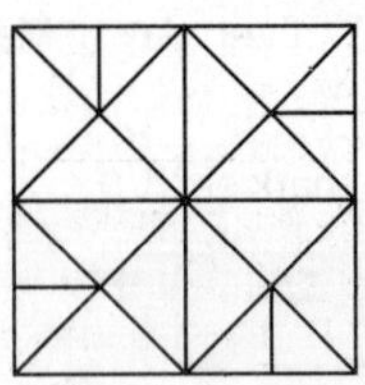

A. 10 B. 14
C. 17 D. None of these

3. Find the missing number, if the same rule is followed in all the three figures.

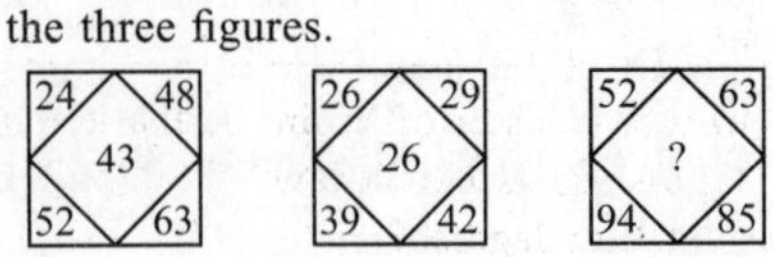

A. 76
B. 56
C. 63
D. 64

4. In a certain code language, 'EMPLOYEES' is written as 'DLOKOXDDR'. How will 'FURNITURE' be written in the same language?

A. ETQMJSTQB
B. GTPNISTQF
C. ETQMISTQD
D. GTPNISTRE

5. Choose a box from the options that is similar to the box formed from the given sheet of paper.

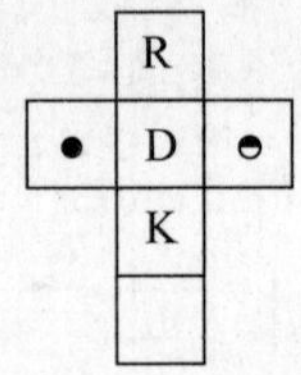

A. 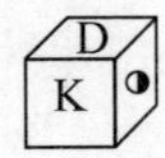

B. 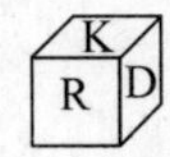

C. 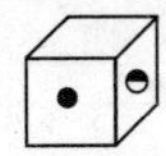

D. 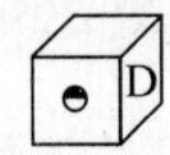

6. Ali walks 10 km towards North. He turns to his right and after walking 2 km, he turns to his left. Finally after walking 6 km, he turns to his left again. In which direction is he moving now?

A. East
B. North-East
C. South
D. West

7. Which of the following options best illustrates the given Venn diagram?

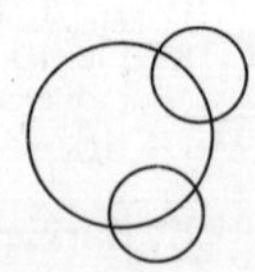

A. Animals, Elephants, Wolves
B. Graduates, Teachers, Human beings
C. Bricks, Houses, Bridges
D. Vehicles, Buses, Cars

8. A square transparent sheet with a pattern and a dotted line on it is given. Select a figure from the options which shows the given sheet when folded along the dotted line.

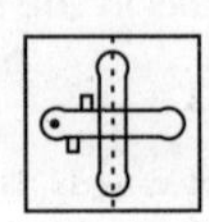

A. 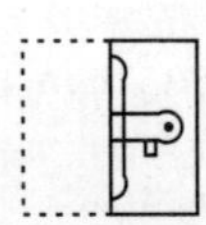

B. 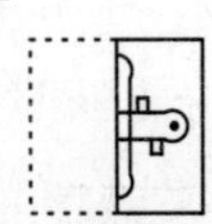

C. 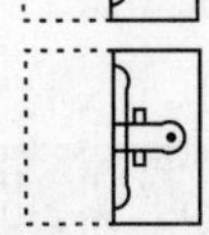

D. 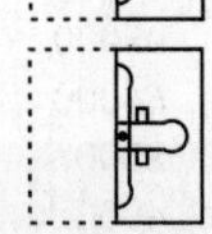

9. If '$' denotes '+', '@' denotes '×', '#' denotes '–' and '*' denotes '÷', then find the value of 12 * 6 @ 4 # 3 $ 6.

A. 12
B. 11
C. 14
D. 10

10. Select the correct mirror image of the given figure.

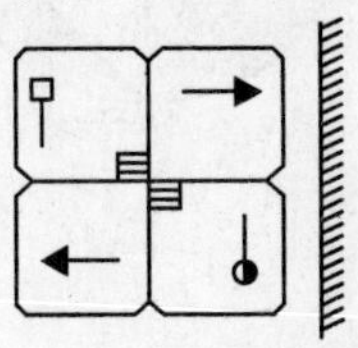

A. 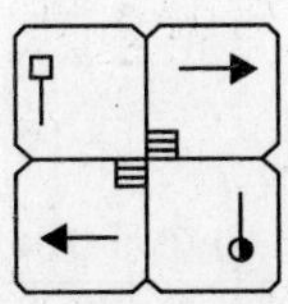
B. 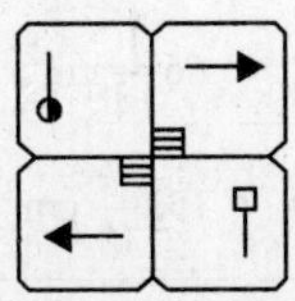
C. 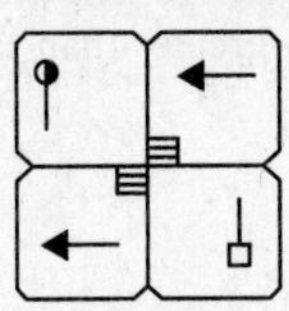
D. 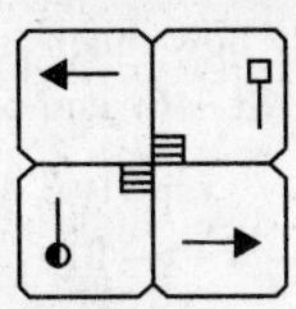

11. Group the given figures into three classes on the basis of their identical properties using each figure only once.

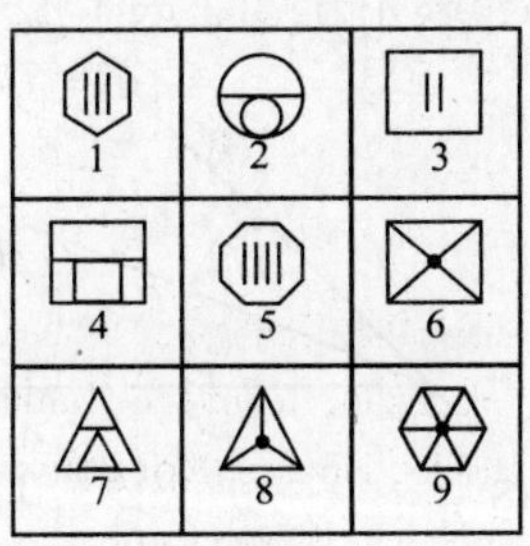

A. 1, 3, 5; 2, 4, 9; 6, 8, 7
B. 2, 5, 7; 6, 8, 9; 1, 3, 4
C. 1, 3, 5; 2, 4, 7; 6, 8, 9
D. 6, 3, 5; 2, 4, 7; 1, 8, 9

12. Select a figure from the options which will complete the given figure matrix.

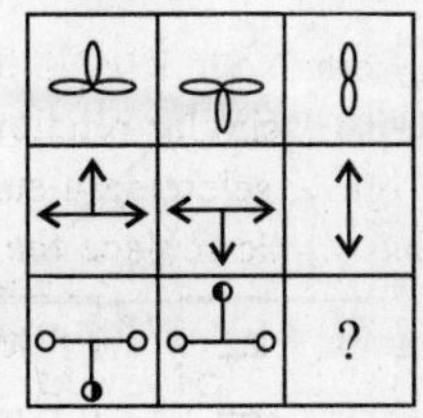

A. 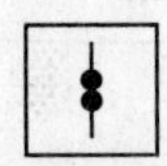
B. 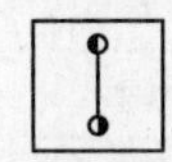
C. 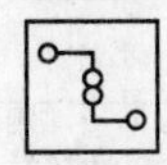
D. 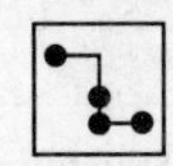

13. Select a figure from the options which satisfies the same conditions of placement of dots as in the given figure.

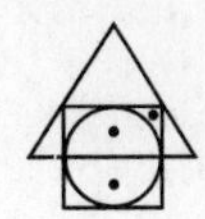

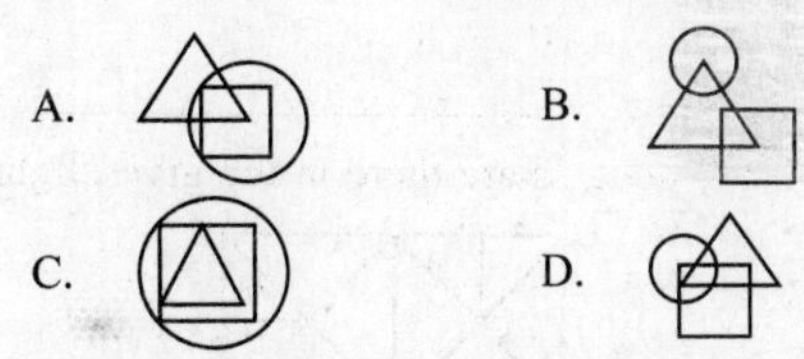

14. If it is possible to make only one meaningful word with the third, sixth and eighth letters of the word ORDINATE, then the third letter of the word formed is the answer. If no meaningful word is formed, then give 'X' as the answer. If more than one such words can be formed, then give 'Z' as the answer.

A. D
B. Z
C. X
D. A

15. Reema is sister of Vipin. Sudha is mother of Vipin. Jagdish is father-in-law of Sudha. How is Reema related to Jagdish?

A. Sister
B. Daughter
C. Granddaughter
D. Daughter-in-law

MATHEMATICAL REASONING

16 . If $\frac{3}{7}$ of 64% of $\frac{x}{21}$ is 1280, then the value of x is ______.

A. 98000
B. 64000
C. 8000
D. 4900

17 . Simplify: $\frac{2^{p-8} \times 8^{q-4}}{2^{p-11} \times 8^{q-5}}$

A. 2^5
B. 2^6
C. 2^3
D. 2^4

18. In the given figure, if $\angle A = 2\angle B$ and $\angle ACD = 2\angle DCB$, then find the measure of $\angle DCB + \angle B$.

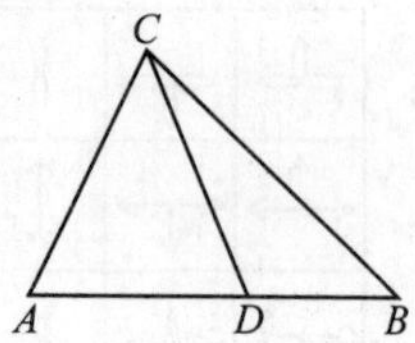

A. 60°
B. 90°
C. 45°
D. 75°

19. Which of the following options represents the value of P shown on the number line?

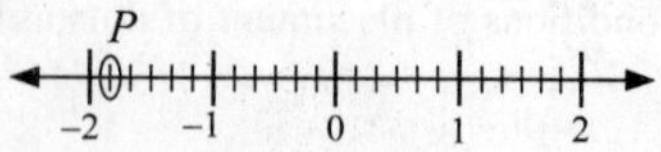

A. $\frac{6}{3}+\frac{1}{3}-\frac{1}{9}+\frac{4}{3}$

B. $-\frac{1}{4}-\frac{3}{2}$

C. $\frac{1}{3}-\frac{6}{2}+\frac{4}{3}-\frac{1}{2}$

D. $\frac{2}{3}-\frac{1}{3}+\frac{6}{3}+2$

20. In the given figure, ACD is a straight line. $AC = CB$ and $BF \parallel DE$. Find $\angle BAE$.

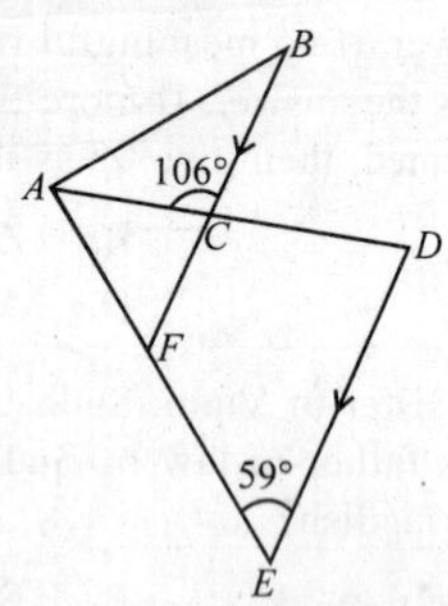

A. 42°
B. 84°
C. 39°
D. None of these

21. Select a pair of integers whose sum is –51.

A. – 42, 93
B. 1, – 50
C. – 93, 42
D. – 1, –52

22. A circle with centre at O and radius 5 cm is given. A right angled triangle AOB is inscribed in the circle. Find the area of the shaded region. $\left(\text{Take } \pi = \frac{22}{7}\right)$

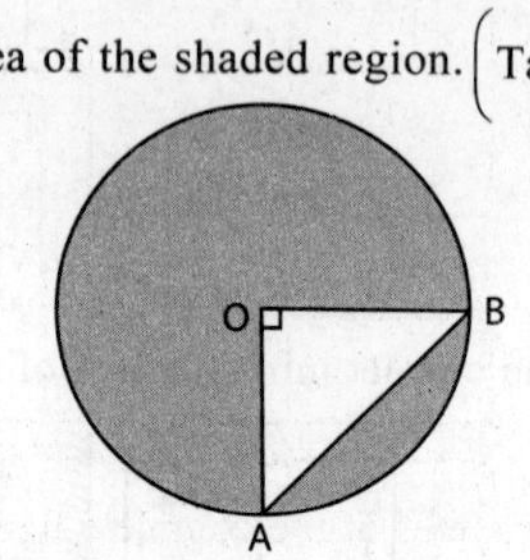

A. $132\frac{4}{7}$ cm^2

B. $139\frac{4}{7}$ cm^2

C. $66\frac{1}{14}$ cm^2

D. $153\frac{7}{17}$ cm^2

23. By how much is $-12x + 2y$ greater than the sum of $-18x + 6y$ and $5x - 25y$?

A. $x + 21y$
B. $-x - 21y$
C. $x + 25y$
D. $x + 36y$

24. By which congruency criterion, $\Delta QPR \cong \Delta QPS$, if $QR = QS$, $PR \perp QA$ and $PS \perp QC$.

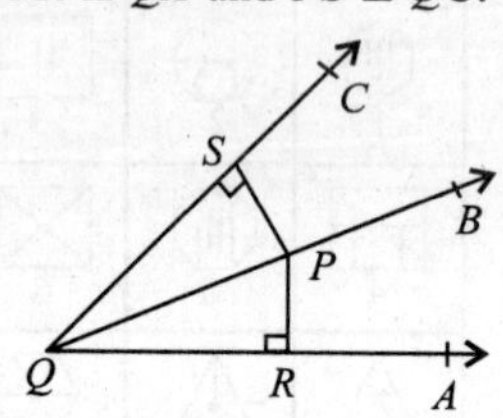

A. SAS
B. RHS
C. ASA
D. SSS

25. Which of the following statements is CORRECT ?

A. If lengths of any two sides of a triangle are 7 cm and 10 cm, then the length of its third side lies between 3 cm and 17 cm.

B. It is possible to construct a unique triangle, if all its three angles are given.

C. An angle of $\left(7\frac{1}{2}\right)^\circ$, can't be constructed using compass and ruler.

D. None of these

26. Study the given figure (not drawn to scale) carefully and select the correct option.

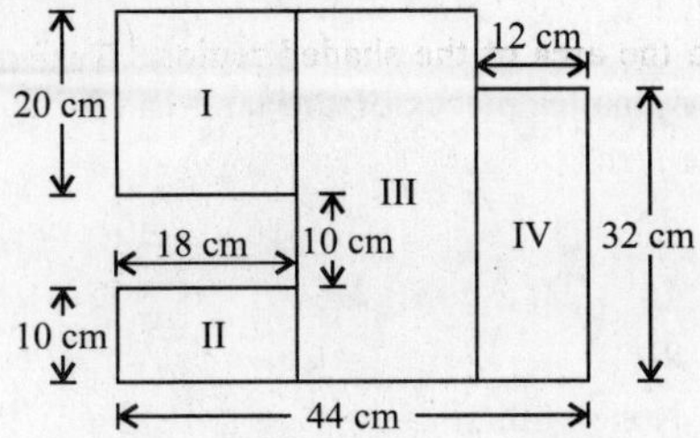

(i) Perimeter of the complete figure is 198 cm.
(ii) Total area of figure II and III is 4 cm^2 less than the total area of figure I and IV.

A. Only (i) is true.
B. Only (ii) is true.
C. Both (i) and (ii) are true.
D. Neither (i) nor (ii) is true.

27. If $a : b = 2\frac{1}{2} : 1\frac{2}{3}$ and $b : c = 1\frac{1}{4} : 3\frac{1}{2}$, then find $a : b : c$.

A. 7 : 6 : 18
B. 5 : 9 : 14
C. 15 : 11 : 14
D. 15 : 10 : 28

28. Solve for x : $\frac{7x+3}{4} + \frac{9x-5}{8} = \frac{16x-3}{16}$

A. $\frac{1}{6}$
B. $\frac{5}{3}$
C. $-\frac{3}{5}$
D. $-\frac{1}{6}$

29. What is the least number of squares that must be added so that the line AB becomes the line of symmetry?

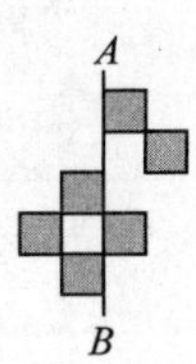

A. 4
B. 5
C. 6
D. 7

30. The sum of two consecutive multiples of 6 is 114. Find the smaller number.

A. 60
B. 66
C. 54
D. 96

31. A sum of money at simple interest doubles itself in 5 years 6 months. In how much time will it triple itself at the same rate?

A. 11 years
B. 12 years
C. 16 years
D. None of these

32. Find the mean of first 7 odd natural numbers.

A. 49
B. 28
C. 21
D. 7

33. Which of the following figures is the top view of the given figure?

A. 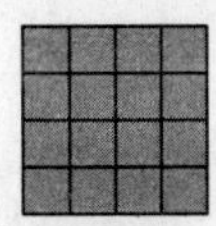
B. 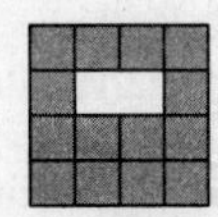
C. 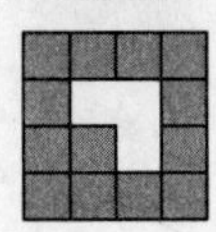
D. 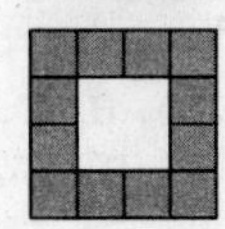

34. What is the order of rotational symmetry of the given figure?

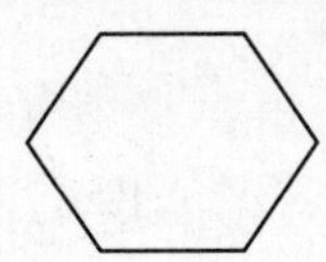

A. 2
B. 6
C. 4
D. 0

35. A bag contains 5 blue gems, 8 red gems and 2 green gems. A gem is drawn at random. What is the probability of getting a blue gem?

A. $\frac{1}{3}$
B. $\frac{2}{3}$
C. $\frac{2}{9}$
D. $\frac{5}{6}$

36. In Shimla, minimum temperature on Tuesday was 25°C. On Wednesday, it fell by 3°C and due to rainfall on Thursday, it further fell by 4°C. What was the minimum temperature on Thursday?

A. 20°C
B. 18°C
C. 22°C
D. 19°C

37. Mr Sharma earns ₹ 64000 per month. He gave $\frac{2}{5}$ of his salary to his son and $\frac{5}{8}$ of the remaining to his daughter and the rest to his wife. Find the share of his wife.

A. ₹ 14400
B. ₹ 24000
C. ₹ 25600
D. ₹ 38400

38. The grades obtained by 30 students of class VII are as follows:

A^+, B^+, A, B, A^+, B^+, A^+, B, B, B^+, A, A, A^+, B, B^+, A, A^+, B, B, A, A, A^+, A^+, B, B^+, B, B^+, A^+, A^+, A

If a student has been selected at random, then find the probability that he has obtained grade A^+.

A. $\frac{7}{10}$
B. $\frac{7}{30}$
C. $\frac{9}{10}$
D. $\frac{3}{10}$

39. Manvi says that she got 16 more marks than 4 times the number of marks scored by Aashi. Form an equation which gives the marks scored by Aashi, if Manvi scored 72 marks.

A. $16x + 4 = 72$
B. $16 + 4x = 72$
C. $16x + 72 = 4$
D. $72 + 4x = 16$

40. A rectangular piece of land is to be sold off in smaller pieces. The total area of the land is 2^{17} sq. miles. The pieces to be cut out are 16^2 sq. miles in size. How many smaller pieces of the land can be sold at the given size?

A. 2^{15}
B. 16^4
C. 2^9
D. None of these

41. Sushma sells an article at a loss of 12%. If she had sold it for ₹ 50.80 more, then she would have earned a profit of 8%. Find the cost price of the article.

A. ₹ 260
B. ₹ 250
C. ₹ 254
D. ₹ 244

42. A rectangular grassy land is 65 m long and 50 m broad. It is surrounded by 3 m wide path. Find the cost of gravelling the path at ₹ 2.50 per m^2.

A. ₹ 1500
B. ₹ 1518
C. ₹ 1815
D. ₹ 1960

43. The number of students in a school increased by 8% annually. If there are 71280 students in the school, then how many students were there last year?

A. 57640
B. 54000
C. 61320
D. 66000

44. The ages of Ruchi and Suchi are in the ratio 6 : 1. The sum of their ages is 56 years. What is the ratio of their ages after 6 years?

A. 27 : 7
B. 26 : 9
C. 25 : 3
D. 29 : 7

45. In an examination, one should get 36% of the maximum marks to pass. A student obtained 113 marks and is declared fail by 85 marks. The maximum marks are ______.

A. 500
B. 550
C. 640
D. 1008

46. State 'T' for true and 'F' for false and select the correct option.

(i) Every natural number is a rational number.

(ii) Every rational number is a fraction.

(iii) Zero is not a rational number.

(iv) The reciprocal of 0 is $\frac{1}{0}$.

	(i)	(ii)	(iii)	(iv)
A.	F	T	T	F
B.	T	T	T	F
C.	T	F	F	F
D.	T	T	F	F

47. Match the following.

	Column-I	Column-II
(P)	If $2700 \times x^6 = 27 \times 10^8$, then $x =$	(i) 6
(Q)	If $pqr = 0$, then $\frac{\left(\left(x^p\right)^r\right)^{2q}}{x^{pqr}} =$	(ii) 900
(R)	$\frac{2\times 2^{n+3}}{2^{n+4}-2^3\times 2^n}+2^2$ is equal to	(iii) 10
(S)	$\frac{\left(3^{-2}\right)^5\times\left(5^{-3}\right)^4\times\left(7^{-4}\right)^5}{\left(2^{-1}\right)^2\times\left(7^2\right)^{-10}\times\left(3^4\right)^{-3}\times\left(5^7\right)^{-2}}$ equals	(iv) 1

	(P)	(Q)	(R)	(S)
A.	(i)	(iv)	(iii)	(ii)
B.	(iii)	(i)	(iv)	(ii)
C.	(ii)	(iii)	(i)	(iv)
D.	(iii)	(iv)	(i)	(ii)

48. In the given figure (not drawn to scale), if $AB \parallel CG \parallel EF$, then find

(i) $2z - x$

(ii) $x + 2y$

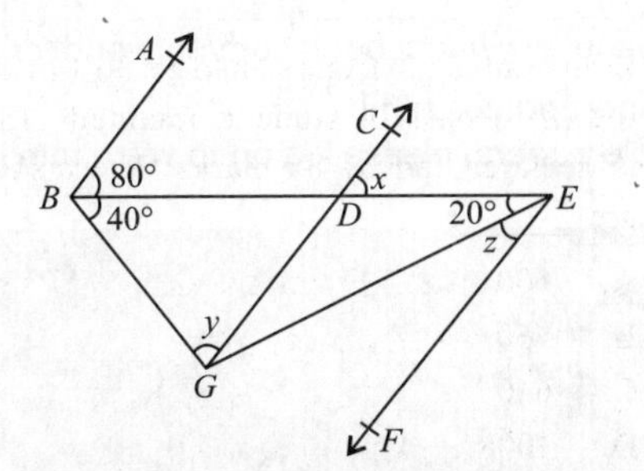

	(i)	(ii)
A.	40°	220°
B.	60°	200°
C.	50°	200°
D.	40°	200°

49. Study the following statements carefully and select the correct option.

Statement-I : A hall is 36 m long and 24 m broad. If allowing area of 40 m^2 for doors and windows, the cost of papering the walls at ₹ 8.40 per square metre is ₹ 4704, then the height of the hall is 5 m.

Statement-II : If the difference between the circumference and diameter of a circle is 154 cm, then the radius of circle is 30.93 cm.

A. Both Statement-I and Statement-II are true.

B. Both Statement-I and Statement-II are false.

C. Statement-I is true but Statement-II is false.

D. Statement-I is false but Statement-II is true.

50. The given double bar graph shows the sale of mobile phones and cars from 2005 to 2008.

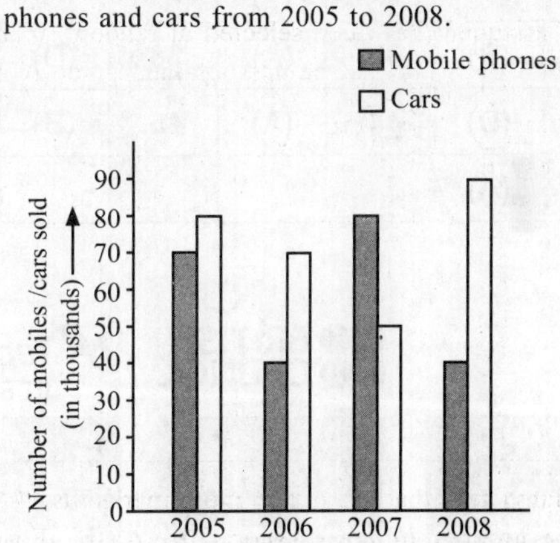

(i) Find the ratio of the total number of mobile phones sold in 2006 and 2008 to the total number of cars sold in 2005 and 2007.

(ii) What is the average number of cars sold from 2005 to 2008?

	(i)	(ii)
A.	8 : 13	72500
B.	13 : 16	72500
C.	8 : 13	97000
D.	16 : 17	89000

SPACE FOR ROUGH WORK

ANSWER KEYS

1.	(A)	2.	(A)	3.	(D)	4.	(C)	5.	(A)	6.	(D)	7.	(C)
8.	(B)	9.	(B)	10.	(D)	11.	(C)	12.	(B)	13.	(D)	14.	(C)
15.	(C)	16.	(A)	17.	(B)	18.	(A)	19.	(C)	20.	(B)	21.	(C)
22.	(C)	23.	(A)	24.	(B)	25.	(A)	26.	(B)	27.	(D)	28.	(D)
29.	(C)	30.	(C)	31.	(A)	32.	(D)	33.	(D)	34.	(B)	35.	(A)
36.	(B)	37.	(A)	38.	(D)	39.	(B)	40.	(C)	41.	(C)	42.	(C)
43.	(D)	44.	(A)	45.	(B)	46.	(C)	47.	(D)	48.	(D)	49.	(C)
50.	(A)												

ANSWERS

CHAPTER 1

Exercise 1A

1. a. 17 b. (–153) c. (–51) d. (–112)
2. a. 23 b. (–108) c. (–28) d. 99
3. a. 5°C b. 540 ft below sea level c. 40 m more
   d. ₹2300 e. (–15°C)

Exercise 1B

1. a. 25, (–10) b. 49 c. –15, 14, 8
   d. –21, –32 e. 100
2. a. One possible answer is given.
   i. (–3) + (–6) = (–9) ii. (–10) – (–3) = (–7)
   iii. 9 + (–9) = 0 iv. 5 – 3 = 2
   v. (–10) + (–3) = (–13) vi. (–5) – (–1) = (–4)
   c. 3000 d. A took 4 more shots than B.

Exercise 1C

1. Positive: positive, positive; negative, negative
   Negative: positive, negative; negative, positive
2. a. 13 b. –300 c. 216 d. 24
   e. 336 f. –495
3. a. 1 b. 9 c. 0 d. –8
   e. –10 f. 11
4. a. –224 b. 8904 c. –3332 d. 1368
   e. –1972 f. –285
5. b. i. 10 marks ii. 13 marks iii. 17 marks
   c. –8°C
   d. i. She made a profit of ₹4000.
   ii. 600 purses iii. A loss of ₹2135

Exercise 1D

1. a. (–8) b. (–27) c. (–7) d. 3
   e. 1 f. (–2)
2. a. 1 b. (–54) c. 99 d. 0
   e. (–86) f. (–1)
3.

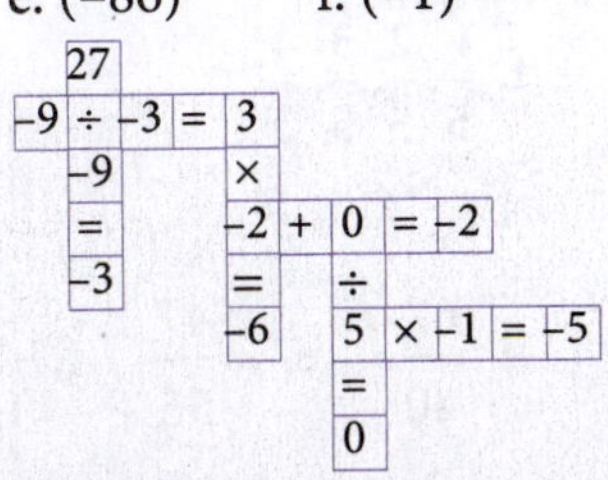

4. b. One possible answer is given: 15 ÷ (–3) = (–5)
   c. Quiz 2 d. 6 old mobiles
   e. 8 years, 456 people

Chapter Revision

A. 1. a 2. b 3. d 4. b 5. c.
B. 1. F 2. T 3. T 4. F 5. T
C. 1. 171 2. 840 3. 990 4. 312 5. 6
   6. (–295) 7. Not defined 8. (–120) 9. (–55)
E. 1. 70 ft 2. 27,250 points 3. 110
   4. 24°C 5. 17 days

CHAPTER 2

Exercise 2A

1. a. $\frac{1}{4}$ b. 25 c. $\frac{3}{2}$ d. 165
   e. $1\frac{10}{17}$ f. $\frac{24}{25}$ g. 208 h. $14\frac{14}{39}$
2. a. $\frac{1}{20}$ b. $\frac{8}{55}$ c. $\frac{25}{36}$ d. $\frac{49}{64}$
   e. $3\frac{1}{5}$ f. $1\frac{31}{50}$ g. $7\frac{11}{15}$ h. $63\frac{43}{50}$
3. a. 100 b. 29 c. 8 d. 11
   e. 800 f. 207 g. 480 h. 20

Exercise 2B

1. a. – vi. b. – i. c. – v. d. – ii.
   e. – iii. f. – iv.
2. a. 12 b. 27 c. 72 d. $\frac{80}{57}$
3. a. $\frac{3}{40}$ b. $\frac{4}{75}$ c. $\frac{1}{12}$ d. $\frac{25}{66}$
4. a. $\frac{2}{3}$ b. $3\frac{1}{2}$ c. $1\frac{11}{28}$ d. $\frac{39}{64}$

Exercise 2C

1. $7\frac{1}{2}$ kg 2. 21 3. 160 4. 3 km
5. $1\frac{4}{15}$ m 6. 250 km 7. 6 servings 8. $\frac{1}{4}$

Exercise 2D

1. a. 1.4 b. 10.4 c. 50.4 d. 8.61
   e. 60.5 f. 452.5 g. 1261.3 h. 576
2. a. 0.15 b. 0.045 c. 0.0003 d. 20.91
   e. 388.62 f. 2.349 g. 13.559 h. 2.1496

3. b. 0.02, 2 c. 12.309, 123.09
d. 2334.50, 23345.0 e. 99999.9, 999999
f. 10.0009, 100.009

Exercise 2E

1. a. 0.04 b. 0.15 c. 0.35 d. 0.00025
e. 0.07 f. 0.525 g. 38.12 h. 27
2. a. 159 b. 2480 c. 0.7 d. 0.2
e. 8 f. 62 g. 9.1 h. 1.74
3. b. 0.1578, 0.01578 c. 25.0056, 2.50056
d. 0.13823 e. 0.1902, 0.01902
f. 100.00001, 1.0000001

Exercise 2F

1. 3 hours 2. 10.8 m 3. 160.125 km
4. ₹132.15 5. 45.6 pieces 6. 60 lamps
7. ₹13.50

Chapter Revision

A 1. d. 2. b. 3. c. 4. c. 5. b.

B. 1. 9 2. 3 3. 300 4. 0.075
5. 2536 6. 0.5

C. 1. T 2. T 3. F 4. T 5. F 6. T

D. 1. d. 2. f. 3. a. 4. b. 5. c. 6. e.

E. b. $2\frac{6}{22}$ c. $\frac{20}{9}$ d. $\frac{300}{49}$ e. $20\frac{5}{6}$

F. 1. 4 2. $\frac{3}{2}$ 3. $4\frac{4}{5}$ 4. $\frac{1}{2}$
5. $2\frac{7}{10}$ 6. $2\frac{13}{32}$ 7. $14\frac{7}{8}$ 8. $46\frac{4}{5}$
9. 1 10. 0.72 11. 1.016 12. 0.00003
13. 0.009 14. 6.25 15. 3.24 16. 0.0309

G. 1. $7\frac{1}{2}$ 2. $\frac{1}{144}$ 3. 72 4. $\frac{5}{9}$ 5. 12
6. 14 7. $10\frac{5}{6}$ 8. $4\frac{22}{25}$ 9. 0.5 10. 0.95
11. 12 12. 400 13. 3.25 14. 2 15. 21 16. 2

H. 1. $\frac{5}{3}$ minutes 2. $7\frac{1}{2}$ calories 3. $1\frac{1}{4}$
4. 17.5 hours 5. ₹42.875 6. 42.6 kg

CHAPTER 3

Exercise 3A

1. Positive rational numbers: b., d., e.
Negative rational numbers: a., c., f.

2.

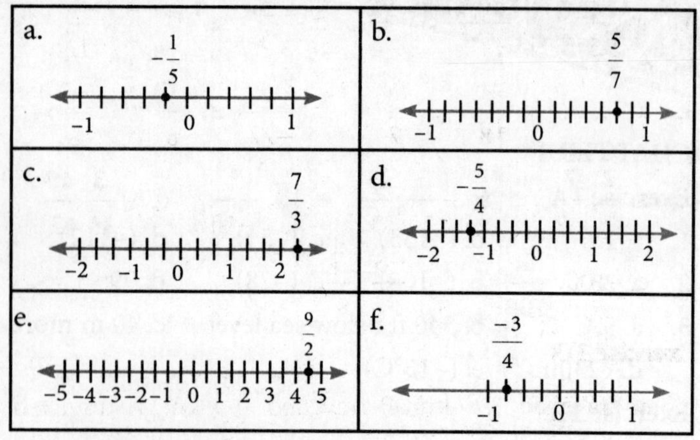

3. Sample answers:
a. $\frac{6}{10}, \frac{9}{15}$ b. $\frac{-8}{14}, \frac{-12}{21}$ c. $\frac{2}{22}, \frac{3}{33}$
d. $\frac{10}{-12}, \frac{15}{-18}$ e. $\frac{6}{8}, \frac{3}{4}$ f. $\frac{5}{25}, \frac{1}{5}$

4. a., b., e.

5. a. $\frac{-3}{1}$ b. $\frac{0}{1}$ c. $\frac{1}{1}$ d. $\frac{99}{1}$ e. $\frac{50}{1}$ f. $\frac{-5}{1}$

6. a. $\frac{5}{7}$ b. $\frac{-2}{13}$ c. $\frac{7}{8}$ d. $\frac{-1}{5}$ e. $\frac{1}{-25}$ f. $\frac{1}{9}$

Exercise 3B

1. a. $\frac{-2}{3}$ b. $\frac{2}{7}$ c. $\frac{4}{9}$ d. $\frac{-11}{5}$ e. $\frac{7}{3}$ f. $\frac{-5}{9}$

2. a. < b. < c. = d. < e. = f. >

3. a. $\frac{3}{7}, \frac{2}{3}, \frac{4}{5}$ b. $\frac{-4}{7}, \frac{-2}{5}, \frac{-1}{3}$ c. $-2, \frac{-3}{7}, 1$
d. $\frac{-8}{4}, -1, 3$ e. $\frac{-13}{12}, \frac{-11}{12}, \frac{3}{5}$ f. $\frac{-8}{7}, \frac{-2}{7}, \frac{-1}{7}$

4. a. $\frac{-9}{5}, \frac{-8}{5}, \frac{-7}{5}, \frac{-6}{5}$ b. $\frac{26}{5}, \frac{27}{5}, \frac{28}{5}, \frac{29}{5}$
c. $\frac{-23}{15}, \frac{-22}{15}, \frac{-12}{15}, \frac{-11}{15}$ d. $-\frac{2}{6}, -\frac{1}{6}, \frac{1}{6}, \frac{2}{6}$
e. $\frac{6}{15}, \frac{7}{15}, \frac{10}{15}, \frac{11}{15}$ f. $\frac{1}{5}, \frac{2}{5}, \frac{3}{5}, \frac{4}{5}$

Exercise 3C

1. a. $\frac{2}{7}$ b. $\frac{1}{2}$ c. $-\frac{1}{3}$ d. $\frac{67}{40}$ e. $-\frac{47}{55}$ f. $\frac{-1}{126}$

2. a. $\frac{62}{45}$ b. $\frac{1}{24}$ c. $\frac{-5}{8}$ d. $\frac{2}{13}$ e. $\frac{-43}{34}$ f. $\frac{-59}{56}$

3. a. $\frac{48}{55}$ b. $\frac{-28}{117}$ c. $\frac{15}{-4}$ d. $\frac{2}{-5}$ e. 10 f. $\frac{1}{12}$

4. a. −2 b. $\frac{-1}{18}$ c. $\frac{6}{7}$ d. $\frac{15}{-77}$ e. $\frac{-7}{6}$ f. $\frac{-7}{8}$

5. a. $\frac{2}{7}, \frac{7}{-2}$ b. $-\frac{3}{11}, \frac{11}{3}$ c. $10, \frac{1}{-10}$ d. $-\frac{3}{13}, \frac{13}{3}$

e. $-100, \frac{1}{100}$ f. $\frac{-8}{19}, \frac{19}{8}$

Exercise 3D

1. A travelled $1\frac{1}{9}$ km, B travelled $\frac{19}{20}$ km, A travelled more distance than B
2. Q is colder by $7\frac{31}{35}$ °C 3. ₹$3\frac{15}{16}$ = ₹3.94 approx.
4. 31 friends 5. $\frac{59}{60}, \frac{1}{60}$

Chapter Revision

A. 1. a 2. b 3. d 4. c 5. b

B. 1. T 2. F 3. F 4. T 5. F

C. 1. positive, less 2. $\frac{a}{b}$ 3. 1

4. Infinite 5. HCF

D. 1. c 2. d 3. a 4. e 5. b

E. a. $\frac{-3}{7}$: $\frac{-3}{7}$

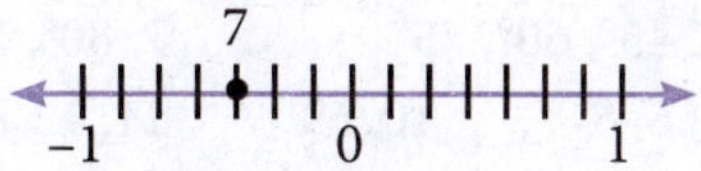

b. $\frac{-6}{5}$: $\frac{-6}{5}$

c. $\frac{-10}{4}$: $\frac{-10}{4}$

d. $\frac{3}{5}$: $\frac{3}{5}$

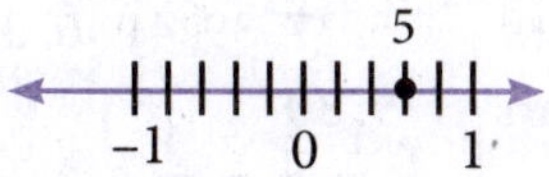

e. $\frac{5}{3}$: $\frac{5}{3}$

F 1. $\frac{-3}{2}$ 2. $\frac{-23}{18}$ 3. $\frac{4}{5}$ 4. $\frac{92}{33}$ 5. $\frac{-1}{8}$ 6. $\frac{-1}{10}$

G. a. $2\frac{3}{28}$ hours b. $\frac{1}{15}$ km c. $\frac{7}{6}$ days d. $\frac{1}{4}$ chocolate

CHAPTER 4

Exercise 4A

1. a. 7^6 b. $(-5)^3$ c. $\left(\frac{8}{9}\right)^5$ d. $\left(\frac{-3}{7}\right)^4$

e. $3^2 \times 23^2$ f. $8^3 \times 13^3$ g. $12^2 \times 11^3$ h. $\frac{5^5}{11^3}$

i. $\frac{13^4}{17^6}$ j. $\frac{(-2)^3}{19^5}$ k. $\frac{(-6)^4}{(-7)^4}$

2. a. 2^6 b. $2^2 \times 7^2$ c. $2^2 \times 3^4$ d. $\left(\frac{3}{5}\right)^2$ e. $\left(\frac{-1}{2}\right)^3$

3. a. 8 b. 9 c. 625 d. −64 e. −128

Exercise 4B

1. a. $\frac{9}{64}$ b. $\frac{-64}{343}$ c. 539 d. −2000 e. −729

f. 1 g. 10 h. $\frac{64}{729}$ i. 1 j. $\frac{25}{27}$

k. $\frac{3}{5}$ l. $\frac{17}{15} = 1\frac{2}{15}$ m. $\frac{3}{16}$ n. $\frac{1}{15}$ o. $\frac{27}{25}$

p. $\frac{7}{529}$ q. $\frac{64}{729}$ r. $\frac{36}{25} = 1\frac{11}{25}$

s. 0 t. 0 u. $\frac{49}{81}$ v. 1 w. $\frac{4}{3} = 1\frac{1}{3}$

2. a. 7 b. 4 c. 2 d. 1 e. 2 f. 1.5

g. 1 h. 0 i. 2

Exercise 4C

1. a. $3 \times 10^4 + 8 \times 10^3 + 2 \times 10^2 + 4 \times 10^1 + 5 \times 10^0$

b. $6 \times 10^5 + 5 \times 10^4 + 3 \times 10^3 + 7 \times 10^2 + 5 \times 10^1 + 2 \times 10^0$

c. $8 \times 10^6 + 4 \times 10^5 + 6 \times 10^4 + 7 \times 10^3 + 3 \times 10^2 + 8 \times 10^1 + 2 \times 10^0$

2. a. 521768 b. 92854
3. a. 2.4×10^4 b. 1.2×10^5 c. 7.39×10^6
4. a. 72500 b. 31500000

Chapter Revision

A. 1. b. 2. c. 3. d. 4. b. 5. a.

B. 1. 7, 8 2. − 2, 3 3. 1 4. $(-5)^5$ 5. $\frac{-2}{3}$ 6. $\frac{2}{3}$

C. 1. e. 2. c. 3. b. 4. a. 5. d.

D. 1. F 2. T 3. F 4. F 5. F

E. 1. $\frac{8}{-3}$ 2. 900 3. −234 4. $\frac{4}{25}$ 5. 1728 6. 11

CHAPTER 5

Exercise 5A

1. a. 15 b. $2n$ c. $-29a^2$ d. -1 e. $-6y$ f. 1
2. a. 11 b. -36 c. -11 d. 15 e. 1 f. 5
3. a. t b. c c. st d. h^2 e. a^2c f. s
4. a. p, $2p$ and pq, $-qp$, $4pq$ b. a, $-6a$ and $-a^2$, $9a^2$, a^2
   c. $7p$, $-p$; $-3q$, q and $5pq$
5. a., d., e., f.
6. a. 2 b. 3 c. 3

Exercise 5B

1. a. -16 b. 94 c. -64
2. 16 cm², 16 cm 3. 5 4. 15

Exercise 5C

1. a. $-3d$ b. $2e + 2e^3$ c. $8a + 3b$ d. $15a - 6b + 2c$
   e. 0 f. $32f + 4g - 6gh$ g. $12a^3 + 8a^2 + 7a + 14$
   h. $11a + 17b + 4c$ i. $18a + 1$ j. $5a + 13b + 26c$
   k. $-x - 9y - 12z - 40$
2. a. $13a$ b. 0 c. $-5abc$ d. $5 - d$
   e. $-2t^3 - 2t^2$ f. $22a - 12b + 16c$
   g. $r - 2s$ h. $12a + 8b - 12c$ i. $8a + 11b - 14c$
   j. $13e - 11s + 8u$
3. $3e + r - 4t$ 4. $10a + 3b$ 5. $3a - 4b - 6c$
   6. $12a + 7b - 8c$
7. a. $21b - 11c + 9d$ b. $a + 22b - 10c + 9d$
   c. $-a + 8b - 2c + 3d$ d. $-a + 23b - 21c + 12d$

Exercise 5D

1. a. $21b^2 - 7bc$ b. $2x^2 - xy - y^2$
   c. $13ab + 5b^2 - 6a^2$ d. $2a^2 + 2ab$
   e. $-6r^2 + 21r$ f. $3a^3 + 4.5a^2 + 1.5a$
   g. $-6e^2 + 6ef + 11e - 11f$ h. $24a^4 - 2a^2 - 5$
   i. $0.2a^2 + 2a - 15$ j. $-20ab^2 + 10a^2b - 16b + 8a$
   k. $\frac{x^2}{4} - 7x + \frac{x}{2} - 14$ l. $xy^2 - x^2y + 3xy + y - x + 3$
   m. $5ax + 5x^2 + 16x + a + 3$ n. $x^2y + 2xy + 2x + y + 2$
2. a. $6a - b$ b. $7a$ c. $5a + 9b$
   d. $6a + 8b + 5$ e. p f. $16kl - 10k$
   g. $5r$ h. a i. $-a$ j. $2a$
   k. $10a + 10ab$ l. $-3y + 12$
3. a. $\frac{x^3}{3} + x^2 - 2x$ b. $10a^2 + 3a - 4$
   c. $18x^2 + 42xy + 12y^2$ d. $2x^2 + 5x - 2xy + y - 3$

Chapter Revision

A. 1. d. 2. c. 3. b. 4. c. 5. c.
B. 1. 0 2. like 3. three 4. $-3d$ 5. $24ab$
C. 1. F 2. T 3. F 4. F 5. T 6. F 7. T
D. 1. d. 2. a. 3. b. 4. c. 5. e.
E. 1. a. $28z - 11$ b. $7a + 16b$
   2. a. $-31y - 2z - 15$ b. $-19a + 6b - 17c$
   3. a. $6p^2 - 18pq$ b. $7s^2 - 28rs + 200r - 50s$
   c. $a^2 + ab + 3a + 4b - 4$ d. $5r^2 - 5rs - 10s^2$
   e. $9e^2 + 7f^2 + 16ef - 5e - 5f$ f. $12x^2 + 7y^2 + 20xy - 4x - 2y$
   4. a. $10b^2 + 10ab - 2ac + 3a - 2bc + 3b$
   b. $a + 11b - 2c + 3$ c. $c^2 - 9ab + ac - 3a - 9bc - 3c$
   d. $17b - c + 6$
   5. a. 20 b. 6 c. 98 d. 0 6. 15 cm², 16 cm

CHAPTER 6

Exercise 6A

1. a. -2 b. 8 c. 2 d. 54 e. $\frac{1}{2}$ f. 2
   g. -4 h. 0 i. -2.5 j. -2
2. $2d = 10$, $d + 3 = 8$, $d - 7 = -2$, $\frac{1}{6} = \frac{d}{30}$
3. a. 10 b. 45 c. 2 d. $\frac{1}{2}$ e. 20 f. 1.78
4. a. 4 b. 3 c. 4 d. 30 e. 2 f. -5
   g. 5 h. $\frac{19}{11} = 1\frac{8}{11}$ i. $\frac{50}{3} = 16\frac{2}{3}$ j. 25
   k. 42 l. -54 m. -5 n. $\frac{8}{3} = 2\frac{2}{3}$ o. -84
   p. -14 q. 101 r. -15

Exercise 6B

1. 93 2. 4 3. 34, 35 4. 41, 43
5. 36, 38, 40 6. 45°, 60°, 75° 7. 80°, 100°
8. 30, 54 9. 6, 8 10. 64 11. 12
12. 18 years 13. 28 14. 45 15. $\frac{7}{6}$

Chapter Revision

A. 1. c. 2. a. 3. d. 4. b.
B. 1. T 2. T 3. T 4. T 5. F 6. T
C. 1. f. 2. e. 3. b. 4. d. 5. c. 6. a.
D. 1. $\frac{-1}{2}$ 2. $\frac{10}{3} = 3\frac{1}{3}$ 3. $\frac{28}{3}$ 4. -100 5. -5.5 6. 9
E. 1. 58, 60 2. 35°, 55° 3. 90
   4. 5 years and 20 years 5. 37, 39, 41 6. 36
   7. 20 years 8. 3 years 9. 30
   10. 16 years, 36 years

CHAPTER 7

Exercise 7A

1. a. 1 : 5 b. 1 : 20 c. 1 : 2 d. 2 : 5 e. 15 : 8
   f. 9 : 10 : 8 g. 66 : 87 : 6 h. 0.2 : 0.6 : 1
   i. 11 cm : 12 cm j. 5 days : 8 days k. 3 g : 20 g
   l. 3 mins : 4 mins m. 1 month : 2 months
   n. 50 paise : 9 paise

2. a. 5 : 3 b. 3 : 5 c. 3 : 8
3. a. 14 : 15 b. 42 : 70 : 45
4. a. 4 : 5 b. A : B : C = 12 : 14 : 15
5. 4 : 15 < 2 : 7 < 3 : 5 6. 11 : 13
7. 90°, 60°, 30° 8. ₹360, ₹270, ₹180 9. ₹160 10. ₹28,000

Exercise 7B

1. a. Yes b. No 2. a. 33 b. 1 3. 20
4. a. 42 b. 0.6 c. 24 d. 84
5. a. 45 b. $\frac{32}{13}$ c. 1.6 d. 40
6. a. 9 b. 6 c. 10 d. 2

Exercise 7C

1. ₹80 2. 135 litres 3. 30 days 4. 45 days
5. 32 days 6. ₹60 7. 21 chocolates
8. 13 men

Chapter Revision

A. 1. c. 2. d. 3. b. 4. a. 5. b.
B. 1. c. 2. ₹4125 3. 45 days 4. 15 : 49
5. 20 : 28 : 7
C. 1. T 2. F 3. F 4. F 5. F
D. 1. c. 2. e. 3. b. 4. d. 5. f.
E. 1. 1 2. 36 : 25 : 24 3. 40 4. 110
5. $10\frac{1}{2}$ days 6. 7
7. ₹1 = 450 coins, ₹2 = 400 coins, ₹5 = 250 coins
8. ₹3,12,500 9. ₹13,500

CHAPTER 8

Exercise 8A

1. a. 0.14 b. 1489.2 c. 1.225 d. 10
e. 6 seconds f. 9 mins g. 25 paise
h. ₹1250 i. 25 g j. 600 g k. 210 mℓ
l. 900 mℓ
2. a. 500 b. 1900 c. 61,700 d. 4000
e. 1600 ℓ f. 55.56 kg
3. a. 72% b. 25% c. ₹2450 d. 12 e. 43.6%

Exercise 8B

1. a. 50% b. 66.66% c. 125% d. 75% e. 550%
2. a. $\frac{3}{10}$ b. $\frac{17}{20}$ c. $\frac{17}{25}$ d. $\frac{9}{20}$ e. $\frac{1}{100}$
3. a. 5% b. 67% c. 150% d. 1205% e. 0.1%
4. a. 0.08 b. 0.14 c. 0.88 d. 0.60 e. 0.51
5. a. 14.28% b. 12.5% c. 22.22% d. 41.67% e. 75%
6. a. 1 : 10 b. 24 : 25 c. 5 : 4 d. 23 : 25 e. 11 : 50

Exercise 8C

1. 16.67% 2. 63.56% 3. 50% 4. Loss of 1%
5. 20% 6. Profit of ₹17,200 7. 33.33%
8. a. ₹10, 12.5% b. ₹53, 15.01% c. ₹1100, 12%
d. ₹2900, 20.6%

Exercise 8D

1. a. ₹1000, ₹11,000 b. 1 year, ₹850 c. ₹545, ₹1035.5
d. 12.5% e. ₹1000, ₹1060
2. ₹45,000 3. ₹29,500 4. 1 year 5. 6.25%
6. ₹4444.44 7. 16.66% 8. 4 years

Chapter Revision

A. 1. b. 2. a. 3. a. 4. d. 5. b.
B. 1. 3% 2. 15 3. ₹225 4. 100
5. $\frac{P \times R \times T}{100}$
C. 1. T 2. F 3. T 4. F 5. F
D. 1. f. 2. d. 3. e. 4. a. 5. b. 6. c.
E. 1. 150 cm 2. 30 g 3. 80 mℓ 4. 0.96 cm
5. 60 m 6. 54 mℓ 7. ₹76.8 8. 3.5 paise
F. b. $\frac{3}{4}$, 75% c. 0.4, 40% d. $\frac{5}{4}$, 1.25 e. 0.85, 85%
f. $\frac{33}{100}$, 33% g. 0.125
G. 1. 33.33% 2. 7.14% 3. 17.5% 4. 20%
5. 1.96% 6. 1.6%
H. 1. ₹2060 2. ₹3500, ₹4060 3. 3 years, ₹600 4. ₹2500, 1%
5. 5 years, ₹1750 6. 1.25%, ₹11,250
7. 2 years, ₹5500
I. 1. 6.25% 2. 10% 3. 45 4. 6.3%
5. 25% profit 6. 0.62% 7. 11.5% 8. ₹587.02

CHAPTER 9

Exercise 9A

1. a. 50° b. 5° 2. a. 118° b. 43° 3. 45°
4. 110° 5. 10° 6. 45°
7. a. 70° b. 50° c. 60°
d. 50° e. 40° f. 108°
8. a. ∠AOD = 130°, ∠BOD = 50°, ∠BOC = 130°
b. ∠AOD = 120°, ∠AOC = 60°, ∠BOD = 60°, ∠BOC = 120°
c. ∠AOD = 100°, ∠AOC = 80°, ∠BOD = 80°, ∠BOC = 100°

Exercise 9B

1. a. 130°, 50°, 130°, 50°, 130°, 50°, 130°
b. 80°, 130° c. 50°, 50° d. 80° e. 50° f. 85°
3. a. 60° b. 120° c. 120° d. 60°
4. a. 37° b. 143° 5. 52° 6. 107°

Chapter Revision

A. 1. b. 2. c. 3. b. 4. a. 5. c.

B. 1. supplementary 2. 22° 3. 112° 4. 50°
5. 180°

C. 1. F 2. F 3. T 4. T 5. T

D. 1. c. 2. b. 3. d. 4. e. 5. a.

E. 1. a. 80° b. 60° c. 80°, 100° d. 72°, 108°
e. 50°, 130°
2. a. 140° b. 150° c. 110° d. 30° e. 140°

CHAPTER 10

Exercise 10A

1. 60° 2. 48°, 60°, 72° 3. 30° 4. 60° 5. 60°
6. 101° 7. a. 110°, 60° b. 25°

Exercise 10B

1. 53° 2. 90° 3. 52.5° 4. 3.7 cm, median
5. 65°, altitude 6. a. 130°, 20° b. 45°, 75° c. 110°

Exercise 10C

1. a. Yes, 3 + 5.5 > 6 b. No, 2.1 + 3 < 5.2
c. No, 4.2 + 4.3 = 8.5 d. Yes, 6.5 + 7 > 13
2. 4 < third side < 18

Exercise 10D

1. a. Yes b. Yes c. No d. No
2. 10 cm
3. 4 m 4. a. $8^{1/2}$ cm b. 15 cm 5. 10 cm, $5^{1/5}$ cm

Chapter Revision

A. 1. a. 2. d. 3. d.

B. 1. 4 + 6.5 > 8 2. 10 – 6 < 4.5 3. longest
4. 90° 5. 360° 6. $PQ^2 + PR^2 = QR^2$

C. 1. f. 2. e. 3. b. 4. a. 5. c. 6. d.

D. 1. 7.5 cm 2. 10 cm 3. 25 m 4. 25 m
6. a. i. 80° ii. 130° 6. b. i. 120° ii. $b = 60°$

CHAPTER 11

Exercise 11

1. a. Corresponding angles are not equal, AC ≠ PR
b. ∠P is not the included angle for RQ and QP.
c. The triangles are congruent.
d. Corresponding sides are not equal.
e. Corresponding sides are not equal.
f. Corresponding sides are not equal.
2. XY = PQ, XZ = PR, YZ = QR, ∠P = ∠X, ∠Q = ∠Y, ∠R = ∠Z

Chapter Revision

A. 1. b. 2. b. 3. d. 4. c.

B. 1. Length 2. equal 3. radii 4. side, angle

C. 1. F 2. T 3. T 4. T

D. 1. b. 2. d. 3. a. 4. c.

CHAPTER 12

Exercise 12A

3. Triangle TYZ

Chapter Revision

A. 1. d. 2. a. 3. b. 4. d. 5. c.

B. 1. parallel 2. supplementary 3. unique
4. included 5. compass

C. 1. T 2. F 3. F 4. T 5. T

D. 1. e. 2. c. 3. f. 4. b. 5. d. 6. a.

CHAPTER 13

Exercise 13A

1. a. 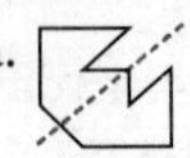 b. 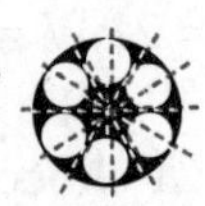 c. 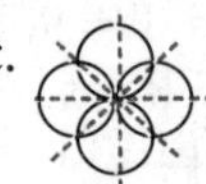 d.  e. 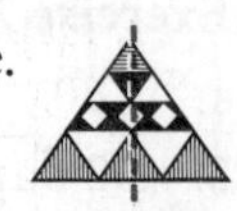
2. a. iv. b. i. c. ii. d. v. e. iii.
3. 32 lines of symmetry
4. a. 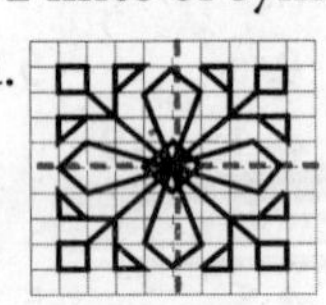 b. 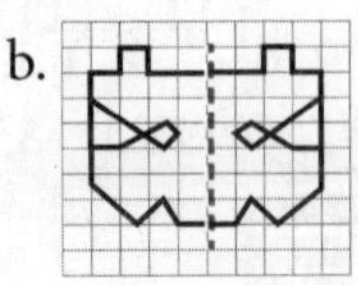

Exercise 13B

1. a., c. 2. a. 10 b. 4 c. 1
3. Square: 4, 90°; Isosceles trapezium: 1, 360°
Parallelogram: 2, 180°; Equilateral triangle: 3, 120°
Regular nonagon: 9, 40°
4. a. L b. R c. R d. N e. L and R

Chapter Revision

A. 1. c. 2. d. 3. d. 4. b. 5. d.

B. 1. e. 2. b. 3. a. 4. d. 5. c.

C. 1. asymmetrical 2. rotational 3. 15
4. rotational 5. $\frac{360}{r}$

D. 1. F 2. F 3. F 4. T 5. T

E. 1. a. A circle has both line symmetry and rotational symmetry. It has infinite lines of symmetry and the order of rotational symmetry is also infinite. Every angle is its angle of rotational symmetry.
2. a. 12 b. 12 c. 12 d. Dodecagon
3. a. No lines of symmetry b. 
c. No lines of symmetry d. 
4. Lines of symmetry: 16,
Order of rotational symmetry: 16,
Angle of rotational symmetry: 22.5°
5. a. 6 b. 5 c. 2 d. 9 e. 7

CHAPTER 14

Exercise 14A

1. One possible answer is given.
   Plane figures: Circle, triangle, square, pentagon
   Solid shapes: Cube, cuboid, cone, cylinder
2. Cylinder: water bottle, chalk piece; Cone: a joker's cap, ice cream cone
3. a. Rectangular pyramid, F = 5, E= 8, V = 5
   b. Pentagonal prism, F = 7, E = 15, V = 10
   c. Hexagonal pyramid, F = 7, E = 12, V = 7
   d. Octagonal prism, F = 10, E = 24, V = 16
   e. Square pyramid, F = 5, E = 8, V = 5
   f. Heptagonal prism, F = 9, E = 21, V = 14
4. a. b. c. d. e. f.

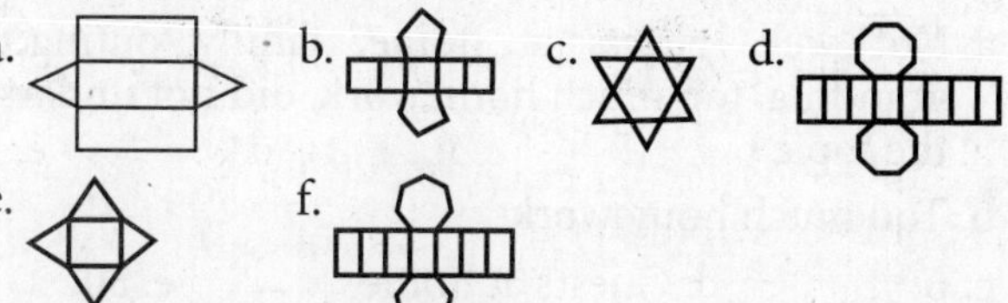

5. One possible answer is given.

6. a. Not a dice b. Not a dice c. Not a dice

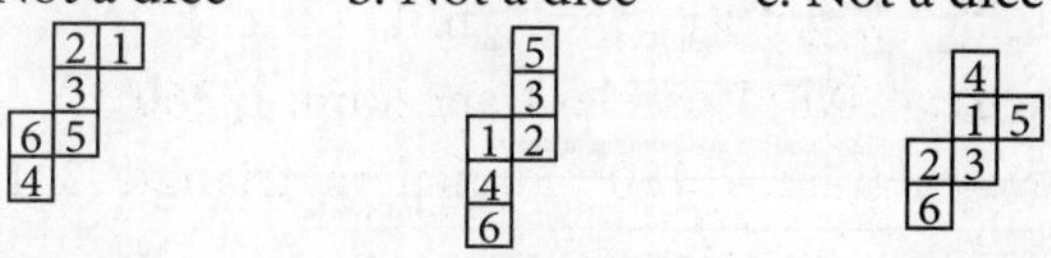

Exercise 14B

1. a. b. c. d. e. f.

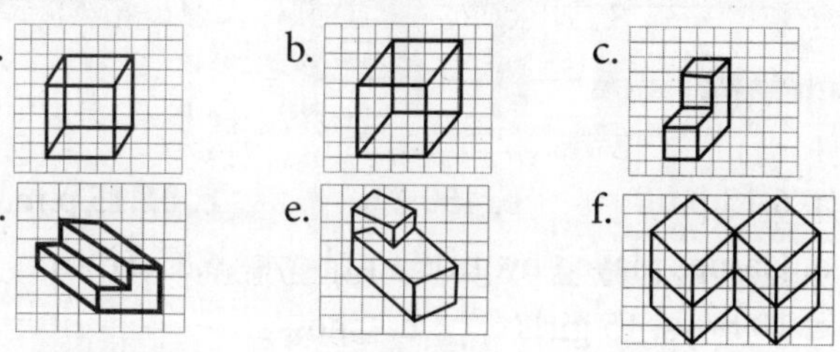

2. a. b. c. d. e. f.

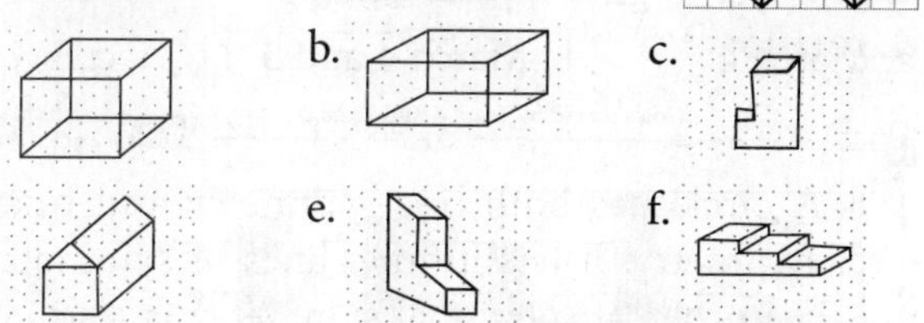

3. 3 different isometric sketches are as follows:

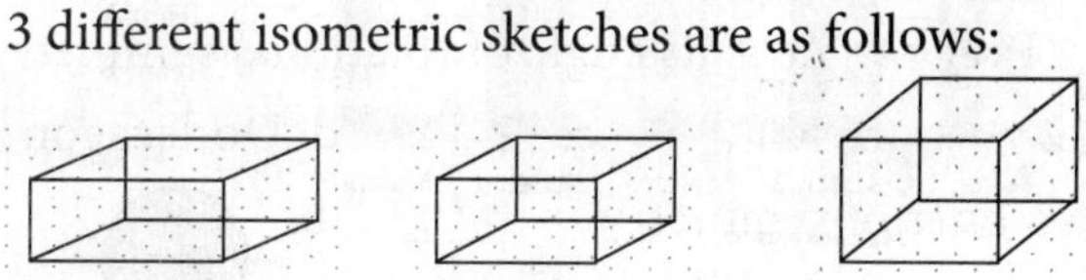

4. Oblique sketch Isometric sketch

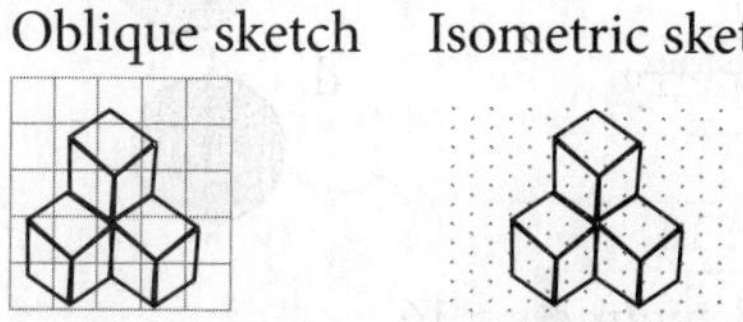

5. Isometric sketch Oblique sketch

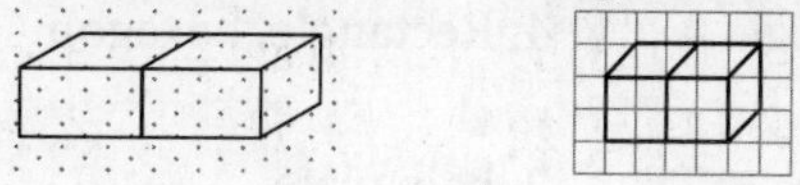

Exercise 14C

1. a. 8 b. 7 c. 8 d. 12 e. 10 f. 9
2. a. Rectangle, circle b. Rectangle, rectangle
   c. Triangle, circle d. Circle, circle
   e. Rectangle, rectangle f. Square, square
   g. Rectangle, circle h. Square, square
3. a. Triangle b. Rectangle c. Circle d. Square
   e. Rectangle f. Circle
4. a. Front, top, side b. Front, top, side
   c. Front, side, top d. Side, front, top
   e. Side, front, top
5. Top view Side view Front view
   a. b. c. d. e.

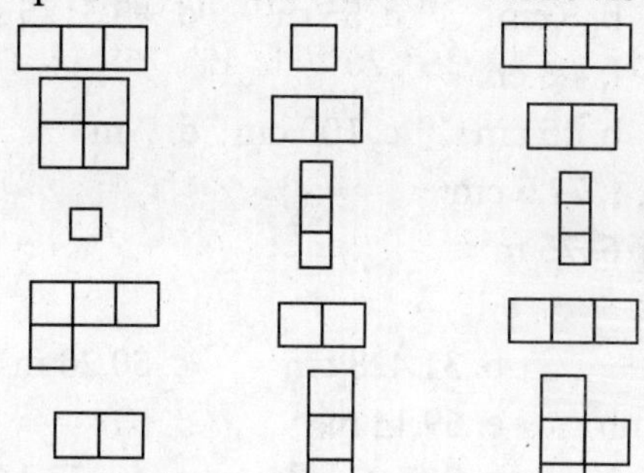

Chapter Revision

A. 1. b. 2. d. 3. d. 4. c. 5. a.

B. 1. edge 2. cylinder 3. 2-D 4. visualising 5. sphere

C. 1. T 2. F 3. T 4. T 5. F

D. 1. Cuboid, F = 6, E = 12, V = 8
   2. Pentagonal pyramid, F = 6, E = 10, V = 6
   3. Hexagonal prism, F = 8, E = 18, V = 12
   4. Cylinder, F = 3 (if top is closed), E =2, V = 0
   5. Tetrahedron, F = 4, E = 6, V = 4

E. 1. 2.

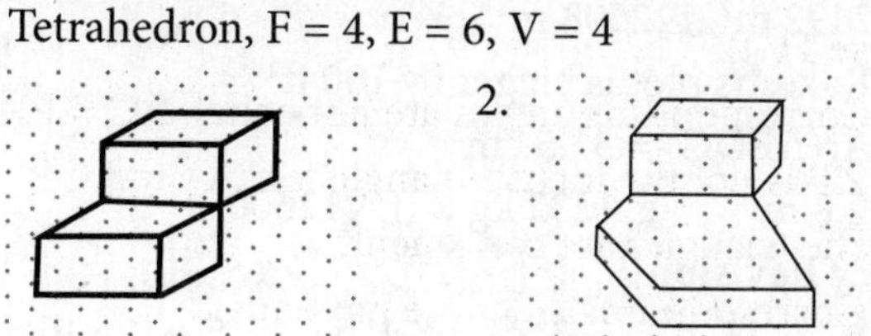

F. 1. c 2. d. 3. b 4. e 5. a.

G.

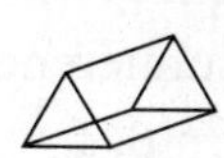

H. Top view Side view Front view
   1. 2. 3.

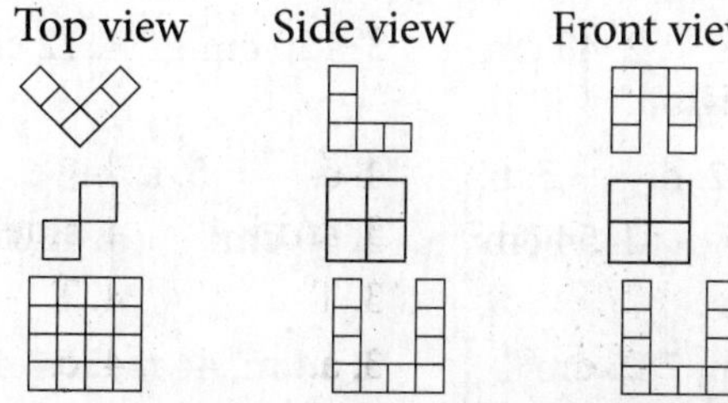

I. 1. Triangle, circle 2. Square, square
3. Triangle, triangle 4. Rectangle, hexagon
5. Rectangle, circle

J. 1. Dice, ice cube 2. ball, plate
3. duster, cylinder 4. cap, pyramid

CHAPTER 15

Exercise 15A

1. a. 36 cm b. 49 cm c. 22 m d. 40 cm
2. a. 300 cm^2 b. 225 cm^2 c. 30 cm^2 d. 64 cm^2
3. a. 25 cm^2 b. 80 cm^2 c. 72 cm^2 d. 15 cm^2
4. Perimeter = 60 cm, Area = 225 cm^2
5. 14 cm 6. Breadth = 50 cm, Area = 4000 cm^2

Exercise 15B

1. a. iv. b. i. c. ii. d. vi. e. iii. f. v.
2. a. 24 cm^2 b. 90 cm^2 c. 35 cm^2 d. 9 cm^2 e. 36 cm^2
3. a. 90 cm^2 b. 5 cm c. 55 m d. 45.3125 sq. ft
e. 125 m f. 4.8 cm
4. a. 56 cm^2 b. 15 cm c. 100 cm d. 7 m
e. 650 m f. 72.5 cm^2
5. 1125 cm^2 6. 75 m^2

Exercise 15C

1. a. 44 cm b. 31.428 cm c. 50.28 m
d. 25.14 cm e. 69.14 m
2. a. 28.28 cm^2 b. 227.07 m^2 c. 45257.14 cm^2
d. 616 cm^2 e. 506.91 m^2
3. a. 10 cm b. 1.91 m c. 20.05 cm d. 8 cm e. 42 cm
4. a. 3 cm b. 5.7 cm c. 1 cm d. 4 cm e. 12 cm
5. a. 15, 94.28 b. 120, 377.14, 11314.28 c. 7.8, 191.21
d. 110, 38028.57 e. 276.57 cm f. 18.5, 268.91
6. 5 cm 7. 2.01 cm^2

Exercise 15D

1. a. 100 b. 0.001 c. 100 d. 1000000
e. 10000000 f. 0.01
2. a. 2492 m^2, 122508 m^2
b. Rakesh's plot is bigger by 100 ft^2
c. Ar(ΔBDC) = 31.5 cm^2
d. 2.8 m e. 1232 kg f. ₹12600

Chapter Revision

A. 1. b. 2. c. 3. d. 4. b. 5. a. 6. c.

B. 1. ½ × base × height 2. 4 3. 60 cm
4. 10000 cm^2 5. 201.14 m^2 6. circumference

C. 1. T 2. F 3. T 4. F 5. T 6. T

D. 1. 22 m 2. 48 cm 3. 120 cm 4. 12 cm
5. 127.5 mm

E. 1. e. 2. d. 3. b. 4. c. 5. f. 6. a.

F. 1. 42 cm^2 2. 54 cm^2 3. 60 cm^2 4. 120 cm^2
5. 544 cm^2

G. 1. 31.4 cm, 78.5 cm^2 2. 14 m, 44 m, 154 m^2
3. 53.4 cm, 227 cm^2 4. 10 m, 62.8 m, 314.2 m^2
5. 220 cm, 3850 cm^2

H. 1. ₹6000 2. 2 m 3. 70 cm
4. 10 m 5. h = 10 ft, b = 20 ft 6. ₹3000 7. 7 m

CHAPTER 16

Exercise 16A

1. 18, 10 2. 48, 66 3. ₹775 4. 11.5 years
5. 29 pages 6. 7403

Exercise 16B

1. a. 7 b. 58 c. 86 d. 36 e. 55
2. a. 6 b. 48 3. ₹45 4. 22 5. 6
6. Foil prints: 20

Exercise 16C

1. a. Not well, guests at home, family outing, sick grandma, too much homework, did not understand the topic
b. Too much homework
c. 6 d. Guests at home e. 30

2.

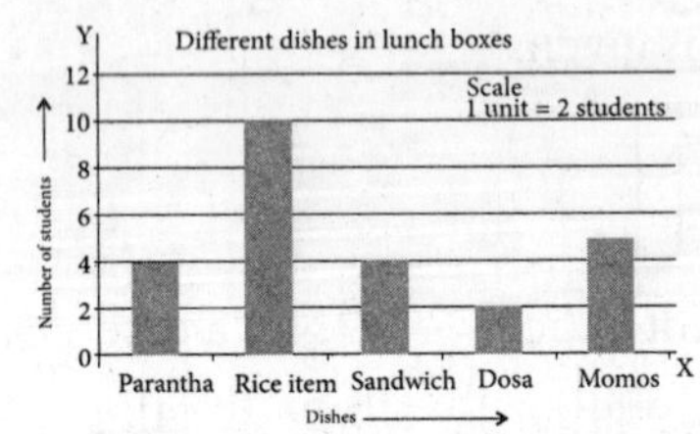

3.

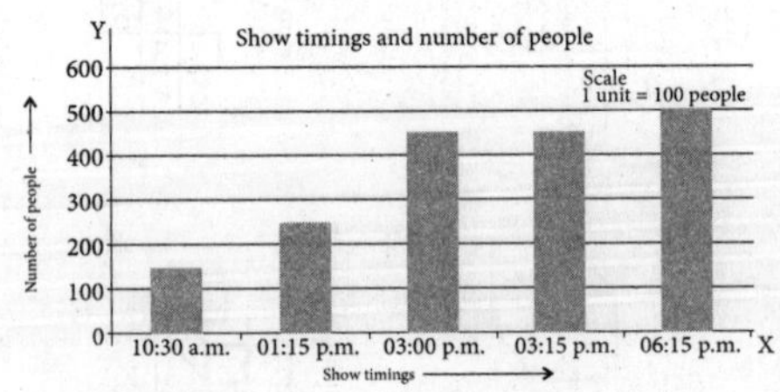

a. 6.15 p.m. b. 450 c. 01:15 p.m.

4. a. Games played by girls and boys b. Carrom
c. 10 boys, 15 girls d. Chess

5. a. Match 4 b. Match 4 and 5 c. 8

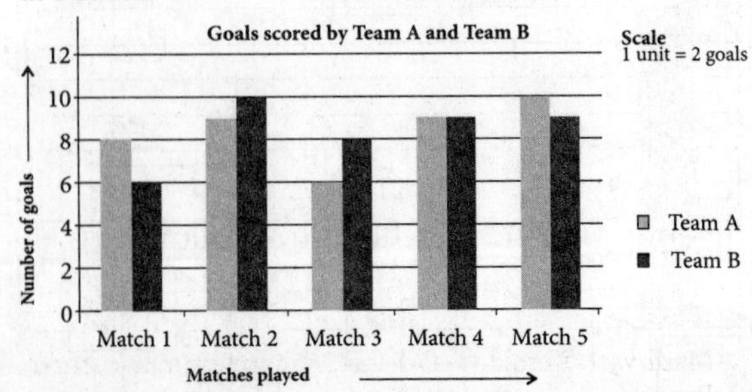

6. a. D b. E c. B

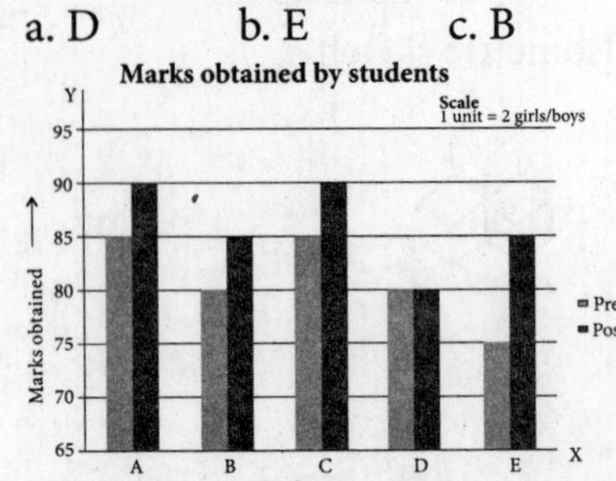

Exercise 16D

1.

Certain to happen	Impossible	May or may not happen
The month of February falling after January	Water will flow from lower area to higher area without any external force.	Team A will win the football match today.
As the side length of a square increases, its perimeter also increases.	A bike without any fuel will run for 100 km.	

2. a. S = {HH, HT, TT, TH} b. S = {7, 11, 13}
   c. S = {i, e, a}
   d. S = {TJM, TJm, Tjm, TjM, tjm, tJM, tjM, tJm}; where T, t are T-shirts; J, j are Jeans; M, m are Mufflers
   e. S = {SC, SP, MC, MP, LC, LP}
3. $P(H) = \frac{11}{20}$, $P(T) = \frac{9}{20}$
4. P(A) = 70% and P(B) = 30%
5. $P(E) = \frac{39}{250}$, $P(H) = \frac{9}{50}$, $P(S) = \frac{43}{250}$,

   $P(G) = \frac{23}{100}$, $P(J) = \frac{9}{125}$, $P(M) = \frac{19}{100}$

Chapter Revision

A. 1. mode 2. 5.6 3. outcomes
   4. sample space 5. random

B. 1. T 2. F 3. F 4. F 5. F

C. 215.7, 152, 125, 387

D. 1. a. Madhya Pradesh b. 2 c. Kerala

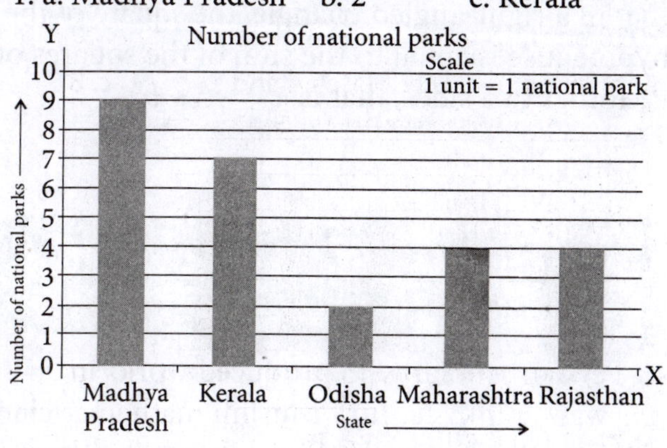

2. a. Doddegowda Deve Gowda b. Inder Kumar Gujral

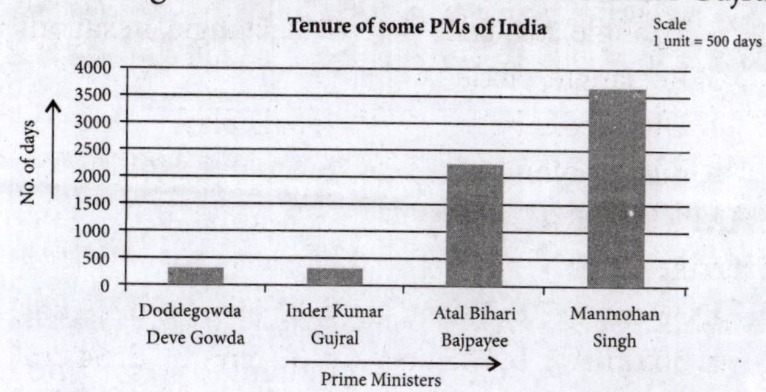

3. a. Tehri b. 48 lakh acre-ft
   c. Bhakra Nangal, Sardar Sarovar

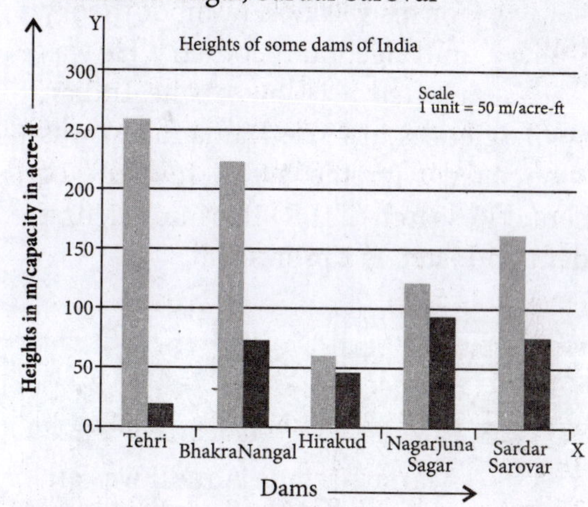

4. $P(H) = \frac{3}{10}$ and $P(T) = \frac{7}{10}$
5. $\frac{2}{11}$ 6. $\frac{1}{2}$
7. a. $\frac{18}{36} = \frac{1}{2}$ b. $\frac{18}{36} = \frac{1}{2}$ c. $\frac{19}{36}$
   d. $\frac{9}{36} = \frac{1}{4}$ e. $\frac{27}{36} = \frac{3}{4}$

Eminent Mathematicians

Chakravarthi Padmanabhan Ramanujam
(1938–1974)

CP Ramanujam was one of the well-known Indian mathematicians. He is known for his work on number theory and algebraic geometry. He was elected a fellow of the Indian Academy of Sciences in 1973. Ramanujam was closely associated with the TATA Institute of Fundamental Research (TIFR) in Mumbai, first as a student and later as a professor.

Girolamo Cardano
(1501–1576)

Girolamo Cardano was an Italian mathematician, physician and astrologer. He was one of the most influential mathematicians of his time and was one of the key figures in the foundation of probability. His book about games of chance contains the first systematic treatment of probability. Cardano is well known for his achievements in algebra. He was the first mathematician to make systematic use of negative numbers.

Maria Gaetana Agnesi
(1718–1799)

Maria Gaetana Agnesi was an Italian mathematician, philosopher, theologian and humanitarian. She is considered to be the first woman in the Western world to have achieved a reputation in mathematics. Agnesi was the first woman to write a mathematics textbook, *Analytical Institutions for the Use of Italian Youth*, which was published in 1748 and was regarded as the best introduction extant to the works of Euler. She devoted the last four decades of her life to studying theology and to charitable work and serving the poor.

Pythagoras of Samos
(c. 570 BC – c. 495 BC)

Pythagoras was a Greek philosopher, mathematician and founder of the Pythagorean brotherhood that contributed to the development of mathematics and Western rational philosophy. He was credited with many mathematical and scientific discoveries, including the Pythagorean theorem which states that in a right-angled triangle, the square of the hypotenuse is equal to the sum of the squares of the other two sides, that is, $c^2 = a^2 + b^2$.

Muhammad ibn Musa al-Khwarizmi
(780 AD–850 AD)

Muhammad ibn Musa al-Khwarizmi was a Persian scholar who produced works in mathematics, astronomy and geography. He was a ninth century Muslim mathematician and astronomer. He is known as the 'father of **algebra**', a word derived from the title of his book, *Kitab al-Jabr*. The term 'algebra' is derived from the name of one of the basic operations with equations (*al-jabr*, meaning 'restoration', referring to adding a number to both sides of the equation to consolidate or cancel terms) described in this book. It provided an exhaustive account of solving polynomial equations up to the second degree and discussed the fundamental methods of 'reduction' and 'balancing'.